History of the British Medical Association

Volume III

1982–2012

History of the British Medical Association

Volume III

1982–2012

Jacqueline Foukas
Sally Watson

British Medical Association

First published in the UK by the British Medical Association, 2013

BMA House
Tavistock Square
London WC1H 9JP

ISBN 978-0-7279-1862-8

Typeset & Printed by Henry Ling Ltd, at the Dorset Press, Dorchester, DT1 1HD
Bound by Skyline Bookbinders, Dorking

Foreword

Love it or loathe it, respect or resent it – and external views of the BMA are and always have been polarised – the British Medical Association is unquestionably one of Britain's most important institutions.

For 180 years it has been, as far as most of the public is concerned, *the* voice of the medical profession, however much the Royal Colleges, the General Medical Council, politicians and other intruders on the turf of medicine may resent that.

Boasting a level of membership that most other trade unions can only envy, it combines its trade union role with that of a professional association. It worries, at its best, not just about doctors' terms and conditions of service, or the structure and management of a National Health Service in which most of its members work, or private patient fees, but about important broader and indeed at times global health issues – from smoking, alcohol and AIDS, to the ethics of medical practice across an enormously broad front. From abortion to reproductive technologies and transplantation to end of life issues and on to torture and much else. On many of these issues, and sometimes with considerable courage, the BMA has proved to be, at least in the eyes of this commentator, on the side of the angels.

This third volume of the BMA's history by Sally Watson, former head of the political division of the BMA, and by Jacqueline Foukas, former head of the council secretariat, covers the association's story over the past 30 years, from 1982 to the middle of 2012.

These have often been turbulent times. There have been two mighty battles in a still continuing war over the introduction of an element of market forces into the English NHS. Tough times over assorted contract negotiations. Long debates about the BMA's own internal constitution and functioning. There is the tortured and still continuing story of revalidation in order to demonstrate a doctor's continued fitness to practise. The nightmare that was MTAS. The long and continuing debate over balancing a medic's responsibility to the individual patient with his or her collective responsibility to manage resources. A somewhat greater tendency than in the past for the BMA to defenestrate its own leaders. Some triumphs and a few disasters.

What emerges from this history are a number of themes. Taken over the long view – and despite the impact of the financial austerity which is currently hitting every part of the public sector – the BMA has proved remarkably effective at defending and promoting its members terms and conditions of service, even if one or two of its victories have in some people's eyes proved pyrrhic: the removal of GPs' personal responsibility for out-of-hours care, for example.

The BMA has proved much less effective, despite the scale of the battles it has fought and the controversy it has helped generate, at deflecting Westminster governments of either main party or indeed the current coalition, from changes to the way the NHS is run and managed in England. From the limited list to the recent battles over Andrew Lansley's Health and Social Care Act 2012, governments in England have tended to get their way, whatever the BMA's views.

In Scotland and Wales, by contrast, and perhaps in time in Northern Ireland, devolution has seen the BMA have a greater influence over NHS policy. Perhaps because the BMA has filled a vacuum in the smaller countries of the United Kingdom where there are fewer powerful voices with views on these matters. Or perhaps because these countries, at least to date, retain a more collectivist view of the world than England.

Devolution, however, has brought its own tensions for the association, not yet destroying but certainly making more difficult an entirely common UK view on both health policy and terms and conditions of service. Within England, the introduction of an element of choice and competition and of freer standing institutions such as NHS Foundation Trusts, along with GP commissioning in its various incarnations, has tended to exacerbate tensions between the various branches of the profession – GPs, junior doctors and consultants – though not yet disastrously.

This history highlights many of those stresses and strains, and some of the internal battles fought within the association to achieve a position that could be presented as united to the outside world.

It charts some of the impact of the feminisation of the profession and of the arrival first of the internet and then of social media. These innovations provided activists with new means by which to challenge the BMA's leadership at times of controversy – exacerbating the long-standing tension that is perhaps inevitable in such a representative organisation between those who, once in office, believe they will achieve most by remaining engaged with politicians and officials, and those who believe that outright confrontation is the only way to get real results. The internet and social media have, however, also brought advantages for the association, hugely improving its ability to communicate with its members and the outside world.

This account also lays out the constructive role the BMA has played in many matters of public health and medical ethics – even when the views it has expressed have discomforted the government of the day, or had to tackle the prejudices of parts of the public and its own membership.

Two things are certain. The first is that amid rising obesity, evolving infections, globalisation and ageing populations, and with technological advance in both science and medicine posing new opportunities and dilemmas, medicine, medical ethics, and the question of how to run health services and reward doctors are matters that are likely to become more, not less, central to public policy. The second is that the BMA will be there holding an important and influential view on them.

This history is littered with lessons about all of that, not just from the past but for the future – lessons both for those would seek to lead the BMA and for those who have to engage with it. It repays the reading.

Nicholas Timmins
February, 2013

Acknowledgements

We were very privileged to be asked by the BMA to write the third volume of its history. This work could not have been produced without the help and encouragement of a large number of people and we are delighted to mention them here.

Firstly, the champion of the project and its co-ordinator throughout, David Pickersgill. David has read and re-read countless drafts, advised us and been the link between us and the BMA from the beginning. This book would not have been possible without him. Neil Poppmacher has overseen every stage of the production and we are very grateful to him for transforming our manuscript into this bound volume or e-book. Editorial advice was provided by Tim Albert and we thank him for his efforts with our manuscript. Sincere thanks are due to Judy Thomas for her many, many hours of wordprocessing support to Sally, unstintingly given and provided to the highest quality. Andy Bainbridge's creative skills and artistic advice have been greatly appreciated. He has designed the cover for the book and the illustrated sections as well as sourcing many of the photographs.

During the course of writing the book, we have interviewed a large number of individuals, who have given their time generously and offered invaluable insights, important factual information and forthright opinions. Others have helpfully commented on drafts. The list of contributors is too long to reproduce, but we are indebted to them all.

We are very grateful to the current Chief Officers, Steve Hajioff, Mark Porter and Andrew Dearden and Chief Executive, Tony Bourne, for reading the final version of our manuscript and for their insightful and supportive comments. Our thanks also to Sarah Connelly, PA to the Chief Executive, for her professional administrative help.

It has been a pleasure to work with the team in the BMA Archive and our thanks to Lee Sands, Lisa Spry and Ben Davies who have efficiently supplied endless committee papers, annual reports, files and photos. Thanks to them also for letting us take over their reading room for days on end. The staff of the BMA Library in London have provided us with huge amounts of information and we thank them for all of their help and advice.

Finally, two other people have lived this project day by day with us, our husbands John Chawner and Lazaros Foukas. We thank them for their constant patience and support throughout the process of writing our book.

Our heartfelt thanks to all of you.

Jacqueline Foukas and Sally Watson
January 2013

Authors' note on the text

Chronology: Readers will notice that some chapters in this book, mainly those covering medico-political events in the first part, are narrated in five chronological chapters, with subsections that cover particular episodes or topics. Chapter 6 covers developments over the whole period which, though important to sections of the profession, have not featured among the major events described in Chapters 1–5. It also includes events in the devolved nations since 1999. Chapter 7 is also mainly chronological, but has separate sections on revalidation and complaints. A number of other chapters are organised by subject. It appeared to us that some issues lent themselves to a chronological telling and others were best explored by subject.

References: We have tended not to reference direct quotations when these have been taken from BMA press statements, minutes of meetings, annual reports or the website. Some BMA reports and publications have been referenced when their full titles have not been included in the text. Generally, we have only referenced sources external to the BMA or used the references to give additional information. We have not attributed or referenced comments or information given to us by the many individuals whom we interviewed in the course of our research: the interviews were conducted on this understanding.

The BMA 'session': References have been made to, for example, the 1995–96 'session'. This is a common BMA term and refers to the BMA year which runs from the end of one Annual Representative Meeting (normally held in late June or early July) to the beginning of the next.

Individuals' titles: We chose to refer to individuals without their medical titles and have normally used first name plus family name throughout. We have, however, stated when an individual was later knighted or received a DBE.

Names of BMA committees: Committee names have changed over the years and we have either referred to them by the names used in 2012 or the names in use at the time of the events being described when this seemed to us to be more appropriate. We hope that any confusion over the use of BMA acronyms will be addressed by the list of abbreviations on page xxiii.

Devolved nations: Where national differences or specific events in individual countries of the UK occurred before devolution in 1999, we have tried to include these in the general narrative. We have then included a section in Chapter 6 to cover developments in each of the devolved nations since devolution. The book inevitably contains a greater weight of material that is relevant specifically to England than to the other nations, reflecting as it does the debates and activity that have preoccupied the BMA at UK level over the 30 year period. The recent tendency to divergence between the nations, with greater autonomy of action by the BMA's national offices, means that future volumes of this history may need to incorporate separate narratives for each nation.

We have had to be selective about issues and events included in this book and some readers may notice omissions. We can only apologise for these and remind readers that it has not been possible to cover every aspect of the BMA's work over the past 30 years in a single volume. Finally, despite our efforts, some errors no doubt remain and we are sorry to those of our readers who find these.

Introduction

As the BMA celebrated its 150th anniversary in 1982 it was just emerging from a rocky period in its history. The organisation's finances had been in crisis following several years of low membership in the late 1970s. But by 1982 new leaders had got to grips with the problems and were introducing unfamiliar business disciplines to ways of working that had changed little since the war. The Representative Body accepted the need for a 20% increase in subscriptions, and this proved to be a turning point. The process of modernisation would continue and accelerate for the next 30 years, during which time the BMA would see consistent growth and expansion, achieving its target of 150,000 members in active practice during 2012.

To mark the 150th anniversary the BMA invited HRH the Prince of Wales to be President for the year. He accepted and took an active interest in the Association's affairs, hosting a reception for Council members at Kensington Palace at which he challenged the profession to re-examine its values, and suggested that 'the whole imposing edifice of modern medicine, for all its breathtaking successes is, like the celebrated tower of Pisa, slightly off balance'. He also caused much scurrying about by urging the BMA to embrace his enthusiasm for alternative medicine. The resulting working party took longer than most to reach its somewhat obfuscatory conclusions.

That year the Annual Representative Meeting (ARM) was held in London, where the royal President was installed with appropriate pomp and ceremony. However the occasion was chiefly remembered for the embarrassing spectacle of hungry representatives at the subsequent reception descending locust-like on the kitchens of the Royal Festival Hall when the canapés failed to appear on time.

As part of the anniversary celebrations, the BMA published the second volume of its history,[1] covering the fifty years since 1932. As well as the second world war, the account included the momentous battle over the terms on which the medical profession would co-operate in the National Health Service from 1948. Elston Grey-Turner's lucid narrative of these events has many resonances with aspects of medical

---

[1] Elston Grey-Turner and F M Sutherland: *History of the British Medical Association Volume II 1932–81.*

politics today, and also gives the lie to the myth, still trundled out by politicians, that the BMA resisted the principles of the NHS. Other turbulent episodes were the unedifying 'Chambers saga' of 1970–74, when the BMA, not for the first or the last time, was convulsed with introspective arguments about its constitution, and a series of bitter recriminations over doctors' pay. These led first to the Pilkington Commission and the establishment of the review body system; then to the general practitioners' charter, following the submission of undated resignations in 1965; and finally to the review body's resignation in 1970 over government interference. The 1970s, a time of industrial unrest throughout the country, was characterised for the BMA by tough negotiations with the government over juniors' and consultants' contracts and over pay beds, all involving sanctions by doctors.

The period also covered major developments in the BMA's professional activities, with the establishment of the Board of Science, strong statements on smoking and on alcohol in relation to road traffic accidents, the determined and ultimately successful campaign for compulsory wearing of seat belts, guidance on advertising, confidentiality and the ethics of transplantation, and the publication of the *Handbook of Medical Ethics*.

This second volume of the BMA's history documents the transition from the 'gracious times' of the 1930s when morning dress was worn on Council meeting days to a 'harsh collectivist world' when the BMA was coming to terms with its identity as a trade union. Yet in 1982 the BMA was far from being a modern organisation – the authors described it as 'very much a club, even a family'. The internet and mobile phones had yet to appear, committee papers were reproduced by hand on an inky stencil machine, the structure was hierarchical and male dominated, the committee rooms wood panelled and filled with smoke, and decision-making was slow and laborious. The NHS was run by administrators, vocational training for GPs had just become mandatory, the first case of AIDS had not yet been reported; GPs' average intended earnings were £18,990 a year and a consultant on the scale maximum might earn £22,270, while a house officer's basic salary was £6,180. Beer was 51p a pint, inflation had come down to 8%, but mortgage rates hit a peak of 18%. Violence reigned in Northern Ireland, and spilled over to mainland Britain with the fatal Hyde Park bombing, corporal punishment was outlawed in schools following a ruling by the European Court of Human Rights, the Ford Sierra was launched and the Falklands War was fought and won.

Dramatic changes were happening – political, social, economic, technological and medical – but even bigger upheavals were to come. The next 30 years would bring new battlefronts, tribulations and crises for the BMA. To meet these challenges it would need to call on all the lessons of its past and muster new resources of imagination and adaptability.

Contents

	Page
Foreword	v
Acknowledgements	ix
Authors' note on the text	xi
Introduction	xiii

Chapter 1   The Thatcher years: 'Steaming through

Errata

Page 17, 7 lines up. The page reference to
GMSC's response to fundholding should read
'see page 43'.

Page 67, 11 lines up. The page reference should
read 'see page 160'.

Page 184, reference 4. The publication
*The Doctors' Tale: Professionalism and Public
Trust* was published in 2003 not 1993 as stated.

Page 222, second paragraph, eight lines down.
SRC should read 'SCR'.

	1
	1
	2
	7
	13
	21
·r	25
	26
	28
	33
	38
	41
	43
	46
	50

Chapter 2	**The decline of the Conservative government:**	
	'Reforming the reforms' 1992–1997	55
	Core values	55
	More NHS reorganisation	57
	Healthcare in London: the Tomlinson Report	58
	Specialist training: the Calman Report	60
	GP out-of-hours negotiations	63
	The local pay campaign	66

Chapter 3	**New Labour: modernisation and negotiation**	
	1997–2007	71
	NHS modernisation and devolution	71
	Change gathers pace: caring for the NHS	74

BMA contract negotiations   82
   Background to the negotiations   83
   Junior doctors' out-of-hours pay   84
   Consultant contract   88
   GP contract   96
   Staff doctors and associate specialists   101
   Reflections   107
The European Working Time Directive   110
Modernising Medical Careers and the MTAS
crisis   113

**Chapter 4   Labour's later years and the financial crisis
2007–2010**   129
Another NHS review   129
Financial crisis   132
Look after our NHS   134
Pensions reform   136

**Chapter 5   The Conservative/Liberal Democrat
coalition 2010–2012**   139
Austerity   139
The Health and Social Care Act 2012   141
Pensions (continued)   145

**Chapter 6   The devolved nations since 1999, pay and
other branches of practice 1982–2012**   149
The BMA in Scotland, Wales and Northern
Ireland since devolution   149
   BMA Scotland   149
   BMA Cymru Wales   152
   BMA Northern Ireland   154
Review body and remuneration   156
Medical academic staff   162
Public health medicine and community health   167
   Community health   171
Armed forces doctors   172
Medical students   174
Private practice   176
   Private practice   179
   Professional fees   179

Forensic medicine 180
Retired members 181

Chapter 7 **The regulation of the medical profession** 183
The BMA and the General Medical Council 183
Revalidation 197
NHS complaints 209

Chapter 8 **The IT revolution** 213
Introduction 213
Access to personal healthcare information 213
Devolved nations 226
The world wide web 227
New technology and services to BMA members 230
Listservers and paperless committees 232

Chapter 9 **The health of the public** 235
Smoking 236
Tobacco advertising and sponsorship 237
Passive smoking 240
Other tobacco-related campaigns 244
Alcohol 245
Nutrition, health and body image 250
Health inequalities 253
Other issues 256
Weapons and warfare 256
AIDS 258
Transport, health and the environment 260
Risk 265
Boxing 265
Alternative and complementary therapy 267
Appendix, Timeline 269
Reports from the Board of Science 1983–2011 269

Chapter 10 **Medical ethics** 275
Reproductive technology 276
Abortion 279
Human genetics 281

Confidentiality   284
Consent and capacity   286
Human rights   292
Organ donation and transplantation   295
End of life issues   299
    Physician assisted suicide and euthanasia   299
    Withholding and withdrawing treatment   304
    Advance directives   308

Chapter 11   The BMA's international work   311
European institutions   312
Immigration   314
International medical associations   318
Third world debt and international sanctions   322
International health care and ethical procurement
of medical equipment   323
Other international work   325

Chapter 12   The BMA and its members   327
Regional services   328
    Workplace services   329
    The growing demand for advice   331
    Joining the call centre revolution   334
Financial and other services   339
Local structures and communications   341

Chapter 13   The BMA's constitution and governance   345
Trade Union Act 1984 and changes to Council   345
Governance Committees 2001–4   347
The modernisation project   352
BMA Council   353
Changes to committees   358
Devolution   362
Appendix, Constitution of Council as
recommended to the 1985 ARM   366

Chapter 14   Inside the BMA   369
Finances   369
    Payments to members   377
BMA staff and departments   378
Presidents   381

Transformation of BMA House   382
Terrorism reaches the BMA   385

Chapter 15   The BMJ Publishing Group   391

Conclusions   413
Appendix, Timeline   417
Index   445

Abbreviations

A&E – Accident and Emergency
ABI – Association of British Insurers
ACMM – Advisory Committee on Medical Manpower
ACMT – Advisory Committee on Medical Training
ADHs – Additional Duty Hours
AFC – Armed Forces Committee
AFPRB – Armed Forces Pay Review Body
AIDS – Acquired Immune Deficiency Syndrome
AoMRC – Academy of Medical Royal Colleges
APMS – Alternative Provider Medical Services
ARF – Annual Retention Fee
ARM – Annual Representative Meeting
ASH – Action on Smoking and Health
BDA – British Dental Association
BMAPS – BMA Professional Services
BMAS – BMA Services
BMJPG – BMJ Publishing Group
BNF – *British National Formulary*
BRPAD – Board of the Representational and Political Activities
    Directorate (later the Political Board)
CARE – Career Average Revalued Earnings
CC – Consultants Committee
CCCMCH – Central Committee for Community Medicine and
    Community Health
CCG – Clinical Commissioning Group
CCHMS – Central Committee for Hospital Medical Services
CCSC – Central Consultants and Specialists Committee
CCST – Certificate of Completion of Specialist Training
CCT – Certificate of Completion of Training
CEO – Chief Executive Officer
CMA – Commonwealth Medical Association
CMO – Chief Medical Officer
CP – Comité Permanent des Médicins Européens (Standing
    Committee of Doctors of the European Community)
CPD – Continuing Professional Development
CQC – Care Quality Commission (previously the Healthcare
    Commission)
CSAG – Clinical Standards Advisory Group
CST – Certificate of Specialist Training

CVCP – Committee of Vice-Chancellors and Principals
DBE – Dame Commander of the Most Excellent Order of the British Empire
DCR – Detailed Care Record
DDRB – Doctors' and Dentists' Review Body
DH – Department of Health
DHA – District Health Authority
DHSS – Department of Health and Social Security
DMS – Defence Medical Services
DMT – district management team
DPH – Director of Public Health
DPP – Director of Public Prosecutions
EWTD – European Working Time Directive
FHSA – Family Health Services Authority
FPC – family practitioner committees
GM – Genetically Modified
GMC – General Medical Council
GMSC – General Medical Services Committee
GP – General Practitioners
GPASS – General Practice Administration System for Scotland
GPC – General Practitioners Committee
HEE – Health Education England
HFEA – Human Fertilisation and Embryology Authority
HIFA – Health Information for All by 2015
HIV – Human Immunodeficiency Virus
HJSC – Hospital Junior Staff Committee
HPERU – Health Policy and Economic Research Unit
HR – Human Resources
ICMJE – International Committee of Medical Journal Editors
IFH – Information for Health
IROs – Industrial Relations Officers
ISTC – Independent Sector Treatment Centre
IT – Information Technology
IVF – In-vitro fertilisation
JAMA – *Journal of the American Medical Association*
JCC – Joint Consultants Committee
JDC – Junior Doctors Committee
JPAC – Joint Planning Advisory Committee
LES – Local Enhanced Services
LHRP – Local Health Resilience Partnerships
LIFT – Local Improvement Finance Programme
LIG – London Implementation Group
LMC – Local Medical Committee
LNC – Local Negotiating Committee
MASA – Medical Association of South Africa

MASC – Medical Academic Staff Committee
MDU – Medical Defence Union
MEE – Medical Education (England)
MEP – Member of the European Parliament
MHRA – Medicines and Healthcare Products Regulatory Agency
MMC – Modernising Medical Careers
MMC – Monopolies and Mergers Commission
MoD – Ministry of Defence
MPIG – Minimum Practice Income Guarantee
MPTS – Medical Practitioners Tribunal Service
MSC – Medical Students Committee
MTAS – Medical Training Application Service
NAFP – National Association of Fundholding Practices
NAHAT – National Association of Health Authorities and Trusts
NHDs – Notional Half Days
NHS – National Health Service
NHSE – National Health Service Executive
NHSME – National Health Service Management Executive (later the NHS Executive)
NHSPS – NHS Pension Scheme
NICE – National Institute for Clinical Excellence
NPfIT – National Programme for IT
OFT – Office of Fair Trading
OHPA – Office of the Health Professions Adjudicator
PACT – Prescribing Analysis and Cost
Padiv – Public Affairs Division
PAs – Programmed Activities
PAGS – Professional Affinity Group Services Ltd
PB – Political Board
PCG – Primary Care Group
PCT – Primary Care Trust
PFI – Private Finance Initiative
PHE – Public Health England
PHMC – Public Health Medicine Committee
PMETB – Postgraduate Medical Education and Training Board
PMS – Personal Medical Services
Powars – Place of Work Accredited Representatives
PPC – Private Practice Committee
PPPFC – Private Practice and Professional Fees Committee
PRHO/FP – Pre-registration House Officer/Foundation Programme
PVS – Persistent Vegetative State
PWG – Permanent Working Group of European Junior Hospital Doctors
QIPP – Quality Innovation Productivity and Prevention
QOF – Quality and Outcomes Framework

RAE – Research Assessment Exercise
RB – Representative Body
RCGP – Royal College of General Practitioners
RCOG – The Royal College of Obstetricians and Gynaecologists
RDPH – Regional Director of Public Health
REDG – Regional Education and Development Group
RHA – regional health authority
RMI – Resource Management Initiative
SAS – Staff and Associate Specialists
SASC – Staff and Associate Specialists Committee
SCMO – Senior Clinical Medical Officer
SCR – Summary Care Record
SHA – Strategic Health Authority
SiMAP – Sindicato de Medicos de Asistencia Publical
SMG – Senior Management Group
SNP – Scottish National Party
SPAs – Supporting Professional Activities
SpRs – Specialist Registrars
SRM – Special Representative Meeting
TCRC – Tobacco Control Resource Centre
TMSC – Medical Schools Council
TUC – Trades Union Congress
UCL – University College London
UEMO – L'Union Européenne des Médecins Omnipraticiens/
  Médecins de Famille (European Union of General Practitioners/
  Family Physicians)
UEMS – Union Européenne des Médecins Spécialistes (European
  Union of Medical Specialists)
UGC – University Grants Committee
UMT – Unit of Medical Time
WAG – Welsh Assembly Government (later the Welsh Government)
WG – Welsh Government
WHO – World Health Organisation
WMA – World Medical Association

Chapter 1

The Thatcher years: 'Steaming through the NHS'[1] 1982–1992

This book begins as Mrs Thatcher's Conservative government, which had been mandated to sort out the deep-seated economic and industrial problems that had come to a head in the 'winter of discontent' of 1978–79, was getting off to a shaky start. Her government later gained popularity through the Falklands war, leading to an increased majority of 144 in the general election of 1983. It then embarked on a radical programme of deregulation and privatisation, with rigorous controls on borrowing to bring down inflation, and a determined attack on the power of the trade unions, culminating in the defeat of the miners' strike in 1985. Then, in the late 1980s, the government turned its attention to the NHS.

Meanwhile, at the start of this period, the BMA was emerging from the pain and gain of industrial action it had taken in the 1970s. Led until 1984 by Anthony (later Sir Anthony) Grabham, a veteran of the consultants' battles with the previous government, it now faced new political challenges. These came mainly from the introduction of management (a concept until then largely alien to medicine), from workforce imbalances in the hospital service, and from financial pressure on GPs, particularly on prescribing.

NHS Reorganisation

In April 1982 a major NHS reorganisation in England abolished the old area health authorities and established two structures above local units: the regional health authority (RHA) and the district health authority (DHA). Family practitioner committees (FPCs) were to continue, with the status of independent health authorities. The BMA did not object, but the loss of experienced area medical officers was a problem for the

---

[1] Stephen Lock, *Steaming through the NHS. BMJ* 1989; 298:619. (The reference is to the then fashionable crime of 'steaming' where "a gang runs amok through a crowded train or carnival demanding money at knifepoint. The aim is achieved through bewilderment and fear . . . The government has used a comparable strategy . . . in imposing its plans for the fourth reorganisation of the health service.")

specialty of community medicine and for the NHS. Area medical committees, with their statutory right to give advice and to be consulted, disappeared and most districts (other than in Wales) chose not to establish an equivalent district medical committee. At regional level the question of medical advice remained a matter of contention, and was not resolved.[2] The tradition of strong professional advisory machinery began to lapse, to be replaced by the beginnings of a new management culture. DHAs were to be advised by a district management team (DMT), which would include a consultant, a GP, a community physician and a district administrator, and were to establish management teams at the next level down: hospital and community units. Most consultant contracts in England would remain with the RHA.

In general practice the independent status of FPCs was welcomed, but the process of enshrining this provision in the Health and Social Security Adjudications Bill became the subject of political machinations. Under pressure from Labour, the government was prepared to drop the clauses relating to FPC independence in order to rush the Bill through before the 1983 election. When the government was re-elected and in a stronger position these clauses were reinstated, though not implemented until April 1985.

Management in the NHS

During the 1970s and 1980s the world of business was following American trends and embracing the 'science' of management, with its proliferation of theories and books, training courses and seminars. The Conservative government had its ideological roots in this world, and had been striving to introduce its disciplines and dynamism into what it saw as a cumbersome and cautious public sector where efficiency was hampered by the pernicious power of the trade unions and professions. The new government had brought in successful business people to look at key areas of public sector activity, notably appointing Sir Derek (later Lord) Rayner from Marks and Spencer to run a programme of efficiency scrutinies on government departments.

The term 'management' first came to the NHS with the 1982 reorganisation, which introduced management teams, though without real powers. Administrators, previously seen as support staff, had been given a more important role and now wanted to challenge established behaviour. By 1983 this was creating friction and the BMA, while

---

[2] Rivett G.G. National Health Service History n.d. retrieved November 2012 from www.nhshistory.net.

encouraging its members to play an active role as members of DMTs or as unit medical representatives (UMRs), struggled with the concept of doctors having managerial responsibility. Were these representative roles, in which doctors would put forward the views of colleagues and try to reach consensus decisions? Or would they be crossing a divide and compromising their professional values by accepting financial responsibility? At this stage the issues were not crystallised, but the BMA generally felt that if important NHS decisions were being taken then doctors should be involved. It also noted that the new management roles would involve additional time and effort, and opened discussions with the Department of Health and Social Security (DHSS) about how to reward doctors who took them on.

As the exchanges trundled on, the government, struggling with a long industrial dispute over pay for nurses and other NHS staff, decided to bring the question of NHS management to the forefront. It asked Roy (later Sir Roy) Griffiths, the managing director of Sainsbury's, to head an inquiry: he turned out to be one of the government's more inspired appointments. Through a combination of personal charm, jargon-free language, and an apparent willingness to engage rather than confront, he built up a high degree of credibility and his report led to genuine debate and real change.

The Griffiths report, *The NHS Management Inquiry*, was published in October 1983. He diagnosed the problem with an often quoted image: 'If Florence Nightingale was carrying her lamp through the corridors of the NHS today, she would almost certainly be searching for the people in charge'. The solution was straightforward and presented as a symptomatic treatment: a general manager would be appointed at each level of NHS organisation (region, district and unit) and would be accountable for the use of resources at that level. Clinicians, and particularly doctors, would be fully involved and encouraged to become general managers themselves. The treatment was actually systemic: if managers were truly empowered, it would bring about real shifts in the traditional balances of power in the NHS.

BMA committees seemed to grasp the far-reaching nature of the proposals without fully visualising where they might lead. It was a worrying departure from the status quo, but it was persuasively articulated and clearly represented current thinking. The BMA debates that followed included much soul searching, and two distinct camps emerged. One clung to the prevailing medical ethos: a doctor was an independent professional whose prime relationship was with the individual patient, and whose first duty was to act in that patient's interests; the health authority was an administrative mechanism to support doctors in their professional practice. This group feared that accepting explicit responsibility for the use of resources would dilute doctors' ability to stand up for individual patients, which amounted to a conflict of interest or even a dereliction of duty. The other group felt that this position was no longer tenable in the face of constrained resources and an increasingly complex medical environment, and that doctors could best protect their patients' interests by being fully involved in management and ensuring that medical voices were in the forefront. In some form and for many years this debate was central to the BMA's medico-political dilemmas, from the terms of joining the NHS in 1948 to the current issue about GPs' role in commissioning.

When the Griffiths report raised this dilemma it was a significant moment. Sir Roy Griffiths had adeptly positioned his report as a discussion document and not as the drawing up of battle lines. The BMA discussed it robustly and ended up rejecting the arguments for non-participation. The modernising view prevailed, though with caveats about the difficulties of reconciling clinical and management roles, and a call for the proposals to be piloted. When the implementation circular was issued in June 1984, the BMA was already talking with the DHSS about the terms on which doctors might take on management roles, and was recommending to members that they become involved. This was a big step: from now on the debate was not *whether* doctors should be involved in management, but *how*.

At first it seemed that Sir Roy's open style was paying dividends, and the BMA and the Department agreed over an appointment process for general managers. Staff were to be consulted and steps taken to ensure that appointees would 'command the confidence of representative members of the management team'.[3] They also agreed on how clinicians who became general managers would be paid, and established the important principle that the job could be part-time. The Central Committee for Hospital Medical Services (CCHMS) and the General Medical Services Committee (GMSC), representing senior hospital doctors and GPs respectively, were convinced that doctors would quickly lose credibility among their colleagues if they gave up all their clinical work, and the rationale for medical managers would disappear. There would also be practical difficulties in returning to clinical practice

---

[3] HC(84)13 Health Service Management: Implementation of the NHS Management Inquiry.

after a period in full-time general management. So they negotiated for cover to be provided for some clinical sessions while doctors undertook a management role, and for administrative support to enable them to take on the extra work.

However, it soon emerged that health authorities did not see the same need as the BMA, or indeed Sir Roy Griffiths, to ensure that doctors played a full part in the new structures. Many of them grasped the opportunity to break out from what they saw as the shackles of medically dominated decision-making. New district general managers quickly decided that a management *board*, with members accountable to the general manager, would be a better model than the old district management *team* with its representative membership. Community physicians felt particularly isolated as few had been appointed district general managers. When the BMA raised cases where the circular's principles had been ignored, the Department showed little interest in enforcing them. The genie of management was out of the bottle, and within a few years various models had emerged (as Sir Roy Griffiths had no doubt expected them to) – from the authoritarian bosses from industry who expected their orders to be followed by a respectful work-force to the inspirational leaders who reconciled differing interests and articulated priorities that all could work towards.

Scores of doctors did take on general manager roles, mostly in units, but also at district and at region. Dame Rosemary Rue, later a distinguished BMA President, successfully combined the post of regional general manager in Oxford with that of regional medical officer. Not all enjoyed the experience, but some relished the challenge, bringing to the role the qualities that had made them successful clinicians. Soon the BMA set up a special group to allow medical managers to share experiences and use their perspective to advise and influence the organisation. The group became a committee, which underwent various constitutional changes, but it has remained an important part of the BMA's determination to represent all doctors.

Griffiths also introduced management budgeting, which had been a key recommendation. Budgets were set up in four demonstration districts. The CCHMS and the Joint Consultants Committee (JCC) took particular interest in this work and monitored progress. But before long information technology problems were getting in the way of the sensible idea that clinicians should be able to monitor their use of resources. When a new NHS director of finance, Ian Mills, arrived from international accountants Price Waterhouse in 1986, he quickly realised that persisting with this scheme would endanger confidence. He pronounced the exercise a failure, and determined on a new start. Working closely with the consultants' committees he chose six new sites and launched the Resource Management Initiative (RMI) with a set of agreed principles and objectives, and a commitment to full evaluation before any extension. The Chairman of the CCHMS, Paddy Ross, was an enthusiastic advocate and his own hospital at Winchester became one of the six sites. He developed a good relationship with Ian Mills, whom he trusted (more than he did the politicians) to carry through the commitment to evaluate. For two years the CCHMS monitored the schemes closely, sending groups of committee members – enthusiasts and sceptics – to visit the hospitals and talk to the consultants involved.

They learnt much, particularly about the need for clinical directorates: management structures at specialty level that would involve clinicians in planning and monitoring activity. In time these replaced general management as the preferred model for medical involvement. But before the promised evaluation, politics intervened and when the white paper *Working for Patients (see p 29 below)* was published in 1989, the government announced that it would roll out the RMI come what may. It then became something very different, focusing on information systems that would cope with the new contracting environment. The profession's willingness to engage in a positive initiative had been thrown back in its face. Paddy Ross took the breach of faith to heart and it undoubtedly coloured the response of the Central Consultants and Specialists Committee (CCSC) (as it became known in 1989) to the white paper.

Medical management has continued to develop in the NHS. The appointment of a medical director in every trust from 1990 gave doctors board level responsibility, while rules on clinical governance from 1999 brought an enhanced role for clinical directors as part of trusts' new accountabilty for quality as well as resources. Medical management has become a recognised discipline with its own faculty.[4] Doctors now expect to be involved in management decisions and many accept formal management roles. Yet the true integration of clinicians into NHS management that Griffiths hoped for has not happened, and the cultural and professional divide between doctors and managers that has characterised the NHS for decades is still evident in the tensions and disputes that regularly arise.

---

[4] The Faculty of Medical Leadership and Management, launched in 2011 by the Academy of Medical Royal Colleges.

Workforce problems

One problem that has dogged the NHS from the start is having the right number of doctors in the appropriate grades to staff its hospitals. It boils down to reconciling four things: hospitals need to maintain safe levels of staffing, particularly at night; doctors need a career structure that offers proper training, reasonable working conditions and the prospect of a consultant post; patients need to be treated by doctors with appropriate training and seniority; and the country needs to control costs by not training more doctors than the NHS wants to employ.

By the beginning of the period covered in this book the imbalance between junior and senior doctors had become acute. For trainees, who were contracted for an average of 90 hours per week (and often worked more), the prospect of becoming a consultant was distant and uncertain. Many hung on as senior registrars into their 40s, while lower down the ladder some qualified doctors were unable to progress and registered as unemployed. In October 1981, in response to the rising concern, the influential House of Commons Social Services Committee published a report on medical education. This became known as the Short Report after Mrs Renée Short, the Labour MP who chaired the committee. It was the latest, and perhaps the most radical, in a long series on this issue by individuals, working parties and even a Royal Commission.

The report's central recommendation, intended to ensure that more hospital care was provided by fully trained doctors, was to double the number of consultants over five years, thereby changing dramatically the balance of the hospital career structure. There would be career posts for all juniors then in training, but the system of 'firms', where each consultant was supported by his or her own team of juniors, would end. With greatly reduced support consultants would have to take on some routine emergency duties themselves, and might need to be resident in hospital when on call.

Within the BMA, the Short Report fanned antagonism between the CCHMS and the Hospital Junior Staff Committee (HJSC). In the 1970s the juniors had taken industrial action over their contract,[5] and the committee, led from 1980 by Michael Rees (who later chaired the BMA's Medical Academic Staff Committee), had gone on to press hard for an improved career structure. They had submitted their own evidence to the Short committee – proposing radical solutions – without

---

[5] Elston Grey-Turner and F M Sutherland: *History of the BMA Vol II 1932–1981*, p 144.

getting it approved by other parts of the BMA. Such insubordination was not well received by the seniors, and there were some tense exchanges, particularly when the junior doctors' committee warmly welcomed the main recommendations of the Short Report while the consultants' committee had serious reservations, expressed with twinkling charm and sharp negotiating skills by its chairman, David Bolt. But after some hard bargaining in (literally, in those days) smoke-filled rooms, the two committees agreed on a joint response that managed to paper over their deep differences.

On some issues there was real agreement. The Short Report had recommended expanding medical student intake from 3,500 to 4,080, but the juniors feared medical unemployment and baulked at an increase. Seniors and juniors agreed and the BMA called for a freeze. Both groups also agreed the need for better manpower data and for the major loophole of honorary contracts to be brought under control. Large numbers of 'research' posts at senior house officer or registrar level were being created on 'soft money', often without real training content and not appearing in any official statistics. A proposal to review the mechanisms for monitoring and controlling the number of overseas doctors in 'training posts' – again often with no training content – was also welcomed. Short recommended legal powers to enforce the existing terms and conditions of service on juniors' working time, which specified an average of 80 contracted hours per week and a minimum of 88 hours per week off duty. But legislation on hours was a step too far even for the HJSC, which agreed with the CCHMS on getting the hours down to 80 as an aspiration, with the caveat that it would be done in a reasonable time scale to avoid having to adopt shift patterns that would compromise continuity of care. And though the Short report focused mainly on hospital medicine, it did note the significance of general practice in workforce planning, and recommended a reduction in average list size to 1700; this was welcomed by the GMSC.

The main battle was over the controversial central recommendation of a doubling of consultant numbers. The final agreed position was to accept the need for a balanced expansion of posts, provided that adequate funding and facilities were made available, quality was maintained and existing consultants were safeguarded. This seemed a disappointing compromise for the HJSC, but was a step forward: CCHMS had accepted the need for consultant expansion, with all its implications for diluting junior support and ultimately changing consultants' working patterns. Having taken the issue as far as it could, the HJSC then shifted its focus to junior doctors' hours of work and medical student numbers.

Led first by Stephen Brearley, then by Robert Hangartner, who later worked for the Department of Health, the committee began a long campaign to reduce hours *(see p 21)*. Under pressure the Chief Medical Officer held a special conference, which resulted in a circular outlawing 1:1 rotas. It also set up district working parties composed of consultants and junior doctors to review other onerous rotas and reduce them to 1:3 where possible. On overall numbers the juniors continued to flag the issue of medical unemployment through surveys and publicity, and persuaded the BMA to accept a tougher policy when the 1984 Annual Representative Meeting endorsed a Council working party's recommendation to reduce medical school intake to below 1979 levels.

Meanwhile the consultants focused on the issue of an expansion of posts. Although the need for an increase had now been accepted, consultants locally continued to resist changes that might mean a return to the kind of routine and out-of-hours duties they thought they had left behind at the end of their training. They had genuine concerns about compromising the quality of care by abandoning their traditional continuing responsibility for patients. But in resisting the appointment of an additional younger and more energetic colleague some undoubtedly also had an eye on protecting their private practices. As workloads increased during the 1980s and 1990s, there was greater readiness to share the burden and the constraint on new posts was usually financial. It was not until much later, with the Labour government's period of investment between 2000 and 2008, that significant consultant expansion of around 5% per annum took place.

In February 1982 the government had largely accepted the Short Report's recommendations and established a 'CMO's initiative on manpower' to implement them. Michael Abrams, the CMO's deputy in England, who was charged with the task, talked cheerfully of moving to a 'consultant-provided service', but was to find this a tough proposition, given its major practical and financial implications as well as the resistance of a still-powerful consultant body. Michael Abrams asked regional medical officers to push ahead with abolishing registrar and SHO posts and replacing them with new 'Short' consultants, who would work with reduced junior support.

But David Bolt had other ideas; he set about dismantling the CMO's initiative, and replacing it with a more practical, more palatable but nevertheless progressive initiative of his own. Although London-based, he worked in a district general hospital, the West Middlesex, and had a good understanding of what motivated consultants. He had been the architect of a proposed new contract in 1978; when it failed – inappropriately priced by the Review Body in 1979 – he and Anthony Grabham had deftly stitched together a deal with the incoming Conservative government. This deal had salvaged key elements, increasing pay by 1/11 for maximum part-timers and giving whole-timers the right to limited private practice. During that time he travelled tirelessly to meetings around the country and was well known by consultants, who warmed to his charm and evident good faith.

David Bolt now sent medical staff committees a commentary on the practical difficulties that the Department's plans might cause: they would increase demands on non-medical staff, create problems in covering consultants' absences and have major financial implications. He then wrote directly to regional medical officers with his own critique of Michael Abrams' paper, appealing to them as colleagues not to implement the changes. His letter concluded: 'It is greatly to be hoped that you and your colleagues, seeing the real problems of hospital staffing more clearly than is, perhaps, possible at departmental level, will not find in this document a pattern of action which you are anxious to pursue.'

Meanwhile he engaged the royal colleges in discussion and in May 1982 published with them in the *British Medical Journal* a proposed alternative solution, on which consultants would be balloted. The article said that there should be a drive for more consultants, but only in the acute specialties of general medicine, general surgery, and obstetrics and gynaecology. New posts would be identified by calling for bids that were justified by workload. Regional manpower committees, working to regional targets, would reduce registrar posts where possible and relate them to senior registrar vacancies.

A ballot was duly held and 85% of consultants supported these proposals. The DHSS had little choice but to enter discussions with the consultants' committee and the plan was put into action. The first year saw 525 bids for new posts. Regional manpower committees set about reviewing registrar posts and plans were made to extend the initiative to other specialties. But 525 new consultant posts was a large financial outlay, and soon the NHS's increasing financial problems began to undermine the progress that had been made.

Over the next two or three years change was slow. A new body, the Joint Planning Advisory Committee (JPAC), was established to set regional quotas and it managed to bring senior registrar numbers under control (including honorary posts, despite reluctance from the royal colleges). But the rate of consultant expansion remained low. Meanwhile, the problems of women doctors – and particularly the lack of part-time training opportunities for them – were coming to the fore, with recommendations from a BMA working party chaired by Ann Blyth increasing the pressure for change. An overseas doctors' training scheme was introduced, with the support of the royal colleges, to improve the content of training as well as to control numbers. In 1983 the government set up a high-powered body, the Advisory Committee on Medical Manpower (ACMM), to make recommendations, particularly on the key supply question: the number of medical students. Their report was with ministers for a year, and when it was finally published in March 1985 the figures were already well out of date. It ducked the issue of numbers, making no proposal to reduce medical school intake.

Government ministers now faced more pressure from the BMA and the royal colleges to deal with the continuing imbalance. They brought in immigration controls for overseas doctors, but with no other solution to hand, the government took the time-honoured step of setting up a working party: in this case a ministerial group, chaired by health minister Barney Hayhoe and including representatives of BMA seniors and juniors, the royal colleges, the departments of health in all the nations, and regional health authorities (representing the employers). On the profession's side the group was led by Anthony Grabham, who had recently retired after a five year term as Chairman of BMA Council and then in a contested election had become the first chairman of the Joint Consultants Committee to come from the BMA rather than the royal colleges. He saw that the pressure that he and others had been exerting provided a great opportunity. Together with the departmental officials, ably led by the deputy chief medical officer Diana Walford, the group worked hard to get a positive outcome. Its report, *Achieving a Balance*, was published in July 1986. It was a concise paper that clearly spelt out how to put the career balance back on track:

- specific incentives for consultant expansion, including 100 new, centrally-funded posts;
- encouragement of early and partial retirement for existing consultants;

- more rigorous control of registrar and senior registrar numbers, with the number of 'career' registrars (those who would stay in the country, as opposed to 'visiting' registrars who would return to their overseas homes) linked to future consultant vacancies; and
- the establishment of a new service grade, at a lower level than any previously mooted 'sub-consultant' grade.

Anthony Grabham was determined to maintain the momentum. Having ensured the alignment of ministerial interests (by then those of Tony Newton, who replaced Barney Hayhoe in 1986) with the success of the plan, and having overcome some reservations from the juniors (led by Peter Hawker, a later chairman of the consultants, then by Dallas Brodie from Scotland), he kept the pressure up to agree the detail of implementation. This was done by a high-level steering group, which published *Achieving a Balance: Plan for Action* in October 1987. It included guidance on how regional manpower committees should implement key aspects, and introduced the concept of the 'safety-net'. This was a review in each acute unit to ensure that the proposed removal of junior posts would not risk unsafe levels of cover or force consultants to work inappropriately in an attempt to fill gaps in junior rotas. The plan also fleshed out the new intermediate service grade, which became known as the staff grade. A difficult negotiation between seniors and juniors finalised the staff grade's terms and conditions, and also settled on mechanisms to ensure that they would not exceed 10% of the consultant establishment. The negotiation hit difficulties over how to reward duties additional to the basic contract; as is often the case the problem was how to make such work pensionable. A solution had not been found when the contract was finally issued in 1988, and it was a continuing cause of dissatisfaction.

For a while those involved in the negotiations felt that they might have brought order to the chaos of hospital staffing. However, signs were beginning to appear that the plan was being compromised by cash problems in the NHS. When the 1988 workforce figures were published, consultant expansion had dropped to 1.5%, below the levels before *Achieving a Balance*. By then, the NHS funding crisis had become the most pressing problem affecting hospitals.

The workforce battles of the 1980s had consumed a great deal of energy. They did not at the time produce dramatic change, though the most severe problems were alleviated by well targeted injections of money. Though it did not materialise, Mrs Short's radical vision had sewn seeds that did take root; underlying shifts in attitude had taken place, towards greater control over numbers and towards consultant expansion as a policy aim. But no ideal model of medical staffing had emerged, and tensions would continue to arise over the coming decades as different aspects of the workforce conundrum competed for priority.

GP negotiations

During the early 1980s GPs became aware that the new Conservative government was contemplating changes to general practice. Their committee, the GMSC, spent time thinking about possible changes to the GP contract, but before discussions could take place, relationships between them and government were strained by the deputising crisis of 1983/84. Many GPs were using deputising services to cover out-of-hours work and these were often provided commercially. The BMA had a financial interest in some of these services through its partnership with a company called Air Call, later known as Healthcall. (It was a relationship which in due course gave rise to conflicts of interest and was terminated in 1999.) The quality of deputising services was variable, and public disquiet began to grow about the extent of their use and about safety issues. Late in 1983, spurred by an example of bad practice that Kenneth Clarke, the Minister of Health, had encountered during the election campaign, and which generated TV publicity, the government decided to act. Without discussion Clarke issued a draft circular proposing radical changes to the regulation of deputising services, putting a limit on their use by individual GPs and giving FPCs a supervisory role.

GPs were furious. They were not used to such direct political interference in what they saw as professional matters, and the GMSC reacted strongly, describing the government's action as Orwellian. They sent an angry letter to the minister rejecting the proposals, and BMA Council supported them by expressing 'extreme disquiet'. This led to a heated meeting between the GMSC chairman John Ball and the Health Minister Kenneth Clarke, two robust combatants who nevertheless found a way to negotiate. A series of meetings was set up with officials to thrash out an acceptable compromise and a new circular was drawn up which tightened the monitoring of deputising services but gave FPCs greater flexibility on how to do this. The crisis passed, but Mr Clarke had flexed his muscles. Although he had made concessions (probably at the behest of the Secretary of State, Norman Fowler) GPs had sensed a new hostility from the government, to which they had responded with heat. More exchanges would follow.

The next skirmish was over the government's introduction of a limited list of drugs that could be prescribed on the NHS. In 1982 the departmental Greenfield Report had looked at making prescribing more effective. The GMSC had given evidence to the review and had largely supported the recommendations. The report rejected the idea of a limited list of products from which doctors could prescribe, and proposed other ways of reducing costs, such as generic substitutions and extending hospital local pharmacopoeias. But out of the blue on 8 November 1984, the morning after a cordial dinner for BMA chairmen to meet the new Chief Medical Officer for England, Donald Acheson (later Sir Donald, and BMA President in 1996/7), the government announced it would introduce a limited list by regulation and without consultation.

The chairmanship of the GMSC had passed to Michael Wilson, a GP from a rural practice in Yorkshire, who had been involved in the committee since the battles between GPs and government in the 1960s.[6] He and his committee reacted strongly. GPs saw the limited list as an unwarranted attack on their clinical freedom and feared it would lead to only the cheapest, most basic drugs being available on the NHS, with patients having to pay for all others. The committee launched a campaign against the change, sending letters to MPs and producing leaflets to explain the potential dangers to patients. An initial meeting between Michael Wilson and the Secretary of State, Norman Fowler, failed to reassure the GMSC, and thereafter the issue was largely handled by Kenneth Clarke. He rebutted the profession's concerns with the characteristic robustness that came to infuriate the BMA when he later returned as Secretary of State trying to drive through Mrs Thatcher's NHS changes.

There was an angry exchange of letters in which Kenneth Clarke and Michael Wilson each accused the other of misrepresentation. The GMSC threatened to use European law to challenge the regulations and wrote to Jacques Delors, the European Commissioner, suggesting that the effective black-listing of some products might contravene the free market. The BMA as a whole supported the GPs' actions, though in practice hospital doctors, used to prescribing from a hospital formulary, were not greatly concerned. Despite this opposition, the limited list came into effect in 1985. It did indeed create bureaucratic problems: many amendments to the list led to confusion over what was or was

---

[6] Elston Grey-Turner and F M Sutherland: *History of the BMA Vol II 1932–1981,* Ch 5.

not included, and there were discussions about a local 'override' procedure and an appeals process. Within a year the Department agreed
to produce a consolidated schedule, and to consider an appropriate
review mechanism. Yet the list was not the disaster that the GMSC
had feared. It had perhaps chosen the battle unwisely: its views had
been disregarded and Kenneth Clarke could contemplate future battles
with greater confidence.

The next confrontation proved more serious. It again involved
Kenneth Clarke, but began not with an unexpected *coup de main* but
with a consultation over a green paper. In April 1986 *Primary Health
Care: An Agenda for Discussion* was published, the outcome of a review
launched two years earlier by the Secretary of State, Norman Fowler,
and carried out by Kenneth Clarke with a team of civil servants. It was
intended to consider changes in general practice for which pressures
had been building up. The GMSC had been seeking improvements,
including better out-of-hours pay, and had sent a list of proposals to the government in December 1985. A 1981 report by Donald
Acheson (then Dean of Southampton medical school) had called for
big changes in primary care in London and had still not been acted
upon. Government think tanks had been highlighting the problem of controlling costs in general practice and had commissioned a
report by accountants Binder Hamlyn. (Though never published, it
was thought to explore the possibility of cash limits in general practice and to recommend changes in how much practice income should
come from capitation – the number of patients on a practice's list.)
Also published about this time was a review of community nursing
by Julia Cumberlege (later Baroness Cumberlege and a health minister, but at the time a health authority chairman), and a consultation
on ways of making FPC complaints procedures easier for patients
to use.

The green paper raised a number of concerns from local medical
committees (LMCs), which were distilled at a special LMC conference
in November 1986. Those present felt that the proposed 'good practice allowance' raised difficulties in principle and in practice, and they
regarded the increase in the proportion of income from capitation with
suspicion. They strongly opposed the theme of a more commercialised
and competitive primary care system, with 'health care shops', 'neigh-
bourhood nursing teams' based outside general practice as proposed
by Cumberlege, and 'service committees' for dealing with complaints.
They did, however, welcome the possibility of more resources.

After spending some time deliberating on its response, the government in November 1987 published a white paper on primary health care: *Promoting Better Health*. The 'good practice allowance' had been translated into the concept of financial incentives for some services, including postgraduate education and staff training. The proportion of payment that reflected list size would be increased, and compulsory retirement would be introduced when GPs reached 70. There were also proposals on cash limits for the premises and ancillary staff elements of general practice expenses; against the background of increasing financial stringency this was a worrying development.

The GMSC broadly welcomed the white paper, though with the caveat that increasing consumer choice would quickly founder if the service was underfunded. The committee strongly opposed the cash limits proposal though failed to prevent it being written into the Health and Medicines Act in 1988. But it felt there was scope for negotiation on the elements of a new contract, and set up a number of working parties with the Department to work through the details.

At first the discussions were constructive. But in March 1988 the DHSS proposed more substantial changes to the contract than had been expected, and the negotiations became tougher. Tension between the government and doctors was increasing. The GMSC negotiators felt they made good progress with officials but were suspicious of ministerial intentions: since January the Prime Minister, Margaret Thatcher, had been conducting a review of the NHS behind closed doors, and rumours about its scope were raising fears that it might significantly affect the negotiations.

In September, in an attempt to clear the air, Michael Wilson met Kenneth Clarke, who had been promoted to Secretary of State in July, and his Minister for Health, Edwina Currie. They issued a statement agreeing on the objectives of the discussions and offering to work together in order to raise standards in general practice, make general practice more responsive to consumers, introduce financial rewards for developing services, and ensure that better information was provided to FPCs in Scotland. The Secretary of State also stated unequivocally that the NHS Review was mainly about the hospital service and would not affect the status of GPs nor impact on their clinical freedom.

The harmony was short-lived. It soon transpired that the Department of Health (DH) had been consulting FPCs directly about possible changes, and within a month of the meeting it had sent out a document: *Key Ministerial Aims for FPCs 1989–91*. The document, on which the GMSC had not been consulted, suggested that FPCs should monitor the prescribing patterns of individual GPs and seek advice from independent medical advisers rather than LMCs. The GMSC strongly objected, but the government pressed on. Against a background of press interest generated by a National Audit Office report[7] critical of the management of family practitioner services, it encouraged FPCs to implement changes, without waiting for the new regulations.

GPs around the country felt that ministers were expressing ill-informed views about their work, and at a meeting of the GMSC in October 1988 LMC representatives pressed Michael Wilson and his negotiators to withdraw from negotiations. The debate was difficult, and the negotiators acknowledged that the climate had changed and a positive outcome looked less likely. But in the end they were supported as it was 'important to remain in the negotiating forum to seek to achieve the best possible outcome for the profession'.

But problems continued to arise, such as an argument with the DH over the use of PACT (Prescribing Analysis and Cost), a system to support GPs, which had been subverted into a management tool for FPCs to monitor prescribing. Then, just before the publication of the white paper *Working for Patients* in January 1989, the DH unexpectedly postponed a scheduled negotiating meeting. This was despite Mr Clarke's assurance three months earlier that the NHS review, which had led to the white paper, would not affect GPs. When it came out the white paper did propose major changes for general practice, including an increase in capitation from 46% to 60%, freedom for patients to change their GP, an FPC-led system of medical audit, indicative drug budgets (another new way to limit prescribing) and a major revamp of the composition of FPCs (only one doctor out of 11 members instead of 15 out of 31). Most significant was a proposal that some GPs could become fundholders, responsible for purchasing hospital care for their patients (*for the GMSC's response to fundholding, see nn*). The GMSC's suspicions of bad faith were confirmed.

From that point the temperature rose still further. The GMSC and Mr Clarke conducted a sharp debate in formal correspondence between them, letters to GPs, and in the media. It began to overlap with the BMA's wider campaign against other aspects of *Working for Patients (see this chapter below)*, and while the GP contract was

---

[7] National Audit Office: *Management of the Family Practitioner Services.* (HC 498) May 1988.

kept apart from the BMA's overall responses, there can be little doubt that the perception of Mr Clarke as chief tormentor of GPs and their committee spilled over into the BMA's characterisation of him as the man who didn't listen to medical advice *(see p 37)*. By the same token it is likely that Kenneth Clarke's experience of the GMSC's resistance to earlier changes now increased his resolve to drive these proposals through come what may. The frequent terse exchanges of letters between Michael Wilson and Kenneth Clarke at this time suggest a fiercely hostile atmosphere in which Mr Clarke's jaunty dismissals of objections played badly with Michael Wilson's uncompromising Yorkshire determination to defend GPs' interests in principle and to the last detail.

GPs attending the next meeting of the GMSC after the white paper were angry, prompting the committee to defend itself by publishing a full report on the negotiations so far. Mr Clarke called this a breach of confidentiality and declared that he would write to all GPs with his version of events. Michael Wilson responded that he had informed officials about the report and had even agreed a form of words with them. Nevertheless, on 23 February, Kenneth Clarke wrote to GPs to inform them of the new contract that he would introduce on 1 April 1990. He would negotiate on some details but would not delay the timing. A special LMC conference was called at which the proposed contract was formally rejected. The conference did, however, mandate the GMSC to negotiate. A series of meetings culminated in a three-day session at the Selsdon Park Hotel in Surrey.

This meeting, in early May 1989, took place against the background of a public war of words that had descended into a slanging match, with Mr Clarke writing to MPs with inflated claims about GPs' remuneration (he included expenses as well as pay), and the GMSC replying: 'Mr Clarke's comparison is like saying the PM's salary is the same as the amount needed to run Downing Street'. There were letters in *The Independent,* and leaks about the bitterness of negotiations and the concessions allegedly wrung out of Mr Clarke. Some Tory MPs became openly hostile to the GPs' committee, and Michael Wilson was subjected to some vitriolic remarks when he appeared before the Conservative Health Committee.

Nevertheless progress was made at Selsdon Park, and the bones of an agreement were thrashed out. A meeting was convened for 4 May with the ministers, then Kenneth Clarke and David Mellor, to try to resolve the outstanding issues. It was a tough meeting which lasted

10 hours, punctuated by breaks for the Secretary of State's cigars. But there was sufficient movement for Michael Wilson and his negotiators to conclude that they should come to an agreement rather than risk a contract being imposed against the profession's wishes. The main improvement they negotiated was in capitation, which would be 55% rather than the proposed 60%, with the difference accounted for by new fees for health checks, child health screening and working in deprived areas. The 11-point document also included increased hours of availability, changes in prevention targets, night visit fees, minor surgery payments, a reduction in seniority payments balanced by a new postgraduate education allowance and a review of rural practice payments. Mr Clarke, who had made concessions, demanded in return that Michael Wilson should 'commend' the contract to doctors in the coming ballot.

This did not satisfy the GMSC. When Michael Wilson brought the proposed contract to them on 18 May, he was strongly criticised for having reached agreement without wider consultation. The negotiators explained that the alternative might have been the imposition of a worse contract. But the committee, reflecting the anger felt by their colleagues about the government's behaviour, could not support their leaders and decided to take no view on the contract in advance of the coming special LMC conference. At this meeting, on 22 June, they debated the contract at great length. Angry speakers felt it would increase workload and administrative burdens and that all-or-nothing payments for hitting targets would be demotivating. They reacted strongly against commending such a contract to the profession. The conference narrowly voted, by 166 votes to 150, to reject the contract and to hold a referendum of GPs.

More than 80% of GPs took part in the ballot and the result was a resounding rejection of the contract by a majority of 76%. The government stood firm, and began a formal consultation on the amendments to the regulations that would be needed to implement the contract. At the end of July Michael Wilson met Kenneth Clarke to convey the results of the ballot, to protest about the proposed timescale for the consultation, and to ask the government to reconsider. Mr Clarke, who was simultaneously fighting the BMA over the wider NHS changes in *Working for Patients*, was in no mood to back down. He agreed to extend the time limits for consultation, but made clear that he would not re-open discussions on the 11 points that he regarded as agreed. On 3 August he wrote to all GPs informing them he would go ahead and introduce the contract.

The GMSC was faced with a classic dilemma: should the negotiators stay at the table and continue to seek improvements or maintain the integrity of their position by walking away? If they walked away they would need to have a positive strategy, such as industrial action, to establish a stronger bargaining position. At the crucial extraordinary meeting of the GMSC in August there were strong voices in favour of mounting an aggressive opposition, but the committee agreed instead to set up a working party to consider alternative strategies and work up plans for possible action later. A major factor in this decision was legal advice that failure to engage with the consultation process would compromise any grounds for industrial action. The working party deliberated through the autumn and considered asking GPs to submit undated resignations from the NHS, an echo of the strategy used successfully in 1965 over the charter for general practice. Meanwhile GMSC members worked hard to respond to the draft regulations, protesting about the unreasonable timescale and the DH's refusal to meet on areas they felt needed further consideration.

Kenneth Clarke kept up the pressure. In October, he reiterated that he would impose the contract from 1 April 1990, with some elements in place from November 1989. The GMSC took legal advice about whether he had powers to impose a contract unilaterally. The prevailing view was that he did. The committee decided to move back from considering industrial action, and instead started compiling a critique of the contract so that its flaws would be exposed to the public. It wrote to MPs, and Kenneth Clarke countered with a leaflet for the public entitled *You and Your GP,* setting out the contract's advantages. This drew howls of anger from grass roots GPs and further protests from Michael Wilson. The anger raged, and as often happened, it was directed at the BMA and the GMSC as well as at the government. At a special conference of LMCs in March 1990, days before the new contract came into effect, there were motions of no confidence in the GMSC negotiators, and frustrated calls for 'professional negotiators' who, some felt, might be better equipped to stop the government riding roughshod over the profession.

Over a long day the LMC representatives came to terms with the reality: the contract would go ahead and there were other battles to fight. The government was pressing on with its wider NHS changes, and this was not the time to waste energy on internal recriminations. The conference reiterated its rejection of the new contract and supported the GMSC in its policy of monitoring implementation and exposing the contract's undoubted defects. It was the only time when a major negotiation between the BMA and government has ended with arrangements imposed that the profession had not, however reluctantly, accepted. Although much of the contract was not substantially different from elements that had been negotiated, the imposition left a bitter legacy and the contract remained deeply unpopular.

Junior doctors' hours of work

The third significant battle at this time was over junior doctors' hours. It began in the 1980s but ploughed on like a submarine through turbulent seas to reach port in 1991, just as the landmark NHS and Community Care Act (*see below*) was receiving Royal Assent. Steps to reduce the hours had been taken in 1982 (*see this chapter, above*) and for a while the problem was subsumed into the more general issue of career structure. Junior doctors hoped that the proposed new consultant posts, together with the 'safety net' reviews, would make progress towards more reasonable working patterns.

By 1988 financial pressures in the NHS had stalled the intended consultant expansion, and junior doctors were becoming increasingly angry at the hours they were working and the lack of a plan to reduce them. Juniors meeting for their annual conference that year were aware that doctors in New York now had legal limitations to the hours they could work. They would also have read a report from Isobel Allen of the Policy Studies Institute on *Doctors and their Careers*, which painted a bleak picture of rock-bottom morale among junior doctors and of the poor outlook for women doctors. The conference took a tough line and called for a statutory limit of 80 hours per week. The HJSC then gave its support to a private member's bill from Lord Rees that sought a limit of 72 hours per week by 1992, reducing thereafter to 60 hours. The bill was blocked by the government, but it created the sort of publicity that the juniors felt was needed. Over Christmas and New Year a group of junior doctors, led by the politically astute activist, Sam Everington, a member of HJSC, created embarrassment for the government and further valuable publicity by chaining themselves to the railings outside the Royal London Hospital.

The juniors' decision to call for legislation caused consternation when they brought it to Council in January 1989; it was a significant departure from previous policy and the consultants particularly were opposed. Momentum was with the juniors, however, who gained the support of the GP members. After a tense debate, with the consultants numerically under-represented at the time (this changed with a new Council constitution a few months later), Council came out in support of a legal limit of 72 hours, with the caveat that it should be implemented 'save in exceptional circumstances'. This policy was endorsed later that year by the Annual Representative Meeting.

This hardened stance, together with the continuing publicity, was enough to put pressure on the government to meet the juniors. The minister, David Mellor, certainly did not want legislation, but would consider ways to speed up the reduction in hours, short of banning rotas more onerous than 1:3 as the juniors had requested. He agreed to seek urgent reports from the district working parties reviewing rotas, but progress stalled again. Though David Mellor had agreed to a 72-hour maximum working week as a long-term objective, little changed and anger continued to build.

As has often happened at the BMA at a time of grassroots frustration, angry members were motivated to stand for election to regional junior doctor committees and to the national HJSC, so that by 1990 the committee's mood was militant and members were calling for more extreme tactics. Sam Everington, a barrister as well as a doctor, highlighted the case of Chris Johnstone, a junior who was taking legal action against Bloomsbury Health Authority for allegedly causing him personal injury by forcing him to work intolerable hours and thus endangering his health and the safety of patients. Sam Everington persuaded BMA Council to take on the funding of the case and thus benefit from the publicity.

Virginia Bottomley, who had succeeded David Mellor as Minister for Health, was increasingly uncomfortable with the publicity on this issue and agreed to meet juniors' leaders again. She had recently published *Patterns of Hospital Medical Staffing,* a report by Robin Dowie of the British Postgraduate Medical Federation, which provided further evidence that junior doctors were commonly working more than 90 hours per week. The report drew an analogy between junior doctors and Victorian chimney sweeps. However, the minister had sat on the report for some months and it was published just too late to be considered by the review body, which infuriated the juniors' leaders. The Chairman, Graeme McDonald, a psychiatrist from Northern Ireland, and his deputies met her in February 1990, with three demands: penal rates of pay for the most extreme hours worked (known as A Units of Medical Time or AUMTs), the outlawing of rotas more onerous than 1:3, and support for an amendment to the NHS and Community Care

Bill to limit working hours. Mrs Bottomley simply offered a conference of 'all the interested parties'. The juniors' leaders later said they walked out of the meeting – though they had been there for two hours.

The HJSC was unsure whether to take part in the conference. Members were reminded that a similar event in 1982 – set up in response to juniors' pressure – had achieved little. Some felt that progress would be made only through more extreme measures. Graeme McDonald, a pragmatic politician who combined a benign manner with a steely negotiating brain, sensed that the tide was running in their favour and persuaded the committee not to pass up this chance to drive forward their demands.

The juniors did attend the conference in spring 1990, and, given the acrimonious climate, achieved a remarkable outcome: a ministerial working group which would bind all the reluctant players – government, NHS authorities, royal colleges and consultants' leaders – to real measures that would improve juniors' working hours. The working group met regularly for the rest of the year with Virginia Bottomley usually attending. Junior doctors impatiently kept up the pressure on their leaders. When a BMA survey showed that almost half of juniors were willing to provide an emergency service only, they called for a ballot on industrial action. But Mrs Bottomley promised an outcome by the end of the year and on 17 December 1990 a heads of agreement document was signed.

The most important step forward was an agreement by all parties that satisfactory training could be delivered within a 72-hour working week, and that this should now be the common objective. It would be achieved by expanding career grade posts (following the programme proposed in *Achieving a Balance*), developing shift and partial shift systems for some junior posts, and being more flexibile over cross-cover between specialties. A number of other principles were agreed: the standard of juniors' accommodation and support would be improved; juniors would not be expected to undertake non-medical duties; there would be new advice on the composition of on-call teams; the royal colleges should review training posts and withdraw educational approval for posts with excessive hours. In addition the parties accepted the need to rationalise the number of acute sites, particularly in cities, reducing the need for cover, and it was agreed that regional task forces would be established to oversee and monitor the changes. The consultant representatives needed to secure protection for their own members, and as a result of tough negotiation secured the agreement that consultants should not be asked to undertake duties that were in the competence of other grades, that they should not be compulsorily resident in hospital when on call, and that the problem of excessive hours should not merely be transferred from juniors to consultants.

The juniors had conducted a hard-fought campaign, and all those in the working group had compromised to bring this momentous agreement to a conclusion. Stephen Hunter, another psychiatrist, replaced Graeme McDonald as juniors' chairman in October 1990. He had done well to wring concessions out of ministers, royal college presidents and hard-nosed consultant negotiators. But when he brought the agreement to the committee for approval, he was given a rough ride. In a pattern now familiar to BMA negotiators, members were disappointed that their highest hopes – for a foolproof, statutory limitation – had not been met, and suspicious that the principles would not deliver results. It was only with difficulty that he secured enough support to allow the working party to continue its work and thrash out the details, which were then published in the form of *The New Deal* in June 1991.

The New Deal was a radical departure from the previous arrangements over juniors' hours. It laid down a pattern of staged reduction which shaped juniors' working patterns for the next decade, when the European Working Time Directive came into play. The agreement specified maximum weekly hours for the three different types of working pattern: on-call rotas, partial shifts and full shifts. The hours would be reduced most quickly for 'hard-pressed' posts and by the end of 1996 would be down to 72, 64 and 56 hours respectively for all juniors. There would be maximum periods of continuous duty, minimum time off and minimum periods of continuous off-duty for each pattern. The main caveat was that in some circumstances those in higher specialist training could still work up to 83 hours per week. This was known as 'the English clause' having been insisted upon by the pioneering heart surgeon and President of the Royal College of Surgeons, Sir Terence English, who was reflecting his college's conviction that the ability to deliver high quality surgical training is seriously compromised by over-zealous restrictions on hours. It was seen as an unfortunate loophole by non-surgical juniors, and inflamed the vocal minority who continued to criticise *The New Deal* as a sell-out.

The New Deal applied throughout the UK and was introduced with an additional in-year pay rise. It was accompanied in England by extra funding for 200 new consultant posts and 50 staff grade posts. The HJSC issued detailed guidance on the new arrangements, helped to set up regional task forces, and worked with BMA regional staff to help juniors make the deal work and ensure that accommodation improved. The main task left was to negotiate the necessary contractual changes to ensure that fewer hours would not lead to lower pay. The job fell to a new team of negotiators, largely anti-*New Deal* activists who had replaced the previous leaders in the 1991 committee elections. But once in positions of responsibility they pragmatically accepted that the opportunities offered by the *New Deal* must now be grasped, and adopted the solution of replacing UMTs by Additional Duty Hours (ADHs). This eased the transition in the short term, but threw into relief the next problem: the relatively low rates of 'overtime' pay *(see p 84)*.

The NHS review and white paper

On 25 January 1988 the Prime Minister, Mrs Margaret Thatcher, was interviewed on the television programme *Panorama*. The NHS had been under pressure for some time and she faced difficult questions from presenter David Dimbleby. Suddenly, she announced that the government was to undertake a review of the NHS. Her cabinet colleagues and civil servants later admitted this came as a surprise.

Problems over the NHS, and particularly over funding, had been getting more serious for most of the decade as the government's financial stringency took ever more painful effect. Doctors were increasingly frustrated at cuts in services and manpower shortages, while patients faced longer waiting lists and more cancellations. At first the BMA took an analytical approach, publishing reports jointly with the Royal College of Nursing, the Institute of Health Service Management and academic health economists at York and Bath universities. These put forward the now generally accepted argument that health spending must grow in order for output to stand still, and highlighted an ageing population, new treatments with increasing patient expectations, and the rising cost of drugs. In 1985 the BMA and its collaborators called for a 2% increase in NHS funding and created enough pressure for the government to announce modest budget increases, although they were to be financed partly by local cost savings.

More reports in 1986 and 1987 kept up the pressure, but the problem was getting worse. GPs and hospital doctors produced evidence of cases where patient care had been seriously compromised. The GPs' committee published a report *Primary Care Under Pressure*, while the consultants committee, led since 1983 by Maurice Burrows, an anaesthetist from Wirral, came up with figures showing that although health spending had grown overall, spending on 'hospital and community health services' had fallen. Over 18 months he wrote repeatedly to the Secretary of State, Norman Fowler, giving details of ward closures and loss of services, and warning of an impending crisis. His political instincts were to operate quietly behind the scenes, but ministers showed no interest in heeding the warnings. In 1986 the new chairman Paddy Ross, a surgeon from Winchester, held a press conference, published the correspondence and commissioned further surveys.

By late 1987 the crisis that Maurice Burrows had warned of had materialised. There were daily headlines about problems in the NHS. One particularly affecting story was the death of a baby whose operation had been cancelled five times, apparently because of the shortage of intensive care beds. The BMA called for an immediate cash injection of £1.5 billion, underpinned by a long-term link between health spending and the national economy as defined by GDP (gross domestic product), and with additional provision for demographic change and pay restructuring.

By December, frustration among hospital doctors was such that the Presidents of the Royal Colleges of Surgeons, Physicians, and Obstetricians and Gynaecologists took the unusual step of making a public statement about the need to increase funding. They met the Secretary of State and gave a 'doorstep' interview outside the Department which had a considerable public impact. A few weeks later came Mrs Thatcher's *Panorama* interview which in turn led, after a year, to the NHS white paper: *Working for Patients*. This turned out to be one of the most significant events of the period covered by this book. It changed the NHS fundamentally, and galvanised the BMA into the most intense campaign it has undertaken in recent times, hugely raising the Association's profile and provoking a leap in membership and bitter resentment from politicians. The campaign has remained embedded in the medico-political folk memory – and has coloured relationships between the BMA and governments ever since.

The review

The review was announced in public but conducted in secret. Naturally this produced fearful speculation about who was involved, what methodology they were using and what was being discussed. The review lasted a year and as the BMA and other representative organisations were excluded rumours abounded that advice was being taken from the

Conservatives' favoured business gurus, including those in the private health sector. The medical profession was not used to being treated as anything other than a key player in a major review of health policy, and the BMA felt the offence keenly. But it was determined to keep channels of communication open, ensure that funding remained in the public spotlight, and exert influence by whatever means possible. The Association submitted a memorandum of evidence in April, focusing on the need for more funding, and a deputation was allowed to follow this up with oral evidence to the Secretary of State, John Moore. He listened politely, but gave no indication of what was being considered.

It emerged later that the review was chaired by the Prime Minister herself, and the members were John Moore, David Mellor, John Major, Malcolm Rifkind (Secretary of State for Scotland) and Peter Walker (Secretary of State for Wales). For the first few months they focused on how to give the private sector a bigger role, increasing competition and the role of health care insurance. But no clear policy direction emerged until August 1988 when Kenneth Clarke replaced John Moore as Secretary of State. He changed the emphasis from funding to delivery,[8] and the discussions then centred on the concept of an internal market. This idea had been put forward by Professor Alain Enthoven of Stanford University who in 1985 had come to Britain to examine the NHS and then published a book with the Nuffield Provincial Hospitals Trust.[9] The change in emphasis enabled Kenneth Clarke to persuade the Treasury to allocate more money to the NHS (£1.8 billion in England) and gave him the momentum to look at other radical ideas.

One was the notion that GPs could be given budgets to buy hospital services for their patients. It had already been floated along with the American model of health maintenance organisations and in October 1988 it was trailed in the media as a possible recommendation. The second big idea was self-governing hospitals: these would be freed from central controls, including national pay agreements, in order to become more competitive. It was sniffed out and leaked by the highly effective Shadow Health Secretary Robin Cook in January 1989, and it came as a bombshell. It indicated that the review might bring an even more radical upheaval than had been feared, threatening not just structures and funding, but the whole infrastructure of professional

---

[8] Rivett G.G. National Health Service History n.d. retrieved November 2012 from www.nhshistory.net.

[9] Enthoven A. *Reflections on management of the NHS*. London: Nuffield Provincial Hospitals Trust, 1985).

accountability and employment conditions that had been painstakingly built up since 1948.

The white paper

There was not much longer to wait, for the outcome of the review was published as a white paper (*Working for Patients*) on 31 January 1989. It was launched with considerable razzmatazz, including an appearance by Secretary of State Kenneth Clarke before an invited audience at Limehouse Studios, which was relayed by the latest teleconference technology to other invited audiences around the country. The BMA was not briefed in advance about the contents, but it was braced for radical proposals and had planned carefully to avoid a knee-jerk reaction. Its first priority was to get information out to members quickly and then in due course to make a considered response. Leading the effort would be the Chairman of Council John Marks, a Hertfordshire GP and veteran campaigner on general practice issues, who had been a leading member of the GMSC before becoming a popular chairman of the BMA's Representative Body, then Chairman of Council in 1984.

The white paper *Working for Patients* was a wide-ranging document, quite as radical as anticipated, and containing surprises that even the assiduous Robin Cook had not divined. It would involve such a shake-up that much of the detail was still to be worked out, and the government promised more working papers to put flesh on the bones. The key elements of the plan were as follows:

- An internal market would be introduced, with separation of purchasers and providers, contracts for 'core' and 'non core' services, and incentives for improvements in cost and quality through 'money following the patient'.
- Some hospitals could become 'self-governing', free of many of the constraints of central NHS planning (including, crucially, the national agreements on employment of staff), and some GP practices (those with more than 11,000 patients) could hold practice budgets with which to purchase hospital services for their patients. The purpose was to give extra momentum to the market.
- NHS management structures would be completely revised. A national NHS policy board would set strategy while an NHS management executive (NHSME) would deal with operational matters; all members would be appointed by the Secretary of State. Regional and district boards would become smaller and have executive and non-executive members, but no 'representative'

members (thus no independent doctors). The boards of self-governing hospitals would have a similar structure. Membership of FPCs would be cut from 30 to 11 members with doctors reduced from eight (out of 15 professional members) to one.

- The resource management initiative was to be rolled out to a further 50 units in 1989, and another 260 by 1991–2, without the evaluation promised to take place in October 1989.
- Indicative drug budgets would be introduced for all general practices 'to place downward pressure on expenditure on drugs', and these would be policed by FPCs.
- The capitation element of GPs remuneration, which had been under active discussion as part of the GP contract negotiations, would go up from 46% to 60%.
- Medical audit, overseen by advisory committees, would be systematically implemented in hospitals and in general practice.
- Consultants' contracts would be managed differently, and devolved from regional to district health authorities. They would include detailed job descriptions, and appointment procedures would be revised to include district managers. The machinery for giving distinction awards to consultants would change, with greater input from managers and the rewards subject to review.
- The white paper applied to all four nations. However, separate working papers were to be issued for Scotland, Wales and Northern Ireland.

The timescale was short, with the first legislative changes to be introduced within four months by May 1989 and the whole system in place by 1991. Geoffrey Rivett, who was working in the Department of Health at the time, wrote: 'The idea of an increased reliance on market forces, albeit forces that were managed and constrained, was so radical that few, even in the Department of Health, understood or agreed with what was happening.'[10]

There was much to worry doctors: the threat to national terms and conditions of service, the increasing influence of managers, and the potential for a two-tier service. But the Association did not want to play into Kenneth Clarke's hands. He had observed at the launch: 'The BMA, in my unbiased opinion, has never been in favour of any change of any kind on any subject for as long as anyone can remember.' So its early comments were muted, focusing on concerns that the

---

[10] Rivett G.G. National Health Service History n.d. retrieved November 2012 from www.nhshistory.net.

internal market proposals were untried and should be piloted, and that such radical reforms would be expensive and rely on still-developing technology. The Association, quite properly, put a great deal of effort into analysing the proposals, particularly how contracts, funding flows, capital charges and budgets might work, and promoted local debates in order to gauge the views of doctors.

On 20 February 1989 the government published eight more working papers. They covered self-governing hospitals, funding and contracts for hospital services, practice budgets for GPs, indicative pre-scribing budgets for GPs, capital charges, medical audit, consultants' contractual arrangements, and implications for FPCs. All were care-fully analysed, though most reinforced existing doubts. How would rigid, predetermined contracts for services increase patient choice? Why was there nothing on how community health and public health services would be paid for and protected from fragmentation? Why was there minimal reference to medical education and research, which would surely suffer in a market based on service provision? Would the ability of self-governing hospitals to pay higher salaries reverse the good distribution of consultants between district general hospitals and teaching hospitals? Would patients trust GPs who held budgets? Was this an attempt to privatise the NHS?

At a more visceral level, two events further alienated sections of the profession and angered its leaders. A few weeks after *Working for Patients*, the government refused to implement a recommendation from the Doctors' and Dentists' Review Body (DDRB) to give con-sultants a specific £1,000 increase and raise the value of the A+ distinc-tion award. Consultants felt this was vindictive and it reinforced their perception, caused by several years of negative press coverage, that the government wanted to punish them. The consultants' chairman, Paddy Ross, heard the news while abroad; it compounded the bitter sense of betrayal that he felt over the government's broken promise on the resource management initiative. Then it was the turn of gen-eral practice. At the end of February, following negotiations that had been critically undermined by the white paper, the Secretary of State wrote to all GPs informing them that his version of their new contract would be going ahead despite unresolved objections. Adding insult to injury, he remarked during a speech at the annual dinner of the Royal College of GPs : 'I do wish the more suspicious of our GPs would stop feeling anxiously for their wallets every time that I mention the word "reform".'

Grass-roots members began to respond to the proposals, and their reaction was much less reasoned than the initial response from the centre. Division meetings were rapidly arranged, often with someone from headquarters giving the latest information, and were frequently overwhelmed by hundreds of anxious members. Although some wanted to work with the government, most were angry, fearful for the future of the NHS, and insistent that the BMA must do all it could to stop the changes.

Anger and reasoned objection fuelled each other. BMA Council held an extended meeting in early March which called for a Special Representative Meeting (SRM) on 17 May to crystallise the Association's position. Particular aspects of the proposals were beginning to dominate the debate. The GMSC, though preoccupied with its battle over the contract, was deeply concerned about the new powers and composition of FPCs and angry at the anathematic proposal for indicative prescribing budgets, which it saw as cash limits. Practice budgets, or fundholding as they came to be known, proved deeply divisive, though the GMSC opposed the policy from early on fearing that it could undermine the doctor-patient relationship. The GPs' committee set up a working group to look at this in detail and identified serious objections, including the likely development of a two-tier service and problems over the proposed financing. The consultants committee, now rebranded as the Central Consultants and Specialists Committee (CCSC) saw self-governing hospitals as the most immediate danger, mainly because they would be able to disregard national agreements on pay and employment.

The government moved fast on fundholding and self-governing hospitals, aiming to pre-empt objections at national level by appealing directly to those at local level, using both carrot and stick. In March 1989 the NHS Chief Executive, Duncan Nicholl, invited hospitals to express interest in becoming self-governing, and in December the government issued a 'prospectus' inviting GP practices with more than 11,000 patients to apply for fundholding. This new strategy posed particular challenges for the BMA *(see p 43 and p 46 below)*.

The royal colleges were drawn into the debate. They shared the BMA's anxiety about the untried nature of the internal market, and feared the erosion of clinical standards under the influence of market forces. They were particularly worried about medical education and research, and by March 1989 endorsed strongly critical evidence submitted to the Social Services Select Committee by the Joint Consultants

Committee (JCC), a heavyweight consultative group with members from the royal colleges and the BMA. The JCC had been used to conducting its business quietly behind the scenes, where in the past it had enjoyed ready access to ministers. But the doors were no longer open. A private meeting did take place between its chairman, Sir Anthony Grabham, and Kenneth Clarke, following the intervention of Sir Roy Griffiths, then an influential member of the NHS Supervisory Board, who was clearly worried about the lack of dialogue. But Kenneth Clarke was not inclined to listen and the JCC held – awkwardly – its first-ever press conference to explain its criticisms.

By April the strength of feeling among BMA members was such that John Marks, advised by the public affairs division and with support from committee chairmen, started to prepare detailed plans for a major publicity campaign. The aim was to make it politically difficult for the government to take forward its reforms. Leading advertising agencies were approached and a special meeting of the Finance and General Purposes Committee considered a proposal from Abbott Mead Vickers involving hard-hitting full-page newspaper advertisements. The committee had a long discussion on resorting to advertising for what many felt should be a rational debate on serious professional matters. But they anticipated the upcoming SRM would exert strong pressure for vigorous action and agreed to take the advertising proposal to the next stage. They approved a £600,000 retainer for Abbott Mead Vickers to work up the plan.

They also set up an action group to co-ordinate the campaign, and its members held a range of views about how political they should become, bearing in mind the BMA's status as an independent, non-affiliated trade union. John Marks was deeply committed to the NHS and felt that the BMA's views on the white paper coincided so closely with those of the Labour Party that he thought it made sense to work closely with them, while carefully avoiding endorsing the party.[11] The Chairman of the CCSC, Paddy Ross, was at that time a member of the Conservative Party, though he publicly resigned in 1990 and Michael Wilson, Chairman of the GMSC, had been crossing swords with Kenneth Clarke for the previous two years. Among the Chief Officers were Alistair Riddell, the Treasurer, a sensible and respected Glasgow GP, and Sandy (later Sir Alexander) Macara, a public health academic who was then Chairman of the Representative Body and later became Chairman of Council. Other senior chairmen on the action group were

[11] John Marks: *The NHS: Beginning, Middle and End?* Radcliffe 2008 p 182.

Colin Smith, Chairman of the Medical Academic Staff Committee, and Eileen Wain representing community medicine. Sir Anthony Grabham, Chairman of the Joint Consultants Committee, remained an influential member of the BMA Council and of the Finance and General Purposes Committee.

The Secretary of the BMA was the formidable and well respected Dr John Havard, who was followed in July 1989 by Dr Ian Field, a medical administrator who had previously worked for the Department of Health, and who shunned the limelight, preferring to use his considerable experience to give advice behind the scenes. Two staff members played an important role. One was Pamela Taylor, head of the public affairs division, a highly motivated and professional public relations expert, who exercised great influence over the elected leaders through her evident organisational skills, a forceful personality, and a glamorous persona proficient in the slick language of a PR world that was unfamiliar to most doctors. Her ally was Dr John Dawson, head of scientific affairs, who had been on the staff of the BMA for 13 years and, though not a natural administrator, was a creative thinker and forceful campaigner who enjoyed radical causes. In 1989 he was already suffering from cancer, from which he died in December 1990, but not before putting considerable energy into what became an increasingly political campaign.

The SRM was held on 17 May at the QEII Conference Centre in London. A special report of Council had been prepared, containing a detailed analysis of the white paper and its weaknesses, and the meeting supported all its criticisms, with emotions building as the day went on. It was a rallying point for a profession under attack and an NHS under threat. The outcome was a series of resolutions condemning the white paper and the government that produced it, and a resounding mandate for John Marks and the Council to press ahead with a vigorous campaign to oppose it, with a further SRM planned for early July at the Swansea ARM.

Two days later, all members received the last of three special newspaper editions produced by staff of *BMA News Review*, with the banner headline quoting what John Marks had said in his speech to Kenneth Clarke: 'Calm down, sit down, slow down'.

The campaign

Advertisements started to appear in the national press almost immediately after the SRM, which itself had generated much publicity.

They were followed in late June by a series of public meetings held in 30 towns around the country: each included a panel of local doctors, nurses and community representatives and was chaired by a senior BMA staff member, who had been well briefed and rehearsed. They started with a specially made video in which the dangers to the much-loved NHS were presented in stark terms by well known actors, including Mark McManus who was at the time starring in the popular TV series *Taggart*. Members of the public could then express their views and question the panel. The meetings were well attended, with some attracting more than 600 people, and they were supported by badges, T-shirts stating *An SOS for the NHS*, and leaflets that were also distributed through GP practices.

The idea was to put pressure on the government. Research done by Abbott Mead Vickers had indicated that Conservative as well as Labour voters were worried about the proposed NHS changes. BMA members and members of the public were encouraged to lobby their MPs and the BMA's experienced parliamentary unit played a full part. It was led by Sue Marks, who had built up good working relationships with MPs across all parties over many years of providing them with information on a wide range of subjects. Meetings were arranged for doctors to explain their fears to MPs, and vast quantities of briefing material were prepared.

By early July it was clear that the campaign was having a significant effect. In his stirring ARM speech, which received a long standing ovation, John Marks was able to quote successive Gallup polls showing heightened public awareness of the issues raised. The government was facing difficult questions from its own backbenchers as well as from the opposition, and there was particular animosity over the wording of the leaflet that had been distributed through GPs' surgeries. This made assertions about the dangers of the reforms in a tone more natural to advertising copywriters than to the usual authors of BMA documents, and led Kenneth Clarke to accuse the BMA of irresponsible and misleading shroud-waving and unscrupulous political propaganda. Indeed some members were uncomfortable with it, feeling it to be unprofessional, and a few of them resigned from the BMA as a result.

Tension over style and tactics had already surfaced in the BMA 'war cabinet'. The group was united in its opposition to the white paper and support for a strong campaign, but they disagreed about the tone. Some feared that an overtly hostile campaign would alienate the government, its supporters and BMA members; others felt a dramatic weapon that hurt the government was justified because all reasonable means of persuasion had failed. Personal and political differences were not far from the surface: some felt John Marks to be brash and irresponsible. They felt that the advertising agency and the public affairs division were wielding inappropriate influence, and were uncomfortable with the political nature of the campaign. Others accused the more cautious members of dragging their heels just when the BMA was starting to make an impact.

Most BMA members strongly supported the campaign. At the SRM a resolution rebutting the doubters was easily carried: 'That this meeting emphasises that the first leaflet had the support of the members of the Representative Body and was entirely accurate.' Membership grew: by June 1,000 doctors had joined or rejoined, with another 1,000 by September.

Nevertheless it looked as if internal tensions might come to a head at the Swansea ARM. John Marks's five-year term of office as Chairman of Council was due to end in 1989, and normally a successor would have been elected at a Council meeting at the end of the week. Traditionally the chairmanship of Council alternated between a GP and a consultant and it was among consultants that discomfort about John Marks' style was most evident. But the consultants' chairman, Paddy Ross, though worried about the campaign, was hoping to succeed Sir Anthony Grabham as chairman of the JCC, and was therefore reluctant to take on the job himself. No other candidate was evident. Many Council members felt that changing the leadership at such a crucial point of the campaign would send the wrong signal to government and jeopardise the campaign. So despite John Marks' reluctance to change his retirement plans, at the Council meeting in May the way had been cleared for him to be re-elected by invoking an obscure clause in the Association's bye-laws which permitted a Chairman of Council to stand for a sixth year if the circumstances were 'sufficiently exceptional'. But dissent rumbled on and in the run-up to the ARM discussions took place behind closed doors over whether someone might stand against him in order to lead the campaign in a less abrasive manner. For a time the rumour circulated that Sir Anthony himself, a proven leader and previous Chairman of Council, might offer his services. He did not. During the week at Swansea Paddy Ross's sense of duty urged him to put himself forward. But colleagues saw that an election, whatever the outcome, would show the government a divided Association and in earnest conversations at the meeting, in hotel bars late at night, and finally in a dawn walk along Swansea's sandy beach, they convinced him not to stand. Sir Anthony Grabham, absent from the meeting because his father was terminally ill, responded to speculation in *The Times* and sent a message of support to John Marks which was read out to the meeting.

John Marks was elected unopposed and the campaign moved on to its next phase. A joint meeting of the Finance and General Purposes Committee and the Council Executive in mid-June had already budgeted £950,000 for stages two and three, which would complete the programme of public meetings, launch large roadside posters, and distribute another leaflet through GP practices. The meeting also approved plans for a conference on self-governing hospitals to be organised by the consultants' committee at Kensington Town Hall. It took place in September and highlighted to the public and to the many consultants who attended the dangers and doubts surrounding the 'opting out' proposals.

The posters were to prove the most controversial part of the campaign. Again designed by Abbott Mead Vickers, they were intended to give visual impact to punchy messages encapsulating the concerns that had already been expressed and were now in the public's consciousness. The 'war cabinet' had been encouraged by several things: the mood at the ARM, feedback from doctors around the country, a report from the Select Committee on Social Services critical of the government's proposals, and a Gallup poll showing that just under three out of four people were opposed to the reforms. They sanctioned the posters as an inevitable escalation of hostilities, though some had to swallow hard at what they regarded as the dubious taste of some of them. They did reject some ideas as too extreme, but the ones they chose appeared during August and September and made an undoubted impact – provoking delight, admiration,[12] shock, horror and anger.

Their themes were that a much-loved NHS was in danger, that patients' interests were being sacrificed to a financial ethos, and doctors' legitimate concerns were being overridden. Each poster carried the strapline: *NHS. Underfunded. Undermined. Under threat.* Some posters were as follows:

- A picture of tins of 'Clarke's Processed Peas': *If the government's plans for the NHS go through, how will the patient feel?*
- A blank page: *A complete list of the medical bodies who support the government's plans for the NHS*

---

[12] Nick Timmins in his book *The Five Giants: A Biography of the Welfare State* (Harper Collins 1995) described the posters as 'of memorable brilliance'.

- A forlorn elderly patient in a hospital bed: *When you're 50 miles from home, every ward is an isolation ward*
- A huge steamroller: *Mrs Thatcher's plans for the NHS*

The final poster targeted Kenneth Clarke with the line: *What do you call a man who ignores medical advice? – Mr Clarke*. This provoked a strong backlash from some members of the BMA and of the Conservative Party, who felt it was offensive. A leader in *The Independent* castigated the BMA for displaying 'the arrogance of doctors' and although John Marks defended the campaign strongly, he later admitted that this had been 'a poster too far, and was ultimately counter-productive.'[13]

The effect of the campaign on the government's position was not clear. Kenneth Clarke, following sustained pressure from the GMSC, agreed that indicative drug budgets would not operate as cash limits. This was welcomed by the GMSC, and the influential health journalist Nick Timmins, then with *The Independent*, reported the agreement as a sign of the government backing down. Kenneth Clarke quickly issued a denial, though his statement had been in writing. Other journalists saw it as evidence that the BMA's campaign was hollow scaremongering. The megaphone had started to overpower other forms of debate and some Tory backbenchers, furious at the BMA's poster campaign, redoubled their support for reforms that would bring this badly-behaved profession to heel.

The fury among the Conservative grassroots was experienced by a team of BMA speakers at a fringe meeting at the Conservative Party Conference in Blackpool in October. The team included John Lynch, a GP negotiator, Paddy Ross, consultant chairman, Graeme McDonald, the juniors' chairman, together with Ian Field the Secretary and Jon Ford the BMA's economist. Their presentations were low key, particularly Paddy Ross's as he was suffering from laryngitis. But they were shouted down by party members wanting to vent their anger. The BMA speakers were told to 'sit down and shut up' and accused of 'ramming socialism down our throats', chairs were overturned, and the BMA team were visibly shaken, pleased to escape with their dignity intact, just.[14]

The poster campaign provoked more arguments within the BMA and at the end of the summer elected members started to discuss the next steps. The Treasurer and others were anxious about the costs

---

[13] John Marks, *The NHS: Beginning, Middle and End?* Radcliffe 2008.
[14] Pier groups and politicians, Harvey Marcovitch. *BMA News Review*, November 1989, p 18.

of the campaign, which had risen from a budgeted £0.95 million to £1.5 million, and members of the Council Executive were worried that they were losing control. They recommended that Abbott Mead Vickers should not be engaged for further phases. They also agreed to develop ways of countering criticisms of their campaign and on 22 September John Marks wrote to doctors setting out a seven-point plan to improve the NHS without the need for the government's untried methods.

At the October Council meeting John Marks acknowledged members' concern over the Kenneth Clarke poster but felt that the furore had passed. He argued strongly that now was not the time to ease off. Council agreed, proposing that they should concentrate on pressing for change before legislation was published. The BMA arranged a meeting with the Secretary of State on 18 October at which it urged consideration of the seven-point plan, but the government's position was firm. It pressed ahead, publishing on 21 November the NHS and Community Care Bill which would implement the white paper as drafted, and enable regulations to be introduced to deal with the rest.

By the beginning of 1990 various groups and working parties in the BMA were discussing with the NHSME the details of matters such as contracts for services, funding and medical audit. It was becoming disconcertingly clear that civil servants were having to make a lot of it up as they went on. This reinforced the conviction that huge risks were being taken with all that was valuable about the NHS. Its most serious problem – lack of money – was not only being overlooked, but exacerbated by the need for more spending to support the new information systems that would be required. As the Association's resolve stiffened, the campaign evolved from a single argument about the white paper to a series of battles on several separate fronts. The 'war cabinet' continued to co-ordinate these battles, but by now the organisation, under John Mark's leadership and Pamela Taylor's energetic influence, was using publicity as a routine weapon and generated a constant flow of press releases, interviews, surveys and local news stories that kept the pressure building.

The bill

Once the bill had been published the BMA launched a major exercise, with the parliamentary unit working flat out, along with their public affairs colleagues and with all those BMA departments that had relevant expertise. They crawled over every word of the draft legislation, suggesting possible areas for amendment, preparing briefings, seeking advice, and drafting amendments. They held countless meetings with MPs. Staff from the parliamentary unit, usually its head, Sue Marks, attended debates late into the night, often accompanied by the Chairman of Council or other committee members. They took notes on who had said what, and these were fed back to inform tactics for the next stage.

Despite these efforts, the changes to the substance of the Bill were minimal. However, the detailed work did bear fruit in other ways. A continuing stream of publicity was generated by sustained engagement with MPs, ministers, doctors, health unions, patient organisations, medical bodies and the various groups that grew up to defend or oppose the reforms (for example, the NHS Support Federation and the NHS Reform Group). Opinion polls, some commissioned by the BMA, showed high and growing levels of concern about the government's plans. A new political party, the NHS Supporters Party, fielded candidates in by-elections, including GPs Chris Tiarks and Christopher Abell in the Vale of Glamorgan and Mid Staffordshire; both had been Conservative seats but were won by Labour. By June 1990 the press were reporting (accurately, as it was later confirmed)[15] that Mrs Thatcher had become so worried that she was considering softening the reforms by allowing a slower implementation.[16] This was quickly denied, apparently as a result of the firm stance taken by Kenneth Clarke, who was now strongly committed to the programme.

The combination of public pressure and behind-the-scenes lobbying produced some important concessions. The first was an independent mechanism to monitor the effect of the reforms on clinical practice. The royal colleges had been pressing for an NHS Evaluation Programme. Kenneth Clarke declined this at first. But he came under pressure from some influential members of the House of Lords who feared the changes might harm patient care, and he agreed to meet some college presidents privately to explore alternatives. He suggested a Clinical Standards Advisory Group (CSAG), but specified that this should not include the BMA, particularly objecting to the involvement of Sir Anthony Grabham, then Chairman of the JCC, whom he regarded as 'one of the cleverest and most difficult negotiators he had

---

[15] Nick Timmins: *The Five Giants: A Biography of the Welfare State.* HarperCollins 1995.
[16] *Financial Times* 18.6.90.

ever come across'.[17] Although attempts by politicians to 'divide and rule' between the BMA and the royal colleges have often succeeded, on this occasion Sir Terence English, President of the Royal College of Surgeons, stood firm against the BMA's exclusion and refused to attend further discussions unless the BMA were involved. Mr Clarke, needing to avoid difficult debates in the House of Lords, relented and included the Chairman of the JCC (thus, indirectly, the BMA) as a member of the new body. The CSAG turned out to be of doubtful effectiveness, but it stood as an important acknowledgement that medical values and expertise still had a role in the running of the NHS.

Another concession was over the employment of junior doctors. It appeared to have been achieved by pressure from the BMA in the form of letters to ministers and lobbying of MPs. But it had been supported by behind-the-scenes work at the ministerial working group on junior doctors' hours, at which Virginia Bottomley and her senior civil servants were seriously engaged at the end of 1990. This forum enabled the team to understand better the realities of working as a junior NHS doctor, as well as to form more constructive relationships with BMA representatives than were possible elsewhere at the time. In January 1991 (shortly after the announcement of the heads of agreement on juniors' hours of work), the Secretary of State announced that junior doctors would remain on national terms and conditions of service, even if working in self-governing trusts. Furthermore, though the contracts of house officers and senior house officers would be held by trusts, those of registrars would be held by the region so that they could rotate easily through different training posts. This crucially recognised that junior doctors' most important role was to receive training and that this activity needed explicit protection from unconstrained market forces. Juniors have fought hard to maintain this principle ever since.

A third concession was over the contracting arrangements sketched out in *Working for Patients*, developed in working paper two, *Funding and Contracts for Hospital Services* and in a later guidance document, *Operating Contracts*. These arrangements had never been tried out, and inevitably were full of gaps and anomalies. One particular concern was that rigid contracts for services, arranged between DHAs and hospitals, would limit a GP's freedom of referral. The NHSME's guidance allowed for some extra-contractual referrals, but they would be limited at first to fundholding practices. Doctors were affronted by this assault

---

[17] Sir Terence English: *Follow Your Star*. AuthorHouse 2011.

on the key professional relationship between GPs and specialists (even though the reality was that in some places the relationship was not all it should have been, with GPs complaining of lack of communication and consultants complaining of inappropriate referrals). This issue was repeatedly raised by the GMSC and by the CCSC in their separate discussions with the NHSME, and the result was an agreement that all GPs would have the right to make extra-contractual referrals. The GMSC regarded this as a significant watering down of fundholding, and emphasised this in its guidance to GPs of June 1990.

At the end of June 1990 the NHS and Community Care Bill completed its passage through parliament and was given Royal Assent. It coincided with the end of John Marks's term of office as chairman of BMA Council, and he stood down at the Bournemouth ARM to a grateful standing ovation. He had led a passionate fight against what he saw as the destruction of the NHS that he had served since he qualified as a doctor on the same day that it came into being in 1948. His successor was Dr Jeremy Lee-Potter, a haematologist from Poole, who had been deputy chairman of the CCSC, but who had kept a low profile in the Representative Body and BMA Council. Although a less accomplished public speaker than his predecessor, he was a cerebral politician who was deeply opposed to the market theory behind the reforms, particularly to self-governing hospitals. He promised to continue the fight, but favoured a more pragmatic approach. Soon afterwards, Paddy Ross succeeded Sir Anthony Grabham as chairman of the Joint Consultants Committee, and was replaced as chairman of the CCSC by John Chawner, an obstetrician and gynaecologist from North Wales. Michael Wilson stepped down as chairman of the GMSC, to be succeeded by Ian Bogle from Liverpool, while Graeme McDonald gave way to Stephen Hunter, another psychiatrist, as chairman of the HJSC. And in November of 1990, Kenneth Clarke, the architect and enforcer of the reforms, became Secretary of State for Education and was replaced by William Waldegrave, who quickly made it clear that he wanted to repair relationships with the profession. So the second half of 1990 marked the beginning of a shift in the BMA's position, though for some time and on some issues the battle lines remained drawn, and members expected to fight on.

Consultants' contracts

Some of the strongest criticism from government and NHS sources during the NHS review was about the employment of consultants.

The new breed of NHS managers found it difficult to understand the arcane arrangements that had evolved since 1948, with whole-time, maximum part-time and part-time contracts, while many consultants still saw themselves more as independent professionals than employees.

Some local managers had tried to introduce simple weekly time-tables for consultants, which rarely took account of their on-call duties and their teaching and other professional commitments. There had also been a difficult re-negotiation of the disciplinary procedures for employed doctors, including the controversial 'paragraph 190' right of appeal to the Secretary of State against dismissal, but the changes had been shelved until the white paper was published. So it was no surprise that one of the working papers dealt with the aspects of consultant employment that most pre-occupied managers: organisation of duties, distinction awards and appointment procedures. Its proposals, which alarmed consultants, included giving local managers control over consultants' working patterns, greater say in their appointment, and greater influence in the distinction award system. Distinction awards were to be reviewable, and would not be pensionable until three years after the award – a crude mechanism to prevent the abuse that awards were sometimes granted just before retirement in order to boost the doctor's pension before recycling the award to someone else.

After the working papers were published, the NHSME quickly set up working parties with the CCSC, including representatives of other groups affected, such as public health doctors in the case of distinction awards. The negotiations were tough but constructive, conducted largely with civil servants, though now also with NHS representatives, and compromises were possible on both sides. It soon became clear that the NHSME did not want to renegotiate the whole consultant contract. The CCSC had been forcefully pointing out that it was good value for the NHS, with most consultants working much more than the minimum for which they were paid, and this was borne out by an authoritative workload survey by the Office of Manpower Economics in 1990.

The NHSME wanted some form of work programme for consultants, and the CCSC was happy to agree, provided that only fixed commitments would be timetabled and contracts would continue to be assessed in notional half days (NHDs) in order to allow flexibility. So 'job-plans' were introduced to make workloads more explicit; these could benefit consultants with too many commitments as well as managers looking to pin down their consultants. An appeal mechanism was specified, the definition of workload was widened, and additional NHDs were made available. Consultants, apart from those working for trusts, remained employed by the RHA although the day-to-day management of the contract was devolved to district level. On appointment procedures the main battle was about the role of the district general manager. The NHSME insisted that he or she must be on the appointment committee and could nominate a deputy. The consultants pointed out that professional members were not able to nominate deputies, but eventually reached a compromise that any deputy must be approved by all the committee members.

On distinction awards, the 'delayed pensionability' idea was felt to be unjust and unworkable: for instance, what if a consultant died in the intervening three years? It was replaced with an age limit for new awards – an unsatisfactorily arbitrary measure, but an improvement on the original proposal. Awards were also made reviewable – a significant departure – but a mechanism was introduced at the CCSC's insistence to protect the cash value of the award if it was withdrawn. This reaffirmed the concept that distinction awards had always been a consolidated element of salary, part of an incremental structure, and were in no sense to be seen as temporary bonus payments. Managers were to have greater input to the C awards by sitting on the awards committee and by introducing a new criterion: commitment to the management and development of the service.

These changes were introduced relatively easily during 1990/91. Consultants had been worried that the new powers of self-governing trusts might mean that they would simply ignore central guidance. But most of the new trusts accepted the circulars without demur, and newly established local negotiating committees, armed with BMA guidance, engaged with trust managers in implementing the latest national agreements rather than negotiating brand new contracts.

GP fundholding

The issue of budget holding, or fundholding as it became known, caused difficulties for the BMA and the GMSC for some years. The GMSC had felt from the start that it would be wrong for some GPs to buy 'better' services for their patients than other GPs could, and that it could lead to a two-tier service. They were also concerned that financial arrangements for fundholding were unclear, could lead to an over-bureaucratic approach, and could compromise patients' trust in their GP.

However, when the government issued its prospectus in December 1989, some practices felt that they should not close the door on gaining advantages for their patients; by mid-1990, 850 practices had expressed an interest. There were difficult debates in the GMSC, which had set up a working party to consider fundholding. Some GPs reported they were being pressured to apply for fundholding status, with threats that development money would be withheld and hints that those who led the way would be generously treated. These reports reinforced the suspicions of the GMSC that GPs were being led into a trap. On the other hand it was clear that many GPs felt they could do a better job than their DHA at arranging services for their patients, and did not want to be held back by theoretical principles. In January 1990 the working party's report, *Funding General Practice*, highlighted concerns about the proposed accounting arrangements, and the GMSC maintained its outright opposition. In June it sent all GPs detailed advice on the problems of fundholding and surveyed their views. The ARM that year confirmed the BMA's total opposition to fundholding.

In September the GMSC had a soul-searching debate days before the regulations were laid. Michael Wilson had been a firm opponent of fundholding, but the new chairman, Ian Bogle, felt that he needed to be pragmatic. The committee issued a policy statement that signalled a shift in position: it still felt that fundholding was detrimental to patients' interests and to the NHS, and that the right principle was to work for equal access to NHS resources, but it would continue to represent the interests of all GPs. This sent a message that the GMSC understood the position of those who embraced fundholding and would not ostracise them for doing so. Of the 850 practices that had expressed interest in fund-holding status, 350 made formal applications and 306 went forward as the 'first wave' of fundholders from 1 April 1991. Some GPs were angry with the GMSC's shift in position, and it caused a row with the BMA public affairs division, which was still in campaigning mode. But Ian Bogle was determined to restore dialogue with the government, and for several years he led the GMSC in an elaborate dance which maintained fundamental opposition to fundholding while at the same time embracing fundholders, considering fundholding issues and taking them up with government, and issuing advice on how to make the system work.

Such behaviour baffles other trade unions, who hold that a binding policy decision precludes representation of members who decline to follow it. Members of BMA committees have also found it baffling:

they have got a particular policy adopted only to find that holders of conflicting views are still encouraged to pursue them. This facility for 'doublethink' is based on the understanding that the BMA and its committees are 'a broad church', and as the only organisation representing all doctors it must accommodate minority strands of opinion rather than cast them out to form rival organisations. Put another way, BMA policy may prefer that doctors organise their affairs in certain ways, but if some of them choose to practise differently – and these forms of practice are perfectly legal and ethical – they are still entitled to advice and representation like any other members. It is a debate that arises regularly and will continue, and of course it does not prevent splinter groups diverting energy into intra-professional battles and taking away members – sometimes later to be offered seats and reabsorbed into BMA committees, having galvanised the BMA into taking greater account of non-mainstream points of view.

In the early 1990s the GMSC worked hard to keep the growing number of fundholders on board. About 300 more practices applied for the second wave and late in 1991 the GMSC organised two conferences – one for fundholders and one for those who had expressed an interest – in order to exchange views and experience and co-ordinate guidance. Because it was seen to be in touch with fundholders the committee was able to conduct a dialogue with the NHSME over developing, together with the JCC, guidance to ensure that patients of fundholders would not have privileged access to services – clinical need was to be the only criterion. The NHSME then invited the GPs committee to join a group evaluating the experience of fundholding, and they accepted the invitation, despite being criticised as selling out. The criticism grew in December 1991 when the Department agreed that all GPs, not just fundholders, would be involved in local discussions about purchasing arrangements, a move which the GMSC welcomed. Ian Bogle had to issue public denials that the BMA had softened its opposition to fundholding.

Clearly there were tensions among GPs and within the GMSC, and it was not long before a new body, the National Association of Fundholding Practices (NAFP), had set itself up. The GMSC was already meeting the NHSME regularly to discuss matters such as revisions to the regulations. It was keen to maintain this position to ensure that, should the question arise, the GMSC would be recognised as having formal negotiating rights for fundholders. With this in mind, and with a third wave of fundholders in place, the LMC conference resolved in 1993 that it 'no longer asserts its opposition to GP fund-holding'. When the GMSC endorsed this policy, however, it was quick to explain that in principle it did not regard fundholding as the best way to organise access to NHS services. The GMSC set up a fundhold-ers subcommittee and a dialogue was opened with the NAFP. As time passed, fundholding became part of the landscape of general practice, and GPs who had opposed it began to see it as a way of protecting their local services. By 1997, 3,600 practices were involved, covering over half of the population of England. Arguments continued about its effectiveness, with many fundholders convinced that it gave them a powerful lever to improve and develop services, and health policy com-mentators arguing that its culture of innovation improved the standard of general practice. Others still felt that encouraging different levels of access to the NHS – the 'two-tier service' – was wrong in principle, and this was the position adopted by the new Labour government in 1997. Within two years of taking office it had abolished GP fundholding.

Self-governing trusts

Returning to the events of 1990–91, a parallel development to GP fundholding was the establishment of self-governing hospital trusts with new freedoms over the provision of services, capital development and the employment of staff. The government used the same strat-egy of appealing directly to local self-preservation and of by-passing central debate, and the CCSC was faced with similar issues of imple-menting a policy of principled opposition in the face of fast-moving local initiatives. The difference was that the potential advantages of fundholding appealed directly to GPs, whereas self-governing trusts appealed largely to NHS managers. Some consultants took a positive view, but most suspected the motives of managers, felt excluded from decision making, and were worried that they could lose their national terms and conditions of service. So the CCSC's task was less fraught with internal political difficulties than the GMSC's.

At first some hospital consultants were attracted by the idea of greater independence from what they saw as the stultifying oversight of the district health authority. In a few well-run hospitals like Guy's in London, where they worked with managers and had confidence in them, the prospect of a return to the days of an enlightened hospital board, powerful enough to stand up to politicians and NHS bureau-crats, was seductive. This was apparently the vision that Ian McColl, senior surgeon at Guy's and later to become Lord McColl and a health minister, had sold to Mrs Thatcher's review team. But Paddy Ross no longer trusted the motives of the government. He had wanted to work cooperatively, but felt bitterly let down when it reneged on promises made about the evaluation of the Resource Management Initiative, and then by its treatment of consultants over the DDRB report. He saw a cynical and dangerous attempt to undermine consultants' professional independence, as enshrined in their contracts and terms of service. Although managers found this independence inconvenient and Mrs Thatcher was thought to be infuriated by it, Paddy Ross firmly believed it was a vital safeguard to patients and a major strength of the NHS. So he determined to warn consultants of the dangers of being sucked into endorsing 'expressions of interest'. These were being strongly encouraged, particularly by the regional health authority chairmen, a group of powerful and often highly political individuals, who urged hospitals to get ahead in what they portrayed as a race with glittering prizes. In April 1989 Paddy Ross wrote a personal letter to all consultants in which, in colourful language, he likened the government to an unscrupulous timeshare salesman on a Spanish beach, with hapless consultants being led into a trap. The letter provoked strong responses from both sides, alerting many to the political nature of what was going on, but also raising hackles because of its overtly critical tone. Among the many replies, one arrived on an embossed card from Harley Street: 'Sir, were I a member of your ridiculous and petulant organisation, I would resign.'

As it became clear that local hospitals were the real battleground, the consultants' committee adopted a strategy of intensive communication with consultants in the hospitals concerned in order to promote informed debate, empower consultants to make their views felt, and highlight the dangers of rushing into trust status. In May 1989 they surveyed consultants in 350 hospitals: this showed that where an expression of interest had gone forward it had rarely been with the agreement or even the knowledge of the consultants. In only seven hospitals had the consultants expressed enthusiasm and in hospitals where they had acquiesced it had been simply to find out more. In June 1989 the committee produced an information pack for consultants and encouraged them to hold ballots. When ballots for the 79 'front runners' were analysed later that year, in only 29 could the hospital claim that senior medical staff supported the application; in 19 they were firmly opposed and in a further 31 undecided. The Chairman of the CCSC wrote to the Secretary of State with these results and urged him to ensure that the views of the consultants were taken into account.

The committee went to considerable lengths to find out what was happening, and sent out regular communications, including summaries of further guidance. The government's *NHS Trusts – A Working Guide* contained worrying details about how employment would be transferred: trusts would be able to change terms and conditions of service at any time after transfer. They would also be able to offer alternatives to the distinction award, and abolish the right of appeal to the Secretary of State against dismissal. The CCSC also circulated information about 'frighteners' and 'sweeteners': threats of recrimination if hospitals did not show sufficient enthusiasm and hints of advantageous funding arrangements for those that did.

Medical staff committees were encouraged to set up meetings, often attended by CCSC officers and/or BMA staff, to discuss trust status and question their managers. The meetings were generally well attended and there was often a sense of fear among consultants about the increased power that managers were likely to wield. But the CCSC representatives received a mixed reception. In hospitals (often large ones with teaching responsibilities) where consultants were confident of their influence with managers and keen to pursue trust status, the BMA's warnings were often dismissed as scaremongering. In other hospitals, however, consultants warmly welcomed the BMA's support and advice in resisting local pressure, or at least in forcing their managers into a more open dialogue. In Plymouth consultants joined other staff and the local community in a sustained campaign against trust status for the Derriford Hospital. It attracted much local publicity and kept up the hopes of the CCSC.

By the summer of 1990, with Royal Assent given to the Bill and a new Chairman of Council in place, the BMA was reviewing its campaign. But such had been the heat and anger over the past 18 months that members were in no mood to ease up. They called for more campaigning, and the public affairs division advised that the most fruitful issue would be self-governing hospitals, with the first trusts due to come into effect the following April. The BMA approved funding for a new campaign, with certain 'flagship hospitals' targeted for particular attention. Arrangements were made to link with other campaigning organisations, including trade unions. It adopted a slogan: *People lose out if our hospital opts out*. The BMA also published an analysis of the first wave applications, which highlighted great variety in the management structures proposed, an absence of information about education or training, and considerable uncertainty about funding. The campaign generated continuing publicity and maintained public doubts, but once the first wave of trusts was in place, it was no longer realistic to try to halt the steamroller.

The consultants' committee began to shift its focus from opposing trusts outright to mitigating any damage caused and protecting senior hospital doctors. With John Chawner replacing Paddy Ross as chairman of CCSC in October 1990 the committee continued its valuable contacts with consultants in actual or potential trusts, and in 1991 held two conferences to support consultants from the first and second waves. Meanwhile a group of BMA staff, led by the CCSC secretariat but including other head office and regional staff with industrial relations expertise, had worked out a strategic response. Conscious of the major threat to the central negotiating function of the BMA, their main recommendation was that the BMA should move swiftly to establish in each trust a local negotiating committee (LNC) to represent doctors in any discussions with managers about terms of service. The committees would be serviced by the BMA through local offices. As with the national negotiating machinery, the LNC would represent not just BMA members but all doctors in the trust, and would thus report back to the medical staff committee. LNCs would aim to establish themselves as the de facto collective bargaining machinery for doctors, seeking formal recognition once their value had been noted. The proposals included details about how the committees would be formed, trained and supported, and preliminary advice about the negotiating strategies they might adopt and the information they would need.

John Chawner gained the support of his committee for the document, which he took through the Council Executive to become BMA policy. There was some debate over tactics – for example in relation to the inclusion of non-members – but it was approved and arrangements quickly put in place to start implementing it. Some industrial relations officers had developed close working relationships with other health unions at local level and were at first uncomfortable about separate machinery for doctors. But they accepted it would be in the best interests of doctors, and worked enthusiastically, in cooperation with central staff, to get LNCs up and running.

The two CCSC conferences for doctors in trusts had much to discuss in terms of the mechanics of LNCs and of the issues that managers might want to discuss. A driving force in the establishment of LNCs was the fear among consultants, arising from bullish statements from government and NHS sources about the need to bring them under control, that trusts would quickly embark on dramatic changes to their contracts. LNCs became a buffer to such ambitions, making any changes subject to a negotiating process. The changes turned out to be less sweeping than feared, and LNCs – with advice from IROs – tied the newly appointed managers in knots over the technicalities so that proposals were often watered down or dropped. One or two trusts, notably West Dorset, put forward more ambitious changes and set off on a long negotiating process, which ran into the ground when it became clear that most of the proposals would be too expensive and that the existing contract was actually good value for money. In practice, the workload for the managers of a new trust was huge, and those appointed to look after medical staff employment were often less expert in the workings of the consultant contract than the consultants themselves, and were in any case soon tied up with the task of negotiating local disciplinary arrangements. After the first few 'waves', trusts became the norm, and changes to doctors' contracts slipped down the agenda. The anticipated threat to national terms and conditions of service had been largely averted.

The aftermath

When Jeremy Lee-Potter took over as Chairman of Council in 1990 he made clear that, while he had strongly supported the BMA campaign, he now felt that with legislation in place the best hope of influencing events had to be through re-establishing a dialogue with the government. Some members of Council thought that a change of tone would be interpreted as weakness, and at the October 1990 Council meeting Jeremy Lee-Potter was given a hard time over his perceived lack of action – notably by two previous Chairmen of Council, Sir Anthony Grabham and John Marks.[18]

His strategy of seeking dialogue was helped when in November William Waldegrave was appointed as Secretary of State, and sent signals that he was willing to listen. Soon after, Mrs Thatcher was replaced as Prime Minister by John Major. Jeremy Lee-Potter quickly wrote to him drawing attention to the resource problems that still plagued the NHS, and asked for a meeting. But any hopes of a fundamental change were misplaced: John Major declined a meeting and rebutted

---

[18] Jeremy Lee-Potter: *A Damn Bad Business – The NHS Deformed* 1997.

the BMA's warnings about financial problems (though they were to meet later in September and December the following year). In May Jeremy Lee-Potter, who believed he had built a good relationship with William Waldegrave, offered to drop BMA opposition to NHS trusts if Mr Waldegrave would agree to pause the programme and evaluate the first wave of trusts; this too was declined.

The government's plan seemed to be to press on regardless, while diverting criticism by introducing other initiatives. They launched a health strategy for England, which eventually became *The Health of the Nation*, that set out priorities and key targets for health. They followed this up with the *Patient's Charter*, which set out rights and expectations for waiting times and complaints procedures. But BMA members on the ground were preoccupied with problems caused by the internal market. These included obvious inequalities from fundholding, with funding running out on block contracts for other patients, difficulties over extra-contractual referrals, and early job cuts proposed by some first wave trusts, such as Guy's and Bradford.

At the 1991 ARM, in a rain-sodden Inverness, there was a perceptible current of dissatisfaction about the BMA's apparent inability or unwillingness to mount effective opposition to what was happening. It became focused on Jeremy Lee-Potter, whose keynote speech failed to rally the troops. At the Council meeting at the end of that week members called for a free-ranging debate, and in a highly uncomfortable couple of hours one member after another mounted a detailed critique of the Chairman of Council's style and lack of effectiveness. However, with support from a few colleagues, he averted a motion of no confidence, and the meeting concluded by affirming its confidence in their chairman. Jeremy Lee-Potter, having listened stoically, agreed to take the criticisms on board and set off on the long journey home to Poole.

The air had been cleared and at the next Council meeting Jeremy Lee-Potter launched an initiative to stimulate debate on other models of health service provision. This centred on a discussion paper *Leading for Health*, written by the then *BMJ* editor Dr Richard Smith from interviews with doctors and health policy experts conducted by Dr Andrew Vallance-Owen, then a member of BMA staff. He proposed four models and an SRM was planned to debate them. But positive proposals rarely inspire the passionate debates that BMA meetings thrive on, and when the meeting took place in March 1992 shortly before the general election, debate focused largely on the still rumbling dissatisfaction over the negative impact of the 'reforms'.

Members were also dissatisfied with the underlying funding difficulties that continued to make headlines. One example was the 'war
of Jennifer's ear'. The Labour Party, with Robin Cook still holding the health brief, had carried on making telling criticisms of the
government's changes to the NHS, which seemed to resonate with a
public still troubled by the doubts raised by the BMA campaign. The
Conservatives had lost several by-elections in which health had been
an issue, and the Labour Party had high hopes of success in the April
1992 general election. In the run-up to that election, the Labour publicists chose to use an actual case of a child whose operation for glue
ear seemed to have been cancelled for financial reasons. The publicity went badly wrong when the child's family objected to her personal details having been revealed, and the message became confused.
This and other gaffes in a poorly-run campaign meant that to general
surprise the Conservative government was re-elected, though with a
much reduced majority. Virginia Bottomley, a former health minister,
became Secretary of State for Health with Brian Mawhinney as her
Minister for Health.

Part of the folklore that has grown up about the campaign against
the 1989 white paper is that its stridency damaged the Association's
reputation and credibility, leading to the BMA being 'excluded from
the table' in the subsequent development of NHS policy. It certainly
took time to regain the confidence of some Conservative MPs, but
there is little evidence that the BMA's access to or influence with government was in any real sense reduced by these events. Changes in the
NHS need to involve doctors, and though governments may find it
convenient to seek support from narrower interest groups they usually
recognise in the end that the BMA, with its representative structure,
provides the most reliable advice on the practicalities of making things
work. The health commentator Chris Ham concluded in his book on
these events: 'The role of doctors in implementation . . . meant that
the BMA retained considerable power . . .'.[19]

If any change in medical influence did take place, it is more likely
that it came not from the campaign, but from an earlier determination
by the Thatcher government to change the terms on which it dealt with
the medical profession. The NHS had been founded on a deal between
doctors and the government, and while there were often strong differences of opinion, governments since 1948 had always felt they should

[19] Chris Ham: *The Politics of NHS Reform 1988–97. Metaphor or Reality?* King's
Fund 2000, p 65.

try to reach agreement with them if they wanted to change the terms of the deal. Now doctors were to be seen as one NHS stakeholder among many: they might be consulted but the government, acting on behalf of the tax payers who funded the service, would determine policy. This change in attitude was clearly evident from 1988 when the BMA and other medical bodies were excluded from the NHS review. Arguably it was the strength and skill of the BMA's subsequent campaign, its ability to express its members' powerful views, and particularly its success in moving into the new arena of the media to get its message across that enabled doctors to retain much more influence than the government had originally intended.

Chapter 2

The decline of the Conservative government: 'Reforming the reforms' 1992–1997

Core values

Over the next five years there were some significant developments for the BMA, hard-fought battles, and notable negotiating successes of the kind more readily achieved with a government whose majority is dwindling to single figures than with a confident administration with a large majority. If the period seemed quiet or uneventful, this is only by contrast with the turbulent battles that preceded it and the renewed spurt of activity that came later with the election of the Labour government.

Funding problems in the NHS continued, with recurring headlines about bed closures, service curtailments and growing waiting times for elective admissions and in A&E. These were exacerbated by frictions arising from the internal market, with new waves of NHS trusts and fundholders gradually changing the dynamics of provision. Virginia Bottomley, as Secretary of State, cheerfully brushed aside problems with repeated assertions that the NHS was treating more patients than ever before, so must be a success. Where elective admissions were cancelled because money had run out, she attributed it to 'over-delivery on contracts', a concept that doctors found it hard to sympathise with.

Jeremy Lee-Potter struggled to command wholehearted support from Council, and at the first opportunity, in 1993, he was challenged by Dr Sandy (later Sir Alexander) Macara, a public health academic from Bristol who had recently been chairman of the Representative Body. His election broke the traditional cycle of the chairmanship of Council alternating between a GP and a hospital consultant. Sandy Macara was hostile to the NHS 'reforms', but by then the time for blanket opposition had passed. His style was to exert influence through engagement, through the development of personal relationships, and through the type of political manipulation that flourishes in the common rooms of academic institutions. It was based on personal charm, strong principles, a sharp intellect and an even sharper memory (including the apparent ability to remember the name of every individual he met, from Secretary of State to junior member of BMA staff).

Mrs Bottomley saw her role as ensuring that the NHS reforms were so well established that they were no longer in the forefront of political debate.[1] The BMA felt that many aspects were still far from settled, but the Association's structure, where each main craft (since 2005 'branch of practice') committee negotiates directly with the government, meant that it fell to these committees to fight the most important battles. As Chairman of Council, Sandy Macara needed to be in a position to support them. He immediately set about changing the public image of the BMA from street-fighting trade union to responsible professional association. He launched the 'Core Values' exercise at the Birmingham Annual Representative Meeting (ARM) in 1994 with a seven-point plan: *Reforming the NHS Reforms*. It started from the politically necessary assertion that the NHS reforms had failed and attacked privatisation and local pay, but went on to concentrate on positive proposals based on the government's own principles of *Health of the Nation,* which the BMA had largely supported. It called for co-operation between purchasers and providers, and for strategic planning to achieve health priorities that were publicly determined and informed by needs and outcomes.

In November a two-day conference was held at BMA House, to which were invited the great and the good of the medical profession, including a limited number of BMA committee members. Keynote speakers challenged participants to address the changing context of medicine. One notable contribution was from Sir Maurice Shock, an educationalist and former rector of Lincoln College Oxford, who gave an eye-opening analysis of the encroachment of consumerism into areas of society that professionals still felt were protected from its influence. A report published after the conference set out proposed core values for doctors in the 21st century, and called for a single body that could unite the views of the whole profession.

Sandy Macara had acted nimbly, with the support of the BMA Secretary, Mac Armstrong, to take the lead among the various professional bodies and respond to a challenge issued to doctors by the Chief Medical Officer (CMO) for England, Kenneth Calman (later Sir Kenneth, and the BMA President in 2008–9) in May 1994. The BMA was first to offer to convene a steering group for the conference and

---

[1] Chris Ham: *The Politics of NHS Reform 1988–97. Metaphor or Reality?* King's Fund 2000, p 19.

so the Chairman of the BMA Council chaired the event. The discussion chimed strongly with Sandy Macara's own ethical and academic interests, and the subsequent report was circulated widely and helped to stimulate further thinking about the changing nature of medical professionalism. But as with Jeremy Lee-Potter's *Leading for Health* initiative two years earlier, it made little impact on ordinary BMA members, whose concerns were more immediate and practical. Yet the exercise did restore some of the Association's 'respectability' with, among others the CMO and various medical bodies, and it ensured Sandy Macara's continuing involvement in key high level discussions.

More NHS re-organisation

In May 1993 the government set up a Functions and Manpower Review to make the structural changes demanded in England by the NHS reforms, notably the establishment of trusts and the growth of fundholding. The changes were managed in phases and they ended with the Health Authorities Act of 1995, which was implemented from April 1996. Regional Health Authorities were replaced by eight regional offices of the NHS Executive (NHSE), previously the NHS Management Executive. They were to be responsible for the remaining regional functions: the regions had been first reduced from 14 to eight, then established transitionally as 'outposts'. District Health Authorities and Family Health Service Authorities were merged (as they had been already in Scotland) into 100 health authorities responsible for purchasing. Centrally the NHS was run by the NHSE with its executive board, which included the eight regional directors alongside senior managers, and its policy board which included eight regional non-executives.

The BMA was not opposed to the changes, but was concerned about crucial functions in medical education, training and workforce planning that had previously been carried out by the regions but which, in the early stages of discussion, appeared to have been overlooked. Eventually, the role of the postgraduate deans was acknowledged as important and they remained responsible for commissioning postgraduate medical education, supported by a regional adviser on general practice and a new body, the Regional Education and Development Group (REDG), drawn from trusts and health authorities. Most workforce planning fell to these REDGs; the BMA felt this to be a significant weakening of the machinery that had existed to implement key national strategies.

There were also concerns over the public health function and the role of the Regional Director of Public Health (RDPH). The posts continued but were transferred to the civil service, a move that the BMA resisted as likely to compromise the directors' independence. Their role became weaker, with many strategic health responsibilities passing to individual health authorities. There was also a debate about medical advice, where it was feared previous agreements might be diluted, but this was resolved with strong guidance about the need for appropriate professional advisory machinery at all levels, and a requirement for the new health authorities to recognise existing local advisory committees.

Another concern had been the BMA's interface with the Department of Health and/or the NHSE over negotiations on doctors' terms and conditions of service. Trusts were now legally responsible for changes to doctors' employment contracts, but in practice nearly all doctors were still employed on national terms and conditions of service, and the usefulness of being able to resolve nationally such fraught issues as junior doctors' hours and discretionary points for consultants had recently been shown. For GPs also, the national negotiating forum was effective and their contractual arrangements were so complex that devolving them would have been hugely disruptive. So the opportunity for the Department of Health to offload its negotiating activity was not taken and the national negotiating bodies continued as before, though with the worrying proviso that NHSE headquarters would continue to support the national pay machinery only 'for as long as it exists'.

The result of the Functions and Manpower Review and the subsequent changes was that for three years following the upheavals of the NHS reforms, the NHS in England was in a constant state of flux. Boundaries and lines of accountability were re-drawn, sometimes several times, and there was a big turnover in health authority staff, including public health doctors who often had to re-apply for their job. It was a pattern that was to become familiar in the NHS.

Healthcare in London: the Tomlinson Report

As early as 1991 it became clear that, if left to its own devices, the impact of the internal health care market in London would be seismic. London's health services had developed around the status and influence of its many world-famous teaching hospitals with their research facilities, high staffing levels and historic buildings. Their costs were higher than those of hospitals providing comparable services elsewhere. They would have had no chance of competing in an unregulated market so steps would have to be taken if they were to survive. Hospital closures, then as now, were politically sensitive, so the government swiftly stepped in to look for a more palatable way to manage the inevitable changes than abandoning London hospitals to the market. Professor Sir Bernard Tomlinson, a former medical chairman of the Northern RHA, was asked to conduct an inquiry into London health care. He worked quickly, drawing on previous work by the King's Fund and the London Health Planning Consortium, and the Tomlinson Report was published in October 1992. Its recommendations were radical and difficult for the government, as they involved closing or merging several iconic institutions and cutting up to 7,000 beds at a time when the public believed that acute services were already under-resourced. But the report also identified the need to improve primary and community care in London, and the implementation included significant investment in primary care within a 'London initiatives zone'.

The government responded with *Making London Better* in February 1993, which largely accepted Tomlinson's recommendations, and pressed ahead, setting up a London Implementation Group (LIG) to take forward practical aspects and commissioning further specialty reviews. The process required tough action from the government, as the threatened institutions fought strongly to defend themselves: St Bartholomew's in particular conducted a high profile campaign supported by the London *Evening Standard*. But the Secretary of State, Virginia Bottomley, was resolute, and despite the government's slim majority overcame opposition from some London MPs and ensured that much of the rationalisation went ahead.

The apparently muted BMA response to the Tomlinson report was explained by the deep-seated view in the central committees, most of whose members came from outside London, that the capital city had for too long attracted more than its share of government favour and resources. After all, the Association had begun in Worcester in 1832 as the Provincial Medical and Surgical Association, with the aim of redressing a perceived imbalance of influence between London doctors and those in the rest of the country, and this perception has never been completely dissipated. More recently the Association has tried to strengthen its local structures, particularly its regional councils, so that debates on reconfiguring services can take place locally.

The BMA's 1993 response did not oppose the principle of rationalisation, and refrained from taking a view on the future of individual hospitals. It made general points about the need to manage change sensitively and to avoid destabilising integrated services, and expressed concern about the statistical basis of some of the conclusions. The main BMA effort then went into its trade union job of looking after individual members who might be affected by the changes. The consultants' committee, led by John Chawner, started negotiations with the LIG to set up a clearing house to help redeploy consultants who faced redundancy, and the medical academics' committee was able to adapt this for clinical academic staff. Meanwhile the GPs' committee worked with a group of London Local Medical Committees (LMCs) to lobby for investment in primary care before further bed closures. They also ensured that GPs were involved in the process through a conference and a ballot of views, and helped to set up a task force to work with the NHSE on improving premises in the London Initiative Zone.

BMA regional staff were able to represent individual members when problems arose, though the feared numbers of medical redundancies did not materialise. Over the next few years further rationalisation took place in London, with mergers of many of the medical schools setting the pattern for a five-sector approach to service provision. This was reviewed again in 1997 under the new government, which led to major capital developments at University College Hospital, St Bartholomew's and the Royal London, before a further radical rethink 10 years later led by Sir Ara (later Lord) Darzi *(see Chapter 4)*.

Specialist training: the Calman Report

In 1991 Stephen Hunter was succeeded as Chairman of the Hospital Junior Staff Committee (HJSC) by Edwin Borman, an articulate South African anaesthetist who, with a group of other juniors, had joined the committee fired up with passionate determination to reduce working hours, and after two years found himself precipitated into the chair. Their success in persuading ministers – and seniors – to sign up to the *New Deal* seemed to motivate this generation of juniors to push harder for more change. While remaining engaged in the *New Deal* implementation (due to continue until the end of 1996), they turned their attention to the variable quality and undue length of specialist training; at that time the average age of appointment to a consultant job was 38 and rising.

The problems for juniors were already well documented, with recruitment and retention causing headaches for employers and exacerbating workload problems for consultants. But what forced the government to act – and offered the politically aware HJSC leadership a chance to advance their agenda – was a legal action by the European Commission against the UK government for breaches of the European Directives on medical training. The commission found a substantial difference between the certificate issued by the GMC to British-trained doctors wishing to work as specialists in Europe, and the accreditation issued by the royal colleges to those wishing to work as specialists in the UK. This double standard showed that the relevant authorities, the GMC and the royal colleges, were not yet taking European requirements as seriously as they needed to.

The government asked the CMO in England, Kenneth Calman, to set up a working party to review the whole question of training. The CMO was aware that the issues went wider than the regulatory ones highlighted by the EC proceedings and encouraged the working party to look for radical solutions. Both juniors and seniors from the BMA were represented, though only after a battle as relationships with the government were still strained following the arguments over *Working for Patients*. The group met five times between September 1992 and February 1993 and, as in the *New Deal* group, its deliberations involved tough battles and difficult compromises. Edwin Borman brought from the Junior Doctors Committee (JDC – as the HJSC became in 1992) a proposal – developed after heated arguments in the committee – for a structured and shorter training programme for specialist trainees, while John Chawner from the CCSC, though supporting the juniors' aspirations to improve training and career prospects, needed to fight for similar safeguards for consultants to those that had been included in the *New Deal*.

The outcome was a report proposing a new model of specialist training.[2] Training would be reduced from 12 to 7 years, the registrar and senior registrar grades unified, and a new certificate of completion of specialist training introduced. This would replace accreditation as a prerequisite for consultant appointment and would be based on an assessment of competence as opposed to time served. Crucially, consultant expansion would be accelerated above the level of the annual 2% that was already supposed to be maintained under *Achieving a Balance*. This would entail a different form of service provision, with more care delivered by consultants; the report described this as a move from a

---

[2] *Hospital Doctors – Training for the Future*. DH 1993 (*The Calman Report*).

consultant-led to a consultant-based service, though it did not explain what the change would mean in practice.

There was a short period of consultation, and the government's intention to implement the recommendations was swiftly announced in December 1993 by the Minister for Health, Brian Mawhinney. As he did so he dashed the optimism of those who had hoped their problems were over by stating that implementation would take place without new resources and would be subject to the capacity of the NHS to absorb the changes into existing budgets. Significant consultant expansion had never previously been achieved without earmarked funding. Although the report had not been explicit about the level of consultant expansion needed, Paul Miller, the JDC workforce number-cruncher (and a future chairman of the consultants committee) estimated that achieving the desired reduction in training time would require 8% per annum expansion over five years. In the same announcement Brian Mawhinney commented that implementing the report required a 'move away from existing medical staffing policies towards more flexible measures which emphasise local decision-making and priorities'. This undermined the expectation that the government would require trusts to follow central guidance when implementing the working group's conclusions.

So although major parts of the Calman reforms – those relating to the structure and organisation of training – went ahead, strategic reform of the medical staffing structure as envisaged was compromised from the start. As predicted, consultant expansion failed to reach the levels needed to facilitate different ways of working. Without central direction, indeed encouraged by the NHSE to adopt ad hoc solutions, trusts made their staffing decisions on the basis of immediate service needs. They quickly started filling any rota gaps with non-standard posts that fell outside any career structure. These were variously called SHOs, staff grades, 'trust grades', or other invented terms. The National Association of Health Authorities and Trusts (NAHAT), which represented employers, published a report recommending that trusts consider appointing two grades of consultant: 'junior' consultants (who would assume much of the on-call responsibility, often be resident, and work largely without intermediate level support) and a much smaller number of 'senior' consultants, with a consulting and management role. This was generally seen as a step too far, but the idea kept resurfacing as the balance of hospital staffing changed, most recently in 2012.[3]

---

[3] Centre for Workforce Intelligence. *Shape of the Medical Workforce: starting the debate on the future consultant workforce* February 2012.

Notwithstanding their disappointment, the JDC still had much to gain by staying involved in the Calman implementation process. The work programme included curricula for new training programmes, national training numbers to enable manpower control to be exercised, expert groups (to look at research, overseas doctors and general practice), and work by the GMC on basic specialist training. In 1995 a new body, the Advisory Group on Medical Education, Training and Staffing, took over the central functions of the previously existing Achieving a Balance, New Deal and Joint Planning Advisory Committee groups and a Specialist Workforce Advisory Group was set up to recommend on training numbers for each specialty.

After a slow start, by 1995 enough progress had been made on the training arrangements for the JDC to negotiate terms and conditions of service as well as transitional arrangements for the new grade of specialist registrar. The NHSE wanted to change the nature of the contract, arguing for an inclusive, professional contract which would not include extra payment for long or unsocial hours, and with pay progression dependent on educational performance. The JDC, under the chairmanship of psychiatrists Andrew Carney from London then Peter Bennie from Glasgow (later chairman of the BMA's Representative Body), strongly resisted. Eventually ministers, conscious of a slim parliamentary majority, conceded and agreed on terms and conditions of service based on those already in use. The Doctors' and Dentists' Review Body (DDRB) then recommended a higher pay increase for juniors than for other groups (up to 6.8% instead of 3.8%) which also pleased the juniors. On the other hand, they did lose an important battle: registrars' contracts, which had been held at regional level together with 50% of the budget for training posts, would now be held by NHS trusts. Despite assurances that trusts would not change the nature of employment contracts and that 'lead trusts' would be designated to co-ordinate registrars rotating between different trusts, this was seen as another worrying step away from the protection of national terms and conditions of service that had been granted in 1991.

GP out-of-hours negotiations

As soon as it was implemented, the GPs' 1990 contract ran into problems: for example, the requirement to offer health promotion led to endless local difficulties over precisely what constituted a health promotion clinic. The GMSC spent much time negotiating changes to make the contract workable. A particular setback occurred when a combination of technical problems over the estimate of expenses and the government's interference with the review body award led to an attempt to claw back what the government called an 'overpayment' of £6,000 to each GP. After an argument, a proportion of the amount was waived, but the term 'overpayment' caused some bitterness.

The contract was tainted from the start by the fact that it had been imposed, and the new GMSC Chairman Dr Ian Bogle lost no time in starting a debate on possible changes. In June 1991 the committee published a consultation document for GPs: *Building Your Own Future*. This was followed in October by *Your Choices for the Future*, then in January by a questionnaire designed to inform a special LMC conference later that year. The issues were wide-ranging, but it was clear that the main bugbear among GPs was their 24-hour commitment to their patients and the amount of relatively unproductive work that this generated 'out-of-hours'. Ian Bogle, coming from a busy inner city practice in Liverpool, felt strongly about this issue himself. He ensured that the GMSC had agreed a clear set of negotiating objectives before it moved forward. But he was optimistic: 'I sense that we are now returning to a position where we can again exert influence, where governments are prepared to listen to our views'.[4] Indeed meetings with the NHSE soon got under way. However, it was not until three years later, that the 'out-of-hours' dispute was finally settled.

At first discussions focused on deputising services, still governed by a restrictive 1984 circular, and how they related to the increasingly widespread GP co-operatives. The GMSC gradually teased out an understanding that practices could make use of deputising doctors (when they were also GP principals) to relieve the burden of out-of-hours cover. Progress was made on different ways for GPs to provide out-of-hours services, including greater use of telephone advice or emergency centres as opposed to home visits, and the GMSC launched a *Help us to Help You* campaign to inform patients. But the government refused to accept the LMC conference's demand that GPs should be able to opt out of their 24-hour responsibility for patients completely. The principle was debated again at the 1994 LMC conference, when the risks of hiving off some of the traditional responsibility of GPs – jeopardising public confidence in GPs and the danger of undercutting by competitive tender were recognised. Negotiations continued on how to reduce the burden of providing the service rather than opting out of

[4] GMSC Annual Report 1992.

it completely, but the issue had become emotive and the GMSC was under pressure to achieve a substantial improvement. In November 1994 the committee rejected as derisory an offer of a £2,000 fixed payment per GP and £9 fee per home visit or consultation, particularly since it was to be funded from reductions elsewhere in the remuneration package.

The DDRB became embroiled. It did not support the NHSE's proposal, and was not prepared to recommend the additional resources the GMSC had wanted. It delayed setting the GPs' fee scale for 1995/96 in the hope that a solution might be negotiated, and attitudes hardened, despite an injection of £15m into cash-limited funding for general practice. The two sides failed to agree, and the DDRB issued a supplementary report in March 1995 setting the fee scale on the old basis. The stand-off was not eased until the summer, when Stephen Dorrell took over from Virginia Bottomley with Gerry Malone as his Minister for Health.

The Conservative government's parliamentary majority was down to single figures. It is not clear how close to the forefront of Stephen Dorrell's mind this was, nor how far he was just temperamentally inclined to avoid confrontation, but he acted quickly to defuse the tension. He thrashed out with the GP negotiators a new package, supported by £45m of new money in an 'out-of-hours development fund', together with a £2,000 annual allowance and a revised £20 night consultation fee. The GPs' committee accepted this and the dispute was settled. It had taken a significant step away from the notion of general practice as a personal service in which patients might expect to see their doctor at any time of the day or night, and towards a more modern, complex arrangement in which levels of care, and access to them, are more differentiated and planned. Ian Bogle and his negotiating team were well aware that they were opening the door to further changes in the future.

Stephen Dorrell quickly picked up that the problems affecting GPs' morale were more deep-seated, and in the autumn of 1995 he asked his minister, Gerry Malone, to undertake a 'listening exercise'. The GMSC had been working on alternative models of provision, with important contributions from two future chairmen – Hamish Meldrum on practice-based contracts and John Chisholm on core and non-core medical services. Worried by evidence from its medical workforce task group of a serious recruitment problem in general practice, the committee seized the chance to discuss new ideas and identified four policy priorities: a clear definition of core medical services, the development of a salaried option, the desirability of some form of quality assurance, and the end of out-of-hours responsibility.

Meanwhile the 'listening exercise' had led to a discussion paper, and the subsequent white papers *Choice and Opportunity* and *Primary Care: delivering the future*. They envisaged major changes to primary care as part of a move to shift more care into this sector. The Primary Care Act of 1997 introduced a new kind of general practice, known as 'personal medical services' (PMS), which allowed alternative providers to enter the market and offer a different range of services from the traditional general medical services. These changes were introduced on a voluntary basis with pilot schemes, and the GMSC, while concerned about the possible role of the commercial sector, largely supported the developments. They also sought to open negotiations on improvements to terms and conditions identified in their consultation document *Core Services – taking the initiative*.

The local pay campaign

The prospect of doctors' pay being settled locally rather than at national level was a big worry for the BMA when NHS trusts were first proposed in 1989, and has resurfaced in 2012. In the early 1990s, as more waves of NHS trusts came on stream (employing 90% of senior hospital doctors in England by 1994), the BMA became embroiled in a bitter battle with the government over the issue. Led by the CCSC, whose members were most affected, it took a resolute stand and was rewarded with one of the very few instances in this history of a government backing down and withdrawing a policy that it had firmly and publicly articulated.

Although trusts had been free to determine doctors' pay since the 1991 NHS and Community Care Act, in fact there was little movement away from national pay scales. The government wanted to keep public sector pay increases down and to link them to increases in productivity and efficiency. The NHSE had become frustrated because trusts were not using use their powers over doctors' pay, and in its evidence for the 1992 DDRB review it signalled that it would propose 'performance-related pay' as part of the mechanism for determining general pay increases. It suggested that this would be largely for senior staff, particularly hospital consultants.

The DDRB reacted coolly, commenting: 'Our collective experience is that performance-related pay schemes present fundamental challenges to pay systems which limit overall earnings' and 'the incentive impact of performance-related pay schemes will be weakened if increased payments for increased performance are seen as being automatically set off against future pay rises.' However it asked both sides to consider the matter further, pointing particularly to performance pay supplements, group schemes, and a review of the distinction awards scheme (particularly C awards), as fruitful areas for discussion.

The CCSC responded positively: it was sceptical about applying 'industrial' performance-related pay schemes to medical work, and spent time examining the academic arguments for and against such schemes, but felt strongly that if changes were to come it was better to agree centrally on some principles rather than allow local free-for-alls. The committee feared that doctors in less 'glamorous' specialties and in disadvantaged areas would come off worse, and that inappropriate incentives would almost certainly overshadow those reflecting clinical values. The principle of rewarding outstanding performance was not at issue: it had after all been the basis of the distinction award scheme since 1948.

So the CCSC started a national debate among consultants about distinction awards and told the NHSE it was willing to enter discussions. The debate on distinction awards – always a contentious subject among consultants – led to some positive proposals for improving their fairness and transparency in the local nominations process. The NHSE agreed to consider these ideas, though it would not meet to discuss them nor make its own proposals. The CCSC sent its recommendations to all consultants and asked medical staff committees to set up local groups to consider nominations for awards, ensuring that all consultants were involved.

In 1993 the government prevented the review body from reporting (see..), and the NHSE continued to avoid meeting the CCSC until in November 1993 it suddenly announced a review of distinction awards, to be chaired by Professor Robert Kendell, a former Scottish CMO. He would report to the Minister for Health by the end of March 1994. Under the terms of reference the review would look particularly at separating the higher awards (for rewarding 'work of national and international importance') from 'C' awards (for rewarding 'local performance').

With some difficulty the CCSC secured two seats on the group and had much to contribute, having recently gathered consultants' views. Discussions were progressing well until a junior civil servant let slip in a meeting that another piece of work on distinction awards was going on, though it would not be shared with the review group. The CCSC chairman, John Chawner, pressed Professor Kendell for more information, which he seemed embarrassed to give. John Chawner refused to let the matter drop and eventually persuaded the Minister, Brian Mawhinney, to investigate. He ascertained, apparently with some annoyance, that the Treasury had commissioned a private consultancy to produce a parallel report and agreed that it must be seen by the review group. When it appeared the alternative report was ill-informed and brought little to the debate, but openness was preserved, and the Treasury's attempt to outflank the minister seemed to strengthen his support for the group's conclusions.

No more had been heard from the NHSE on local pay until, in evidence to the DDRB in 1994, it hardened its stance, stating that from the following year pay bargaining would be carried out locally on the basis of performance-related pay schemes. It took this position despite the DDRB's advice not to, and having declined all of the CCSC's requests to discuss the matter. It did say that it would discuss with the BMA and other staff unions an 'enabling clause': an amendment to national terms and conditions of service that would allow an element of pay to be determined locally. When the DDRB published its report it had shifted its position, and seemed to support the government, encouraging the parties to discuss ways of introducing local pay.

The report was badly received by BMA committees, which opposed the principle of local pay negotiations for doctors. With support from BMA Council, the CCSC began to campaign against local pay, beginning with those who would be most involved in implementing it: the members of Local Negotiating Committees (LNCs). By this time the CCSC had developed strong communications with LNCs, and it sent out advice, backed up by briefing papers, on how to counter any local proposals that might pre-empt the government's initiative. Consultants did not want to spend their time negotiating over pay with local managers, who they knew faced financial and political pressures: it was the DDRB's job to resolve this at national level, using a wider perspective. The campaign quickly generated strong support from consultants.

The NHSE refused to discuss the detail of local schemes to implement performance-related pay, merely proposing the wording of an enabling clause, which was duly rejected by the negotiating committees for seniors, juniors and community medicine/community health staff.

With the help of the public affairs division, the CCSC, leading the campaign, generated debate in the press and briefed MPs. Although it is difficult to engage public sympathy on doctors' pay, the arguments against local and performance pay attracted some support, perhaps because of continuing concern about the apparent commercialisation of the NHS. However, the government seemed unwilling either to mount a robust defence or to enter into meaningful discussions.

At the ARM in Birmingham there was an emotional rejection of local pay – hardly a debate as no-one spoke in favour of it – with a standing ovation for John Chawner who pledged to continue the fight, reiterating the dangers to the NHS of moving away from national pay determination. The CCSC followed this up with a special meeting for consultants in August at the QEII Conference Centre in London. At an advanced stage of planning a national rail strike was called for the day, but staff organised coaches and were rewarded by a strong attendance of more than 400. But there would be a second setback to the publicity effort. On the day of the conference, the IRA announced it would renounce its campaign of violence and enter negotiations with the British government. This major breakthrough dominated the evening news and morning papers, leaving little space for the hoped for coverage on local pay. Fervently though consultants shared the nation's delight at this historic development, many wished the timing of the announcement could have been different.

Nevertheless, the conference made an impact in the medical press, and it certainly reinforced the CCSC's determination to resist local pay. There had been angry calls at the London meeting for industrial action, and when the CCSC met in the autumn, its new chairman, James Johnson, a chairman of the juniors in the 1970s, found himself setting up a working group to consider a range of sanctions that might be applied if the government imposed the enabling clause, as it now threatened to do.

As the year came to an end the dispute continued to build, following the classic pattern of hardening resistance in public while developing a solution behind the scenes. The BMA and the CCSC resolutely opposed the enabling clause, while the government stuck to its line that it would be introduced from 1 April 1995. Meanwhile, the Kendell Committee completed its work in October, recommending greater involvement of managers with the C awards system. The government neither accepted the report nor issued it for consultation, but as BMA pressure grew, finally agreed to discuss its recommendations.

The Kendell Committee had proposed separating distinction awards into 'national' and 'local' awards, and in suggesting that these were a form of performance pay it had opened a way forward.

At last the CCSC was able to meet officials on this matter, including the CMO and the HR director of the NHSE, who seemed keener to discuss practical solutions than the rhetoric of their political masters had suggested. The CCSC negotiators had no objection to making substantial changes to the C awards scheme, which many consultants saw as unfair and inflexible. They insisted that the money in the scheme should be retained as part of consultant remuneration, and that any new scheme should continue using national criteria based on professional achievement. Once they had agreed a mechanism for protecting the funding – in the form of minimum numbers of points to be allocated by each trust – the way was clear to replace C awards with a new discretionary points scheme. Negotiations continued through much of 1995, but by January the CCSC Chairman was able to suggest to the Secretary of State that the government's objectives could now be met without the troublesome enabling clause.

As the February 1995 publication of the DDRB report came near, and with it the moment when the government would have to announce its decision on the enabling clause, which could trigger industrial action, there were hasty late-night phone calls between civil servants and the CCSC office. Days before publication, James Johnson was summoned to see Virginia Bottomley, to be told quietly that the government did not want a dispute and would drop the enabling clause. He resisted the urge to exult, and the CCSC returned to finalise the discretionary points agreement. It was implemented in April 1996, and involved considerable co-operation between LNCs and trust managements.

The DDRB's report, written before the government's change of heart, devoted several pages to a recommendation for 'transitional local pay', a scheme that would allow trusts to pay consultants – but not juniors – a locally determined increase, with specified limits, which could exceed the national scale. But the recommendation was redundant because the enabling clause had been dropped. The question of local pay would only arise where national terms and conditions of service had been abandoned, and since trusts were soon busy reinforcing their commitment to national terms and conditions by introducing the nationally agreed discretionary points scheme, the DDRB's recommendation was redundant.

Chapter 3

New Labour: modernisation and negotiation
1997–2007

NHS modernisation and devolution

In May 1997 a new Labour government was elected with a large majority and the nation was gripped with optimism. The BMA had worked cordially with the Secretary of State for Health, Frank Dobson, during his years in opposition, when, as the local MP, he had often attended events in BMA House. In office, he talked about abolishing the internal market, returning to collaboration rather than competition, and undoing the damage inflicted by the 1990 reforms. By the end of 1997 a white paper, *The New NHS – Modern, Dependable,* had appeared, followed in 1998 by a green paper *A First Class Service.* They were to bring more upheaval to the English NHS: the abolition of the eight NHS Executive (NHSE) regional offices, and the establishment of nearly 500 Primary Care Groups (PCGs) to take over commissioning from the health authorities. But they put a new emphasis on quality and regulation by introducing clinical governance and setting up the National Institute for Clinical Excellence and the Commission for Healthcare Improvement. The BMA welcomed these innovations and looked forward to a constructive relationship with the government over the development of NHS policy.

But by the time that Ian Bogle, a Liverpool GP and former General Medical Services Committee (GMSC) chairman, was elected Chairman of Council in 1998, a major event had occurred that would make the BMA's task immeasurably harder: the revelations about paediatric cardiac surgery at Bristol Royal Infirmary that had outraged the public and would continue to generate scandalous headlines as the events were inquired into and reviewed *(see Chapter 7).* Ian Bogle came to the role determined to restore the BMA to the position of influence that some felt the stridency of its 1990 campaign had sacrificed, and although he was able to keep open the channels of communication with government, he was repeatedly forced onto the back foot by more high-profile cases of medical misdemeanour: the gynaecologists

Rodney Ledward and Richard Neale, the Harold Shipman murders and the Alder Hey organ retention scandal. The BMA did not defend those who had fallen short, but public respect for doctors was damaged. And ministers, always sensitive to headlines, were sometimes tempted to add their voices to generalised calls for retribution. Thus the BMA found itself crossing swords with the government to defend the vast majority of competent and conscientious doctors from unjustified criticism.

Within two years Frank Dobson had fulfilled one of Labour's pre-election promises and replaced GP fundholding by giving all GPs a role in commissioning. But though the words had changed, the emphasis on commissioning was to ensure the continuation rather than the abolition of the internal market. By then the NHS was once again beset by financial pressures, with waiting lists increasing and services curtailed. In October 1999 Frank Dobson was replaced by Alan Milburn, who had been his health minister, and who as a New Labour figure enjoyed greater influence with Downing Street. He was more inclined than Frank Dobson to pursue policies that had been identified with the Conservative government – particularly greater private sector involvement in the NHS, supported by competition and market forces. His determination to develop a radical agenda was encouraged by the severe financial 'winter pressures' that hit the NHS over his first few months, when opinion polls showed falling public confidence in the NHS.

At the height of this crisis in January 2000, the Prime Minister, Tony Blair, was pressed on NHS funding by David Frost in a TV interview. As Mrs Thatcher had done 12 years before, he made an unexpected commitment – apparently without the agreement or knowledge of the Chancellor of the Exchequer. He promised a substantial increase in NHS funding: 5% in real terms for each of the next five years to bring health spending up to the average of other EU countries. The Treasury came up with the money, announcing the first tranche in the March 2000 budget, and allowing Alan Milburn to launch his ambitious *NHS Plan* in July. Meanwhile Sir Derek Wanless, a distinguished banker, was asked to review the long-term financial requirements of the NHS, a major exercise which, when published in 2002, provided the rationale for further funding increases.

The *NHS Plan* envisaged real investment in the NHS, including more doctors and nurses, with modernised pay systems, more acute beds and hospital investment, better access to GPs, and various initiatives for improvement to be overseen by a modernisation board. Clearly it was an opportunity to be grasped. Ian Bogle added his name to a list of signatories to the plan, including other health organisations and unions, who declared: 'We all support the process of modernisation and reform, and welcome the direction of travel: to reshape the NHS from a patient's point of view'. He was criticised by some within the BMA for explicitly endorsing government policy and thereby compromising the BMA's independence. Others objected that specific proposals could not be supported, such as the inadequate provision for extra GPs and a proposed restriction on consultants' ability to do private practice for seven years after being appointed. But Alan Milburn had deliberately engaged organisations such as the BMA while preparing the plan, and Ian Bogle felt that signing up to a general statement lost nothing but gained a seat at the negotiating table. The BMA did have a seat on the modernisation board – filled by the Chairman of Council – as well as seats on many of the other groups and project teams.

Meanwhile Ian Bogle and the Council had been trying to counteract the media 'doctor-bashing' that arose from medical scandals. He set up a steering group to review NHS funding, which included representatives of patients' groups, nurses, the private sector and the pharmaceutical industry as well as the BMA; it published its report in 2001.[1] The report reiterated that the only realistic way to fund the NHS was from general taxation; this had been the BMA's long-standing policy. More controversially, it called for an open acknowledgement that resources would never meet demand, raising the spectre of rationing, and argued that NHS services should no longer be described as comprehensive. This meant that a greater role for the private sector was inevitable, and should not be opposed on principle. The report generated discussion, and was followed in September 2001 by *Leading Change*, a 10-point plan for improving both health care and trust in doctors. But by then the funding issue had already been settled by the *NHS Plan*, while the news agenda was dominated by the Shipman Inquiry, which began in June and continued, with regular reports, for two and a half years.

Another radical development was the new government's decision to devolve significant powers, including responsibility for health, from the UK government in Westminster to national governments or assemblies in Scotland, Wales and Northern Ireland (following the Good Friday Agreement in 1998). This had been signalled before the election, and the BMA had already been thinking through the implications

---

[1] *Healthcare Funding Review*: BMA February 2001.

for its own structures and organisation. The BMA functioned as a UK organisation, run largely from London but with offices and active national councils and committees in Scotland, Wales and Northern Ireland. The English health department had traditionally led over NHS policy and negotiations for doctors, with the national administrations generally following their line but, in the case of Scotland and Northern Ireland, retaining the ability to adapt any decisions to their own circumstances. BMA committee structures reflected this, with representatives of all nations present, though English members were a large majority.

The first instincts of the UK Council and of the national bodies were that doctors saw themselves as a UK-wide profession, and that this solidarity must be maintained. Nevertheless, members in the newly devolved nations could see that they would need to develop new structures and, after years of a Conservative government that had particularly alienated voters beyond the borders of England, some felt that greater self-determination might offer promising opportunities. On the initiative of the Secretary, Dr Mac Armstrong, himself a Scot (and later Chief Medical Officer (CMO) in Scotland), the BMA moved quickly to upgrade its facilities and boost its staffing in the devolved nations, commissioning early in 1999 a new Edinburgh HQ, at a cost of £2.5 million, followed later by improved accommodation in Belfast and Cardiff (*see also chapter on devolution*). Meanwhile Council set up a working party to look at constitutional changes.[2] The BMA national councils were strengthened and the national branch of practice committees given authority to negotiate on devolved matters, though the Representative Body remained the policy making body for the BMA throughout the UK. But it soon became clear, initially during the consultant contract negotiations in 2001–2, that the impact of devolution would assert itself most strongly through the reality of democratic accountability when big decisions affecting members' interests were to be taken.

Change gathers pace: caring for the NHS

By the end of 1999 the BMA had already embarked on a landmark series of contract negotiations (*see below*), starting with the junior doctors. These negotiations and their fall-out were to preoccupy the Association for more than five years. Meanwhile Alan Milburn pursued a relentless programme of change within the NHS, working closely

---

[2] Supplementary Annual Report of Council 1997–98.

with Downing Street where policy was increasingly determined, and where Simon Stevens (later CEO of the private health care provider UnitedHealth in Europe and in the US), was the influential health policy adviser.

The agenda of patient choice was driven forward, with competition between a plurality of providers, incentives for the private sector to get involved and hospital star ratings to promote 'creative discomfort'. On top of this were rigorously enforced central targets – on waiting times and clinical performance indicators – together with increasingly muscular regulatory regimes, with the Commission for Healthcare Improvement becoming the Healthcare Commission in 2004. Foundation Trusts were proposed in 2002, though not implemented until 2004 after a difficult passage through Parliament; they were the only aspect of the NHS programme that caused significant division within the Labour Party. A further NHS reorganisation in 2002[3] saw PCGs replaced by beefed-up Primary Care Trusts (PCTs) that would receive direct financial allocations. Health authorities were replaced by 28 strategic health authorities (SHAs). Hospital building projects forged ahead, largely financed through the Private Finance Initiative (PFI), a policy started by the Conservative government but hugely expanded under Labour. By 2009 £12 billion worth of projects had been approved.[4] The BMA had opposed PFI since 1996 because it offered poor value for money and committed hospitals to high levels of repayment for a long time. (This concern has since been borne out in critical reports by the Public Accounts Committee and National Audit Office[5] and in 2007 the government was obliged to refinance the crippling PFI debt of some hospitals.) At the time, however, many local doctors welcomed the schemes, agreeing with managers that it was the only way of improving outdated and dilapidated hospital buildings.

Another big change was a new tariff system for hospital treatment, *Payment by Results,* which would alter hospitals' financial incentives and thus, in time, their priorities and behaviour more dramatically than might have been thought when the consultation paper *Reforming NHS Financial Flows* was published in October 2002. Meanwhile, there was also change in primary care, with NHS Direct set up in March 1998 to

---

[3] The NHS Reform and Health Care Professions Act 2002.

[4] HPERU briefing: *The PFI and the NHS* 2009.

[5] Public Accounts Committee May 2007 and September 2008: *Making changes in operational PFI payments*. National Audit Office June 2010: *The performance and management of hospital PFI contracts*.

provide health advice from call centres, investment in practice premises through the local improvement finance programme (LIFT – another form of private finance initiative), Personal Medical Services (PMS) with more and more GPs opting for salaried contracts and the development of various models of GP commissioning.

The NHS was breathless at the speed of change. There was staff turnover with every re-organisation, jargon-spouting project teams for each new initiative, and the emergence of a 'target culture' among managers that, despite the rhetoric about local decision-making, was clearly driven by the centre. Doctors mainly wanted to get on with treating their patients and they struggled to keep abreast of the latest schemes. While some thrived and saw opportunities for clinicians to take a lead, many remained sceptical, fearing that targets and initiatives would not offer real solutions, but simply distort priorities. But for a while the most noticeable change was the substantial increase in money available for new developments; this had been desperately needed for years and was now widely welcomed.

The BMA's position too was broadly welcoming, at first. Committee representatives were involved in the various groups set up by the Modernisation Board and its Modernisation Agency. Although there was little opportunity to influence the overall direction of government policy, they were able to provide input into the operational aspects. But as relationships with the government became strained over the difficult contract negotiations that were underway and over the heavy-handed measures being demanded in the wake of Bristol, Shipman and other medical scandals, concerns grew in BMA committees that the reforms were not heading in the right direction. The BMA repeatedly expressed its objections in principle to PFI, greatly increased private sector involvement and the distortion of clinical priorities by inappropriate targets. But the government was intent on its path and outright opposition was neither called for by members, nor a practical proposition.

The divergences between the NHS in England and in the other nations started to set in. The *NHS Plan* was an England document, and though the increased investment applied to all four countries, the other nations chose to make different changes with less emphasis on choice, market mechanisms and private provision. The agenda of BMA Council and other UK committees became increasingly dominated by English problems, while the Councils and committees of the devolved nations held separate discussions with their own administrations.

In June 2003 Alan Milburn unexpectedly resigned and was replaced as Secretary of State by John Reid. Soon after James Johnson, a Merseyside surgeon and former chairman of the juniors and seniors committees and the Joint Consultants Committee took over from Ian Bogle as Chairman of BMA Council. James Johnson shared with his predecessor the view that the BMA had more to gain by engagement and dialogue than by shouting from the sidelines, and he worked hard to ensure that BMA representatives were actively contributing to debate with the government at every level. John Reid showed no inclination to slow the pace of change. His *NHS Improvement Plan* introduced more rigorous waiting-time targets, together with enforced patient choice of provider, including private sector alternatives, to be supported by electronic booking and better information. After the 2005 general election, Patricia Hewitt replaced him as Secretary of State, and in January 2006 introduced *Our Health, Our Care, Our Say* which called for a shift of resources from hospitals to the community and put pressure on GPs to offer new services (such as a 'life check') and to increase hours of access. But the PCTs, as commissioners, were ill-equipped to deliver strategic change of this kind. On the provider side, trusts had responded to the incentives to become entrepreneurial – investing in PFI projects, seeking foundation trust status, expanding and merging – so that they generally outgunned the PCTs by showing that the demand for their services was higher than ever.

The effects of the demand-led financial pressures became increasingly clear. The 2005–6 financial year ended with significant deficits, despite the emergency measure of allowing about £637 million of NHS money to be moved from ring-fenced training budgets into service provision. This caused not only bad feeling, but also real infrastructure damage as it reduced the number of training posts for some health professions (such as physiotherapists) and cut study leave for doctors. The deficit worsened in 2006 as PCTs struggled to meet the conflicting demands of shifting resources to the community, paying for the continuing rise in acute emergency admissions, and meeting tougher performance targets on waiting times, patient choice and other ministerial priorities. They also faced yet another restructuring exercise: reducing 28 SHAs to 10, and halving the number of PCTs.

The NHS Chief Executive, Sir Nigel Crisp, retired in March 2006, accepting some measure of responsibility for what had become a real financial crisis. 2007–8 would be the last of the five years of significant spending increases put in place by the Chancellor of the Exchequer Gordon Brown. Patricia Hewitt was under pressure to act and in November 2006 she announced she would bring NHS finances back into balance by March 2007. Many trusts and PCTs had to take drastic steps and imposed staff redundancies and hasty service reductions. The Doctors' and Dentists' Review Body (DDRB) toed the line and recommended that GPs should have no pay increase, and employed doctors just a flat rate increase of £1000. Even so, the government felt this was not draconian enough, and phased the award so that anything more than 1.5% would not be paid until November.

Remarkably, the target of balancing the finances was met by the NHS in England as a whole and by all but 82 NHS organisations. But there had been a loss of momentum and morale. In October 2007 the government announced that NHS spending would increase at 4% for each of the next three years, which was higher than expected, and it was evident that waiting times had reduced dramatically since the Labour government came to power. However, the sense remained that the 'boom and bust' period had distorted priorities, with clinical decision-making, quality of care, and concern for patients coming well behind financial considerations, political targets and a drive for marketisation and commercialisation.

The constant barrage of policy initiatives had made many BMA members, particularly in England, increasingly uneasy. The idea of contestability in service provision, respectable economic doctrine though it may have been, seemed to translate too often at local level into schemes designed to hive off discrete activities to private providers. In primary care, GP practices were put out to tender under the provisions for Alternative Provider Medical Services (APMS) that had been introduced in 2004. Contracts were awarded both to groups of GPs and to corporate private providers. Referral management schemes and clinical assessment centres, run by consultancies on lucrative contracts, were interposed between primary and secondary care to challenge existing local treatment patterns, further destabilising the financial position of already struggling hospital departments. In some places better professional dialogue between GPs and consultants could have improved patient care for patients and saved money, but most of these new schemes, far from fostering such dialogue, tended to create barriers to communication. Local clinicians, rarely consulted, felt alienated, and their fears were enhanced by a media campaign criticising the recent increase in GPs' pay.

Another initiative was a network of treatment centres set up to reduce waiting lists by carrying out routine elective surgery. Some were run by the NHS but the government also commissioned about 35 Independent Sector Treatment Centres (ISTCs). Controversially, these were procured centrally in two waves and awarded five-year contracts. To encourage entry into the market the contracts were paid in advance at a premium rate (costs were 12% higher than in the NHS[6]) and with a 'guaranteed fixed value': this meant that they would be paid even if the specified volumes of work were not delivered (as on the whole they were not). Local doctors reacted strongly, fearing ISTCs would destabilise hospital departments by 'cherry picking' their workload and leaving the NHS to cope with the more complex cases. Patients, GPs and consultants were excluded from referral decisions, and in the first wave the operations were done by surgeons brought in from overseas with no mechanism to follow up treatment or deal with complications. The BMA pressed these concerns repeatedly with the NHS Executive (NHSE) and in 2005[7] published a report which asked for the NHS to be allowed to compete fairly with the private sector, highlighting the fact that the ISTCs did not provide training for juniors. A new principle of 'additionality' was established for the second wave, whereby NHS staff could work in ISTCs, but only if they were not in designated shortage groups and were working in addition to their NHS contracts. Various groups investigated the value of ISTCs.[8] They found no evidence to substantiate claims of poor standards of care (the Healthcare Commission was critical of the quality of data produced by ISTCs, which did not allow useful comparisons with the NHS), but neither was there evidence that they had significantly reduced waiting lists, since they were only providing about 2% of elective care. As the first wave of contracts ended in 2009, the ISTC initiative had cost £1.2 billion[9]; by then the government acknowledged that the extra capacity was no longer needed and stopped their central procurement.

'Systems reform' in the NHS attracted considerable concern at the 2006 Annual Representative Meeting (ARM) in Belfast. Faced with a large number of motions the Chairman of the Representative

[6] HPERU Briefing: ISTCs 2009.
[7] BMA: *Impact of treatment centres on the local health economy in England* 2005.
[8] Healthcare Commission July 2007. House of Commons Health Committee 2006. Audit Commission 2008.
[9] King's Fund Briefing: *ISTCs* October 2009.

Body, Michael Wilks, and his agenda committee wanted to encourage an informal and open debate. They therefore scheduled a free discussion of all of these motions, when contributions from the floor would be taken randomly and no formal votes would be held. Briefing papers were made available, and a long debate took place in which representatives expressed strong views. Some speakers objected in principle to any private sector involvement in the NHS; others wanted specific changes in particular policies; a third group had already set up their own private companies to bid for services and embraced plurality.

But the debate was so wide-ranging and unstructured that the written summary, brought back the following day by rapporteurs, far from crystallising policy positions that had emerged, provoked more heated debate. Having abandoned the rigid but well-honed standing orders that normally provide a methodology for reaching decisions, the Chairman of the RB struggled to deal with objections, emergency motions and points of order. The debate descended into disorder with no clear policy established. The resulting four page summary document agreed that government policy was unsatisfactory, but then went on to offer a series of random and at times contradictory diagnoses and possible treatments. It asserted in one sentence that a clear strategy was needed for the 'commercial private sector' but that there must be no further involvement of the commercial private sector in providing NHS care. It committed the BMA to develop options for an English health service without a purchaser/provider split, but supported the development of commissioning. It listed 46 separate points for Council to take into account.

When Council started to consider the document it spent some time fruitlessly trying to make sense of what the ARM wanted, in particular struggling to agree on a definition of 'commercial private sector', which some felt would include, for example, APMS run by GPs. Council took the only practical action and set up a working group. This led to arguments over who should be members, reflecting the tensions that had already surfaced. One vociferous group wanted strong opposition to government policy; another was concerned but wanted the Association to be constructive. The Chairman, James Johnson, sympathised with the second group to such an extent some felt he should not chair the working party. Although this was rejected as the subject matter was so central to the BMA's activity, a leading protagonist of the opposing faction, Jacky Davis, was appointed deputy chairman to ensure balance.

The group set to work on two fronts. It adopted a slogan *Caring for the NHS* which became the theme for a campaign by the public affairs division. BMA members were encouraged to lobby their MPs, using the new 'political wizard' online tool. In November, the BMA joined other NHS trade unions to lobby Parliament under the banner of *NHS Together*. This was co-ordinated by the Trades Union Congress and reflected growing concern about privatisation, redundancies and NHS cuts, even among unions that had strong links to the Labour party. Early in 2007, the Chairman of Council, together with the consultants' and GPs' chairmen, visited hospitals and practices in the north west, where the SHA was introducing a number of Independent Clinical Assessment and Treatment Centres, somewhat to the bewilderment of local doctors and patients. These visits were well received, and in a few cases BMA regional staff were able to help local groups challenge specific proposals. But nationally the programme of putting services out to tender rolled on.

Meanwhile the working group had set itself the demanding task of reviewing NHS policy, taking written and oral evidence from groups and individuals, BMA and external, medical and non-medical. It was a time-consuming process which provided many insights and a mass of material for the health policy and economic research unit staff to distil, but possibly it took the debate too far into the realms of health policy theory and away from the unifying practical solutions that Council was looking for.

The report, published in May 2007 for consultation,[10] proposed an alternative vision for the NHS. Its central idea was to redefine the core values of the NHS by having an NHS constitution supported by a charter that would make clear what services would be provided. A form of this was eventually adopted by the government in its 2008 NHS constitution. The report also argued that the NHS would best be delivered by an organisation with an independent board of governors, accountable to Parliament but distant from day-to-day political interference. This idea gathered some support, including from the King's Fund and the Picker Institute, and also from the public (according to an opinion poll conducted for the BMA in June 2007). But the government did not take it forward. Locally the report proposed integrated provision and commissioning similar to the Scottish model, and it advocated more local autonomy. The controversial issue of private sector involvement

---

[10] *A Rational Way Foward for the NHS in England* BMA May 2007.

was dealt with firmly by the statement that the private sector's role should be to support – but not supplant – the NHS, and that it should only be used where there was no capacity for NHS provision.

Momentum was lost soon after the document was published with the fallout from the medical training application service crisis and the departure of James Johnson as Chairman of Council *(see below)*. At the ARM in Torquay, where uncertainty prevailed about the Association's future direction, the report received a lukewarm response; representatives expressed concern about a lack of detail on local structures, about the potential for misunderstanding in its call for clarity on rationing, and about the need for immediate action. Nevertheless, Council was asked to take the work forward and more papers were published in the following months *(see below)*.

BMA contract negotiations

During the first few years of the new millennium the BMA went through a particularly turbulent period as it negotiated big contractual changes, first for junior doctors, then for consultants and GPs, and later for doctors in the staff and associate specialist grades. These negotiations were conducted separately and their stories will be told individually, but in some ways they constituted a single episode for the BMA: common themes from the first three were identified in a 'learning the lessons' exercise in early 2004. It was a time of bitter conflicts and recriminations between the BMA and the government, between and within BMA committees, between individuals, and between the grass roots and the centre. It was also a time when emotions ran high and tears were shed – publicly and in private; a time when deadlines loomed over late-night discussions and last-ditch revisions, and when anger boiled over in meetings around the country and no-confidence motions were tabled. The BMA's credibility was called into question, large sums of money were spent, and often a positive outcome looked unlikely.

Yet the negotiations – particularly the first three – turned out to be remarkably successful. Junior doctors achieved average pay increases of at least 28%, while over the first three years GPs' pre-tax pay increased on average by 58% and consultants' average pay rose by 25%.[11] At the time, however, there had been such strong views, such high expectations and such compromises, and the new contracts involved such

---

[11] National Audit Office: *Pay Modernisation: A New Contract for NHS Consultants in England*. April 2007.

changes in ways of working that few members experienced the warm feelings of just reward and renewed motivation that might have been hoped for. And before long the government's negotiators were being criticised by the Audit Commission and the National Audit Office for having underestimated the financial impact of the performance-related or work-sensitive elements of the new contracts: the quality and outcomes framework (QOF) for GPs and the change from notional half-days to programmed activities (PAs) for consultants. Supported by what felt like an orchestrated outcry in the press, the government quickly started to claw back the increases, with minimal pay awards for GPs and consultants in the two years following the initial three-year agreement, while juniors' pay decreased as their hours went down. The gains were further eroded by a pay freeze from 2010.

Background to the negotiations

Each negotiation had a different genesis, going back to long-standing areas of dissatisfaction and unresolved issues from previous negotiations. What united them was the feeling across the profession that doctors had been undervalued, with pay falling behind that of other professions, and comparing badly with the rewards now available in the booming financial and business sectors. After years of frustration the government was now actually willing to enter into pay talks – under the banner of 'pay modernisation', a condition of the huge investment in the NHS announced by Tony Blair at the beginning of 2000. The numbers of doctors and nurses were to increase substantially, but they were to work more efficiently and their pay systems were to be streamlined. Alan Milburn set out more details in his *NHS Plan* of July 2000: by then the juniors had completed their negotiations, already benefitting from Alan Milburn's new tone and from the loosening of government purse-strings. For the other groups, however, 'pay modernisation' gave the signal that money would be on the table and that negotiations would be possible, something that both consultants and GPs had been battling to achieve for several years. Even then, it was not until after the general election of summer 2001 that negotiations formally got under way.

In the meantime, the government had also started 'modernisation' talks with the other NHS staff unions in what became the *Agenda for Change* programme. This was an ambitious scheme to harmonise terms and conditions of service for manual, clerical, technical and professional staff groups – and to bring them into a single pay system,

without endless rounds of separate negotiations. The unions representing these staff already worked together in the General Whitley
Council, but were essentially independent and sometimes competing.
The NHS HR director, Andrew Foster, expected the BMA, also in
the General Whitley Council, to take part, but as the juniors' negotiations were already concluded and a new consultant contract was under
discussion it was eventually agreed that groups covered by the DDRB
(as well as NHS senior managers) would be excluded from *Agenda for
Change*. This caused some resentment from the other staff unions, and
it took time to rebuild relationships. *Agenda for Change* was a remarkable negotiating achievement and took far longer than anticipated, concluding in 2003. But it achieved its aim of simplifying the pay and
grading system for most NHS staff, and although there were winners
and losers, all unions bought into it.

Junior doctors' out-of-hours pay

The origins of the juniors' negotiations lay in the changes that had
followed the *New Deal* of 1991. At that stage the juniors' over-riding
priority had been to reduce hours and to adopt working patterns that
did not include long periods of high intensity on-call work. Hours had
come down, though not as fast as the juniors had wanted, but those
in the hardest-pressed posts still felt that unreasonable demands were
being made on them. This was exacerbated by the fact that the number
of consultants had not expanded at the levels expected by the Calman
Report – and also by poor pay. Units of medical time (UMTs) had
been replaced by additional duty hours (ADHs), a form of overtime
but paid at less than the rates for standard hours. The juniors' committee had long argued in vain that ADHs should attract penal rates for
the most onerous rotas. The basic pay for juniors had increased substantially, but when those doing considerable overtime compared their
pay with colleagues doing little out-of-hours work the difference felt
inadequate and their anger, never far from the surface, was inflamed.

In 1999 the DDRB again rejected a strong BMA case for double ADHs for hours worked in excess of those contracted. The Junior
Doctors Committee (JDC), impatient for action and pointing out that
on Christmas Day most first-year doctors would be working for only
£4.02 per hour, surveyed juniors and a surprising 95% indicated that
they would be willing to take industrial action. An angry cohort at the
annual conference, encouraged by the negotiating chairman, Nizam
Mamode, a charismatic and independent-minded trainee transplant

surgeon, demanded and won a commitment to a formal ballot over industrial action by the end of the summer if the matter of out-of-hours pay was not resolved.

Fired up, the juniors quickly escalated the issue into a full-scale campaign, known as *Situation Critical*. They garnered support at the ARM in Belfast, with campaign T-shirts sported throughout the city, and a speech of such emotion by the juniors' chairman Andrew Hobart that he left the platform in tears. Over the summer, committee members took the campaign around the country with a programme of publicity material and mess visits, enthusing juniors and raising expectations of a successful outcome.

Meanwhile, the NHSE continued to stonewall, as it had been doing with all the BMA's negotiating groups since the 1997 election. But towards the end of the summer the juniors' campaign began to make an impact, and the NHS Director of Human Resources, Hugh Taylor, became involved in discussions, indicating that at last the matter was being taken seriously. The NHS tabled an offer of increased pay, and in the week preceding the September meeting of the juniors committee – the deadline that had been set for a decision on industrial action – the juniors' negotiators discussed the offer long and hard – and rejected it.

Some of the negotiators wanted a hard-line strategy: the JDC was now in dispute with the NHSE and would ballot for industrial action. However, during the weekend the Chairman of the BMA Council, Ian Bogle, had been asked for his advice and he counselled returning to the negotiating table. He reminded the juniors that under trade union law decisions on industrial action were a matter for the BMA, and he suggested that the BMA would not support it unless all attempts at a negotiated solution had been exhausted. Ian Bogle was a respected figure as Chairman of BMA Council and as a former GMSC negotiator and chairman and the juniors accepted his advice. But his intervention brought into play a conflict that often surfaces in BMA negotiations: between the autonomy of a branch of practice to take decisions on matters that affect its members, and the role of the wider BMA in ensuring that such decisions do not impact adversely on other branches of practice or on the BMA itself. In this negotiation it was to become a major issue.

Over the next two days negotiations intensified. Ian Bogle used his channels of communication with the government to press for an improved offer, and this was made and considered at a meeting that carried on late into the night before the JDC meeting. Ian Bogle was away from BMA House at a formal dinner, but the JDC negotiators sought his advice again and he returned to the building. He then became involved in the negotiation, making a personal call to the Secretary of State, Frank Dobson, and urged the negotiators to accept the terms offered. They did so reluctantly and without full accord; Nizam Mamode in particular wanted to press harder. Unwisely, the two sides agreed a joint press statement announcing the deal, and this was published the next day, before the JDC meeting began. Committees always react badly if they suspect they are being bounced into merely endorsing a decision that is theirs to make, and the JDC castigated its leaders, asking them to go back to the table to fill in important missing details.

Negotiations continued during October and November amid mounting tensions between members of the JDC and recriminations over what had happened in the run-up to the September meeting. In December, after an acrimonious debate in which votes of no confidence in the chairman and negotiators were eventually defeated, the committee formally rejected the proposed agreement and resolved to prepare for a ballot over industrial action. The BMA's Council Executive Committee held an emergency meeting four days later to consider this and discussion focused on whether the exacting legal requirements for embarking on industrial action had been met. One condition was that a dispute must exist, and members of the executive – essentially the chairmen of other branch of practice committees – were not convinced that all the necessary steps had been taken to fulfil it. It was agreed that a formal letter be sent to Hugh Taylor confirming that the offer was not acceptable. The juniors' leaders were disappointed and suspicious at the lack of support, but they quickly drafted the letter, took legal advice to ensure that it met the requirement for a dispute, and sent it. They then started preparing for a ballot.

In early January informal approaches were made to Hugh Taylor, and he agreed to meet JDC leaders to see whether anything could be done to improve the offer. Meanwhile, concern was growing in other parts of the BMA about the juniors' militant stance and the Council Executive held another emergency meeting, on 15 January. Some members were angry that the letter to Hugh Taylor had been couched as a step towards a dispute rather than a genuine attempt at a solution. They complained that the juniors had wanted industrial action from the outset and that this was inappropriate; some still remembered the bitterness caused by the BMA's last formal sanctions in the 1970s. Consideration of the risk of industrial action to the standing, reputation and finances of the organisation, and indeed of the consequences of failure, is always an agonising debate for a trade union, and one in which legislation has made life tougher for unions in recent years. Where there are differing branch of practice interests there will also be internal political considerations and at this time both consultants and GPs were pressing hard to open negotiations on their own contracts. The Chairman of the Central Consultants and Specialists Committee (CCSC), Peter Hawker, in particular made clear that the chances of doing so would be jeopardised if the BMA were to embark on industrial action. The juniors felt strongly that it was for them to determine their own negotiating strategy and for the BMA to give support. It turned into an unpleasant meeting which exacerbated the feelings of suspicion and hostility that already surrounded the negotiations.

Nevertheless the JDC continued preparing for a ballot, while the Chairman of Council and the BMA Secretary, Mac Armstrong, tried to exercise some control by setting up a mechanism for all expenditure to be centrally approved. This made the juniors' negotiators suspicious of advice coming from central BMA departments and put the staff in a highly uncomfortable position. Members on the ground were confused: having voted for a ballot on industrial action and been whipped into a fury, they now felt in the dark. This put more pressure on the negotiators, and some juniors started discussing whether they should split from the BMA.

However, negotiations with the NHSE had resumed. Nizam Mamode had worked hard to build a rapport with Hugh Taylor and in early February there was a breakthrough when a revised offer included the substantial improvement that the rate for out-of-hours work was no longer lower than the basic salary. JDC felt that the offer could now be put to members (though not before they had criticised the negotiators for a failure of communication). The new arrangements involved banding posts according to the intensity of the out-of-hours work needed, with supplements of up to 100% of basic salary payable for the highest level (those non-compliant with the *New Deal*). It also included better rates for those on part-time contracts, known as flexible trainees. The committee organised a special conference, supported by a major communications exercise on the details of the offer, and in April this conference recommended acceptance. The decision was confirmed in a referendum of juniors which came out 79% in favour. After more negotiations over some of the new arrangements, including the criteria and process for banding of posts, together with a robust appeals mechanism, the contract was implemented in December 2000, to be fully in place by December 2002.

The controversial ballot was not needed, and views differed over whether the threat of industrial action had helped achieve the resolution. The contract succeeded in its aim of giving employers an incentive to reduce hours, and juniors who were working intensively benefited financially. But the value of this contract was always going to decline with time, and it was unfortunate for junior doctors that the 2008 financial crash and its consequences intervened before they could negotiate a revised form.

Consultant contract

The basic form of the consultant contract had altered little since 1948. The government had avoided major review during the 1990s, despite dissatisfaction from NHS managers and repeated media criticism of some consultants' enthusiasm for private practice. Since the early 1990s the CCSC had been looking at possible areas for change, conscious of consultants' growing dissatisfaction with the open-ended nature of their commitment, of the anomalies created by the maximum part-time/whole-time differential, and of managers' lack of understanding of how the contract worked.

As soon as the new government was elected in 1997, the committee asked for talks on changing the contract. It took a year for the NHSE to agree to meet, and over the next two years meetings were subject to an extremely frustrating stop/start process. Whenever discussions got under way, there would be a ministerial announcement or press leak indicating a change of mind by the government, and talks would be broken off. The suggestion in the *NHS Plan* in July 2000 that newly-appointed consultants would be contracted exclusively to the NHS for their first seven years (this became known as the 'seven lean years' proposal), came out of the blue when the CCSC was in regular discussion with the NHSE about the consultant contract. The NHSE would give no further details on the proposal, which led to a breakdown in the negotiations. In February 2001 another surprise government publication, *Proposals for a new approach to the consultant contract*, appeared just as talks had resumed.

It was not until September 2001, after a further break for that summer's general election, that negotiations started in earnest. By this time the CCSC had lost faith in the Secretary of State, Alan Milburn, and was disappointed by his failure earlier in the year to defend some consultants who were being unjustly pilloried in the press for events linked to the Alder Hey organs scandal. It seemed to the consultants' leaders that Alan Milburn bore particular ill will towards consultants; it was rumoured that he kept on his desk a dossier of examples that could be used opportunistically to show consultants in a bad light. What progress had been made – on the distribution of intensity supplements – they attributed to Hugh Taylor, the NHS Director of Human Resources, who though a tough negotiator at least appeared to want agreement. Now he was succeeded by a new director, Andrew Foster, who was keen to replicate the processes and principles of the *Agenda for Change* negotiations, which he was leading. From the CCSC's point of view this just caused further delay.

So the discussions started in a difficult atmosphere, and the prospect of an agreement seemed as far away as ever. The meetings were sometimes chaotic, partly because NHSE documents were often late, and partly because the NHSE team, composed of civil servants and NHS representatives, found it harder to deal with a diverse group of elected consultants than with the full-time union officials they had negotiated with over *Agenda for Change*. The consultants had been preparing for negotiations over several years, developing ideas through consultation with members and intensive away-day sessions. They had evolved an imaginative proposal to redefine the contract into fixed and flexible sessions, allowing emergency work and rota commitments to be taken into account, and building in time for non-clinical work. They had also discussed strategies and teamwork, though some differences of approach persisted. The chairman of the CCSC was Peter Hawker, an intelligent and forward-looking, though at times mercurial gastro-enterologist and previous chairman of the JDC. His deputies were Derek Machin, a urologist, a dogged negotiator and stickler for detail with long BMA experience, and Michael Goodman, another gastro-enterologist, erudite and fond of complicated theories. The team also included Mark Porter, a recently appointed consultant but also a former negotiator and chairman of the juniors, later (in 2012) to become Chairman of BMA Council, and representatives from Scotland, Wales, and Northern Ireland, and from public health and clinical academic staff, who had the same form of contract. The group started out with clearly articulated common aims, but their differing perspectives were to prove divisive.

By spring 2002, external pressures had started to mount. Consultants had been informed and consulted about the negotiations but they were worried about the government's intentions and impatient for an outcome. This mood was reflected in and escalated by a 'ticking clock' campaign in the newspaper *Hospital Doctor* that criticised the negotiators and put pressure on them to conclude a deal. Although progress had been made on key issues, major problems still existed about the availability of data on workload to underpin the costing of the contract. The CCSC had long argued that consultants were routinely doing many hours of work beyond their contracts and surveys by the Office of Manpower Economics had supported this. If all work was to be paid for under a new contract it was important to know what this would cost. The NHSE produced different figures, indicating less extra work, and though a joint exercise was done to try to reconcile the differing data, the NHSE was unconvinced; it was later heavily criticised for underestimating the costs of the contract.

By May the 'elephant in the room' of the 'seven lean years' proposal, which was strongly opposed by the CCSC, had not yet been tackled, and members of the team disagreed about whether leaving it to the end was the right strategy. Responding to the pressure and frustrated by NHSE intransigence, the negotiators set a deadline of the seniors' conference in June for conclusion of the negotiations. Relationships then broke down badly when Derek Machin, who had been leading the negotiation, was found to have reported to local colleagues some criticism of them made by a member of the NHSE team which he regarded as unjustified. He had acted out of loyalty, and the incident had followed an argument about inappropriate reporting by the other side, but it was a breach of the rules of confidentiality that necessarily apply to negotiations. The NHSE made the most of it, demanding that Derek Machin be removed as a negotiator. It became clear in the agonised discussions about how to respond to this that the BMA team was far from united; they acquiesced and Peter Hawker took over the lead for what were to be the final, frantic weeks.

At about the same time, tensions between the consultants' and juniors' committees came to a head. Juniors had a substantial interest in the kind of contract that they would have when they became consultants, and the JDC had asked to be represented in the negotiations. Relationships between the two committees – particularly between some of the individuals – had been poor since the juniors' contract negotiation two years earlier. The consultants had turned down the request, which made the JDC suspicious that the consultants might 'sell them down the river' by agreeing a deal on the 'seven lean years' that would affect new but not existing consultants. At a late stage the consultants relented and invited the JDC chairman, Trevor Pickersgill, to attend meetings when the question of newly-appointed consultants was discussed. He went to the meetings, but was in a difficult position not having been involved in earlier discussions, which antagonised the juniors further and probably contributed to their eventual opposition to the contract.

In the final two weeks before the seniors' conference there were intensive meetings. The prospect of facing an impatient consultant body impacted far more on the consultants than on the NHSE, and hasty agreements were reached on the main outstanding issues. These included the value of work done outside normal working hours, the transitional arrangements for moving onto the new pay scales, and the treatment of newly appointed consultants. The 'seven lean years' idea was finally sidestepped: instead any consultant wanting to do private practice would have to work extra hours for the NHS, a condition that the CCSC negotiators felt would not be onerous in view of the hours that most consultants were already working. But the arrangements would still differ for consultants in their first seven years: two additional PAs instead of one would be the price for the right to do private practice, and they would have a higher ratio of clinical commitments to other work.

Documents were still being finalised late into the night before the conference and copies of a framework agreement were still being photocopied and rushed to the hall as it began. Most of the negotiators felt that they had secured a good deal and they presented it in positive terms. However, the suspicious murmurings among the juniors, in *Hospital Doctor* and at the grass roots had created a groundswell of concern. Important detail was missing from the framework, and members of the conference were sceptical about a contract whose financial advantages were far from clear, and which seemed to give managers new opportunities to exercise inappropriate control over their work. Despite these danger signals, the next day the CCSC agreed to back its leaders, who argued that consultants would appreciate the deal once they had time to consider its advantages. The committee gave its formal support to the contract, and agreed that it should be presented to members in a positive light.

As the committee prepared for a series of roadshows, the juniors' conference and committee were expressing serious concerns, the differential treatment of new consultants appearing to confirm their suspicions. At the ARM in Harrogate a few weeks later open animosity broke out between the seniors and juniors. A motion supporting the proposed contract was carried, but there were bitter recriminations from the juniors about how the debate had been handled. And from the first roadshows it became clear that consultants were fearful of a new contract that was incomplete, different from what they knew and seemed to give managers too much power. They were also angry about how government and managers had treated them in recent years and felt the BMA, which should have stood up for them more effectively, was now presenting them with a fait accompli. They expressed this anger in no uncertain terms to the committee members and staff who travelled the country to present the contract at hundreds of meetings in hospitals, halls and hotels. As the summer wore on, the meetings became increasingly hostile, fuelled by an active *Vote No* campaign, with JDC leaders, prominent among its adherents, handing out leaflets at roadshows.

It was at this time that new electronic forms of communication began to play a key role. The BMA had previously kept members informed through newsletters, mail shots and *BMA News*, which until 2001 had been a monthly publication. But doctors were increasingly using e-mail to talk to each other, and websites were springing up where communication was more immediate and less moderated. Contributions became emotional, heated, personal and even abusive – a shocking departure for a profession that had been accustomed to somewhat formal communications. Information and misinformation spread rapidly in a way that is now familiar, but then took many by surprise. The *Vote No* campaign was orchestrated through meetings and documentation, but also through a community of like-minded critics on the new website doctors.net. This new strand in the machinery of democracy has played an increasingly important part in medical politics ever since.

The NHSE conducted its own roadshows, briefing NHS managers about what the contract might mean for them, and it was not long before the infamous 'Slide 9' came to the attention of consultants. On this slide Andrew Foster asserted: 'BMA think managers will not use the contract' and listed seven 'tools that must be used', including 'only paying for work already done to the deserving few who do the most'.[12] This confirmed members' suspicions about the intentions behind the contract, and also opened up a toxic divide between England and other parts of the UK, particularly Scotland. This aggressive style was seen to be specific to the English NHSE; the slide was not being used in Scotland nor the other nations, which now had their own governments or assemblies. Although party to the UK negotiations, the devolved governments had their own channels of communication with their doctors, where they generally preferred to cultivate a less hostile relationship. Both governments and negotiators in these nations now became frustrated with the damage that they felt the English NHSE was causing.

Although it was clear to those attending the BMA roadshows in England that the contract was not being well received, there was no opportunity during the hectic summer for the CCSC team to regroup. Peter Hawker, under attack in the media and under personal domestic stress, responded by becoming more bullish. He believed in the contract and had put himself on the line for it. He was encouraged by Peter Terry, the chairman of the Scottish consultants, who reported support for the contract in Scotland, where the mood of the roadshows was quite different.

Andrew Foster seemed unperturbed by the contract's hostile reception and was unrepentant over slide 9. However, when the CCSC negotiators took stock in late August, it was clear that any ballot would reject the contract, and they decided to pause and seek clarification of some key issues. The NHSE returned reluctantly to the table, but could not be persuaded to make the changes needed to allay concerns. At this stage the frustration of the devolved nations overpowered any resolve to maintain UK unity and the Scottish consultants accepted the invitation to pursue talks at national level which might lead to a separate deal. This caused concern and some resentment in England, but it was an early illustration of the reality of devolution: the possibility of achieving a better solution for a local electorate will often outweigh theoretical considerations of maintaining wider unity.

The 'clarification' documents that resulted from these now separate talks showed for the first time variations in the agreements that might be reached in the different nations of the UK. The minor clarifications proposed by the NHSE cut no ice with angry audiences at the continuing roadshows in England, and the CCSC team disagreed

---

[12] *A new consultant contract: The Framework Agreement* DH summer 2002.

about whether to proceed with a ballot. Eventually they decided to go ahead, and when the ballot took place in October the results showed that 66% of consultants in the UK rejected the contract, though in Scotland 54% voted in favour.

On the morning of the October meeting of the CCSC, where the results were due to be announced, Peter Hawker dramatically resigned. The ballot result was announced to the press by his deputy, Derek Machin, who had not been involved in the final stages of the negotiation but had associated himself with the contract and defended it at roadshows. He seemed a haunted figure as veterans of the *Vote No* campaign – the juniors' leader Paul Thorpe, and Nizam Mamode, now a consultant – stalked menacingly at the back of the press conference. The committee resolved that Derek Machin would hold the reins of the CCSC until proper elections could be held in December. It also asked the government to re-open negotiations; the request was refused. The CCSC surveyed consultants on reasons for the rejection and on possible ways forward.

At the December meeting the principles of democratic accountability took effect and the old guard was swept out. A young psychiatrist, Paul Miller, who had been deputy chairman of the JDC, was elected chairman. The chairman of the negotiating committee was Nizam Mamode, who had thrived on the success of his negotiation of the juniors' out-of-hours deal, crossing swords with Peter Hawker and openly criticising the BMA. Paul Miller, as part of a recently completed MBA, had taken a module in crisis management and this was to prove invaluable as he set about rebuilding confidence. The new negotiators would eventually secure a successful end to the consultant contract saga, but for the first six months there was stalemate. The government in England refused to return to the table, while negotiations started in Scotland and then in Wales. Some English trusts began to consider implementing the rejected contract locally, and the CCSC urged consultants to resist and make use of their existing contract. In May 2003 the committee called a special conference of Local Negotiating Committee (LNC) representatives to reinforce this advice and show that the CCSC wished to re-engage with local consultants. On the eve of the conference the NHSE, in a clumsy move to regain the initiative, issued guidance to trusts encouraging local implementation. It was badly received at the conference, and helped to reunite consultants behind their new leadership in resisting attempts to impose a contract they had rejected. Industrial action began to be discussed.

Still the government made no move until in June 2003 the Secretary of State, Alan Milburn, unexpectedly resigned and was replaced by John Reid. He saw that the situation needed to be resolved, met the CCSC leaders and within weeks concluded a six-point heads of agreement. After intensive negotiations, with new faces on the consultant side – including juniors' representatives – and a new political steer on the government's side, agreement was reached on improvements to the original framework. The changes were not fundamental, but they ended the differential treatment for new consultants, improved job planning (with an appeal mechanism), and specified that routine work during out-of-hours periods must be voluntary and paid at an enhanced rate. These amendments – along with the passing of time, acclimatisation to the newness of the contract, and the sense that grievances had been listened to – were enough to convince 61% of consultants in England to vote in favour of the contract in a new ballot in October 2003. Meanwhile changes had been agreed in Scotland, with differences mainly around the definitions of standard and premium time, the status of appeal panels, and the future of distinction awards (which in England had become clinical excellence awards). In Wales they had found an alternative solution – amending the existing contract. Ballots overwhelmingly ratified these agreements, and by January 2004 agreements reached in Northern Ireland and on behalf of clinical academic staff had also been supported.

Many details still had to be agreed, but the contracts were successfully concluded, with final implementation from April 2004. There was also an option to remain on the old contract, which a few consultants took up. The process of agreeing job plans was time-consuming and required local involvement by the BMA's industrial relations officers, but it did bring about more realistic dialogues with managers about what consultants actually did than had previously been possible. The outturn of an average of 11.5 PAs per consultant was much closer to the CCSC's repeated assertions about consultants' workload than the average of 10 PAs that the NHSE had preferred to believe. Implementation was eased by the backdated increases that transition to the new scales provided for some. It was not long before the National Audit Office,[13] noting that the cost of the contract was greater than expected, doubted whether it was giving good value for money. However, it largely achieved the government's objective of introducing transparency about what

---

[13] National Audit Office *Pay Modernisation: A New Contract for NHS Consultants in England* April 2007.

consultants were doing, and for consultants it brought for the first time a way of assessing – and if necessary limiting – the different types of work in their contract. Although the recent severe financial pressures have led some trusts to try to tamper with the contract by reducing the Supporting Professional Activities (SPA) element, neither consultants nor employers have wanted to make significant alterations to its overall form (until the government called for new talks following recommendations from the DDRB as this book was going to press).

GP contract

Before the change of government in 1997 the GMSC had been making progress towards replacing the unpopular 1990 contract. Although the new Labour government had decided that, apart from abolishing fundholding, they would develop primary care along the lines and spending plans that the Conservatives had determined, they were reluctant to hold specific discussions about a new contract. Meanwhile GPs were becoming increasingly dissatisfied with overall pay levels. The BMA's evidence to the DDRB in 1997 showed that their pay had fallen so far behind that of comparable groups that they would need a 50% increase to catch up. When the DDRB responded with only some modest increases, GPs started to call for the GMSC to leave the DDRB mechanism. At the same time growing numbers of GPs were opting to take up the relatively attractive terms on offer for locally-based PMS contracts, introduced by legislation in the dying days of the Conservative government but implemented under Labour, a development that threatened the status of the GMSC as the national negotiating body for GPs.

The GMSC's negotiators had for some time been developing proposals for a radically different form of contract that would address not just pay, but also recruitment problems and variations in quality. Notwithstanding the 1995 improvements in out-of-hours provision, many GPs were dissatisfied over their inability to control their growing workload under what some called the 'John Wayne' contract: 'A GP's got to do what a GP's got to do.' Discussions took place with the NHSE over setting up primary care groups in England, but the government continued to resist negotiations on wider aspects of the contract. But when the DDRB early in 2001 published a fee scale with increases of only 1.6% there was an outcry.

The General Practitioners Committee (GPC) (as the GMSC had become) argued that a revised contract was needed and demanded negotiations. But the government – at the same time dragging its heels over pressure for contract negotiations from the consultants – would not agree to talks. The GPC responded with a campaign, *Crisis in general practice,* which drew public attention to the problems of recruitment and low morale. It published jointly with the Royal College of GPs a report making the case for 10,000 more GPs. Discontented GPs were becoming angrier and relationships between the GPC and the government reached a low ebb. In April 2001 the committee announced that it would resort to the time-honoured tactic of balloting GPs on their willingness to offer undated resignations from the NHS unless there was satisfactory progress on contract negotiations. The government was in the throes of a general election and unable to respond. The ballot went ahead and 86% of GP principals said they would consider resignation.

Such belligerence shortly before the general election infuriated the government but seemed to have the desired effect. In the summer of 2001 the government announced that negotiations would commence, and that they would be led not by the NHSE but by the employers' organisation, the NHS Confederation. The chief negotiator was to be Mike Farrar, a civil servant turned NHS manager, who had negotiated with GPs before and in whom they had some confidence. Meanwhile the GPs' committee kept up the pressure with a survey of GP opinion, conducted by ERS Market Research. It was published in October 2001 and provided dramatic evidence of poor morale, with 82% reporting workload stress, 48% intending to retire before age 60 and 28% contemplating leaving general practice.

Negotiations began in earnest later that month, and continued until the following spring. The GPC's negotiators were led by John Chisholm, the committee chairman, a clever, knowledgeable and principled leader, unfailingly courteous and perpetually late, who was supported by four elected negotiators with strong personalities and wide experience: Simon Fradd, Peter Holden, Hamish Meldrum and Laurence Buckman. Mary Church, Tony Calland and Brian Patterson represented the Scottish, Welsh and Northern Irish GPCs. The GPC had a tradition of disciplined team-working, and they also had special training on the concept of 'principled negotiation' – the seeking of positive outcomes for both sides. The outside facilitator who provided the training had also worked with the Confederation's negotiators; members of both teams later felt this had helped to build mutual understanding.

The negotiations started well. Jointly, and with the help of academics, the teams developed a vision of a new kind of practice-based contract with incentives for high quality. Resources would be distributed according to patient need. Under a complex formula different funding streams would deliver a global sum, together with substantial payments for quality – under the innovative Quality and Outcomes Framework (QOF) – and incentives to develop particular services (Directed, National and Local Enhanced Services). After intensive discussions over the Easter weekend, agreement was reached on the shape of a proposed new contract. This became a framework document, *Your contract your future*. At this stage it had no financial details but it was sent out for consultation in early summer. The GPC used roadshows to explain and listen, but made no recommendation. The atmosphere was more constructive than it had been at the consultant roadshows, although some GPs were apprehensive about the different nature of the contract. The Local Medical Committee (LMC) conference endorsed the framework in June and in a ballot in July 75.8% of GPs supported it – as a basis for continuing negotiation. Already at this stage, however, some voices in the GPC were sceptical, fearing that the contract would harm general practice. The negotiators had worked closely together and with the Confederation, and shared a close understanding and belief in the contract, but they did not convince the whole GPC and a group of dissenters was always in evidence.

The next phase was more difficult. Working goups were set up to deal with the complexities of the new contract. The timetable began to slip, and documents from the Confederation were often late. Work on pricing did not start until September 2002, and the GPC negotiators were worried because the necessary data on practice income and resources had not been produced. GPs on the ground were becoming impatient and in response to their pressure a deadline of January 2003 was set for an agreement, to be followed by a ballot in February and implementation in April.

But as winter approached it became clear that the costing and pricing information had not yet been collected. Although GPC leaders were negotiating with the Confederation and not the government, they sensed that ministers were closely involved. At one point the Confederation negotiators reported that they had been instructed to alter an underlying assumption about the proportion of income that would be derived from the QOF as opposed to the global sum; the GPC negotiators realised that if GPs' expenses turned out as they anticipated under the new contract this could lead to a substantial rise in income, and they were at pains to explain this. The government did not accept the analysis. In November came unexpected news that implementation might be delayed for legislation, and the negotiators met ministers to seek assurances that the government remained committed to the negotiating process. By the end of the year not all the pieces were in place, and the GPC decided to postpone the ballot, with an agreement scheduled for 20 February.

Tension increased day by day as the government's draft summary of the points of agreement failed to appear until late January. The GPC and LMCs were angry and suspicious and the negotiators were under growing pressure. Further negotiations took place, and some significant elements were agreed more easily than the GPC negotiators had anticipated. Once both sides had agreed that practices would have discretion over what services they provided, it was a small step to agree that primary care organisations might choose to commission out-of-hours cover in different ways, and that practices might opt out of providing it. This had been a long term objective for the GPC – indeed the government also saw 24 hour responsibility as a major deterrent to recruitment of young GPs – and when discussion turned to the price of opting out, the negotiators were pleasantly surprised to find that the Confederation was content to settle for the rather modest average figure of £6,000. The pensions implications of the contract – specifically the 'dynamisation factor' – were not discussed until an all-night session late in the process at a weekend meeting in Sheffield. The government later tried to renege on this part of the deal, but the agreement had been reached transparently and ultimately it stood. On 19 February a document was at last agreed with the Confederation. The next day, however, the Department of Health (DH) announced that it could not accept a key part of the document: the allowance for diseconomies of scale in small practices that formed part of the complex formula for allocating money to practices. The GPC leaders protested to ministers, but after yet another late night ministers refused to change their mind.

The new contract was finally announced a day late on 21 February. But because the talks had continued right up to the wire, no supporting documents were available and GPs started to suspect that information was being withheld. These suspicions were exacerbated five days later when the documents finally appeared on the BMA website, but without any pricing information.

The roadshows preceding the ballot began on 3 March, and with the documents now available the negotiators began to hope that they could assuage GPs' fears.

However, on 12 March, later known as 'Black Wednesday', the BMA sent out letters to practices that provoked outrage. The BMA's switchboard was jammed and websites and e-mails throbbed with angry criticism of the negotiators and the BMA. The letters had contained figures indicating the global sum that each practice might expect to receive under the new formula. Considerable work had been done on the highly complex formula, but the information that the negotiators had been pressing for had arrived late, and the final stages of the agreement had been rushed, leaving insufficient time to scrutinise the letters and consider their impact before they went out. Many practices believed they were set to lose large sums. The GPC was caught unawares, and members' fears were confirmed when, if they did manage to get through the switchboard, nobody could reassure them that the problem was being dealt with.

Over that weekend the negotiators held three long teleconferences with the NHS Confederation. Clearly they had to soften the negative impact of the formula, and those who best understood the technical aspects of the contract were tasked with finding a solution. Meanwhile at an angry emergency meeting of the GPC, members did not hold back in their criticism of the letters. Within a week the GPC met again to consider a proposal for the Minimum Practice Income Guarantee (MPIG) – a scheme in which the previously proposed transitional payments were made permanent – and agreed to back it. More negotiations were needed to finalise the supporting documents, which were put up on the BMA website on 2 May, although they only became available in printed form on the day of the Special LMC Conference on 14 May.

All the emotions that GPs had experienced during the long and difficult negotiations bubbled to the surface at this conference, held at the Connaught Hall in London. GPs had been angry about their pay and workload for years; their hopes had been raised at first but then they had lost confidence in the negotiating process. They had been furious over the global sum letters and were now being asked to support a contract that was under fierce attack by dissenters within the GPC. The negotiators were heavily criticised, though not vilified in the way that some, shamefully, had been on websites. But they stood firm and united, with John Chisholm defending with dignity and passion a contract that he strongly believed would improve the quality of general practice. The conference respected the negotiators sufficiently that the crucial vote was not framed as a confidence issue, but focused on the contract itself. In an atmosphere of great tension they voted not to support the contract unless certain improvements were negotiated within six months. As with the consultants eight months earlier, grass roots opinion had asserted itself and the elected leaders had been told that the deal was not good enough. Unlike the consultants' leaders, however, the GPs' leaders remained in place, and unity was preserved for the next phase.

Following the conference, the strength of the relationship between the negotiators and the NHS Confederation came into play again as the Confederation showed itself willing to be flexible. Agreement was reached on the points of concern within two weeks, avoiding the loss of the necessary legislation slots, and GPs were balloted from 31 May: just under 80% voted in favour of the contract, with the ballot counted on a UK basis, there being no substantive differences between the contract in England and in the devolved nations.

Staff doctors and associate specialists

As negotiations for the juniors, consultants and GPs took much longer than anticipated, the equally frustrating problems facing doctors in the staff and associate specialist grades did not come to the top of the agenda until 2003. A much smaller group of doctors, on whom hospital departments often depended, they had long felt overworked and undervalued. They had struggled to make their voice heard within the BMA, being represented for many years through the non-consultant career grades subcommittee of the CCSC (and its predecessors the associate specialists and medical assistants subcommittees). So it was a major step forward when in 2002, under the leadership of Mohib Khan, an associate specialist in urology, they became a fully fledged branch of practice committee, the Staff and Associate Specialists Committee (SASC), with the same delegated authority to determine their own affairs as the consultants, juniors and GPs.

The committee faced particular problems. First, it represented disparate groups of staff. The part-time post of *clinical assistant* was intended for GPs doing hospital work, but over time had also accommodated hospital and community health doctors who were no longer in training. The staff grade had been created as an intermediate grade in 1987 as part of *Achieving a Balance*, while associate specialists were personal appointments at a senior level for those who had an important role in their department but would not progress to consultant. Second, it was a group with greater than average proportions of women and overseas-qualified doctors, often working part-time, and finding themselves in these grades for various reasons, such as immigration status, the vicissitudes of the career structure or personal choice. These different strains were reflected in the composition of the committee, which was subject to more internal tensions – of gender, status, ethnicity, and even religion – than other BMA committees. Third, as a new committee it faced a big learning curve getting to grips with the BMA's democratic processes and the wider medico-political environment, rendered steeper by its members' expectation that they would usually be treated as second-class citizens.

Nevertheless the new committee set out with great optimism to achieve improvements in pay, career progression and status. Their optimism was fuelled by hopes that the new Postgraduate Medical Education and Training Board (PMETB), set to take over from the Specialist Training Authority, would create a permanent route onto the specialist register that would not just rely on formal qualifications. The committee surveyed its members on their aspirations for a new contract and commissioned a report from PricewaterhouseCoopers on workload and job weight in the staff and associate specialist grades, which supported their case to the DDRB for significant improvements in pay. The concept of a single pay spine, allowing progression between the staff and associate specialist grades, was established as an important objective, and early in 2003 the committee started a major communications exercise focused on *Recognition and Reward* conferences around the country. These were well attended and helped to create momentum for formal negotiations. The SASC was encouraged when, later that year, the DH issued a consultation document *Choice and Opportunity: modernising medical careers for non-consultant career grades (England)*, which recommended a single pay structure for SAS doctors, a mechanism for career progression through the accreditation of competencies, and an infrastructure for continuing professional development (CPD).

The committee pressed for negotiations but throughout 2004 the DH procrastinated. Three things were holding up progress. First, new money was no longer available for 'modernisation'; indeed the high costs of the GPs' and consultants' contracts were already ringing alarm bells. Second, *Modernising Medical Careers* (MMC) (*see below*), which had begun with improvements to the SHO grade, was now looking at changing the whole hospital staffing structure, with talk of a

Sir Anthony Grabham (left), Chairman of the Joint Consultants Committee, and Paddy Ross, Chairman of the Central Consultants and Specialists Committee, pictured in the annual report of Council 1989-90 .

A small demonstration outside BMA House in London in 1990 calling on junior doctors to strike for a 72-hour week.

MRS. THATCHER'S PLANS FOR THE NHS.

DON'T LET HER STEAMROLLER THE WHITE PAPER THROUGH. WRITE TO YOUR MP TODAY.

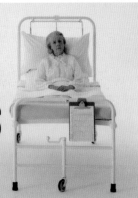

IT'S NOT A LOCAL ANAESTHETIC IF THE HOSPITAL'S 50 MILES AWAY.

DON'T LET THE WHITE PAPER DESTROY LOCAL SERVICES. WRITE TO YOUR MP TODAY.

WHAT DO YOU CALL A MAN WHO IGNORES MEDICAL ADVICE?

MR. CLARKE.

THE DOCTORS BELIEVE THE NHS WHITE PAPER WILL DAMAGE PATIENT CARE. TELL YOUR MP YOU CARE.

Posters used in the BMA's campaign against the NHS White Paper, 1989.

Virginia Bottomley, the Health Minister, and Stephen Hunter, Chairman of the Hospital Junior Staff Committee, with the agreement reached on changes to juniors' hours, 1990.

Colin Smith, (left) Chairman of the Medical Academic Staff Committee, and John Chawner, Chairman of the Central Consultants and Specialists Committee, pictured in 1991.

Pictured in 1992 are, left to right, Jane Richards, future Chairman of Representative Body from 1995 to 1998, Sir Alexander Macara, then Chairman of Representative Body, and Peter Kielty, a General Medical Services Committee negotiator.

Edwin Borman (left), Chairman of the Junior Doctors Committee, and Ian Bogle, Chairman of the General Medical Services Committee, pictured in 1992.

Jo Hilborne, Chairman of the Junior Doctors Committee, 2005-07

Ram Moorthy, Chairman of the Junior Doctors Committee, 2007-08

Junior doctors march to draw attention to the MTAS crisis, March 2007.

Hamish Meldrum, Chairman of Council, and Vivienne Nathanson, Director of Professional Activities, at the NHS Together rally in London, 2007.

Laurence Buckman, Chairman of the General Practitioners Committee (centre), leads a delegation to Downing Street to present a *Support Your Surgery* petition in July 2008. Also pictured (left to right) are Beth McCarron-Nash, Prit Butar and Natalie Teich.

John Chisholm, Chairman of the General Practitioners Committee, 1997-2004

Peter Hawker, Chairman of the Central Consultants and Specialists Committee, 1998-2002

Paul Miller, Chairman of the Central Consultants and Specialists Committee, 2002-06

Medical students, led by their Chairman Ian Noble, protest about the loss of free hospital accommodation at the Edinburgh ARM, 2008.

Richard Lewis, Welsh Secretary (left), delivers a card to First Minister Rhodri Morgan to celebrate the 60th anniversary of the NHS, 2008.

A march in support of the NHS in London in 2010, during the BMA's *Look After Our NHS* campaign.

new 'service grade', which might impact upon the staff and associate specialist grades. Third, the government had decided to set up NHS Employers, a new organisation that would take over in England all the central negotiating functions previously carried out by the DH. This was taking time to organise.

It was not until early 2005 that the DH finally agreed to negotiate. With NHS Employers now up and running, this agreement took the form of a mandate which stipulated the scope, timescale, and a financial envelope of £75 million for the negotiations. Such formal constraints at the outset were new, but the SASC was keen to get on and with an eye to avoiding the pitfalls that had been highlighted in the BMA's *'Learning the Lessons'* exercise *(see p 107)* they set up a 'core team' of negotiators, including representatives from each of the devolved nations. (The SASC was clear that it wanted any agreement to be reached on a UK basis and the DH mandate had specified that the negotiations should cover all four nations. NHS Employers, however, is an England organisation and on the other side of the table the devolved nations were represented by their respective governments, who did not regard themselves as bound by any outcome – this proved to be a difficulty). But with differing factions in the committee, repeated changes of leadership of the negotiating team had brought a legacy of suspicion and mistrust and this continued throughout the negotiations.

For the next 15 months progress was slow. Although the MMC proposal for a 'service grade' had not been clarified, NHS Employers insisted that the associate specialist grade should be closed. This appeared to block hopes of substantial career progression, but on the other hand it was the mechanism by which the status of a new substantive grade could be enhanced. The negotiators were uncomfortable, but agreed to continue the discussion, with the arguments increasingly focusing on the upper salary level for the new grade and on the 'window of opportunity' for becoming an associate specialist before the grade was abolished. But closing the grade was to prove a controversial issue, and when the negotiations were concluded, Mohib Khan, the committee chairman, felt unable to defend it as part of the package, and dissociated himself from the agreement.

The negotiators were also getting discouraged over developments with the PMETB and the application process for entry to the specialist register. Article 14 of the new specialist medical order had established a new experience-based route to specialist registration as an alternative to the certificate of completion of specialist training (CCST), but application was proving to be burdensome and expensive, and it looked as though few associate specialists would be able to take this route, particularly since opportunities for 'top-up training' were limited.

It became clear that the new contract would not be implemented by April 2006 as originally specified, and this became another bone of contention as it confused the issue of the funding envelope. The negotiators pressed unsuccessfully for any settlement to be backdated and the negotiations dragged on tetchily until the summer. The negotiating team appeared unable to agree whether they should take the money on the table, at a time when the government was cutting back on expenditure, or walk away and risk no agreement. In July NHS Employers made clear that they would move no further, and talks were concluded, with the negotiators reluctantly agreeing to put the offer to a ballot.

When the negotiators took the offer to the SASC, they presented it in a negative light. The debate was confused and bad tempered, and the committee failed to agree on a ballot. By this time personal and national tensions were evident in the team: as with the consultants, the SAS committee in Scotland had a good relationship with their health department and took a more favourable view of the offer. The Scottish chairman was Dr Sally Winning, a positive and upbeat character who was clearly frustrated by the UK leadership. This added to the sense of disarray.

Throughout the negotiations the Chairman of Council, James Johnson, and other experienced negotiators had given informal help and advice, though it was sometimes viewed with suspicion. Now the SASC called for help from the wider BMA, and although NHS Employers was at first adamant that they could not reopen negotiations, they eventually agreed to meet and 'clarify' some areas of difficulty. This enabled fuller briefing material to be prepared, so that when the SASC met again in the autumn the debate was better informed. It was still clear that the advantages of the contract had to be weighed carefully against some disadvantages, but this time the committee agreed that the offer could be put to the vote.

First, however, because the negotiation was with NHS Employers, the deal had to be agreed by ministers; it then had to be approved by a shadowy body called the Public Sector Pay Committee, which had been established in the Treasury as additional hedge against inflationary public sector pay deals. On 23 November 2006 the negotiated agreement was finally signed off between the SASC and the NHSE team, including the representatives of the devolved nations, as suitable for approval by ministers. But ministers remained silent and fears increased that the deteriorating financial position in the NHS was jeopardising the agreement. This was confirmed in February when an extraordinary letter arrived from Lord Hunt of King's Heath, the Health Minister, requesting a signed assurance from both sides that, if the costs turned out higher than expected, NHS Employers and the BMA would 'manage this without recourse to further public funding'. The government had clearly been embarrassed by its failure to anticipate the costs of the consultant and GP contracts, but this approach was unprecedented and clumsy. The force of such a signature was far from clear, and to ask doctors to move to a new contract and then bear the financial risk themselves was clearly unacceptable. The BMA offered full details of the costings that underpinned the agreement, which the Treasury already had access to, but made clear that these had been arrived at in good faith and that further undertakings would not be appropriate.

The SASC began to campaign against the government's inaction. It set a deadline of 27 July, after which it would withdraw from the agreement and hold a special conference to consider appropriate action. As the deadline passed, the differences between the UK committee and the Scottish SASC worsened. Scottish SASC, concerned about losing an agreement because of a problem in England, decided that any ballot should be counted separately in Scotland. This was in direct breach of a policy decision taken by UK SASC at the outset of the negotiations in 2005. Members of SASC UK were angry and Mohib Khan in particular felt this was a betrayal. The matter was referred, as a formal dispute, to the BMA's Board of the Representational and Political Activities Directorate, which held a special meeting in July 2007 and voted heavily in favour of the Scottish committee's point of view, no doubt considering that the situation required a pragmatic rather than a forensic approach.

In September the DH wrote again with further concerns about costs, but the terms were less threatening and an approach was agreed to the collection and monitoring of financial information. But still there was no ministerial approval. On the first anniversary of the signing of the contract, the SASC organised a petition to Downing Street for its release, supported by a campaign of letters to MPs. It called a special conference which (after a delay caused by a postal strike) was held in London on Saturday, 1 December 2007, with video links to meetings in Edinburgh, Belfast and Cardiff. The SASC was by then co-chaired by Mohib Khan and Awani Choudhary, who both remained downbeat about the contract. But members, encouraged by a survey, felt that the SASC should try to re-engage with the government and get the contract out to ballot.

Three days later came news that the government had approved the contract. But there was a sting in the tail: in England half of the pay increase involved in moving onto the new contract would be deferred for a year. The BMA, with regional staff in attendance, organised a series of roadshows to explain the contract to members. A ballot was held in March; it was separately counted in Scotland, but not in Wales or Northern Ireland. In the end the only national variation in the contract was more favourable assimilation arrangements in Scotland. The ballot had a low turnout, but the contract was accepted by 60% of voters overall, and by 79% in Scotland.

Implementation was from 1 April 2008. The old associate specialist grade was closed and a new grade of specialty doctor took its place, with a lower maximum salary. Existing staff doctors could apply for regrading in the first year only, and the SASC put a huge effort into producing guidance on how to transfer to the new grades. The process was slow to get off the ground: many trusts dragged their heels, apparently to avoid the cost of new contracts. Constant local and national pressure was needed to ensure that the contract was made available. By 2011 it had been taken up by 81% of staff grades and 72% of associate specialists. Assimilation rates were faster in Wales and Scotland but there were difficulties in Northern Ireland.

After a long and difficult process, doctors in the SAS grades finally had a modern contract, which, like the consultant contract, involved agreeing job plans and forcing managers to recognise the contribution that they were making. Soon after the contract was announced in February 2008, the health minister in England, Ann Keen, released extra funds for development opportunities for SAS doctors, and money was also made available in Scotland and Wales (though this funding was later threatened). SAS doctors achieved less than consultants or GPs, but they had secured both recognition of their role and real investment, including funding for a network of designated clinical tutors and associate postgraduate deans. A decade after they became a separate branch of practice within the BMA, SAS doctors have become a more confident and coherent group, and bodies such as the royal colleges, Medical Education (England) and LNCs now recognise them as equal participants.

Reflections

After the first three negotiations, those who had been involved felt bruised and battered. Members welcomed their higher salaries, but had found the process worrying and fraught with risk. The BMA asked an internal team to review the events, and this was published as *Learning the Lessons* in February 2004. A GPC team conducted its own review, as did the NHS Confederation. The experiences were digested, and important changes made to negotiating structures and processes.

A remarkable feature of the negotiations was the strong exercise of the democratic accountability of the negotiators to the wider membership. In each case there came a critical point at which a ground-swell of grass roots opinion asserted itself, the negotiators (if they survived) were sent back for a better deal, and notwithstanding government insistence that the terms were not negotiable, improvements were achieved. This showed that the BMA's democratic structures can work well, though the process can be dangerously volatile. The events gave BMA leaders a strong reminder of the need to keep in touch with grassroots opinion. And they learnt valuable lessons about communications, particularly over members' very different expectations in the electronic age.

Another major issue was the degree of autonomy exercised by different branches of practice, and more recently different nations. Great efforts have been made since the low point of the consultant negotiations to ensure much closer liaison between the branches of practice and with BMA Council. The Political Board (previously BRPAD), which was set up in 2002, has the role of ensuring that potential internal BMA disputes are resolved as quickly as possible, as it did during the SAS negotiations in 2007 (*see above*). There has also been a move towards 'cross-branch of practice working', whereby policy is developed in broadly-based working groups (actual or virtual) rather than separately by each branch of practice. Successive Chairmen of Council have also found it useful to hold regular informal meetings of branch of practice and national chairmen to ensure that information is shared.

But the branches of practice remain separate, with their own secretariats. They are the official negotiating bodies and are accountable to members within that branch of practice through their own representative structure, long recognised as a crucial part of the BMA's credibility.[14] Since devolution in 1999 the same considerations apply to the national councils or committees, which is why the Articles of the Association allow these committees to have full delegated authority to take decisions in their own areas without reference to the BMA Council. There are caveats: they must not without full consultation take actions that 'may affect materially the interests of another part of the profession', and they must 'take all reasonable steps' to implement BMA policy decisions. It is a structure based on largely autonomous bodies pursuing their own interests but it works because each is closely tuned in to its own members, who actively hold it to account. But it can also be unwieldy at areas of overlap or when the bodies compete for political attention or resources, and when real conflicts arise the structure comes under serious stress.

The role of BMA Council is an added complication (see Chapter 13). It remains legally responsible for the Association's affairs both under trade union law (as the directly elected principal executive committee) and under company law (as the BMA's board of directors). So the Council, and particularly its Chairman, must retain an overview of major negotiations but cannot get involved in the detail, which is the job of the branches of practice. Constitutionally this function is fulfilled by the Political Board, but there is always potential for friction over roles and responsibilities, particularly when the Association's reputation or finances might be at stake.

All four negotiations achieved better working conditions, particularly better levers over workload, though some of the financial gains were subsequently eroded. Some doctors felt that explicit contracts had undermined their professional ways of working, though most recognised that contracts generally were becoming more explicit and this was not an unreasonable price to pay for having more control. The buy-out of GPs' out-of-hours responsibility drew public criticism and, because many alternative service providers were inadequately monitored, damaged confidence in primary care more than might have been expected. But many GPs were relieved to have divested themselves of an onerous and unproductive responsibility which they argued did not need to be a core element of modern general practice. The funding formula for general practice has brought about innovation and quality improvements, but its imperfections – its over-emphasis (following

---

[14] Elston Grey-Turner and F M Sutherland: *History of the BMA* Vol II 1932–1981 p 293 (settlement following Chambers 1974).

ministerial intervention) on a quality and outcomes framework that some feel is not sufficiently demanding, its continued reliance on the MPIG, and the failure of primary care trusts to make proper use of local enhanced services (LESs) – have drawn some criticism.

The accusation is sometimes levelled against the BMA that its negotiators are more grasping than is appropriate for the representatives of an ethical profession. Well, the members who elect them to achieve better working lives for doctors have high expectations and do not hesitate to hold their representatives to account if they fail to deliver good results. Those with whom they negotiate expect the BMA to fight hard for its members: the health minister Lord Warner commented: 'Those of us who have negotiated with the BMA over the years know that the GP negotiators play hardball as well as any industrial trade union'.[15] BMA negotiators equally expect governments to play hardball and know that over the sixty years since the beginning of the NHS their actions have more often than not been intended to depress doctors' pay *(see p 156 DDRB)*; indeed in the same memoir[16] Lord Warner goes on to describe the steps he took to claw back money from the settlements reached with the BMA in 2003, and the government's reneging on its pensions agreement of 2008 by targeting doctors for particularly high contributions is another clear example of this. It is a tough environment in which the BMA's representatives cannot pull their punches, and when opportunities arise to restore eroded positions they must be taken.

Nevertheless it should not be thought that BMA negotiators would pursue these aims without regard to their wider professional responsibilities, to the NHS and particularly to their patients. It is these responsibilities that motivate doctors most strongly, and members look to the BMA to agree arrangements that enable them above all to provide better quality of care; this was the major driver in the GP contract with its QOF, and it is the reason why employed doctors resist 'production-line' working patterns in favour of those that maintain a high degree of personal responsibility and allow time for professional development. In a financially squeezed NHS, the continued assertion of those values by doctors – and by the BMA – is a vital protection for patients.

---

[15] Norman Warner: *A suitable case for treatment: the NHS and Reform. Grosvenor House* 2011, p 119.
[16] Norman Warner: *A suitable case for treatment: the NHS and Reform. Grosvenor House* 2011, p 125.

With the passage of time, these contract negotiations can be seen as a substantial achievement for the BMA. The painful experiences involved in concluding them were part of the inevitable rough and tumble of introducing major change by consent in a healthy democratic environment. The negotiating teams kept going through difficulties and setbacks and were able to achieve agreements that were accepted by members and that delivered better outcomes than expected. But the negotiating environment has changed dramatically since then, from a booming economy with heavy investment in modernising public services to a crisis-driven economy in which a coalition government has prioritised deficit reduction, with public services as the main target. The prospect of a return soon to national negotiations of the scope of those discussed here seems tiny. But the issues that they raised, particularly in relation to the importance of democratic accountability, should not be forgotten.

The European Working Time Directive

The 1991 *New Deal* brought junior doctors real reductions in their hours of work, with a final target of a maximum of 72 hours a week on duty with 56 hours worked by 1996. There were hiccups along the way, with difficulties meeting some of the targets and, following successive NHS re-organisations, a weakening of the regional task forces which played an important role in keeping up the pace of change. But the agreement remained in force until it was overtaken by the cruder but more potent requirements of the European Working Time Directive.

The directive had been adopted in 1993 but it was not until after a period of Conservative prevarication that the government started to bring it into effect. It was a piece of health and safety legislation intended to protect industrial workers from excessive working hours, and initially junior doctors were one of the few exempted groups. But it applied to other employed doctors and in 1998 the consultants' committee agreed with the NHSE how it was to be implemented for hospital consultants and non-consultant career grades. This involved invoking certain derogations that allowed some of the more prescriptive provisions to be applied more flexibly, for example by allowing regular rest breaks to be 'swept up' into periods of compensatory rest to be taken at other times. The maximum weekly working time, however, remained at 48 hours. The CCSC thought that, while in some ways it felt inappropriate for professionals to have their hours rigidly restricted, it was worth pressing employers to recognise their legal responsibility, particularly as the lack of a mechanism to limit workload was a problem for consultants before the 2003 contract. Local negotiating committees were encouraged to engage with trusts on implementing the new agreement, and consultants were asked to keep diaries so they could show where they were working over the limit. It was an uphill struggle to get trusts – and many consultants – to take this process seriously, but some were able to get their workload reviewed, and the diaries that were kept did provide useful evidence for negotiations.

The exclusion of junior doctors from the directive was viewed in Europe as a temporary measure to give member states time to plan for full implementation, and a consultation was launched on how this might be achieved. The JDC, still in campaigning mode on the question of hours, started to lobby in Europe for juniors to be included sooner rather than later. A survey showed that juniors wanted their working week reduced to 48 hours, rather than the 56 specified in the *New Deal*. In May 2000 the European Parliament voted to start applying the directive to junior doctors within four years, bringing maximum hours down to 48 over nine years. The UK government, conscious of the difficulties it would cause in staffing hospitals, resisted the move but was outvoted. The Working Time (Amendment) Regulations were laid in 2003, to take effect in stages with full implementation of 48 hours in August 2009.

The juniors' committee, led by Paul Thorpe then by Simon Eccles, believed that a 48 hour working week was enough to allow proper training, and quoted the examples of Australia and several Scandinavian countries where this was already happening. They recognised there would be difficulties. It would involve substantial re-organisation of rotas, greater use of cross cover, and in the longer term, rationalisation of hospital sites. The biggest problem would be ensuring adequate cover at night, a challenge increased by judgements in the European Court of Justice (the SiMAP case in 2000 and the Jaeger judgement in 2002), which ruled that time spent in hospital on-call would be counted as work and thus included in the total of 48 hours. This differed from the *New Deal* which had counted some on-call time as rest, enabling hospitals to use on-call rotas, which offered better continuity of care than full or partial shifts. Much work went into designing working patterns that could fit the new requirements, including an imaginative *Hospital at Night* project, based on the Australian experience. The

JDC issued detailed guidance on new rotas and the necessary rebanding process, incorporating pay protection for those in post and an appeal mechanism where rebanding had been done inappropriately. These agreements cushioned juniors from the immediate financial impact of reducing their hours. The BMA's regional staff pursued many banding appeals over the years and won most of them, forcing employers to be particularly careful about how they changed juniors' working arrangements.

The first stage of implementing the directive was in August 2003, when posts that were not *New Deal* compliant became unlawful, with a further reduction to a maximum of 58 hours in 2004. There was much anxiety about whether the NHS would cope, and the JDC issued hard hitting publications – *Time's Running Out* and *Time's Up* – to remind trusts of the need to prepare. But the date came and went without disaster, and most trusts appeared to comply.

The real impact of the directive was more gradual. With more deadlines looming in 2007 and 2009 there was a continuing pressure to reduce hours and to focus on designing working patterns that accommodated the required rest periods. This caused confusion in several countries because the directive was unclear as to when compensatory rest might be taken. In January 2004 the European Commission launched a consultation on this and other problematic issues – the reference period over which hours could be averaged, the right of individuals to opt out and the impact of the SiMAP and Jaeger judgements on the definition of working time. In 2005 new proposals emerged to amend the directive, abolishing the opt out and allowing collective agreements to vary the definitions of compensatory rest and of 'active' and 'inactive' time. However, these made slow progress through the European Parliament and Council of Ministers. A further consultation was launched in 2008, and the BMA, working through its Brussels office, lobbied strongly against a definition of working time that would exclude time on-call in hospital. But even after a conciliation process no agreement was reached, so the original working time directive stayed, with no clarification of how compensatory rest should be taken.

Meanwhile hours had been coming down and onerous on-call patterns gradually reduced, leading to a steady erosion of pay. Hospitals had generally taken the easy option of adopting full shift patterns as the most practical way of complying with the directive, which after all was primarily intended to cover industrial workers. Juniors disliked full shifts because they felt they compromised continuity of care, and they also found them socially disruptive. Furthermore, full shifts, particularly in surgical specialties, had a negative impact on training because they reduced the time spent on supervised elective work. In 2008, with the deadline for the 48 hour limit approaching and only 50% of rotas compliant, the JDC, led by Andy Thornley, surveyed juniors and found 64% believing that they would need more years in training in order to reach the right level of competence. But only 30% wanted the Directive to be delayed. The JDC had campaigned for years to protect juniors from dangerous or unsocial working hours and while recognising its shortcomings had embraced the directive as a way of maintaining momentum in an NHS that was usually slow to change. The committee had also felt that women doctors in particular needed the directive's legal protection to enable them to balance domestic and professional commitments. So the JDC continued to support it, aware that it could not be ignored anyway.

The strongest criticisms came from surgical trainees, who were generally a minority within the JDC. They had dissented at the outset from the committee's enthusiasm for the working time directive and increasingly felt that the new working patterns were reducing their opportunities for training. They were supported by many consultants and by the Royal College of Surgeons, which pressed the government for an opt out for all surgeons, something the directive did not allow.

The JDC's stance led to a serious disagreement with the organisations representing surgical trainees, who felt that their genuine concerns were not being understood. The JDC leaders worked hard to maintain dialogue, finding common ground in pressing to improve the quality of training, but relationships remained tense. When the time came to implement the 2009 changes the government sought derogations in respect of a small number of the most hard-pressed rotas to allow a longer period to find ways to re-arrange work, and once again the deadline passed without disaster. But when the JDC repeated its survey of juniors a few months later they found a widespread feeling that working patterns had become more intense and antisocial, with 59% on full shifts, and 49% worried that they were missing training opportunities, while feeling under pressure to cover rota gaps.

Modernising Medical Careers and the MTAS crisis

When Labour came to power in 1997, specialist training had been shortened (following the Calman Report), but consultant numbers had not grown as intended. The workforce problems that had dogged hospitals

since the 1980s persisted: local staff shortages, worry about career progression, lack of flexible training opportunities, imbalances in some
specialties, heavy workload. More recently 'trust doctors' had prolifer-
ated: non-standard junior posts designed to fill service gaps but with no
job security and no training content. Recruitment problems had also
become apparent in general practice, and the NHS continued to rely on
overseas doctors – including many from the EU – to keep it going.

The Medical Workforce Standing Advisory Committee had
agonised ineffectually over the appropriate number of doctors, but
in 1997 its third report finally grasped the nettle. It recommended
that the UK should aim to be self-sufficient in doctors, which would
mean an increase of about 23% in medical school intake that year.
The new Labour government embraced the policy and between 1997
and 2007 medical school places in England grew by 71%, with several
new medical schools starting up. Within the BMA only a few hard-
headed trade unionists, remembering the golden rule that professions
wishing to maintain their pay and status should limit supply, dared to
question the wisdom of this development. They were silenced by the
overworked majority who longed for reinforcements and approved of
self-sufficiency.

Pressures built to rethink the traditional staffing structures. With
the supply of doctors increasing, employers were becoming frustrated
at the constraints on how they could be employed while the profession
was still dissatisfied with career prospects. In 2000 the DH published
A health service for all the talents, a consultation document intended to
rationalise workforce planning for medical and other NHS staff. Most
of the recommendations were implemented through the *NHS Plan*,
published at the end of the consultation period, which included a substantial 'modernisation' programme with further increases in the number of doctors and other clinical staff. A controversial recommendation
for doctors had been the introduction of a post-CCST (Certificate of
Completion of Specialist Training) – but sub-consultant – specialist
grade. The profession opposed it vociferously and NHS employers
were lukewarm, so it was not pursued in the form proposed (though
variants have often resurfaced since).

The other significant proposal was the long overdue modernisation of the senior house officer grade, which was taken forward
through a further consultation.[17] The result was *Modernising Medical*

---

[17] *Unfinished business: proposals for the reform of the SHO grade* DH 2002.

Careers – a co-ordinated response from all four UK health departments published in 2003. It proposed foundation programmes of two years, one before and one after registration. This would be the first stage in a new competency-based and more flexible training structure, covering hospital medicine and general practice and with a Certificate of Completion of Training (CCT) replacing the CCST. It also proposed two types of hospital consultant: those with generic skills and those who would have longer training to achieve 'deep specialisation'.

This was the beginning of a process which imploded four years later in the Medical Training Application Service (MTAS) disaster. Modernising Medical Careers (MMC) became the banner under which all discussions on medical training and workforce took place. The DH set up a project team with strong involvement from the devolved nations. It also set up an MMC Delivery Board with sub-groups for particular tasks, and with Professor Alan Crockard from the Royal College of Surgeons as National Director. The new foundation programmes were duly piloted, but meanwhile the MMC team became more ambitious and began to develop a far-reaching plan for a new medical career structure. However, unlike *Achieving a Balance* or *The New Deal*, this never became an agreed strategy or even a definite proposal. It was constantly evolving, with documents appearing from time to time, but often in draft with enigmatic diagrams of possible career paths that raised questions but did not offer answers.

For many years civil servants and NHS managers had been frustrated by the medical profession's stranglehold over the organisation of training – and thus medical staffing – which they felt got in the way of the most efficient, and cheapest, ways of providing the service. Now the all-powerful medical royal colleges had been sidelined, first through the creation of the Specialist Training Authority, then from the end of 2002 with its replacement by the Postgraduate Medical Education and Training Board – still a medical body, but appointed by the government and somehow more aligned with a corporate NHS than its predecessors. Officials rather than doctors were driving the agenda, and the proposals changed with each public presentation. Documents began to refer to an explicit 'service grade' through which trainees might pass as they notched up competencies on their way to their certificate, but there were important unanswered questions: how did this relate to the existing staff and associate specialist grades, and what would happen after specialist registration? The differentiated consultant grade was no longer mentioned; the consultant grade was now said to be beyond the remit of MMC.

The juniors' committee, despite its misgivings, was determined to engage with MMC. With seats on the delivery board it was able at first to influence the process, successfully arguing that the foundation programme should be delayed for further evaluation. It pressed forward its policy for a single 'run through' training grade to follow the foundation programme. The board made good progress on principles during 2004/5 and started to develop new competency-based curricula. The juniors raised concerns about the end-point of training and about the dangers of shortening it too drastically, but these were brushed aside in the rush to work out the detail of transition to the new grade.

By 2006 the MMC enterprise was fuelling its own momentum. August 2007 was set as the start date for the foundation programmes and for appointments to a new specialist training grade. Patricia Hewitt, who had taken over from John Reid as Secretary of State in England in May 2005, was preoccupied with the latest financial crisis in the NHS, and was presumably being briefed by her civil servants that this new training scheme would solve some problems and was on target.

But those juniors who were involved in the working groups were becoming alarmed at the speed of events. The transition arrangements would involve a single, national selection process for all applicants: SHOs moving into the new grade, existing specialist registrars (SpRs) progressing to the next stage of their training, and applicants coming in from overseas, including the EU. The process was to be completed between February and August 2007. But most of the curricula had still to be produced and concerns about career flexibility had still to be addressed. More importantly there had been no discussion about the number of posts that would be available, the number of candidates who would be involved, nor the selection process that would be used.

After these concerns had been dismissed as a distraction, the JDC concluded that the process should be delayed. It prepared a paper listing the risks of a 'big bang' implementation, including potential problems with the computer system that had still to be procured, and the danger of using selection methods that had still to be tested. As this paper was being finalised, in early March the Home Office announced that it was changing the immigration rules which had allowed certain categories of 'highly skilled migrants', including doctors, to train in the UK without a work permit. This would affect the numbers of overseas doctors coming to the UK, but also the status of those already here in training. The JDC became heavily involved in lobbying both the Home Office and the DH for transitional measures to ease the situation of overseas doctors already in the UK, and managed eventually to obtain some concessions, but this added considerably to the confusion about how many would be involved in the MMC application process.

The situation was about to get worse. In June the DH announced that 9,000 posts were available for specialty training, with another 5,000–6,000 in the pipeline; with up to 30,000 doctors applying for posts, this was clearly inadequate. The JDC called for more posts, and raised concerns about the proposed automated selection process, which was being developed outside the Delivery Board and seemed to rely on an unsubstantiated form of knowledge testing in which the JDC could not feel confident.

In late July, the JDC issued its *Call for Delay*, calling for the timetable to be suspended while crucial issues were addressed. The report was widely publicised and the juniors' leaders met key figures, including the Secretary of State's political adviser Matthew Swindells, but their warnings were not heeded. Within the Department too many hopes and reputations were riding on the project for it to be allowed to run into the sand.

In September, the DH announced that 23,000 training posts were now available – undoubtedly an improvement but still thousands short. The JDC then launched a *Train not Drain* campaign with local meetings and mass e-mails to junior BMA members. By the end of the year, with applications due by 22 January 2007, the computer system – the Medical Training Application Service – had been procured by the DH but without input or scrutiny from the MMC Delivery Board, and the application and selection process had been determined, though guidance on how to use it had not yet been issued.

After the event there were recriminations about why, at this stage, the JDC had not been able to make *Call for Delay* stick. The juniors had kept other BMA committees and Council informed of its concerns, but the issues had seemed technical and the ability to influence the big picture limited. Perhaps in retrospect the JDC could have been more determined in galvanising the BMA Council into active support, though it is clear that all the relevant informaton was shared – both internally and externally with members – or perhaps the other committees – particularly the consultants, who were also represented on the Delivery Board – should have been more alert to the dangers.

Whatever the reason, the BMA now faced its persistent dilemma of whether to remain involved and try to help solve the problems, or to withdraw and oppose from outside, thereby risking exclusion from the negotiating table with no way of helping the affected members. The BMA's elected leaders tend to fall on the pragmatic side of this dilemma – perhaps through organisational culture or perhaps because of their medical training. Though the arguments are always hotly debated, with strong pressure from grassroots voices to take the more dramatic action, it is usually the 'engage and fix' line that will prevail. On this occasion, at its December 2006 meeting the JDC received a deputation from RemedyUK, a pressure group of junior doctors that had just been set up to oppose the MMC process. The Remedy representatives urged the JDC to support a protest march, but the committee declined, judging that MTAS could not now be stopped, and decided to keep struggling for whatever practical changes and improvements could still be made.

In the final weeks before implementation the JDC representatives tried to ensure that information and support would be in place and issued a final press release on 12 January highlighting likely problems. They had managed to secure minor improvements over matters such as ranking choices, limiting applications and handling clashes of interview dates, and also some clarification for international medical graduates. But their request to add 48 hours to the time allowed for shortlisting was turned down, and they had had no input to the proposed marking and selection systems.

MTAS opened for applications on 22 January and that weekend the computer system crashed, unable to cope with the volume. It was soon rectified but widespread mistrust began to turn into panic. This was fuelled in the run-up to the first round of interviews, due to begin on 28 February, by consultants on interview panels who were finding the shortlisting process – based on a predetermined marking system – difficult and unsatisfactory, and were sharing their concerns on websites. The interviews were chaotic: co-ordinating such a huge exercise was always going to be challenging, with large numbers of juniors and consultants simultaneously tied up in interviews all over the country. Now the shortlisting fell apart. Many juniors were not notified in time to get to their interviews, while others found that invitations clashed, and more than 11,000 (almost a third of applicants) were not offered interviews at all. Where interviews did go ahead the unfamiliar application process, which placed all the emphasis on candidates' written statements, produced howling anomalies in the shortlists, with well qualified trainees not being offered interviews while less suitable candidates went forward.

There was a huge outcry from juniors, who feared that they would be left without a post. The JDC responded quickly: Jo Hilborne, the Chairman, wrote to the Secretary of State before the end of February asking her to suspend the process, but the request was declined. Anger built among juniors and consultants, and every day brought showers of e-mails, letters to the press and a rising sense of crisis. RemedyUK had set up a web forum in which doctors felt they could vent their anger more freely than through the structures of the BMA or its official website; its leaders, juniors who unlike the JDC were untainted by involvement in the development of MMC, were able to voice anger in extreme terms that chimed better with juniors' emotions than the more analytical tone of the BMA. The anger became directed increasingly against the BMA and JDC, with the JDC leaders, already at their wits' end trying to press the government for action, having to spend time defending themselves.

The JDC now had strong support within the BMA, particularly from the consultants' committee. The two committees had enjoyed good relations since the consultant contract of 2003, and on 5 March the consultants' chairman, Jonathan Fielden, signed with Jo Hilborne another letter to the Secretary of State calling for the current recruitment round to be suspended or the whole exercise to be postponed for a year. The Chairman of Council, James Johnson, was abroad on BMA business during the critical first week of March, but he made strong representations in support of the juniors on his return.

The Secretary of State had little choice but to listen. On 6 March she made a statement recognising that there had been problems with the first recruitment round and set up a group, chaired by Professor Sir Neil Douglas, President of the Royal College of Physicians of Edinburgh, to review what had happened and report within three weeks. But the membership of the review group was dominated by the royal colleges and did not include a BMA representative. In many ways Jo Hilborne would have preferred to have stayed on the outside and join RemedyUK in unadulterated criticism. But she felt that her first responsibility was to help the thousands of juniors already caught up in the process. Jonathan Fielden and James Johnson, less exposed to direct criticism from members, were generally 'engage and fix' supporters and they were clear that the BMA should have a seat on the review group. They pressed for this, and not waiting for an invitation Jonathan Fielden turned up at the group's first meeting. Once admitted, he insisted that the juniors be represented, and Jo Hilborne was allowed to attend, first as an observer and then as a full member.

Over the next two weeks the group met repeatedly, physically and electronically. The central question was whether processes that had already been completed should be allowed to stand, or whether they were too deeply flawed to be rectified by changes at the next stage. As different proposals were put forward and crawled over on websites the temperature continued to rise – juniors had differing ideas about the solution, but all felt they had been treated badly and wanted this to be acknowledged. RemedyUK, with the agility of a web-based organisation not constrained by democratic structures, gathered support for its march, which took place on 17 March in London, with another event in Glasgow: 12,000 doctors turned out, attracting great publicity and an address by David Cameron, the Conservative leader who was hoping soon to be Prime Minister. The JDC recognised that RemedyUK was providing an important mouthpiece, and supported the march. This meant that the BMA was able to provide posters, placards and other resources, and members were encouraged to take part. But it was RemedyUK's event, and as tension increased between the organisations, it enjoyed taunting the BMA with having been left behind in the race to represent juniors' views.

Five days after the march the review group published its solution. Some applications would be reviewed. In England more posts would be filled at the second round, but to get to this stage all participants would be offered one interview, as opposed to up to four as originally envisaged. (In the other nations the numbers taking part were smaller so more interviews could be offered.) Jo Hilborne was restricted by the rules of confidentiality from consulting widely, but the other JDC officers shared her concern that this proposal disadvantaged about 11,000 juniors whose offers of more than one interview would now be withdrawn. They decided that 'engage and fix' had not worked, and she withdrew from the review group; Jonathan Fielden then also withdrew.

There followed a period of disarray. A group of junior doctors' mothers, some of whom had taken part in the march, added to the pressure by starting their own web forum. More consultants got involved: some had been so appalled by the shortlisting and interview process that they had withdrawn on the spot, and they suggested that similar action should be co-ordinated should the circumstances arise again. A group of distinguished academic consultants, outraged that some of their brightest trainees had been overlooked for interviews, set up Fidelio, another web-based pressure group to add to the chorus of dissent.

The BMA's withdrawal from the review group had had a bracing effect, with other members acknowledging that they too had been unhappy. For two weeks Professor Douglas worked tirelessly to bring views together through phone calls, e-mails and ad hoc discussions, (which included BMA representatives, whose input was recognised to be critical even though they had formally withdrawn). New proposals began to emerge which would enable the outcome of round one interviews to count if appropriate, but allow applicants to revise their original preferences, and then to be interviewed for their first preference post, including those who had not originally been offered an interview. More posts would then be filled at a greatly modified second round. This still represented a major adjustment of original expectations, but it felt fairer, and Jo Hilborne and the JDC once again had to search their souls as to whether to back the proposal or remain disengaged. With strong encouragement from Jonathan Fielden and James Johnson, Jo Hilborne agreed to return to the review group.

By this time nothing would have dispelled the sense of injustice felt by juniors and it was hugely tough for Jo Hilborne and her colleagues to deal with the criticism that assailed them from all sides. Her no-nonsense Yorkshire manner and common sense approach may not have conveyed the passionate anger that many juniors wanted to hear, but it served her well in withstanding the pressures of leadership through perhaps the most intense political crisis the BMA has seen in recent times, while carrying out an acute clinical role in South Wales (she was a trainee in obstetrics and gynaecology) and looking after her three school-age children. Together with her deputies, Tom Dolphin and Andrew Rowlands, and with the support of the small JDC secretariat led by Peter Corpe, she battled on, unclear about where it was all going to lead.

From early April, when the BMA representatives returned to the review group, there was a long period of frantic activity and continuing anxiety for juniors The group focused on the practicalities of getting large numbers of new interviews organised against a background of complete confusion about the overall numbers. More EU doctors than expected had applied and it seemed that about 34,000 doctors had applied for no more that 23,000 posts. The juniors' committee pressed strongly for guarantees that no juniors who had been in training posts should lose their employment as a result of the debacle.

Meanwhile recriminations raged about what had gone wrong. At the end of March, the MMC director, Professor Alan Crockard, had resigned, blaming the DH for problems with the computer system. In the face of constant publicity about the plight of junior doctors, many of whom it was thought might leave the country, the Secretary of State had to acknowledge that the application system had failed, and apologised. However, the Chief Medical Officer in England, Sir Liam Donaldson, under whose area of responsibility medical training fell, felt obliged – whether by his duty as a civil servant or by personal commitment to MMC, with which he had been closely involved from the start – to take a less conciliatory line: he needed to avert the danger of the whole project being destroyed by fallout from the application system and he continued to defend the principles of the new training scheme.

By now the juniors' anger was directed as much against the review group's attempts to find solutions as against the original problems. Riding on this tide of outrage, RemedyUK decided to launch a legal challenge. They were granted a judicial review, in which the BMA (as a member of the review group) was named in the action as an interested party. This polarised opinion: some juniors wanted the BMA to support the judicial review (rather than give evidence in opposition to it), while others wanted the BMA to defend its role in the review group as a responsible attempt to pursue the 'least bad' outcome for the juniors caught up in the process. This had been advocated by James Johnson at the BMA Council meeting on 18 April, though the juniors' conference nine days later was highly critical of the BMA's stance and spent the whole morning debating a motion of no confidence in the JDC's leadership. The motion was defeated, but the juniors remained deeply divided. The JDC started to e-mail junior members, giving as much information as possible about the rescue package for round one. They also tried to ensure that the appropriate BMA staff were geared up to give individual help. In the middle of May, the 'modified MTAS' that had been planned for round one was still posing planning problems, and its credibility was finally destroyed when security breaches came to light as applicants' details were made public. The Secretary of State then announced that MTAS had been formally abandoned; shortlisting and interviews would revert to traditional methods. She set up an inquiry under Professor Sir John Tooke, Dean of Peninsula Medical School.

This provoked another wave of anger from junior doctors, who feared that their applications had been invalidated. The JDC leaders were attacked viciously on websites: one had to move out of his home for a weekend following a threat to burn it down. The BMA set up an informal support team involving the juniors' leaders and their secretariat, senior staff, members of the web team and public affairs – and importantly members and staff from the consultants committee. They met nearly every day to report back from meetings, agree responses, and co-ordinate communications – developing a discipline by which all statements were cleared electronically before going out. The Chairman of Council was kept informed and used his channels of communication with the DH and others to keep up the pressure. Some of the key players disagreed over the tone of messages, with the juniors keen to respond sympathetically to the angry feelings of their members, while the Chairman of Council remained strongly focused, with the surgical single-mindedness that was his hallmark, on actions that would achieve a positive solution to the practical problems. These differences were essentially about means rather than ends, and were usually resolved, but in early May a draft letter was circulated by the Academy of Medical Royal Colleges (AoMRC), intended as a joint communication advising juniors to make the best of the proposed interview round. The BMA juniors and consultants felt its tone was too conciliatory towards the DH and, despite attempts to amend it, the letter was not sent.

At this point there was a critical lapse of the BMA's internal processes. A few days later, on 17 May, a letter appeared in *The Times*, co-signed by Jim Johnson and Dame Carol Black, Chairman of the AoMRC, which made some of the same points as the earlier abandoned draft, and, fatally, expressed support for the English CMO, Sir Liam Donaldson, and his role in improving junior doctors' training. Within hours, *Times Online* had received hundreds of responses, many from appalled junior doctors who wanted to dissociate themselves from the views expressed. The letter had not been cleared through the BMA's internal channels in the usual way though it had been seen by the press office, where staff had advised against submitting it. But James Johnson, probably in a combination of haste, irritation at the prevarication over the earlier letter, and confidence in his own judgement and right to sign up to views which he personally shared, insisted that it should go.

The matter quickly snowballed. Some felt that it had been a worthy action to defend the CMO, a colleague who had come under strong personal attack, but the overwhelming response to the letter was that it failed completely to respond to the anger and anxiety of junior doctors, setting the Chairman of Council at odds with his members. Letters of resignation from the BMA started to arrive and members of Council quickly concluded that their Chairman's position was untenable. Had James Johnson been a popular chairman who commanded the loyalty of his council, there might have been a rallying of support and an opportunity to put the record straight. But the truth was that over many years of leadership in the BMA – as chairman of the medical students, juniors, consultants, the Joint Consultants Committee and then BMA Council – notwithstanding his huge energy, extensive political knowledge and relentless hard work, he had too often displayed an impatience and a dismissiveness that left people feeling slighted. Council debates had often been tetchy, with some members feeling they had not been heard. So few now moved to support him, and some were not sorry to see the tables turned. There was no formal vote and efforts were made to avoid a public row: James Johnson resigned, a sad end to a career of outstanding service to the BMA.

The Association needed to regroup quickly. The role of Deputy Chairman of Council had been created only a few years earlier: its first incumbent, still in post, was Sam Everington, a London GP who had never led a branch of practice, but had been a maverick and increasingly respected presence on various committees and on Council for many years. He had made particular contributions in the field of equal opportunities and anti-smoking (as well as his high-profile work for juniors in the 1980s), and brought to bear a legal qualification and a previous political role as an adviser to the Labour Party. He now found himself precipitated into the chair of Council, with internal strife erupting over recent events, and external criticism raging about how the BMA could have let things go so wrong for junior doctors.

In the week following the letter in *The Times*, on 22 May RemedyUK's judicial review took place, with the BMA giving evidence to defend its role in the review group. The JDC did not want to go head to head with RemedyUK, and the spectacle of the BMA doing so in court made junior doctors even angrier. But the judicial review did help to clear the air by ruling (in terms that were far from a ringing endorsement of the actions of any party) that the review group had not been illegal and that its recommendations were therefore competent. On 24 May the Secretary of State issued a statement proposing the new way forward, with a greater proportion of posts to be filled at the second round.

As soon as practicable, on 5 June, BMA Council held an emergency meeting. The annual election for Chairman of Council was already scheduled for later that month, and Council agreed that new candidates could now come forward and make their statements at the ARM in Torquay. The Council also considered a paper from the Director of Representational and Political Activities on *Regaining the Confidence of the Profession*, which identified the need for the Association to improve its consultation and communication with members, while also putting in place some new internal disciplines to improve levels of co-operation and trust, within Council and between committees.

Over the next month Sam Everington bravely held the reins, his reputation for an independent stance insulating him from association with the previous problems that Council members now dwelt upon. Slowly the juniors' situation began to improve: new interviews took place, gradually introducing hope that most would find posts. A new protocol was adopted for BMA committees to share and approve documents more widely. This established – at least on these issues – an effective working discipline, which was quickly put to use in the preparation of evidence for the Tooke review. Towards the end of June, as Gordon Brown took over as Prime Minister, Patricia Hewitt was replaced as Secretary of State by Alan Johnson. Following the Torquay ARM, Hamish Meldrum was elected as the new Chairman of Council. He had been a GP negotiator for the new contract and now resigned as chairman of the GPC to take on the challenge of chairing a Council that was full of tension and mistrust. It was a task that would require all his resources of charm, common sense, industry and determination.

The Tooke Report, *Aspiring to Excellence*, appeared in October 2007. It gave a lucid diagnosis of what had gone wrong with MMC and MTAS, and proposed clear recommendations for the future. It criticised much of the thinking behind MMC and also the DH's handling, suggesting that the mechanisms that had been put in place 'smacked of an aspiration to mediocrity'. It challenged the medical profession once again to take responsibility for postgraduate medical education in order to reassert professional values and expectations of excellence. The central recommendation was for a new organisation, NHS: Medical Education England, with equivalent bodies in the devolved administrations. Its task was to re-examine the purpose of postgraduate training and ensure that the right steps were taken, working with a new competent authority formed by a merger of the PMETB and the GMC's education arm. The Tooke team consulted again on the recommendations before issuing a definitive report in January 2008. As part of this process, the BMA held a special conference in October 2007, at which junior representatives predominated. Discussion of the report provided an effective 'truth and reconciliation' mechanism within the BMA, and more widely in the medical profession and the NHS. It generated substantial support for the proposals, calmed the juniors by acknowledging how badly they had been treated, and encouraged reflection on the lessons to be learnt.

The 2007 recruitment exercise had in the end been managed so as to ensure that the vast majority found suitable posts, or had hopes of doing so next time. In the BMA, Jo Hilborne stood down as JDC chairman with some relief, and was replaced by Ram Moorthy, a senior surgical trainee and former outspoken critic of MTAS, which enabled him to command the confidence of those who had suffered while leading them back to constructive engagement. The government's response to the Tooke report was less wholehearted than that of the medical profession. Some of the recommendations went ahead, including the creation of NHS: Medical Education England, which then set up a programme board and a number of subgroups, with substantial BMA representation, to plan and execute future recruitment exercises. But many were supported only in principle or referred on for further consideration in the context of other programmes, and crucial issues about the structure of the medical workforce – the growing problem of numbers and what sort of career doctors were being trained for – were ducked. The basic training structure remained in place, and juniors continued to be anxious about having to commit to a specialty immediately after the foundation programme.

There was an uncomfortable postscript to the events of this chapter, which illustrates a jeopardy attached to the high media profile that is now part of the role of the BMA's senior elected officers – and of other leaders of the profession. A short time after James Johnson left the chair of Council, questions and allegations were raised about his clinical practice that led to his suspension from duty by his employing trust. After a long period of uncertainty and further investigations, the matter came before a Fitness to Practise panel of the General Medical Council (GMC). The ten-week hearing generated lurid press coverage, which referred inter alia to 'conflicting pressures' arising from James Johnson's duties as Chairman of BMA Council, and vilified him personally. But he was cleared of all the serious charges; the panel found that no patient had suffered because of his care, rejected any allegation of clinical incompetence and decided that his fitness to practise was not impaired. The whole process had taken three years, during which time he had been unable to work. With characteristic determination he undertook a period of retraining and was able to resume practice as a breast surgeon.

Chapter 4

Labour's later years and the financial crisis 2007–2010

Another NHS review

By the summer of 2007 there was not only a new Chairman of BMA Council, Hamish Meldrum, but also a new Prime Minister, Gordon Brown, and a new Secretary of State for Health in England, Alan Johnson. Notwithstanding the investment and changes made since 1997, Alan Johnson quickly saw that the NHS was still a source of political concern. He launched another review, led by the distinguished surgeon, Sir Ara Darzi, who had come to political prominence through the NHS Modernisation Board and had already led *A Framework for Action*, a major review into health services in London. In it he had set out a radical agenda to close some hospitals and replace them with a network of 'polyclinics'. Sir Ara combined clinical credibility with strong convictions, and Gordon Brown made him a junior health minister as Lord Darzi in his 'government of all the talents'. Alan Johnson asked Lord Darzi to consider extending the London blueprint – still out to consultation – to the wider NHS. He worked fast, issuing an interim report in October 2007,[1] followed by the final paper *High Quality Care for All: NHS Next Stage Review* in June 2008. Meanwhile the London Strategic Health Authorities had set up a consortium known as Healthcare for London to take forward the ambitious programme set out in *A Framework for Action*.

The BMA was still recovering from a particularly hard knock. For the first time during the period covered by this book membership went down in 2007 by about 1,000 following the Medical Training Application Service (MTAS) crisis; most of those resigning had been juniors. The Association faced a major challenge to re-establish confidence, both internally and externally, in a climate where financial problems were prominent. Staff and associate specialist doctors were deeply frustrated by the lack of any movement on their contract (*see Chapter 3*), and GPs were being criticised in the media in what the General Practitioners Committee (GPC) suspected was an

---

[1] *Our NHS, Our Future: NHS Next Stage Review interim report*. DH 2007.

orchestrated campaign by the government to portray them as over-paid and reluctant to extend surgery opening hours. On top of this, in a breathtaking ram-raid late in 2006 the government had announced that it would renege on a key part of the 2003 GP contract deal – the 'dynamising' factor used to determine the uprating of GP pensions, and that it would do so retrospectively. Both working and retired GPs would lose out financially. The GPC resisted angry calls for indus-trial action and launched instead a legal challenge. It was eventually successful, but the impact of the government's action on morale was severe.

In 2007 GPs had received no pay increase, and other doctors only a little more, further reduced by government staging. The BMA Council was feeling the pain of its Chairman's resignation and had become inward-looking, concentrating on structures and processes that the new chairman, Hamish Meldrum, could see were important to dispel the legacy of mistrust, much as he would have preferred to focus on external events. The work done for *A Rational Way Forward (see p 81, above)* was developed by an enhanced Council working group that published further papers on, for example, an NHS consti-tution, and on education and research. But while there was still a broad consensus of concern about 'marketisation' of the NHS, key issues proved divisive when it came to firming up policy. Opinions varied on the role of commissioning and the mechanism through which fund-ing should flow (which the original document had fudged), and argu-ments continued about how far the private sector should be involved. It looked for a while as if the Darzi review might be an opportunity to reunite the profession in support for a new direction for the NHS. Lord Darzi, who was still a practising doctor, made encouraging statements about the importance of engaging clinical leaders, and about the need to place quality at the centre of all decisions. And he envisaged a consultation process that would give local clinicians, in spe-cially convened 'clinical pathway groups', the opportunity to redesign services.

The BMA responded energetically. The consultation process fitted in well with its strategy to engage members through its local structures. It encouraged local representatives to get involved and to nominate members of clinical pathway groups. It sent these group members briefing materials and asked them to feed back regularly to regional councils, which held special meetings to engage with Strategic Health Authorities (SHAs) about the review. But it was not long before optimism began to recede. Healthcare for London's plans were causing alarm and confusion: a newly invigorated London Regional Council warned that the closures would endanger services to patients and lead to staff redundancies (though the moves to reconfigure some specialist services gained support among consultants). And in the wider review, reports were coming in that local consultations had been patchy: of the 97 representatives nominated through local BMA structures, only a handful had felt involved. Some had heard nothing, and many felt they were being asked to endorse proposals that were being developed elsewhere, perhaps by the management consultants to whom the government routinely looked for advice.

As this was going on, the GPs committee had a confrontation with the government on its demand for longer surgery opening hours. Annual contract negotiations had started again at the end of the initial three-year deal, but were proving difficult because of the very different nature of the new contract. Nevertheless, progress was being made on redefining a role for the DDRB, and on the fraught question of access to surgeries. The committee saw practical problems with longer opening hours, particularly for practice staff, but it recognised that both public and government were pressing for change, and it proposed ways of improving access while allowing practices discretion to organise hours to suit local circumstances. The government rejected these proposals out of hand, instead proposing a more rigid scheme that required practices to offer an extra 30 minutes of access time for each 1,000 registered patients. This came with a threat that more draconian measures would be imposed if it were not accepted.

The GPC reacted angrily and refused to negotiate under these conditions. It consulted members and GPs voted overwhelmingly in favour of the first and less unacceptable proposal. But they felt they were given Hobson's choice, and there were calls for a robust rejection of both. The GPC judged that public opinion was not with them, and accepted the first option under duress, but issued a strong statement of its lack of confidence in the government's handling of the NHS and its opposition to further expansion of the commercial sector. As the package of changes to opening hours was implemented – funded through reallocating existing money – the GPC launched a campaign to raise public awareness of the increasing danger of encroachment by private companies into general practice, and to express its concerns about the Darzi review. The GPC chairman, Laurence Buckman, noted that 'the surge in morale of three years ago has been frittered away by government and the level of mistrust has never been higher.'[2]

It was against this background that Council considered its response to *High Quality Care for All*. In March 2008 the Chairman of Council had written to Lord Darzi drawing his attention to flaws in the process that members had highlighted. By the summer, when the final report was published (to coincide with the 60th anniversary of the NHS), attitudes had hardened, particularly among GPs. The Association, while welcoming some of Lord Darzi's aims, had serious concerns. In particular members were disappointed at the continuing emphasis on market-based solutions, while the idea of a network of new, GP-led health centres – a development of the polyclinics idea, which would be superimposed on existing services – was seen as a threat to practices and had no support at all. The GPC's locally-based *Support your Surgery* campaign had put the case for improving current services rather than creating a new layer of provision as an opportunity for the commercial sector, and had considerable support, including a petition to Downing Street signed by 1.3 million patients. Some MPs objected that patients had been inappropriately pressured into signing but the GPC countered that many patients had been unaware of the waste of resources that the government was contemplating.

In March 2008 there was good news when the result of the BMA's judicial review over the pensions dynamisation issue was announced. The court found that the Secretary of State had acted unlawfully by retrospectively altering the agreement, and the Department of Health (DH) was obliged to reinstate the original level of dynamisation for 2004–6. This involved the payment of around £75 million of arrears and interest to those doctors affected. The success was gratifying and a vindication of the cost and effort that went into mounting the case. But taking the government to court did not help already strained relationships, and may well have hardened hearts in Whitehall against the BMA's criticisms of what was happening in the NHS.

Financial crisis

In the autumn of 2008 came the world-wide financial crash that was to impact so disastrously on the nation's economy and thus on the pay, pensions and career prospects of those employed in the public sector. It was clear at the time that the events were seismic, and everyone

---

[2] GPC Annual Report 2008.

experienced the sense of dislocation and changing expectations that came with the daily reports of collapsing financial institutions and falling stock markets. The NHS was insulated at first by the settlement following the 2007 Comprehensive Spending Review, which had allowed for 4% annual increases in spending for three years, despite the tighter financial circumstances. Public sector pay was already constrained and a new agreement on NHS pensions was coming into force, with a later retirement age and increased contributions. It was not until 2009 that the need to make further substantial NHS savings started to be articulated, with a programme known as Quality Innovation Productivity and Prevention (QIPP), and in 2010 a requirement to cut management costs by 30%, a cap on tariff payments for acute trusts, and a target of £20 billion efficiency savings by 2015.

The implementation of the Darzi reports continued well into 2009. The BMA continued to brief and receive feedback from its local representatives, who reported some positive developments, such as new metrics to measure aspects of quality (which Lord Darzi had proclaimed would be 'the organising principle of the NHS').[3] On the whole, however, they were sceptical. The most contentious development was the network of GP-led health centres, to be open from 8am to 8pm, with walk-in access: it transpired that the government had ordered every Primary Care Trust (PCT) to put these out for tender, irrespective of local need or demand.[4] So in every PCT an arduous and expensive bidding process had to be established, and GPs in every practice were obliged to consider the likely impact on their own services. Private providers rushed to mount bids. Some would employ salaried GPs; others proposed working with existing GPs to form new entities, often bidding against other local GPs. Many practices challenged the need for a new service, but PCTs said they were under orders.

Many GPs felt they lacked the technical expertise to prepare the necessary tender documents. So they were attracted by the offers of private companies to coordinate the bid on their behalf, seeing this as a means of survival in a hostile commercial environment, and as a more responsible option for their patients than leaving the field to unknown private operators. The process was divisive, sometimes causing partners to disagree. In the end, most contracts for the new centres were

---

[3] Lord Darzi: *High Quality Care for All: NHS Next Stage Review final report*. June 2008.
[4] Rivett G.G. National Health Service History n.d.retrieved November 2012 from www.nhshistory.net.

won by existing GPs bidding defensively. The government seized on
this as evidence that GPs had endorsed the exercise, particularly relish-
ing the fact that in Hamish Meldrum's area his own practice had made
the successful bid. As predicted, relatively few patients made use of the
centres when they opened. Some, notably in urban centres, were able
to supplement existing provision usefully, but by the time plans were
fully developed the extent of the financial crisis had become clear, and
the scheme was allowed to lapse when the new government took over
in 2010. It had cost £250 million[5] to put in place.

Look after our NHS

The BMA Council was again becoming frustrated with the government's handling of the NHS in England and by early 2009 the differences of a few years earlier reasserted themselves. One group wanted
to campaign openly against government policy with marches and alliances to pressure groups. Another group, including the leaders of
the main branches of practice, were uncomfortable with a stance that
appeared ideologically based, or wholly negative, and preferred to raise
their concerns pragmatically through the many channels in which the
Association could exert influence. The 'activists' group were pressing their views in other forums, such as the *Keep Our NHS Public*
pressure group and the London Regional Council, which was actively
involved in co-ordinating responses to the changes being made by
Healthcare for London. They were adept at keeping Council under
pressure to enforce the Representative Body's policy against increasing private sector involvement in the NHS, using the full machinery
of democracy – websites and listservers as well as procedural
devices.

There were some difficult debates, but by May Council settled
on a way forward that all could support, launching a campaign under
the banner of *Look after our NHS,* with an initial budget of £200,000.
It would oppose the commercialisation of the NHS but would focus
on positive principles: high quality, comprehensive healthcare, which
should be publicly funded through central taxation and publicly provided, based on cooperation not competition, and putting patient care
before financial targets while seeking value for money. A campaign
group was set up and staff resources, particularly in the communications directorate, were concentrated on an intensive programme of

[5] Rivett G.G. National Health Service History n.d. retrieved November 2012 from
nhshistory.net.

activity, including a brochure, information sheets, a dedicated website, a regular newsletter, advertisements in the medical press, and campaign materials for a stand and press event at the Liverpool Annual Representative Meeting. The BMA commissioned surveys which showed that both the public and doctors generally accepted a role for the private sector, but opposed a market in healthcare. They also showed that the public did not really understand the government's plans and that doctors disagreed about what should be the focus of a campaign. The campaign did generate significant publicity over the summer, but the campaign group felt that insufficient impact had been made. They redoubled their efforts, and a dedicated member of staff with campaigning expertise was taken on. They envisaged two phases: the first would aim to persuade doctors to support the BMA's message, and to gather local examples of problems arising from the healthcare market; the second would use posters and leaflets, and an electronic cartoon Christmas card, to promote the messages. Events with other organisations and with MPs would also be organised.

The BMA invested considerable time and money in the campaign and it made sure that the government's NHS policy stayed in the public eye. In September 2009 it seemed as if progress had been made, when the new Health Secretary Andy Burnham, a former Minister of Health who took over from Alan Johnson in June 2009, controversially reached agreement with the NHS unions on an 'NHS preferred provider' policy. This appeared to establish an important principle: competitive tendering for health services should only be invited where the NHS provider would not or could not provide that service to an appropriate standard. The exact wording of the statement had been carefully thrashed out in the Social Partnership Forum, an increasingly influential group (with BMA representatives) in which ministers briefed the unions on NHS policy issues and listened to their views. Andy Burnham seemed to value the relationship, and while he staunchly defended the need for competition, he appeared more sympathetic than some of his predecessors to concerns about unnecessarily destabilising good NHS provision. But the doctrine of competitive tendering had become firmly embedded. The *Transforming Community Services* initiative (whereby PCTs were required to put their provider functions out to tender) was steaming ahead, with local managers going to great lengths to ensure that their bidding processes complied with the requirements of the government's Co-operation and Competition Panel and EC procurement law. These were difficult to reconcile with the preferred provider policy and its message was quickly buried by the NHS hierarchy.

By 2010 the *Look after our NHS* campaign had run its course. The campaign group was disappointed that it had not gained the hoped-for momentum but found it difficult to justify more expenditure. The BMA had not persuaded the government of the dangers of commercialising the NHS, but with a general election coming it now began to focus increasingly on how to influence future NHS policy after a likely change of government.

Meanwhile during 2009 events were overshadowed by an outbreak of a new strain of influenza (the H1N1 virus, known as 'swine flu'). The government had prepared extensively for the expected pandemic and the GPs' committee worked with the DH to ensure that GPs would have proper guidance, a planning checklist, and sufficient vaccine. As the outbreak spread and public concern mounted, the GPC and the Public Health Medicine Committee helped to keep doctors briefed on developments and advised on communications to patients. It was also the GPC's job to agree contractual arrangements with the government to cover the extra work involved in the vaccination programme, which required the negotiators to take a firm stance over the need to release time from other duties.

Because of the preoccupation over the flu pandemic, there was little further change to GPs contractual arrangements that year and the improved formula for annual uplift that had been put in place in 2009 was not used. The hospital sector was also beginning to feel the effects of new financial constraints. Trusts were putting pressure on consultants' contracts, particularly reducing Supporting Professional Activities, and local planning for service reconfigurations was undermined by the imperative of realising savings through simple cuts.

Pensions reform

In 2008, after a long negotiation between the NHS trade unions and NHS Employers, major changes were introduced to the NHS Pension Scheme. The schemes in Scotland and Northern Ireland were technically separate from the scheme in England and Wales, but the negotiation effectively covered the UK and similar proposals were made for all three schemes. The NHS Pension Scheme applies to all NHS staff and the negotiation was therefore conducted through the NHS Staff Council, of which the BMA is a member. A senior member of staff from the BMA Pensions Department joined the other unions in the negotiation, with close involvement from the Chairman of the BMA Pensions Committee, who for much of the period concerned was Andrew Dearden, a GP negotiator from Wales, and later BMA Treasurer.

The context of the negotiation was the dawning realisation that the combination of final salary benefits and a population that was living longer was putting severe strain on many pension schemes. Once the local government scheme had been reformed, the Treasury turned its attention to the NHS scheme, with its close to 2.5 million (active, deferred and in payment) members.[6] The government agenda was to make the scheme more financially sustainable, which would probably mean increasing the age of retirement, considering basing pensions on career average earnings rather than final salary, and increasing contributions. The unions were naturally unenthusiastic, but they wanted other changes and were prepared to negotiate. The process took several years: the unions had to fight for detailed information and on several occasions the Treasury raised objections, causing urgent representations to be made through the Public Sector Pensions Committee, a group co-ordinated by the Trades Union Congress which had a channel of communication to the Cabinet Office. But finally an agreement was reached.

A key element was to continue with a final salary scheme (other than for GPs, who retained their dynamised career average arrangement), which most unions felt was the biggest prize. On the other hand normal retirement age would go up to 65 for new joiners after April 2008; this was reluctantly accepted by the unions as in line with general trends in society. There were also banded increases in employee contributions and, importantly, a cost-sharing agreement which recognised the possible need for future increases but capped the amount that employers could be asked to contribute, apparently 'future-proofing' the deal. The increased contributions were tough for BMA members, as the highest earners, but by the time the changes went out to consultation in 2007-8 the cold reality of the new financial climate was setting in: members swallowed hard and accepted the increases as the price for pension benefits that were still good by most standards. Little did they know that the agreement would be torn up almost before the ink had dried *(see Chapter 5)*.

In January 2010 the NHS launched a *Choice Exercise*, during

---

[6] NHS Pensions Agency: *Annual Accounts* March 2011.

which members were given a one-off opportunity to opt to remain in their old scheme (known as the 1995 scheme), now closed to new entrants, or to join the new 2008 scheme. The main difference was the normal age of retirement – 60 in the old scheme and 65 in the new – though both schemes had smaller changes, including the option to take more pension as a lump sum, new arrangements for topping up pensions, the abolition of the earnings cap for members of the old scheme and greater flexibility in the run up to retirement. The higher contribution rates – 8.5% for the highest earners – applied to both schemes. Members needed detailed advice on their individual circumstances in order to make their decision, but would soon have to do their financial planning all over again (*see Chapter 5*).

Chapter 5

The Conservative/Liberal Democrat coalition
2010–2012

Austerity

The general election of May 2010 was widely expected to lead to a change of government, but the Conservative party failed to achieve an outright majority. It was only after five days of political wrangling that David Cameron was able to form a government with the Liberal Democrats, the first UK coalition since the second world war. In the week after the election the two parties' leading figures put together the *Programme for Government*, starting with the two manifesto statements and ending with some hastily cobbled together compromises, particularly over the NHS.

The new government focused first on the economy. Ministers quickly discovered that the financial situation was worse than expected, and the coalition made clear in an early budget that its highest priority would be reducing the deficit, with significant cuts in public spending to be announced by the end of the year. It imposed a two-year pay freeze for public sector employees earning more than £21,000 a year, and set up a review of public sector pensions.

In primary care overall funding increased slightly to allow for higher staff costs, and central negotiations continued to make minor adjustments to the GP contract. But a survey carried out by the General Practitioners Committee (GPC) in 2011 showed most GPs were expecting their incomes to decline. Meanwhile, as Primary Care Trusts (PCTs) were merged and scaled down, Personal Medical Services (PMS) contracts, covering around a quarter of GPs, came under threat as they came up for renewal. Other issues of concern were a continuing debate over the possible abolition of practice boundaries (a policy first proposed by the previous government) and problems over the introduction of a new telephone number, NHS 111, for patients with urgent health problems. There was also an adjustment to the GPC's structure: another GPC survey had confirmed the growing concern among salaried and freelance/locum GPs ('sessional' doctors who make up at least a fifth of GPs) about the same committee (GPC) representing both employers and employees at the same time. A working group concluded that one committee would be stronger than two, and made constitutional changes to enhance the role and influence of the sessional GPs subcommittee within the GPC.

The coalition government said it would protect NHS spending – but not increase it. In the previous year Sir David Nicholson, the NHS Chief Executive in England, had challenged the service to save £20 billion by 2015, so it was clear that, with increasing costs and demands, 'standing still' would mean major economies. For hospital doctors this policy led to pressures on services, to attempts by employers to reduce the availability of Supporting Professional Activities (SPAs) in contracts and to local service reconfigurations. The Consultants' Committee (CC), led by Mark Porter, produced guidance for members on how to ensure that these would be based on clinical considerations, not just financial ones.

Pressures for change were also driven by the imminent oversupply of Certificate of Completion of Training (CCT) holders[1] (those who have completed their training and are looking for a consultant post), and the consultants, juniors and SAS committees started to consider new working patterns ('trained doctor' or 'consultant-present' provision) which envisaged more out-of-hours care being delivered by fully trained doctors, with the main role of juniors being to be trained, as in general practice. These models might improve patient care and juniors' training, but with funding constrained they might also downgrade consultant work or lead to a new subconsultant grade.

Junior doctors, led in the BMA by Shree Dhatta (who later co-chaired the Junior Doctors Committee (JDC) with Tom Dolphin) became increasingly concerned about the impact of full shift working on training, with clinical tutors expressing anxieties about how much longer the standards necessary for signing off trainees as competent could continue to be met. These concerns had already been identified in a review of the impact of the European Working Time Directive (EWTD) led by Professor Sir John Temple, a former President of the Royal College of Surgeons of Edinburgh, which concluded that if training were to be delivered within a 48 hour week, it would need to be very differently organised.[2] The government recognised that the

---

[1] Centre for Workforce Intelligence: *Starting the debate on the future consultant workforce* May 2012.
[2] Professor Sir John Temple: *Time for Training. A review of the impact of the European Working Time Directive on the quality of training.* Medical Education England May 2010.

EWTD might be causing problems, but swept this into the basket of issues that could be dealt with in some future adjustment of Britain's relationship with the EU. Meanwhile a further consultation process was launched in Europe to clarify the law, this time through the 'social partners' – European trade unions and business/employer organisations. It was due to be completed in 2012; if agreement were reached it would be in the form of a proposal for new legislation which member states can accept or reject but not amend.

By this time new contracts for juniors had long been overdue. The changes agreed in 2000 had been intended to reduce hours and once this had happened their value decreased and they became unwieldy for employers, with disproportionate pay differentials for slight alterations in working patterns creating an incentive for appeals over banding. The JDC had begun to press for a new contract in 2008 and the government asked NHS Employers to consult the four health departments on the possible scope of any negotiations. The pay freeze and period of austerity put the issue on the back burner, but it was expected to become a high priority for juniors as soon as the financial climate became more favourable.

The Health and Social Care Act 2012

One of the coalition's most significant initiatives was the Health and Social Care Act, probably the most radical structural change in the NHS in England since 1948. The health journalist Nick Timmins[3] has described how the new dynamic of a coalition government meant that policy about the NHS in England was developed 'on the hoof', and how this led to a volatile and convoluted two-year political battle to enact it. The process undoubtedly distracted the NHS from reducing costs and from focusing strategically on reconfiguring services. For the BMA, responding to the bill was a time-consuming and politically difficult exercise: the whole profession shared concerns about the scale and some aspects of the proposed changes, but there were sharp divisions on policy and on tactics. These differences surfaced particularly in BMA Council, which since 2005, reduced to 34 voting members, had been torn between its role as a corporate board and its wish to lead policy development by acting as a representative debating chamber. Despite Hamish Meldrum's patient diplomacy, Council struggled to maintain a united position on the bill.

---

[3] Nick Timmins: *Never Again? The story of the Health and Social Care Act* The King's Fund/Institute for Government July 2012.

David Cameron had promised during the election campaign 'to end the damage caused by pointless and disruptive re-organisations of the NHS', and the *Programme for Government* confirmed there would be 'no more top-down reorganisations of the NHS'.[4] But in the white paper *Equity and excellence: Liberating the NHS* published in July 2010 the Health Secretary, Andrew Lansley proposed changes far more sweeping than anyone had anticipated. He had been shadow health secretary for six years and, as Nick Timmins showed, many of his proposals could be traced back to his policy statements and speeches during that time. As far back as 2005 he had floated the notions of greater GP involvement in commissioning, a larger role for a pro-competitive economic regulator, and a right for independent providers to supply NHS services. But other elements were added during the discussions preceding coalition: compulsory participation by GPs in commissioning groups, giving local authorities responsibility for most public health services, and sweeping away PCTs and strategic health authorities. When the bill appeared it was a huge and complex document of some 550 pages, which left no room for doubt about the radical nature of the proposals. Sir David Nicholson, the NHS Chief Executive in England, described it as 'the only change management system you can actually see from space, it is that large'.[5]

The BMA, taken aback by the scope of the proposals, joined in the early chorus of concern. But it did not want to reject the idea that doctors – as those best placed to understand patients' needs – should have greater influence in shaping services. The GPs' committee particularly, while concerned about the practical details and (as with the debate over fundholding 20 years earlier) about the impact of financial responsibility on the doctor/patient relationship, was keen to explore how it could be made to work. So the BMA's initial position was one of critical engagement, though from the outset there was dissent from those members of Council who had long suspected that privatisation was the government's real motive. The Association's detailed response did not condemn the government's plan outright but highlighted serious concerns, including the lack of any role in commissioning for consultants or for public health doctors. By the end of 2010 worries were building up in all quarters about the plan's practicality. The House of Commons Health Select Committee, chaired by the influential former Health Secretary, Stephen Dorrell, questioned the thinking behind

[4] *The Coalition: Our Programme for Government.* Cabinet Office May 2010.
[5] *Financial Times* 9/12/10.

the proposals and its impact on the NHS's financial imperatives. The King's Fund suggested that the coalition was heading 'too far, too fast'.[6] And the Royal College of GPs (RCGP) under its new President, Clare Gerada, was worried that GPs were being cast as 'the new rationers'. Within the coalition there were signs of political concern about the growing public opposition.

Andrew Lansley convinced the government to stick to its guns and the bill was launched in January 2011 with few modifications to indicate that concerns about the white paper had been listened to. Larger doubts then started to surface. The GPs committee had been discussing with the Department of Health the detail of how GPs would be involved in commissioning, but it feared that not enough support would be made available. Meanwhile PCTs were already being dismantled and experienced staff disappearing. Even the moderates on BMA Council became suspicious when they saw that the bill proposed reducing the Secretary of State's role and giving fierce powers to the regulator, Monitor, in order to enforce competition. Council hardened its stance, and called for a Special Representative Meeting (SRM) for 15 March.

In the run-up to this meeting, significant opposition to the bill was mounted not only by the Labour Party but crucially by senior Liberal Democrats, notably Baroness Shirley Williams. She generated much publicity by tabling a critical motion for the party's coming conference, due to take place just before the BMA's meeting. The motion, calling for big changes to the bill, was carried, to the embarrassment of the party leader and Deputy Prime Minister, Nick Clegg. With the tide now running strongly against the bill, the BMA's SRM agreed that the best outcome would be its withdrawal. But when it came to tactics, after a tense debate the meeting decided that the BMA should campaign against the bill's more damaging aspects rather than oppose it entirely, and the earlier stance of critical engagement was supported. So plans were made for a campaign, and a series of meetings took place with MPs and peers.

By now the coalition government was in some disarray, with some cabinet members giving the impression that they had not fully understood the political implications and now regretted having given Andrew Lansley so much scope. His belief in his plan was implacable, but by mid-April the pressure was such that the Prime Minister took the highly unusual step of making him announce a pause in the legislation process to allow the government to 'listen, engage and amend'.

---

[6] King's Fund press release 7/10/12.

Over the next two months an independent but government-appointed body, the Future Forum, chaired by former President of the RCGP, Steve Field, would review the concerns and report back.

Time will no doubt reveal whether this was an astute political move to derail the opposition to the bill with the intention of carrying on regardless or a desperate ploy to buy time and regroup. Whatever the government's motivation, the Forum went about its task energetically and produced a report – most of which was accepted by the government – that recommended several important changes to the bill's provisions without affecting its fundamental impact. The BMA worked hard to have an effective input, meanwhile continuing to scrutinise the bill in detail, preparing briefings for MPs and peers and looking for opportunities for amendment. In Council, however, the pause widened the division between those who wanted to influence by engagement and those who wanted outright opposition. At the Annual Representative Meeting (ARM) in late June, soon after the Forum reported, the latter group carried the day and, against the advice of the Chairman of Council, the ARM called for the bill to be withdrawn.

The BMA continued to publicise its concerns as the bill passed through the Commons and the Lords. It consulted and informed members, and continued to work with parliamentarians on hundreds of clauses and more than a thousand amendments. Particularly during the passage through the House of Lords, where Baroness Williams continued to have a key role, there was much to play for. But the pro-campaigning group on Council pointed out that making amendments was not the same as the total withdrawal that the ARM had demanded. Following acrimonious Council meetings and the use of Twitter and other social media by the campaigners, the BMA changed its stance to one of formal opposition, to the frustration of the more pragmatic members, who felt progress could still be made. Nick Timmins commented later that Dr Meldrum faced the problem that every Chairman of Council faces when the BMA gets in a major dispute with the government: 'A chunk of the Association's membership always wants confrontation while the Council's officers almost always believe that remaining engaged with ministers is more likely to produce results.'[7]

There was a wobble during the bill's passage through the Lords as Andy Burnham, the shadow health secretary, began to draw some of the royal colleges into opposing the bill. He argued that many of

---

[7] Nick Timmins: *Never Again? The Story of the Health and Social Care Act.* The King's Fund/ Institute for Government. July 2012 p 87.

the positive changes could be made without legislation. Sensing an opportunity to make an impact, some of the 'campaigners' on BMA Council organised a social media campaign to encourage members of royal colleges to use their right to call extraordinary meetings or votes to pressurise their colleges into demanding the bill's withdrawal. The campaign gained momentum, and the President of the Royal College of Physicians came under attack from members for attending a Downing Street summit organised for 'constructively engaged' organisations. But the turnouts to some college meetings were low, and the moment passed when finally Baroness Williams was persuaded by Earl Howe, the Conservative health spokesman in the Lords, that having been amended the bill was now safe to proceed. It received royal assent at the end of March 2012.

The BMA was able to share credit for some significant changes that had been made during the passage of the bill. These included:

- removing a proposed national tariff which would have allowed competition between providers on price;
- changing the role of Monitor from promoting competition to enabling integration and co-operation;
- including a consultant and public health doctor as well as GPs in Clinical Commissioning Groups (CCGs);
- introducing new provisions on patient information and confidentiality;
- reversing plans to subject 'failing' NHS foundation trusts to a private sector insolvency process; and
- reinstating certain duties for the Secretary of State: to secure a comprehensive service and to have national oversight for education and training (with the establishment of Health Education England (HEE)).

Whether these changes have been enough, with the continuing involvement of the BMA and its members in implementing the new structures, to prevent the damage to the NHS that many feared, and indeed to improve and strengthen it, is a judgement to be reached by future historians.

Pensions (continued)

The coalition government quickly focused on public sector pensions as a major opportunity to reduce public expenditure. Lord Hutton, a former Labour health minister, Secretary of State for Work and Pensions and Business Secretary, was appointed to chair the independent Public

Service Pensions Commission. In March 2011 he produced a report which recommended linking retirement age to the state pension age, and replacing final salary schemes with Career Average Revalued Earnings (CARE) schemes, though it did acknowledge that public sector pensions were not necessarily the 'gold-plated' benefit often criticised in the press.

Before negotiations got under way on these proposals, the government made some unilateral changes. They changed the rate of increase of pensions in payment from RPI to the lower CPI where they had legal powers to do so (this change alone reduced the cost of past service benefits in public sector pension schemes by £175 billion). They also announced further staged increases in contribution rates from April 2012: the highest earning doctors, whose contributions had already risen to 8.5% after the 2008 changes, now faced contributions of 14.5% by 2014.

This was clearly bad news for doctors, who had so recently accepted higher contributions and longer working (for new entrants), believing that the cost sharing agreement which limited further increases in employers' contributions would protect the NHS pension scheme (NHSPS) for the future. The BMA pointed out that the scheme was now in good health with contributions paid in between 2009/10 and 2015/16 set to exceed benefits paid out by £10.7 billion. Civil servants on a similar salary to a senior doctor would contribute significantly less, increasing from 1.5% to only 7.5%. Doctors joining the service at 25 would pay an extra £200,000 in contributions and would have to work to age 68, raising serious issues about physical capability in some specialties. For hospital doctors the value of a CARE scheme would be about 30% less than the current final salary scheme. The imposition of the higher contributions felt more like an opportunistic additional tax on higher earning doctors than part of a well considered plan, and anger in the profession mounted as doctors calculated what they would lose and struggled to understand why they were being targeted.

The other NHS unions were also angry and talks with the government made little progress. The TUC called for a day of action in November 2011, which the BMA supported (though not at that stage agreeing to industrial action). The government tabled a 'final offer' – which included some protection for those close to retirement – in December 2011; the BMA decided to survey its members on their response. From that point, without major concessions by the government, a confrontation was always the likely outcome. Even if they accepted the need to reduce the deficit and the responsibility falling on higher earners at a time of recession, doctors felt the government had acted unfairly and a stand must be taken. The survey, to which 44,000 members replied, showed about 80% wanted to reject the offer and about 65% were prepared to take some industrial action. Repeated approaches to the government failed to resolve the impasse so when Council held an emergency meeting in February 2012, it had little option but to call for a ballot on industrial action.

There have been calls for industrial action by the BMA at various points in the narrative of the last thirty years; on several occasions preparations have been started, but each time a solution has emerged – to the relief of those who would have to take the decision to go ahead. Industrial action is a high risk activity for any union, but particularly so for the BMA, whose influence is very dependent on public support and trust in doctors, and whose members find it difficult to contemplate action that could compromise their professional responsibility to their patients. The BMA had not taken industrial action since 1975. Since then the laws on trade union activity had become more restrictive and several unions had been faced with injunctions after challenges to their balloting procedures. The technical preparation needed for the ballot was immense, with lawyers consulted at every step, databases thoroughly checked and updated, and roadshows held around the country to ensure that members fully understood the issues. The BMA deliberated over what form of industrial action to take, and each branch of practice was asked to draw up detailed proposals, bearing in mind that only a fifth of those responding to the survey had said they would support an outright strike. The ballot took place in May – the latest increases in contributions having come into effect in April – and the outcome, on a 50% turnout, was more decisive than many had expected: 79% of GPs, 84% of consultants and 92% of juniors voted for industrial action.

The action, which involved providing urgent and emergency care only, was to take place on 21 June. Doctors were to turn up for work in order to be available for urgent needs, but would postpone non-urgent duties, giving as much advance notice as possible. GP surgeries would be open and each practice would decide what could safely be postponed. Great efforts were made in the run up to the action to minimise inconvenience to patients and to reassure them about safety. Within the profession there were strong feelings on both sides about the appropriateness of the action, with some advocating an even more militant stance while others deplored any resort to withdrawal of labour. The media coverage was generally hostile, focusing on the relative generosity of doctors' pensions rather than on whether they were being unfairly targeted.

The BMA's impression was that the action was generally well supported, though it was difficult to measure participation since doctors were at work anyway; certainly a clear message was delivered about doctors' grievances. Services had not been seriously disrupted, though some clinics and operations had been cancelled, and an IPSOS/MORI poll carried out shortly afterwards suggested encouragingly that 49% of the public had supported doctors and only 29% had supported the government's position, while 69% accepted that doctors had tried to minimise harm to patients.

But the action had not created enough pressure to force any movement from the government and discussion continued at the Bournemouth ARM, with positions hardening and doctors now having to choose between backing down or taking stronger action. The ARM, still fired up from the action the previous week, voted to continue the fight. The meeting marked the end of Hamish Meldrum's tough five-year term of office as Chairman of Council: he had been uncomfortable with industrial action but had accepted members' wishes and had led the campaign vigorously. His successor as chairman was Mark Porter, leader of the consultants and before that of the juniors. This change allowed for a pause for reflection, and a decision on the next steps was delayed until the next Council meeting in mid-July. Mark Porter used the time to meet the Secretary of State and reiterate the BMA's desire to find a solution through further talks. Andrew Lansley indicated that there would be scope for discussing the relationship of the proposed contribution increases in years two and three to the tiered structure of contributions, and also that talks would begin on the implications of working to age 68 or beyond (an issue of great concern to doctors). So on 18 July the Council decided to suspend its industrial action pending the outcome of these talks – but not to rule out further action should no progress be made.

At the time of writing the pensions dispute remains unresolved, but the prospect of industrial action appears to be receding as a new Secretary of State in England, Jeremy Hunt, keeps hopes alive of further discussions. The issue has been dangerous and divisive for the BMA, with differences emerging between GPs and hospital doctors and between England/Wales and Scotland, as well as between individual colleagues and partners. Pension reductions may turn out to have been the major battleground of the new era of austerity, or this may be the first of a series of further painful encounters, which will test to the limits the BMA's resilience and effectiveness.

Chapter 6

The devolved nations since 1999, pay and other branches of practice 1982–2012

The BMA in Scotland, Wales and Northern Ireland since devolution

One of the major political changes over the past 30 years has been the devolution of powers in 1999 from the UK government at Westminster to the Scottish Parliament, National Assembly for Wales and Northern Ireland Assembly. Since then health services in the three devolved nations have developed along very different lines from those in England. In each country the BMA has had to establish working relationships with new governments, including new negotiating structures for doctors' terms of employment. It has also had to develop new policy-making processes in each of the nations in order to influence and respond to the increasingly divergent local circumstances. At the same time the national BMAs have wanted to stay part of an integrated and united UK BMA. There have been tensions, which have generally been smoothed over. On the whole the BMA has dealt pragmatically with the challenges of devolution, preferring the evolution of new ways of working to radical structural change; this has allowed the national offices to make the most of the opportunity to establish influential positions with relatively inexperienced governments needing authoritative advice on health policy matters, while retaining access to the support, resources and shared knowledge of the UK BMA and its central departments. But as political circumstances continue to diverge, particularly in Scotland where the prospect of independence is being debated, the BMA may need to contemplate more fundamental structural changes than might have been thought conceivable at the beginning of the 1980s.

BMA Scotland

The BMA in Scotland had a proud history and clear identity long before devolution, with elegant if spartan premises in Drumsheugh Gardens, Edinburgh, an active council and committees, good relationships with national institutions and a long line of independently-minded chairmen of Council and medical Secretaries. In anticipation of the new demands that devolution would bring, the BMA acquired premises in Queen Street, Edinburgh, where a 19th century grade A listed building was refurbished to provide top quality accommodation for a new Scottish Office; it was officially opened in 2001. Under successive chairmen of Scottish Council – Arthur Morris, John Garner, Peter Terry and Brian Keighley – supported by Scottish Secretaries Brian Potter, Bill O'Neill and Martin Woodrow (the first non-medical incumbent), BMA Scotland developed into a modern and well-regarded organisation with a strong media profile and high visibility among members.

During the first term of the Scottish Parliament a Labour/Liberal Democrat coalition moved quickly to take ownership of the NHS in Scotland. Following an earlier acute services review it reduced the number of trusts in 1999 from 47 to 28. In 2000 clear differences began to emerge with the publication of *Our NHS*, which encouraged a more collaborative approach than the English *NHS Plan* with its emphasis on choice and plurality. The Arbuthnott review of NHS funding in Scotland introduced social deprivation as a major factor for distributing resources, and in 2001 the Scottish Executive departed from the English purchaser/provider orthodoxy by replacing separate health boards and trusts with unified health boards. The 2003 elections, when the Scottish National Party (SNP) gained seats, marked greater divergence. In 2004 the Labour-led coalition set up 14 health boards to provide services in an integrated system, together with about 40 community health partnerships.

At the same time the Scottish government asked the distinguished oncologist Professor David Kerr to chair a review of the future shape of the NHS. Its substantial report,[1] published in 2005, was adopted as the blueprint for Scotland's NHS over the next 20 years, and has underpinned a distinct consensus for an integrated, collaborative and publicly-provided health service. In 2007 the SNP formed a minority government and built on this approach, outlawing private provision in general practice in 2010 and introducing pilot schemes for direct elections to health boards. The SNP strengthened its position in the 2011 elections and looked likely to continue to develop the NHS along these lines.

---

[1] *Building a Health Service Fit for the Future*, 2005.

The BMA in Scotland has broadly supported these changes and has made its views heard on specific aspects. It has been particularly influential in encouraging the government to lead on public health issues, such as legislating against smoking in public places (which was implemented in advance of the rest of the UK), and more recently the introduction of minimum pricing for alcohol. These developments have clearly put pressure on the UK government to follow suit, a situation that enables the BMA to co-ordinate its public health lobbying across the four nations.

But on contractual issues the Scottish BMA has had to battle hard: first for appropriate negotiating structures, and then for agreements that may differ from those in other parts of the UK. This process caused some tensions within the UK BMA, whose broad policy is that doctors will be in a stronger position with uniform pay and conditions than with locally varying arrangements. But differences quickly emerged during the consultant contract negotiations of 2002–3 and the SAS negotiations of 2005–7 *(see p 105)*. When negotiators in a devolved country enjoy better relationships with government than the UK negotiators at Westminster, pressures to take a better local deal become hard to resist – and different agreements were reached. In practice the differences were slight – in the case of the SAS contract they related only to the assimilation arrangements – but once the principle of variation had been established further issues were bound to arise. Thus in 2007, although the Doctors' and Dentists' Review Body (DDRB) continued to recommend on a UK basis, the Scottish government chose to implement its award more generously than other parts of the UK. The basis of the general practice contract remains uniform across the UK, but in Scotland different Directed Enhanced Services have been agreed, and at the time of going to press the Scottish government seems likely to make different changes to the contract from those that may be imposed in England. For junior doctors, again on a UK contract, different relocation arrangements are in force. Scottish consultants still have distinction awards rather than clinical excellence awards, but the Scottish government froze them in advance of the wider public sector pay freeze in 2010. This issue was then subsumed into the DDRB's UK-wide review. Meanwhile a major difference opened up over medical student finance, with students from Scotland and other EU countries, but not those from other parts of the UK, having their tuition fees paid by a government agency.

The BMA has handled the 2012 pensions dispute (*see p 145*) as a UK matter, but feelings ran particularly high in Scotland, where the scheme is separate, though subject to the Westminster government's influence because of funding. After the UK-wide action was suspended hopes of a separate solution in Scotland led to calls for a further Scottish ballot, though when this was held it did not provide a mandate for industrial action.

In 2012 the two governments agreed that a referendum on independence for Scotland would take place in 2014. The terms of any such independence, or of the devolution of greater powers without full independence, known as 'devo-max', remain to be clarified. But clearly this raises major issues for the BMA in Scotland and for the UK BMA, impacting initially on the political climate as each side of the debate seeks to maximise the attractiveness of its favoured route, and in the longer term potentially on the very nature of the BMA.

BMA Cymru Wales

Before devolution the Welsh BMA had a strong identity, even though the Welsh and English health services were in most respects a single entity. It had good relations with the Welsh Office, its chief medical officer and the network of chief administrative medical officers (CAMOs) who remained influential at district level until after devolution. Under its Chairmen of Council since devolution – Terry Morris, Tony Calland, Andrew Dearden and Stefan Coghlan – and medical Secretaries Bob Broughton and Richard Lewis – the Welsh BMA has been able to foster a good personal relationship with its members (based on fraternal medical traditions) while at the same time adapting to the challenges of devolution. It set up new offices in Cardiff Bay, expanded staff in areas such as public affairs and industrial relations, and adopted new technology for its communications. In 2008 Welsh Council was reformed to establish a smaller, directly elected and more effective body. BMA Cymru Wales is also strongly engaged with Welsh civic society, maintaining relationships and undertaking collaborative work with a range of voluntary and professional organisations.

The first term of the Welsh Assembly from 1999 had a majority Labour government. It did not have legislative powers and took time to work out its vision for the NHS in Wales, initiating strategic reviews of acute services, primary care and human resources. The Welsh Assembly Government (WAG) turned for advice to the BMA, which was prepared to co-operate with reconfiguring trusts and establishing local health groups to bring them together with health authorities. This collaborative model developed further when health authorities were abolished in 2001 under the *Improving health in Wales* initiative. They were replaced by 22 local health boards, and under the WAG's second term from 2003, when it had increased legislative powers, these were reorganised, again with support from the BMA. They became co-terminous with local authorities, though (as in other parts of the UK) the intention to improve links between health and social care proved difficult to achieve.

During this time the Welsh BMA's strong relationship with the WAG proved fruitful when, after UK negotiations ran into difficulties in 2002, it agreed a separate contract for Welsh consultants. However, when serious problems arose over the contract in 2004/5, it became clear that this had been over-ambitious for an inexperienced government with limited capacity. The costs had been underestimated, leaving the WAG unable to fund some agreed clinical sessions. The NHS in Wales fell so far behind its target dates for implementation that the BMA Welsh Council endorsed a resolution of no confidence in the WAG from the Welsh Consultants Committee, and relationships were damaged until the contract was fully implemented.[2]

After the 2007 elections a coalition was established between Labour and Plaid Cymru, and, as in Scotland the movement away from the market driven health economy towards an integrated, collaborative service was made definitive. The strategy set out in *One Wales: a progressive agenda for the government of Wales* brought an end to any remaining private provision of NHS services, the internal market (Foundation Trusts had never been established in Wales) and the Private Finance Initiative. It clearly positioned the NHS in Wales as publicly owned, funded and provided, within an expanded welfare state with no prescription charges and free hospital car parking. In 2009 seven new, larger health boards – responsible for planning and delivering all services – were established to streamline the new system, with most public health services provided through a separate body, Public Health Wales.

After these changes Wales was hit by austerity and the government, which reverted to Labour in 2011 and became known as the Welsh Government (WG), argued strongly that it was worse off than other parts of the UK. The problem of long waiting times got worse

---

[2] John Jenkins. *The Serpent the Staff and the Dragon – The story of the BMA in Wales 1852–2007.*

and it was still difficult to recruit juniors, GPs and doctors in some hospital specialties. Meanwhile proposals for major rationalisations were undermined by lack of funds for transferring work to the community, and also by the geography of Wales which caused problems over access to A&E. BMA Cymru Wales has maintained talks on these issues, and has taken the opportunity to reinvigorate its divisions to play a key role in local discussion on reconfiguration proposals.

On employment it has taken time to establish appropriate channels of communication with which to negotiate changes to doctors' terms and conditions of service. The consultant contract was negotiated directly with the WAG, but BMA Cymru Wales then had to take a firm stand by withdrawing from the Welsh Partnership Forum, a multi-union consultative body which the WAG was seeking to use as a negotiating body for all staff. Eventually it was agreed that BMA Cymru Wales would be included in joint discussions on common issues such as pensions, but would deal separately with the WG on doctors' employment. Other than the consultant contract, which is an amended version of the old contract and includes commitment awards instead of discretionary points, there have been fewer differences than in Scotland, though in 2008 the WAG unlike the other nations agreed not to withdraw free accommodation for first year trainees. Welsh-domiciled medical students are also protected from increased tuition fees wherever they study in the UK through free grants which top up their student loan.

Like BMA Scotland, BMA Cymru Wales has found its devolved government receptive on public health issues, particularly on smoking-related policy, and has run a successful campaign on banning unsupervised suntan salons. Wales had a draft Bill on presumed consent for organ donation ahead of other parts of the UK.

BMA Northern Ireland

Long before devolution the Northern Ireland health service had developed differently, with administrative units covering both health and social services. Doctors' terms and conditions of service were also technically separate, but in practice they closely mirrored those in the rest of the UK. This was also the case with pay, though the DDRB's remit was not formally extended to Northern Ireland until 2007. The BMA in Northern Ireland played an important role in supporting doctors through the professional challenges of the troubles and, as in Scotland and Wales, the chairmen of the national Council post devolution – Maurice Dunlop, Brian Patterson and Paul Darragh – were respected figures in a close-knit medical community.

Preparation for devolution did not start in Northern Ireland until the Good Friday Agreement in 1998. The Assembly was not set up until December 1999, and then suspended for a year. An Executive in Northern Ireland began reforms, establishing local health and social care groups (which did not, however, hold budgets), initiating an acute services review, and consulting on a public health strategy. The Northern Ireland BMA developed relationships, and moved into new premises in September 2001. But momentum stalled and the Assembly and its executive were suspended again in October 2002.

During the period of direct rule, which lasted until 2007, BMA Northern Ireland developed its role by negotiating a new consultant contract and by implementing GP and SAS contracts. It also increased links with the Irish Medical Organisation. The two bodies held a joint conference in 2004 and this has led to further meetings and shared work on all-Ireland issues such as health inequalities, which is promoted through an annual event for MEPs as well as through the UK BMA. But the main political focus was on re-establishing devolved government and there was little impetus to change health service structures. Although a long-term Review of Public Administration was launched, elements of the English system – an internal market with private sector involvement – were allowed to continue in a structure characterised as 'permissive managerialism'.[3] This was reinforced by the Appleby Report of 2005 recommending stronger incentives to reduce waiting times and increase productivity.

Once the Assembly was restored in 2007 the executive began to look at new structures for the health service, starting with the first stage of the reforms identified in the Review of Public Administration which was to reduce 18 trusts to five. Again the BMA helped to fill a vacuum of policy advice by building relationships with politicians with little experience of national government. By 2009 more changes were taking place with a single Health and Social Care Board, together with a Patient and Client Council and a Public Health Agency. In 2011 a panel of health policy experts produced *Transforming Your Care*, a strategy document which was expected to set the pattern of service development. Unlike Scotland and Wales, Northern Ireland is choosing an internal market, delivered through local commissioning groups.

---

[3] S Greer. *Four Way Bet; How devolution has led to four different models for the NHS* 2004.

And like the rest of the UK, it is also starting to rationalise A&E services and transfer some services from hospital to community. The Northern Ireland BMA is broadly cooperating with these developments, and in particular has welcomed an emphasis on clinical leadership, a strategy it has influenced through its own 2010 document *Vision and Recommendations for a Health Service*, and also through its 10-year strategy on the future of general practice. As in other parts of the UK, however, it is increasingly concerned about the severe lack of resources.

Relationships with the executive and the health minister have been good, allowing a more favourable agreement on access to general practice than in England. But conflicts have arisen, for example over the executive's aggressive stance in freezing clinical excellence awards from 2010, leading BMA Northern Ireland to launch a legal action to resolve the problem. There was also serious concern over proposed cuts in primary care funding: it led to vigorous action and a campaign in which 30,000 patients' signatures were collected.

Review body and remuneration

It has long been recognised that doctors' pay from the NHS is such a contentious issue that it is best determined by an independent body. Since 1963, following a Royal Commission,[4] this has been the Review Body on Doctors' and Dentists' Remuneration (DDRB). But over the DDRB's long history the government has often refused to accept its recommendations, and this has led to regular conflict with the BMA. During the 1960s the government, trying to impose a prices and incomes policy, interfered repeatedly, leading to the review body's resignation and sanctions from the BMA.[5] A new review body was appointed in 1971 with assurances about its independence, and despite further interferences, doctors had large pay increases during the inflationary 1970s. By 1980, shortly before the period covered by this book, the pay level of career grade doctors had reached a peak: broadly the 97.5th percentile of the earnings distribution.

Since then a pattern of government interference has continued. The government failed to implement in full the DDRB's recommendations in 17 out of the past 30 years. It phased the award 10 times,

---

[4] *The Pilkington Report 10 February 1960* (Report of the Royal Commission on Doctors' and Dentists' Remuneration).
[5] The sanctions, described in Vol 2 of *The History of the BMA* (p 300), involved non-cooperation in NHS administration and refusal to sign sickness certificates. 70% of doctors responding to a ballot also expressed willingness to withdraw from the NHS.

allowing part to be paid from the due date of 1 April but holding back the balance until later in the year: this reduces the cash value of the award while ensuring that the ultimate salary levels are those recommended by the DDRB. At other times the government cut the size of the award, declined to implement specific recommendations, or (as in 1993 and during the public sector pay freeze starting in 2011) simply constrained the DDRB's role.

On several occasions the review body's terms of reference have been amended. In 2000, the government inserted a clause requiring the DDRB to take into account its targets for output, expenditure and inflation – despite the BMA's protest that this would weight the balance in the government's favour. Also, the DDRB was to advise the Secretary of State for Health and the relevant ministers in the devolved nations rather than the Prime Minister. In 2003 the DDRB was allowed to consider evidence on regional variations in labour markets and in 2007 its remit was extended to Northern Ireland. At the same time an additional clause made it take discrimination laws into account, and the reference to output targets was replaced with a wider strategic aim of placing patients at the heart of the DDRB's activities.

The DDRB's recommendations, and the government's decisions, are set out in the following table.

Year	DDRB recommendation (% increase)	Implementation by government	
1982	5.5	Partial	DDRB had recommended restoration of previous year's 3% abatement. Government declined.
1983	8.8	Phased	
1984	6.8–7.5	Phased	
1985	6.2	Phased	
1986	7.6–9.5	Phased	
1987	7.0–8.25	In full	
1988	7.3–8.1	In full	
1989	8	Partial	Govt declined specific recommendation of £1,000 for consultants.
1990	9.5–11.5	Cut, phased and partial	7% across the board, consultants, £1,000 declined again.

Year	DDRB recommendation (% increase)	Implementation by government	
1991	9.5–10.5	Phased	
1992	5	In full	
1993	No report	1.5%	
1994	3	In full	
1995	2.5–3.0	In full	
1996	3.8–5.3	Phased	
1997	3.4 (+0.35 for depreciated pensions)	Partial	£60m recommended for GPs to reflect job weight. (Distributed in 1998 as deprivation payments, local GMS development schemes and seniority.)
1998	4.2–5.2	Phased	
1999	3.5–4.3	Partial	£50m recommended for consultants. (Distributed in 2000 as intensity supplements, discretionary points.)
2000	3.3	In full	
2001	3.6–6.8	In full	
2002	3.6	In full	
2003		In full	
2004	3.225	(3 year deals)	
2005			
2006	0–2.0	Phased	
2007	0–£1,000/£650	Phased (not in Scotland)	
2008	2.2	In full	
2009	1.5	In full	
2010	0–1.34	Cut	
2011–13	Pay freeze	n/a	

Events that have affected the DDRB's considerations, the government's decisions or the BMA's response to them in particular years are briefly mentioned below:

- In 1987 the reason given for a higher award to salaried doctors was the cost of defence body subscriptions. These had been rising for some time with the increasing costs of negligence cases, but in 1987 the defence bodies announced increases of up to 87% for the following year. The DDRB noted that, while GPs had their subscriptions reimbursed through their expenses, salaried doctors had to meet these costs from their own pockets. The BMA made representations to the defence bodies and to the DHSS but without effect, and then made a strong plea to the DDRB for relief. Although it is not the DDRB's role to devise solutions to employment issues that should have been settled elsewhere, nor to arbitrate where negotiations have failed, the temptation to invite them to do so was strong and on this occasion the DDRB surprisingly took the bait. It came up with a novel but ill-thought-through solution which produced more problems and showed the dangers of seeking to blur the DDRB's true remit.

The recommendation was that employers would reimburse two thirds of the defence body subscription to whole-time salaried doctors, or those who were employed part-time but working wholly for the NHS. This threw up a number of anomalies, particularly that of maximum part-time consultants, who were carrying out the same NHS commitment as whole-time consultants, yet did not receive reimbursement for their subscriptions because they were deemed part-time. After a couple of years it was clear that the arrangement was impractical and instead the legal norm (already applied to other NHS staff) was adopted that employers are liable for the actions of their employees. Until then consultants had been carrying their own liability insurance as an element of their much-valued sense of professional independence, alongside their right to private practice. At a few hundred pounds a year it seemed an emblem of professionalism worth preserving. But once subscriptions had risen beyond £10,000 in some specialties it quickly became a luxury, and the NHS Indemnity Scheme was introduced from 1 January 1990.

- In 1990, in the heat of the BMA's battle with the government over the NHS white paper, the government cut and phased the award, and also rejected for a second year running the DDRB's recommendation of an additional £1,000 for consultants. This was seen as a vindictive act, particularly since the Minister for Health had assured the DDRB in evidence that its recommendations would be implemented in full unless there were clear and compelling reasons not to do so.

- Towards the end of 1992 the Chancellor of the Exchequer made an autumn statement, which restricted all pay increases in the public sector to 1.5% for a year. The Prime Minister wrote to the DDRB and other review bodies telling them this would be imposed and asking them not to make any recommendations for that year. However decisions were needed on other issues, such as the number and value of distinction awards, practice expenses for GPs, and fees for ophthalmic medical practitioners; the Prime Minister suggested that on these the DDRB might make recommendations as normal. The DDRB was not pleased by the government's unilateral action and replied that it would only consider these issues if its independence were guaranteed. The BMA was willing but the government was not, and the DDRB therefore declined to issue a report in 1993, with the outstanding matters resolved in direct negotiation between the BMA and the Department of Health (DH).

- In 1997 the BMA looked at the earnings of comparable groups and concluded that restoring doctors' pay to its appropriate position would require a 50% increase; clearly the DDRB's recommendation was going to be disappointing. At the same time GPs felt that being part of the BMA's evidence machinery (and being compared with consultants) was stopping them from pressing for bigger increases so they started to talk about other ways of determining their pay.

- Between 2003 and 2006 the DDRB's role was reduced when an across-the-board 3.225% increase was implemented each year to give effect to the negotiated cost-of-living element of the GPs' and consultants' new contracts. At the end of the period the government wanted to peg down public expenditure and the NHS faced financial deficits. The DH had asked for a 2.5% increase, but then the Chancellor of the Exchequer asked all pay review bodies for an upper limit of 1% and the Health Secretary changed the DH's evidence to fall in line with this request. The BMA reminded the DDRB of its independence, but was disappointed when it came close to following the DH line.

- In 2007 the DDRB again exasperated the BMA by its apparent willingness to comply with the government's wish to use public sector pay restraint as a policy weapon. The BMA may have underestimated how much being excluded from determining pay settlements for three years had distanced the DDRB from the rationale for the contract deals that had been negotiated. The DDRB seemed to take at face value media criticism that doctors were overpaid, and recommended only small increases. The UK government then rubbed salt into the wound by phasing the award, though the Scottish government chose not to do so. GPs, who had borne the brunt of the media criticism, were awarded 0%; this revealed a lack of understanding by the DDRB of the complexity of GP's new contractual arrangements and provoked an attempt by the Minister for Health, Lord Warner, to exclude the DDRB from a role in determining GPs' pay. Admittedly, the detail of the contract baffled many, and it took patient effort by the BMA's economist Jon Ford and negotiators on both sides to set down an explanation which clarified the DDRB's role for the future. The contract's reliance on income from several different funding streams – a global sum, a Quality and Outcomes Framework and payments for particular services, tempered by the Minimum Practice Income Guarantee – meant that complex negotiations were needed each year to reflect adjustments to these elements at the same time as an uplift to cover practice expenses.

- Soon after the coalition government came to power in 2010 it imposed a two-year pay freeze across the public sector in England for all staff earning more than £21,000 a year. (For GPs who were independent contractors this was implemented through contract negotiations.) The devolved nations also adopted a pay freeze until 2013. Although the DDRB would thus not have to make recommendations for two years, it decided that it would continue to collect information on recruitment, retention and motivation and would consider potential legal implications of pay policy. The BMA also decided to continue to submit evidence tracing any comparative decline in incomes, and reporting on non-pay elements. In December 2011 the government announced that it would end the pay freeze from 2013, though it would seek 1% public sector pay awards for the next two years. In 2010 the government asked the DDRB to review the consultants' clinical excellence and distinction award schemes in all the nations. The review was completed in the summer of 2011, but publication was delayed until late December 2012, when the government announced that negotiations would take place on significant changes to consultants' – and juniors' – employment terms.

The BMA has sometimes looked at alternatives to the review body system – probably direct negotiations. When the DDRB's role was reduced to accepting joint evidence on three-year arrangements that had already been agreed, the pay of GPs and consultants forged ahead. In addition, question marks have repeatedly arisen over the DDRB's independence and its apparent reluctance to come into conflict with government. On the other hand, average medical earnings have remained around the 97th percentile over the past 10 years, with increases usually staying ahead of government pay norms,[6] and staff in review body arrangements have consistently done better than those who are not.[7] The review body system was set up to avoid regular and destructive conflict between doctors and the government, and this remains a relevant consideration. The risks of relying on direct pay bargaining are perhaps greater now in the modern, fragmented NHS: a renewed impetus for local pay, a greater plurality of providers/employers, and an increasing supply of doctors with fewer new posts. The DDRB also provides a fair and authoritative mechanism for resolving inevitable differences about the relative worth of different branches of practice: thrashing out such differences in negotiation could become deeply divisive for the profession, and could weaken the BMA's bargaining position. However, in practice the DDRB has tended to duck major issues of relativities, which has led to dissatisfaction when changes in workload or responsibility have not been adequately reflected.

In summary, the BMA has so far preferred to remain with the existing system, while keeping it under review. At the time of writing the recession and pay freeze have put the DDRB's main role on hold, and although its continuation in a monitoring role offers some reassurance about an eventual return to ordered consideration of pay increases, uncertainty about the future is such that the BMA must plan for a number of possible scenarios for determining doctors' pay.

Medical academic staff

The BMA's Medical Academic Staff Committee (MASC) became a full committee in the late 1970s. Since then it has fought – and won – some tough battles on behalf of a group that includes teachers and researchers with world-wide reputations but whose pay and working conditions often lag behind those of their NHS colleagues. Clinical academics are

---

[6] DDRB 40th Report 2012.
[7] Michael Short: *The earnings of workers covered by the pay review bodies: evidence from the LFS* February 2008 OME.

usually employed by universities and hold an honorary contract with the NHS, under which they undertake clinical duties alongside NHS colleagues. But ensuring that their salaries are broadly comparable has been difficult. In 1979 an historic agreement with the universities established the Clinical Academic Staff Salaries Committee, with membership from the BMA, BDA, Association of University Teachers and the Committee of Vice-Chancellors and Principals (CVCP). Its remit was to ensure that NHS salary levels were reflected in the pay of clinical academic staff. But there was rarely a year during the 1980s and early 1990s in which this translation was achieved without a bitter battle. This was for three reasons: universities were relatively independent, two different government departments (health and education) were involved, and those in universities often resented the higher salaries paid to clinical academics.

The MASC had to mount annual campaigns, with letters to MPs, ARM resolutions and meetings with both Secretaries of State, to press the government to release the extra funding that universities usually needed to pay the full amount to their clinical staff; all too often it did not arrive until late in the year. After a particularly difficult battle in 1996, when the chairman of BMA Council wrote to the Prime Minister threatening a ban on university job advertisements in the *BMJ*, the government finally grasped the nettle and instructed the Higher Education Funding Council for England to enable medical schools to meet any extra costs arising from the translation of NHS pay awards.

Since then, translation of the basic pay award for clinical academics has been relatively straightforward, but MASC has had to be vigilant in other areas. The collective bargaining machinery within the universities was overhauled several times, with the Universities and Colleges Employers' Association taking over from the CVCP in 1995, then further new arrangements following the recommendations in the Dearing Report of 1997[8] and the Bett Report of 1999.[9] Bett helpfully recognised that clinical academic staff had special problems because of the conflicting pressures of research (by then driven by the Research Assessment Exercise (RAE)) with teaching and clinical work. The MASC argued successfully for the new national council to have a special subcommittee for clinical academic issues. This principle was

---

[8] The National Committee of Inquiry into Higher Education. July 1997.
[9] *Independent Review of Higher Education Pay and Conditions.* Report of a Committee chaired by Sir Michael Bett 1999.

continued when revised machinery, the Joint National Committee for Higher Education Staff was set up in 2002, later supplemented by a Stakeholder Forum in 2002–3.

Meanwhile in 2001 the government commissioned a review[10] of the difficulties caused for clinical academics and their employers by having to report to a university and to the NHS. This led to *The Follett Principles*, which insisted on joint working between the university and NHS employers to integrate their separate responsibilities. The MASC strongly supported these principles and has often relied on them in solving practical problems for clinical academic staff, such as countering the suggestion that VAT should be charged on the supply of university staff for NHS services with a Memorandum of Understanding between employers to clarify the relationship.

Led by Colin Smith, then by Professor Michael Rees, previously chairman of the juniors, MASC was fully involved in negotiations for the new consultant contracts in England and Scotland in 2003. It was able to ensure that they were implemented for clinical academic staff, and later extended to senior academic GPs. Agreement was not reached in Wales nor in Northern Ireland, where a version of the English contract was eventually imposed in 2012. Growing financial pressures in universities meant that clinical academics have been more vulnerable to redundancy than NHS staff, and the MASC has worked closely with local BMA staff to ensure that consultation processes are followed and alternative solutions considered.

As well as its actions on pay and conditions, the MASC has also pressed for better career structure and progression for clinical academic staff. Over the past 30 years the number of posts has fluctuated, and there have been two major crises of recruitment and retention. In 1981, the Conservative government announced that, as part of its austerity drive, higher education funding would be reduced for the next three years. But by the following year the Secretary of State for Education, Sir Keith Joseph, was looking for even more reductions. The effects were felt more keenly in medical schools than in other academic departments: 14% of clinical teaching posts were lost between 1981 and 1985, compared with 10% or less in most other departments. The problem was exacerbated because the government determined student numbers and the universities could not reduce them.

---

[10] Department for Education and Skills. *A Review of Appraisal, Disciplinary and Reporting Arrangements for Senior NHS and University Staff with Academic and Clinical Duties*. Professor Sir Michael Follett and Michael Paulson-Ellis. September 2001.

In 1983 the MASC, together with the British Dental Association, set up a high powered body, including deans of medical schools and representatives from the royal colleges and the Joint Consultants Committee, to monitor and then publicise the effects of university cuts on medicine. The group commissioned regular surveys and these showed that academics were having to prioritise teaching and fund-raising and that research time was being squeezed out. Most lost posts were among those aged 30–35, which jeopardised the future of academic medicine, with potential effects on the whole profession.

In 1985, the MASC, chaired by Colin Smith of Southampton (who led the committee energetically for the next 20 years), decided to step up the pressure. He sought a meeting with Sir Keith Joseph who flatly denied that there was a crisis in academic medicine. In its response to the 1986 Social Services Committee report on university cuts, the government complacently suggested that any impact on medical services was marginal because the NHS was able to compensate by funding teaching posts. In April a MASC survey showed a 20% reduction in clinical academic staff since 1980, that some vacancies were unfilled, and that most medical schools had or were expecting overspends or shortfalls and were struggling to maintain research infrastructure. The committee organised a conference, at which the Chairman of the the CVCP, Professor Sir Maurice Shock, suggested that universities were facing a decline of 30% in their funding between 1980 and 1990. The conference helped to raise public awareness and the MASC then organised a series of meetings with MPs and members of the House of Lords, many of whom were surprised to learn of the extent of the problem.

By the late 1980s, Kenneth Baker, who had replaced Sir Keith Joseph as Secretary of State, realised that the cuts had 'reached the bone', and the University Grants Committee (UGC) found the money to create 50 new clinical academic posts. At the same time, Lord Croham was appointed to review the role of the UGC, and in 1988 Kenneth Baker's Education Reform Act created the new Universities Funding Council, a body with executive rather than advisory powers (which was replaced in 1992 by the Higher Education Funding Council for England and its equivalent bodies in Scotland and Wales).

But policy initiatives designed for the NHS or for higher education often overlook the impact on academic medicine and soon the problems reappeared. In the late 1990s the Committee of Vice-Chancellors and

Principals commissioned the Richards Report[11] which recognised that 'clinical academics work under greater pressure and receive less reward than NHS doctors and dentists' and the MASC drew these findings to the attention of the House of Lords Select Committee on Science and Technology, which expressed concern. As medical student numbers grew in the early 2000s, and as the demands of the RAE squeezed out teaching time, the strain on clinical academic staff again became acute. In 2001 there were 79 vacant clinical chairs and the number of whole-time honorary contract holders had fallen by 16% since 1992; by 2004 junior academic posts had fallen by 23%.

The 2003 Higher Education white paper brought unwelcome increases in tuition fees but did acknowledge the problems and intro-duced some measures to address them, including a review of the RAE. The significant step forward came with the publication in 2005 of the Walport Report, commissioned jointly by the university and health sectors.[12] Accepted by the government, this set up a new integrated career pathway for clinical academic trainees. In England this would be funded through academic clinical fellowships run by the National Institute for Health Research; 200 'new blood' senior lecturer posts would also be set up. In Scotland clinical lecturer posts in the univer-sities were funded through the Scottish Clinical Research Excellence Development Scheme.

The MASC welcomed this initiative and hosted a conference on academic careers at which Sir Mark Walport spoke, and which led to a continuing stream of work for the MASC in supporting academic trainees with guidance documents, further annual conferences and later a joint subcommittee reporting to MASC and the Junior Doctors Committee (JDC). In the fall-out from the MTAS debacle in 2007 (*see Chapter 3*) MASC members played a key role in ensuring that the pro-cesses for application to the integrated training scheme were reviewed and revised.

The MASC has also championed the particular problems of women in academic medicine, producing an influential research-based report in April 2008, co-ordinated by Anita Holdcroft, a co-chair of the committee, which highlighted disadvantages both in career pro-gression and in pay. And throughout its history the MASC has pressed, often jointly with the Medical Students Committee and the Board of

---

[11] *Report of the Task Force on Clinical Academic Careers* chaired by Sir Rex Richards. July 1997.
[12] UK Clinical Research Collaboration with Modernising Medical Careers at the DH.

Education, for improvements in the undergraduate curriculum, a particular interest of longstanding MASC member and recent chairman, Peter Dangerfield, a senior lecturer in anatomy from Liverpool.

Public health medicine and community health

The specialty of public health medicine, known in the 1980s and 1990s as community medicine, has perhaps experienced more change and upheaval than any other group of NHS doctors over the past 30 years. In 1974 the public health function had been moved from local authorities to the NHS, with the post of Medical Officer of Health abolished and many experienced staff lost. In 1982 more senior posts were lost when Area Health Authorities were abolished. Barely had the dust settled when in 1983 the Griffiths Report introduced a new breed of regional and district general managers. They were not all attuned to the importance of public health and many of them left out a public health doctor when they assembled their district management teams. The Central Committee for Community Medicine and Community Health (CCCMCH) represented these doctors and was led from 1984 to 1988 by David Miles. It fought resolutely to reverse this trend. And by 1986 the situation had improved: all but 15 district health authorities had a district medical officer on their management team.

Meanwhile, a further review was taking shape, led by the distinguished physician and epidemiologist Donald Acheson, who had become Chief Medical Officer in England in 1983 (and who later, as Sir Donald Acheson, served as President of the BMA in 1996–97). His report followed an inquiry into a food poisoning outbreak at the Stanley Royd Hospital in Wakefield in 1984 which had identified serious community medicine failures. The Acheson report was to look at the future of public health and the specialty of community medicine, and the CCCMCH, seeing it as an opportunity, submitted substantial evidence. The report was published in January 1988,[13] and despite concern that no extra resources were envisaged, the CCCMCH, now led by Eileen Wain, the first woman to chair a BMA branch of practice committee, was pleased to take part in a DH working party to apply the recommendations. At the time the government was conducting the NHS review behind closed doors, and this gave the BMA a rare opportunity to work constructively with the Department.

---

[13] Acheson D. *Public Health in England: Report of the Committee of Inquiry into the Future Development of the Public Health Function.* London (HMSO) 1988.

The report redefined the function of public health: it would be responsible for the health of populations, for working with other relevant bodies (such as family practitioner committees and local authorities), and for controlling communicable diseases and infection. Each district and region would have a director of public health (DPH) and one of their important responsibilities would be to produce an annual report. These changes were implemented in a circular of December 1988[14] and were welcomed by the BMA. However, any sense that the importance of public health had finally been recognised was quickly washed away by the white paper *Working for Patients*, which barely acknowledged its existence.

Through the turmoil of the reforms that followed the white paper, public health doctors found themselves, as health authority employees, on the purchaser side of the purchaser/provider divide. Health authorities tended to see this as a largely financial activity and at first overlooked the opportunity of supporting purchasing decisions with informed medical advice. But the BMA gave repeated reminders, and in 1993 a governmental committee chaired by former deputy CMO Michael Abrams confirmed in guidance[15] that public health advice should be a key part of all purchasing decisions. By then, however, the Functions and Manpower Review was advocating the abolition of regions and the merger of district health authorities with family health services authotities. This duly took place with the Health Authorities Act in 1996. The CCCMCH, led by Lindsey Davies then by Stephen Watkins, became involved in fighting hard for health authorities and local authorities to have the same boundaries. They also fought for regional directors of public health, whose independence was threatened by the absorption of regions into the DH, and eventually ensured that they would remain on NHS terms and conditions of service even though they had become civil servants.

Meanwhile, the issue of medical advice to providers was never satisfactorily resolved. The Central Consultants and Specialists Committee (CCSC) argued that input from public health specialists was vital and issued advice to this effect. But the Abrams report only paid this lip service and in practice it turned out to be an area where the political drive for competition triumphed over professional co-operation. It has proved difficult even for clinical consultants to secure adequate involvement in providers' contracting decisions, let alone

---

[14] HC (88)64.
[15] HSG(93)56.

public health doctors. Through the various iterations of policy on commissioning this remained a major weakness of the purchaser/provider separation.

After Labour was elected in 1997, three further waves of reorganisation in England meant that the structure of public health had to be redefined, with repeated contractual changes for the doctors involved. The greatest disruption came in 2002 when primary care groups converted to primary care trusts (PCTs) and health authorities were abolished. Once again the issue of public health advice seemed to have been barely considered. DPH posts were transferred from health authorities to PCTs but the applications were managed insensitively, with a two-round process in which existing directors had to compete for their jobs in the first round and remaining jobs were filled by advertisement in a second round which was open to non-medical applicants. The processes were challenged by the Public Health Medicine Committee (PHMC), as it became, led through this turbulent period by Eddie Coyle, then by Peter Tiplady followed by Chris Spencer Jones. They secured some improvements, but more experienced public health doctors were lost, and the process was repeated when the number of PCTs and Strategic Health Authorities was again reduced in 2006. Meanwhile, other public health doctors needed support when the Health Protection Agency was established in 2003, taking over from the Public Health Laboratory Service and other organisations.

Increasingly, the PHMC has had to become a robust advocate for the special role of doctors in a multidisciplinary specialty. Sometimes this involved determined resistance when the DH failed to honour long-standing agreements, for example when it tried in 2007 to move DsPH onto 'very senior manager' pay scales. At other times the committee has positively promoted medical values, for example through three well-attended conferences on the role and contribution of public health doctors in 2008–9.

Since 2010 the coalition government has initiated another reorganisation of public health in England as part of the NHS and Social Care Act 2012. The proposed changes were set out in the white paper *Healthy Lives, Healthy People* in November 2010, and they constituted a radical upheaval, with most public health responsibilities transferring out of the NHS. Local public health functions were to pass to local authorities, which have a new statutory responsibility to commission public health services for their population, led by a DPH, a chief officer of the authority. They were also to be responsible for advising clinical commissioning groups. Certain health protection functions also fall to local authorities including immunisation, screening and control of infection; these are to be co-ordinated with NHS bodies through local health resilience partnerships (LHRPs). This model opens up an even wider divergence in public health provision across the UK than existed before. While joint working with local authorities is encouraged in each nation, none of the devolved administrations has handed over this responsibility to them: Scotland has kept public health clearly within its integrated health boards, while in Wales (though health boards retain population health responsibilities) most functions are carried out by Public Health Wales, and in Northern Ireland by the Public Health Agency.

A new body, Public Health England (PHE) has been set up as an executive agency of the DH to replace the Health Protection Agency and the Treatment Agency for Substance Abuse. It will handle national health protection emergencies and through regional outposts will provide information and intelligence, analysis, best practice dissemination and outcomes data for public health programmes.

The PHMC, co-chaired by Keith Reid and Richard Jarvis, had to respond vigorously to these changes. The committee was broadly in favour of transferring responsibility to local authorities, given the impact on public health outcomes of a much wider range of social determinants than those within the remit of the NHS, but had various concerns about organisational and resource issues. It also had major worries about the transfer of staff, their job security, their terms and conditions of service under employers with whom the BMA has no direct negotiating relationship, and whether, as civil servants or local government officers, they would still be able to speak out on public health issues. The committee was assured that medical trainees in the specialty will retain NHS contracts and will be overseen by Health Education England, but still has concerns about career development in a non-NHS service. Early indications were that another group of senior medical staff were leaving at a time when 60% of trainees in the specialty are non-medical.

However, the PHMC took an important initiative when the white paper was published and set up a task force of all the key public health leadership organisations chaired by Lindsey Davies, President of the Faculty of Public Health and a former chair of the committee. A large conference of public health practitioners took place in January 2011 which led to a position statement, *Public Health: Our Voice*. This has enabled the public health community to co-ordinate its response to the white paper and negotiate significant improvements, in particular the requirement for directors of public health to be properly qualified (through the Faculty of Public Health) and appointed (with input from PHE).

Community health

Until 2002/3 the CCCMCH also represented doctors working in community health, a disparate group with different levels of training and experience and no clear career structure. They were mainly employed as clinical and senior clinical medical officers providing services in child health, mental health, and family planning. In both the NHS and the BMA there were tensions and disputes about their lines of accountability. In 1986, as the Acheson review got underway, the BMA set up a forum to look at the child health services, a particularly fraught area. Chaired by George Duncan, the experienced regional medical officer for East Anglia, it aimed for a dialogue between GPs, paediatricians and the community health doctors (who were doing much of the work) about how to improve service standards and career prospects. The CCCMCH welcomed the review but quickly became concerned that the voice of community health was being drowned out. George Duncan stuck to his task despite a bitter battle over whether paediatricians should take over the whole service. By 1987 the Annual Representative Meeting (ARM) accepted a report advocating that the service should be consultant-led, but with career progression and proper training for doctors already working in the area.

The forum was converted into a working party, which continued to thrash out the details. Some senior clinical medical officers would become consultants while others, along with the clinical medical officers, would move onto hospital terms and conditions of service in the associate specialist or staff grade. The BMA working party reported in 1989, and the DH then set up a joint working party with involvement from all the health departments, the British Paediatric Association and the relevant BMA committees, led by Sandy Macara, then chairman of the Representative Body (RB). It produced an interim report in 1992 and a final report in 1993 which included model job descriptions and training programmes for the new specialty of community child health or community paediatrics. It had been a grinding process, and implementation at first was slow.

However, it did provide a model for other branches of the community health service, and in 2002 the senior and chief medical officer grades were finally assimilated into the hospital grading structure. A particular battle was fought over the position of SCMOs in family planning who were at first excluded from the specialist register – and thus from consultant posts – because their discipline was not recognised as a specialty. The committee lobbied for change and under its chairman Stephen Watkins, a veteran campaigner, supported a legal test case that eventually led to the establishment of family planning as a specialty.

Although doctors working in the community health services are now part of a recognised career structure, they continue to have less security than their hospital colleagues. Under the DH's *Commissioning a patient-led NHS* initiative, which was launched on an unprepared NHS in 2005, PCTs were asked to concentrate more on commissioning activities and to shed their provider functions. Under the *Transforming Community Services* initiative in 2008–10, community services were put out to tender and established as separate or sometimes 'arm's length' organisations, which might be merged with other trusts or run by private providers, social enterprises, community foundation trusts, or a contractually distinct subgroup of the PCT. The BMA, and other NHS unions, fought hard to gain some protection of terms and conditions of service – particularly pension rights – when staff were transferred, but there was great disruption, and in some areas a loss of integration with other local services.

Armed forces doctors

The Defence Medical Services (DMS) have seen a marked decline over the past 30 years. In the early 1980s there were still three separate services with proud traditions, though as forces medical pay lagged behind the NHS and pay increases were lower than those of non-medical officers, they struggled to recruit and retain doctors. Since 1994 the services, while retaining their separate identities, have been under a single command. The eight UK military hospitals have been closed and replaced with a major NHS-run centre in Birmingham. Increasingly reserves have been used on active service: for example from April to October 2009 they provided nearly a third of operational output in Afghanistan and field hospitals were manned alternately by regulars and reserves.[16]

---

[16] AFPRB 2010 DMS Report.

Service doctors, like others (such as medical academics) working as a minority group within large organisations, have a particular need for a professional organisation to represent their interests. During this period the Armed Forces Committee (AFC) increased its activity and profile, ensuring that their voice is always heard, even though trade unions are not recognised within the armed forces. The committee holds a well-attended annual conference, liaises with the Ministry of Defence (MoD), NHS authorities and the Surgeon General and through the BMA briefs MPs and the press.

A key activity has been giving written and oral evidence to the Armed Forces Pay Review Body (AFPRB), which produces a supplementary report each year on DMS doctors and dentists. During the 1980s the AFC persuaded the AFPRB to address specific problems of differentials with non-medical officers and with the NHS hospital service, and to remedy a pensions anomaly that, together with the clawback of pay after short-service commissions, was causing doctors to leave the services. Recruitment and retention improved after a review carried out in 1984 by the former CMO in England Sir Henry Yellowlees and the introduction of the 'x factor' supplement in 1988, intended to reflect the 'special conditions of service life'. The committee also pressed the review body on specific areas of disadvantage, such as lack of access to extra-contractual earnings and employer responsibility for medical indemnity. These were addressed but there was still a 33% shortfall in specialist manpower.

The Gulf War forced the MoD to acknowledge the critical importance of the defence medical services. In 1991 military medical pay went up by 20%, but the next year the award was staged as it was for NHS doctors (though not for others in the armed forces). Cuts in the armed forces were announced, as well as the closure of military hospitals, in the *Options for Change* report. Morale fell again and more closures and reductions were announced in 1994–5. Although the 1995 Bett report[17] recommended improvements to the career structure and terms and conditions of service for the armed forces, the government delayed its response and recruitment and retention continued to suffer. Meanwhile, the increasing use of reserves led the AFC to work with other BMA committees to press for NHS employers to allow time off for doctors in the reserves.

---

[17] *Managing People in Tomorrow's Armed Forces: Review of the Armed Forces Manpower, Career and Remuneration Structures, 1995.*

In 1997 the new Labour Defence Secretary, George Robertson, appeared sympathetic and promised to restructure and revive the DMS. New arrangements were negotiated to improve the pay of civilian medical practitioners but medical staff continued to leave the services. The AFC gave evidence to the Defence Select Committee, pressed the AFPRB to re-introduce a lead payment and in 2001 the BMA appealed to the Prime Minister. The MoD then established the Medical Manning and Retention Review which looked at differentials with civilian doctors and dentists and in 2003 this gave the AFPRB evidence which allowed it to recommend a second increase of 6.8% in addition to the 3.2% that had already been paid in April 2003. A further increase of £6,500 was paid late in 2006, and recruitment improved. This continued for several years, though in 2009 manning levels were still only 74% of target.

The austerity programme introduced by the new government in 2010 impacted severely upon the MoD, which has made clear that the 11,000 military redundancies expected by 2015 – with more to come in the future – will include doctors. Future provision is being planned on the basis of studies[18] which recommend an even greater proportion of reserves, and changes in the terms and conditions of service (and pensions) of all those in the armed forces are expected.

Medical students

At the 1991 ARM the medical students' chairman, Ian Wilson (later a deputy chairman of the consultants committee and of the RB), caused great amusement by ostentatiously sporting a cardboard replica of the formal chains of office then routinely worn at the meeting by senior committee chairmen. The mockery was light-hearted but had a serious purpose as part of a campaign by the students to achieve equal status with other BMA committees. They finally succeeded 10 years later when the Medical Students Committee (MSC) was granted equivalent autonomy to the other branch of practice committees. This completed a transformation in the role and influence of medical students within the BMA. In 1982 there were about 6,000 associate members, represented by an informal 'group', which became a committee six years later. By 2012 student membership had reached 22,220 and the committee had a representative in each medical school, an active presence on the BMA website, a seat on council and an annual conference. Members receive a monthly *Student BMJ* and a special students' edition of *BMA News*.

---

[18] *Army 2020, DMS 2020, Future Reserves 2020.*

There are good strategic reasons for the BMA to attract student members and numbers were boosted by a revitalised campaign to recruit medical students at freshers' fairs, and by a decision to waive the first year's subscription in return for signed direct debits for the second and third years. But MSC members are more than recruiting agents for the Association. Those sitting on other BMA committees, on Council and at the ARM have a tradition of punching above their weight and their contribution – often challenging and iconoclastic – is taken seriously. The MSC has to deal with significant issues affecting medical schools that neither wider student organisations nor NHS bodies are well placed to address. These have generally arisen in three main areas: student finance; curriculum and welfare; and the transition to NHS foundation programmes.

Whenever new policies are adopted over the cost of higher education, the MSC has to fight to remind governments and the public that medical students face special problems, with longer courses and restricted ability to earn money in the vacation. In the 1980s grants failed to keep pace with medical students' extra costs and in the 1990s there were problems over the availability and flexibility of student loans. The MSC carried out regular surveys of medical student debt and by 2010 these showed medical students owing about £24,000 after five years. The MSC has used this evidence to campaign vigorously against proposals such as topping up or increasing tuition fees that would deter applicants and work against the aim of widening access to medical careers. They have also lobbied for better support for medical students from the NHS Bursary Scheme. The BMA forecasted that those starting medicine in 2012 would have a debt of about £70,000 on graduation.

On education and welfare, the MSC developed a regular dialogue with the GMC and its education committee, giving important input to consultations on the curriculum, including *Tomorrow's Doctors* in 2005 and its revision in 2009. It also made strong representations to the GMC and to the Medical Schools Council (TMSC), about barriers to access to medical studies in relation to testing and immunisation for blood-borne viruses and to disability. Building on the Medical School Charter, agreed with TMSC in 2005, it published for several years a *Rough Guide to Medical Schools*, providing information on how well schools measure up to the criteria that students see as important.

The committee strongly defended the interests of overseas medical students already in the UK over issues of immigration status. In 2007, for example, the Home Office suddenly changed the rules, and some students were threatened with having to return home before completing their pre-registration training.

On the transition to pre-registration training, the committee has annually monitored the availability of PRHO/FP posts, often having to press for extra posts when there was danger of a shortfall. During the period of *Modernising Medical Careers* the MSC became closely involved in consultations on the new foundation programme and its application process, continuing to monitor and evaluate its development. In 2008, led by its charismatic chairman Ian Noble (who tragically died in a motorcycle accident in 2010) the committee joined the JDC in campaigning to maintain free hospital accommodation for FP1 trainees. Members slept in tents at the Edinburgh ARM and in London to draw attention to the issue, and met some success when the NHS in Wales (which suffers from a shortage of junior doctors) agreed not to withdraw the accommodation.

Private practice

In the mid-1980s consultants engaged in private practice were becoming worried that the provident associations, particularly BUPA, were unreasonably holding down the level of the fees they could charge. The two provident associations BUPA and PPP dominated the market. There were few commercial insurers in the field and it was an unchanging world in which professional practice was conducted along traditional lines, with little external regulation. Within the BMA, private practitioners were represented by the Private Practice Committee (PPC), chaired from 1982 by John Chawner, a gynaecologist from North Wales working mainly in the NHS but, like many other maximum part-time consultants, interested in the private sector because it gave a degree of independence from the state. The PPC had a broad remit, also dealing with a large range of fees for medical services, reports and examinations that fell outside basic NHS or general medical service contracts, so it worked closely with the GPs and consultants committees.

In 1983 relations with BUPA improved, facilitated by the fact that a previous, highly respected senior member of BMA staff, Dr David Gullick, had become its medical director. The consultants' committee arrived at an 'understanding' with BUPA that consultants would not increase their fees so that premiums could be kept down to encourage private health insurance. But by 1985, in a period of high inflation, Bupa (as it became) had not raised its benefit levels. The consultants' committee felt betrayed and when Bupa refused to move, with the

PPC's backing, it broke the agreement. It recommended that consultants increase their fees, and a year later suggested a 10% increase where fees had not gone up since 1982.

This was clearly an unsatisfactory situation. Doctors appeared to be at the mercy of the provident associations, with no lever to persuade them to increase the benefit levels, which effectively determined what consultants could charge. The PPC, with input from the consultants' committee, set out to change the balance of power, setting up a working group to produce a schedule of fees for private procedures that the BMA might then recommend to members. It was a huge task, requiring an objective rationale for the level of fees and their relativities. Considerable data was collected on the range of procedures and as the work progressed David Gullick, now retired from Bupa, took on the painstaking task of reviewing data on fees charged for more than 1,000 private operations, and ascribing relative values to them. Schedules were then produced with input from specialty groups and the BMA published them in 1989 as *Private Consultant Work: BMA Guidelines.*

The response to the guidelines was good. They came with advice about responsible private practice, including the novel suggestion that consultants should be open with patients about their fees. And there were indications that the exercise was working when Bupa published its own revised schedule of benefits, based on the Office of Population Censuses and Surveys' classification of surgical procedures. It was always recognised that the guidance would need to be adjusted, and the committee, now known as the Private Practice and Professional Fees Committee (PPPFC), undertook an extensive revision, under a new chairman, David Pickersgill, a GP from Norfolk and later BMA Treasurer. The BMA's economic research unit looked at other countries with insurance-based healthcare, notably Australia where a major relative values study had been undertaken. Those values were compared with updated data on fees and a new schedule produced. For the first time the fees payable to surgeons and anaesthetists were separated (previously, to anaesthetists' chagrin, the fee was split at the discretion of the surgeon). The new guidelines were sent to all consultant members in August 1992.

But by then the world had changed. The commercial values championed by the Conservative government since 1979 had begun to impact on professional practice, with the liberalisation of advertising and the growing interest of competition authorities such as the Monopolies and Mergers Commission (MMC). Soon after the revised guidelines appeared, the Office of Fair Trading (OFT) referred them to the MMC, which announced that it would investigate a possible monopoly in the supply of private medical services. The formal process of defending the guidelines in written and oral submissions took considerable effort. The BMA argued that the publication of fees was in the public interest and was a useful source of information for patients. However, in a stern ruling in 1994 the MMC determined that the BMA was part of a 'complex monopoly' which constrained competition for medical services, and that the guidelines should not be published. The Secretary of State for Trade and Industry agreed and the BMA withdrew them and gave an undertaking not to advise members on private fees. Many felt the ruling to be perverse. The MMC's own data showed that 70% of the health market was influenced by the benefit schedules of Bupa and other provident associations, and also that consultants' fees had declined since 1986, and that increases in private medical insurance subscriptions had been caused predominantly by rising hospital costs.

The fees exercise did not markedly increase fees for specialists, but for a short time it took the initiative away from the provident associations. Since then, specialists have found it difficult to fight their corner in an increasingly commercial private healthcare market, dominated on the one hand by the two major insurers – Bupa and AXA PPP with 66% of subscriptions between them[19] – and by five large private hospital groups accounting for 77% of the market on the other. Since 1994 the fees of specialists have hardly increased, while the OFT has continued to raise questions about their role in restricting, distorting or preventing competition. In 2002–3 the practice of fee-setting by local groups of anaesthetists was challenged as anti-competitive and in 2012, following a market study[20] in which the role of anaesthetic groups was again questioned, the OFT referred the private healthcare market to the Competition Commission for investigation. The outcome could resolve some of the longstanding problems that have affected private practice, but could equally create new difficulties for specialists who wish to practise independently.

This exacting legal framework has forced the BMA to find new ways to counter some aggressive commercial tactics from insurers and private hospitals. In 1997 the PPPFC separated into a Private Practice Committee (PPC) looking after specialist practice, a Professional Fees Committee and a Forensic Medicine Committee.

---

[19] *Laing's Healthcare Market Review 2011–12*, table 3.14 p 206.
[20] Office of Fair Trading: *Private Healthcare Market Study*, April 2012.

Private practice

Led since the split by Derek Machin, a surgeon from Liverpool, the PPC has engaged closely with all the main players in the private sector, influencing developments where possible but more often challenging initiatives that might harm professional practice or individual practitioners. These have included, on the insurance side, incentive schemes for those who agree to limit fees, arbitrary reduction of benefits for particular procedures, and more recently the linking of recognition by the insurers (previously a matter of ascertaining competence) to an agreement over fee levels. On the hospitals side, facilities have been blocked for doctors in less lucrative specialties or who are thought to be also using the facilities of a rival group.

At the same time new models of provision are emerging, such as Circle, which proposes a 'partnership' with consultants. NHS Foundation Trusts are looking to work with private providers in developing their private patient facilities (though this is to be investigated by the Competition Commission). Meanwhile, since the financial downturn of 2008, the number of private policy holders has declined, and with medical indemnity costs still increasing, many consultants have found that keeping a small private practice is no longer viable.

Another aspect of the PPC's role is developing quality guidelines. In this there is scope for constructive dialogue with the insurers and hospital groups, and the PPC organises regular events to take forward new initiatives. With the appearance of new forms of regulation – both of practitioners and of premises – the PPC has had a major role in identifying problems and then working with regulators to find practical solutions. The introduction of clinical governance and appraisal in the NHS created a need to ensure that practitioners active in both sectors could be overseen without duplication of processes; the principles adopted here have then had to be extended to revalidation. Similarly much discussion has been necessary with the Care Quality Commission (CQC) (previously the Healthcare Commission) to adapt the complicated regulations about registering and inspecting providers of healthcare services to avoid onerous and disproportionate requirements (including substantial registration fees) being imposed upon individual private practitioners.

Professional fees

The BMA's work in negotiating and recommending fees for work outside doctors' main NHS contracts has also had to adapt to competition law. Following the Competition Act 1998, the BMA held discussions with the competition authorities and agreed to discontinue publishing certain suggested fees for services which can be provided by any doctor. Guidance on certain matters (such as fees for GP locums and deputising services, medico-legal fees and work for central government departments or under the collaborative arrangements with local authorities) is now generic, covering the factors to be taken into account by doctors in setting fees and giving guidance on relevant legislation. Nevertheless the Professional Fees Committee, led from 1997 by Peter Holden and from 2006 by John Canning, has had much to do: where fees are not determined by a national agreement, they are recommended for services that can only be provided by the patient's own GP or other attending doctor (such as fitness certificates for travel, employment, insurance or education purposes), and any agreements must be negotiated and regularly updated. It was agreed in 2003/4 that for most of these the annual increase would be linked to GPs' net NHS remuneration (leading to an initial increase in many fees). In maintaining these agreements the committee keeps channels of communication open with a wide range of organisations and departments. This enables problems to be raised, advice to be given, for example over the application of VAT to certain categories of medical work, and disputes to be pursued, as with the various organisations that provided medical services to the government following the privatisation of the Benefits Agency in 1996, and with insurance companies over the quality of insurance medical reports and the fees payable for them.

Forensic medicine

A small expert group, the Forensic Medicine Committee, chaired by George Fernie then by Michael Wilks, looks after the interests of forensic physicians, pathologists and psychiatrists, together with crematorium medical referees (to be replaced by medical examiners), and medically trained coroners. Before responsibility for prison medical services was transferred to PCTs, the committee was involved in lengthy negotiations to improve the pay of prison doctors. The BMA argued that responsibility for forensic medical services should be transferred from police authorities to the NHS, and worked with the Faculty of Forensic Medicine over discussions with Offender Health, a co-ordinating body between the DH and the Ministry of Justice.

The committee has also taken the lead within the BMA in contributing to the changes that have been made in death certification since the Brodrick Report *Deaths in the Community* in 1985. It also led the response to the consultation that followed the Shipman Inquiry and the subsequent reforms involving the appointment of medical examiners and the establishment of the national coroner service.

Retired members

The Association has a significant level of membership amongst retired doctors – over 11,000 in 2012. They obviously do not use many of the services provided for members still in employment, and they are no longer as involved in Council and national committee work as in the past. However, they often provide the officers for those divisions which are active, and they have a dedicated seat on Council. In 2003 following pressure from the Treasurer to do more for retired members and give them a voice in the Associations affairs, a retired members forum was established which meets annually and sends representatives to the ARM. In addition, annual lunches in each region are organised to enable retired members to meet and be briefed on current issues, whilst enjoying an informal opportunity to meet with past colleagues.

Chapter 7

The regulation of the medical profession

The BMA and the General Medical Council

Relations between the BMA and the GMC, which had been seriously compromised in the early-1970s when many doctors refused to pay the annual retention fee, had by 1982, been on an even keel for some years. However, the BMA started to become preoccupied about elections to the GMC and whether the BMA should continue to sponsor candidates and, if so, how. It was also concerned about the GMC's electoral scheme, the constitution of its council, the increase in the size of the annual retention fee and its procedures for disciplining doctors.

During the 1980s the major issue relating to the GMC came from a Bill, presented to the House of Commons in April 1984, by Nigel Spearing MP. Mr Spearing had noted that, while the GMC had the power to impose penalties on doctors found guilty of serious professional misconduct, it had no power to 'impose disciplinary measures for a lesser degree of culpability'.[1] His amendment to the Medical Act 1983 had been prompted by the widely publicised case of Alfie Winn whose GP had failed properly to examine or treat him during a home visit in January 1982 when he also behaved discourteously towards the patient and his parents. Alfie Winn died four days later of meningitis. Although the GMC was critical of the GP's conduct, it did not feel that it amounted to serious professional misconduct. The doctor was found guilty of serious professional misconduct when he appeared before the GMC on another matter shortly afterwards. This case was one of the first to call into question the medical profession's ability to deal with doctors who failed their patients. The BMA was alert to the implications of the case and the fact that the tide was turning when it came to the public's opinion of the profession. In May 1984 the BMA's GMC Working Party agreed that 'public interest in the matter of the disciplining of doctors by the GMC was unlikely to diminish'. Mr Spearing's proposed amendment ran out of parliamentary time, but the interest generated by both the case and the amendment presaged a

---

[1] Explanatory memorandum to the Bill to amend Section 36 of the Medical Act 1983.

maelstrom which, in the years ahead, would almost consume the GMC and test to its absolute limits the fitness for purpose of self regulation.

In the 1990s the GMC woke up to the uncomfortable truth that an approach to medical regulation which had changed little since 1858 was no longer good enough. As it admitted later: 'By the early 1990s it was clear that public attitudes and expectations were changing fast. Too many doctors were seen by the public as limited in their willingness and ability to communicate effectively; to act promptly to protect patients from poor practice; to be open about risks and unjustified variations in performance; and to admit to the errors that are an everyday occurrence in judgement-based clinical decision-making.'[2] In 1995, as the GMC started to modernise, it published *Good Medical Practice*, which listed the duties of a doctor and, by linking these duties to registration, set professionally-led medical regulation in a new direction.

An important innovation was the introduction of the GMC's performance procedures in 1997, following legislation laid two years before. For the first time, the GMC would not just be concerned with doctors whose performance or conduct had reached a crisis point, but would assume new powers allowing it to compel failing doctors to undergo retraining.[3] In more serious cases it could restrict a doctor's practice or suspend him or her from the register. The BMA supported these proposals, though with the proviso that the costs of retraining would not fall upon the individual doctor. Sir Donald Irvine, a former President of the GMC, has since written that the GMC's decision to go with what became the performance procedures of the 1990s was not a result of strongly proactive action: 'Such action had to be dragged out of the council, as many of the medical members glanced over their shoulders, perhaps quite understandably, at what their colleagues might say in other places, such as the craft committees of the BMA.'[4] In October 1995 and March 1996 BMA Council debated a number of concerns on job security, voluntary removal of one's name from the register and interim suspension. The BMA was keen to ensure that failing doctors were identified and helped. It recognised that the new procedures would close a loophole in the GMC's processes, but a

---

[2] Page 7 of *Changing Times, Changing Culture: A Summary Review of the Work of the GMC Since 1995*, GMC, 2000.
[3] These powers were contained in the Medical (Professional Performance) Act 1995.
[4] Sir Donald Irvine, *The Doctors' Tale: Professionalism and Public Trust*, 1993. Quoted in paragraph 24.4 of the Fifth Report of the Shipman Inquiry, *Safeguarding Patients: Lessons from the Past – Proposals for the Future*, December 2004.

potentially far-reaching change was being introduced and the BMA's job was to make sure that the changes would be fair.

In June 1998, a year after the performance procedures were introduced, the GMC found James Wisheart, John Roylance and Janardan Dhasmana, three doctors at the Bristol Royal Infirmary where 29 babies had died following complex heart surgery, guilty of serious professional misconduct. The hearing had received massive publicity with widely broadcast images of tiny coffins standing on the pavement outside the GMC's headquarters. This was the beginning of almost a decade of devastating accounts of medical malpractice, when detailed inquiries and reports would shine a spotlight into every aspect of medical regulation, leaving both public and doctors wondering how such terrible cases could have occurred. 'Looking back, it's a sorry tale', wrote Sir Donald Irvine. 'The stark reality is that from the beginning of 1858 right up to the early 1990s, statutory self-regulation as operated by the GMC failed the public and conscientious doctors.'[5] Leading BMA figures made no attempt to hide what had become a critical situation, refusing at the 1998 ARM to back a motion stating that self-regulation served the interests of doctors and patients very well. Laurence Buckman, who was to go on to chair the BMA's Working Party on the GMC, told the meeting that the motion was complacent and deceitful: 'Self-regulation has covered up when it should have exposed, has supported when it should have punished, has allowed poor practice to continue when it should have protected and re-educated unfortunate colleagues.'[6]

Increased access to healthcare information, a rise in consumer expectations and a general decline in deference to 'authority' throughout the 1980s and 1990s had led to, as the BMA put it in a document in 2008, the 'death of deference'.[7] This was not necessarily a bad thing. The report continued that 'alongside the aim of patient choice, the doctor-patient relationship is expected increasingly to move toward a two-way interaction with a growing emphasis on a partnership approach to deliver a negotiated outcome in respect of decisions concerning a

---

[5] Sir Donald Irvine, 2006 *A Short History of the General Medical Council* Medical Education 2006 40:202–211 (quoted on page v of *Good Doctors, Safer Patients*, a report by the Chief Medical Officer, 2006).
[6] Quoted in a BBC on-line article, Special Report, *Self regulation has failed*, published 8 July 1998.
[7] Page 5 *The Role of the Doctor – Building on the Past, Looking to the Future*, BMA Health Policy and Economic Research Unit, 2008.

patient's care.'[8] But it did mean that the dreadful cases about to emerge would do so to a critical press and a disillusioned public. The challenge for the BMA, in the context of these cases and almost overwhelming attacks on the integrity of the GMC, would be to decide how far it should go to defend self regulation and the GMC. It would have to make some hard decisions about the organisation whose establishment it had lobbied for in 1858. It would have to defend the profession in the face of unprecedented attacks and to reassure public, press and politicians that most doctors were principled and hard-working. It would also have to distance itself from deviant doctors: as Alexander (later Sir Alexander) Macara, the Chairman of Council, said in 1998: 'The BMA is not in the business of defending or protecting bad doctors. In fact we would prefer to get rid of them.'[9]

For 18 months between the Bristol case in June 1998 and the convictions in December 2000 of William Kerr[10] and Clifford Ayling[11] on charges of indecent assault, a number of alarming cases became public. The guilty findings of serious professional misconduct against the three doctors at Bristol Royal Infirmary were followed in September 1998 by the erasure from the medical register of the consultant gynaecologist Rodney Ledward for serious surgical errors and the arrest of Harold Shipman on suspicion of murder. A year later came the first indication of the Alder Hey Children's Hospital organ retention scandal.[12] Shipman's subsequent conviction in January 2000 of 15 murders was, in turn, followed in August by the striking off of Richard Neale[13]

---

[8] Page 5 *The Role of the Doctor – Building on the Past, Looking to the Future*, BMA Health Policy and Economic Research Unit, 2008.

[9] *Doctors must earn respect says BMA leader*, BBC News on-line 12 June 1998 (accessed 7 March 2011).

[10] William Kerr, a retired psychiatrist, was convicted of indecent assault on 18 December 2000. He was found to be suffering from cognitive impairment and discharged with his name being placed on the sex offenders' register for five years. In April 2001 he applied for voluntary erasure from the medical register and this request was granted in May 2003.

[11] Clifford Ayling was convicted of 12 counts of indecent assault relating to 10 of his female patients on 20 December 2000. An initial complaint about Ayling had been made to the GMC in March 1998 and the health authority had asked the GMC to expedite this in September 1998. He was subsequently erased from the medical register on 14 July 2001.

[12] The report into events at Alder Hey stated that more than 2000 organs had been removed without consent and many were never used for research purposes.

[13] Richard Neale, an obstetrician and gynaecologist, was erased from the medical register on 23 August 2000 having been found guilty of serious professional misconduct in relation to the treatment of 12 of his former patients. In 1985, Neale's name had been removed from the Medical Register of Ontario in Canada. Neale did not disclose this to either his next employer in the UK or to the GMC. The GMC was informed of Neale's erasure in Canada in 1985/6, but took no action.

and the conviction, in December, of both William Kerr and Clifford Ayling. These cases were particularly shocking for their severity, their volume, their co-incidence of timing – and for the fact that the doctors concerned had completely betrayed the trust placed in them. The role of the GMC gave cause for deep concern. Should it have acted earlier to curtail the actions of these doctors? Was its role to protect patients or doctors? Government hostility towards the institution was growing. Frank Dobson, when Secretary of State, said that the GMC should have erased from the medical register all three doctors involved in the Bristol case. His successor, Alan Milburn, was said to be 'incandescent with anger' at the GMC President, Sir Donald Irvine, after the Shipman case.[14] Opinions vary about the seriousness of health secretaries' intentions with regard to abolition of the GMC. Some who were involved at the time believed that the politicians were saying what the public wanted to hear and had no intention of taking the regulation of doctors under government control, but others maintain that these threats were credible and that the GMC escaped abolition by a whisker.

The BMA's attitude towards the regulatory body hardened and the March 2000 Council recorded a 'general feeling of deep disillusion with the current functioning of the GMC and in particular its leaders' reaction to media coverage following the conclusions of the Shipman trial'. Only two years earlier, at the 1998 ARM, the meeting had expressed its 'full confidence in the GMC, in its professional and lay members and in its disciplinary and performance review procedures'. However, by 2000, the Representative Body was in no mood to back the beleaguered GMC and resolved that it had 'no confidence in the GMC as currently constituted and functioning and calls upon it to initiate urgent reforms of its structures and functions in consultation with the profession.'

The BMA continued to draw attention to the trust that patients still had in their doctors, carefully drawing a distinction between the vast majority of doctors and the actions of aberrant individual members of the profession. Research commissioned from Mori by the BMA in March 2001 showed that doctors, more than members of any other profession, were most trusted to tell the truth with 89% of those questioned saying that they trusted doctors to tell the truth (up 2% on the results of research conducted a year earlier). 'Patients read about

---

[14] *BMJ* editorial, *The GMC: where now? It must put the public first but listen to doctors and be bold with its reform'*, *BMJ* 320: 1356 doi: 10.1136/bmj.320.7246.1356 (Published 20 May 2000).

high profile cases and they want action taken against individual bad doctors,' commented Ian Bogle, Chairman of Council. 'But they do not make false links between very different kinds of problems and they know that doctors are doing a good job in difficult circumstances . . . There is a danger that if you keep saying that public confidence has been eroded, it will become a self-fulfilling prophecy. That is not good for patients, doctors or the NHS.'[15]

Given the backdrop of unprecedented negative publicity received by the medical profession these survey results were remarkable. Besides showing that the public was capable of distinguishing between the majority of doctors and the deviant few, it also appeared to demonstrate that the public's respect for the profession of medicine, if not its deference, still endured. But the profession was not out of the woods: it still had to convince sceptical and influential critics that it could be trusted to regulate itself and deal firmly with failing doctors. The GMC was grappling with reforming its structures and its council, with its every move scrutinised by the government, media and the BMA, where a number of long debates about the GMC's future were held as the GMC's troubles deepened. In May 2000, after the embarrassing revelation that a doctor who had been struck off for racial abuse and neglect of patients had been elected to its council, the GMC had to promise to reform its election procedures. In December, it voted to reduce its size and increase lay membership, but this had led to objections that some specialties would not be properly represented. It came up with an idea for a GMC 'conference' of about 100 members who would then elect a council of about 25. Although this plan did not command the confidence of the BMA and others and would ultimately fail, it is important to recognise that it emerged from the GMC's realisation that radical proposals were needed to address its inadequate constitution and governance arrangements.[16] The BMA said that it welcomed 'the GMC's acknowledgement that there are some fundamental flaws within the organisation' and placed upon record its appreciation of the work that the GMC had undertaken to try to address these flaws. However, by the end of 2000, medical bodies were losing confidence in the GMC's ability to develop coherent plans for its future and in January 2001 the BMA, with the Joint Consultants Committee (JCC) and the Academy of Medical Royal Colleges (AoMRC), proposed

---

[15] *Medical scandals leave trust in doctors unshaken, The Guardian*, 7 May 2001.
[16] See the initial report of the GMC's Governance Working Group, dated 18 September 2000, and considered by BMA Council on 11 October 2000.

'11 principles of GMC governance'. These included the proposals that the council should have about 50 members and that the conference idea should be dropped. The GMC met in February and considered the BMA/JCC/AoMRC model but decided to stick with its original idea, though with some changes.

The Joint Consultants Committee was led at this time by James Johnson, who also chaired the BMA's Working Party on the GMC. With his energy, astuteness and straight talking, he made it clear to BMA Council in March 2001 that the GMC was pressing ahead with an unacceptable model. Some felt that the GMC needed to be saved from itself and work continued behind the scenes to persuade its leaders that, by clinging to their preferred model for reform, they were heading for confrontation with other professional bodies – and probably a government-imposed settlement. James Johnson told BMA Council in July 2001 that failure to reach a consensus on a new GMC structure would signal the end of self regulation. By this time the BMA and others had exerted sufficient pressure for the GMC to start edging its way towards accepting most of the 11 principles of governance.

The sticking point was the size of council. The GMC wanted 35 members; the 11 principles had proposed 50. During a long BMA Council debate in July 2001, James Johnson recommended that, since the GMC had given way on many other points, the BMA should settle with 35 members. Several members bridled, believing that this number was too large to be effective and too small to be representative. But they were also aware that professional unity was at stake. The BMA therefore agreed to a 35-member council and sent its Chairman, Ian Bogle, to negotiate further with the GMC concerning the operation of a restructured GMC.

In the wake of Shipman's conviction, the ARM's no confidence resolution and in the face of a hostile media and government the GMC, in 2000 and 2001, had come close to disarray and the BMA in general, and James Johnson in particular, played a significant part in helping to pull it back from the brink. Through a combination of brutal honesty, hard bargaining and persistence the GMC realised that it could not continue to advocate changes to its constitution that were unacceptable to the profession's representatives. A modernised GMC came into operation in July 2003. The size of the council went down from 104 to 35 and the proportion of lay members increased from 25% to 40%. It was now led by its new President, Sir Graeme Catto, a widely respected and well-liked expert in renal medicine who had taken over at the beginning of 2002. All of Sir Graeme's sharp intelligence and affability were needed over the next few years as, almost immediately, the new council faced the fall-out from some of the most searching, wide-ranging, detailed and forensic investigations ever undertaken in relation to any profession.[17] These were published between September 2004 and July 2005 and looked closely at the activities of a group of particularly notorious doctors and led to some radical proposals from the Labour government, determined to prove that it was willing to act on the recommendations of the various inquiries.

Meanwhile, considerable advances had been made in other ways to regulate doctors and check their performance. By the time that the government published its final set of proposals in the Health and Social Care Bill in November 2007, the regulatory and quality landscape had changed unrecognisably since the 1980s. In the late 1980s about £10 million was allocated each year to medical audit,[18] and medical audit advisory groups were established during the early 1990s. The Labour government introduced *Standards for Better Health*[19] a set of core standards that NHS services had to address and which were subject to inspection by the Healthcare Commission. The National Institute for Health and Clinical Excellence (NICE) was set up to produce guidance on the clinical and cost effectiveness of treatments and national service frameworks were issued. In 1995 the GMC had broken new ground with the publication of *Good Medical Practice,* setting out, for the first time, a code of practice which included the duties of a doctor. In addition, the GMC had, since the 1990s, initiated a series of reforms to its structure and procedures and had signed memoranda of understanding with bodies concerned with clinical governance in both the public and private healthcare systems. In 1999, the concept of 'clinical governance' was introduced which placed a 'duty of quality' on all providers of NHS services. The obligation to take part in clinical governance was embedded in the standard general medical services

[17] Ayling Inquiry *Independent Investigation into how the NHS Handled Allegations about the Conduct of Clifford Ayling.* Cm 6298 (TSO, September 2004). Neale Inquiry *Independent Investigation into how the NHS Handled Allegations about the Conduct of Richard Neale.* Cm 6315 (TSO, September 2004). Shipman Inquiry *Safeguarding Patients: Lessons from the Past – Proposals for the Future,* Cm 6390 (TSO, December 2004). Kerr/Haslam Inquiry *Independent Investigation into how the NHS Handled Allegations about the Conduct of William Kerr and Michael Haslam.* Cm 6640 (TSO July 2005).
[18] Figure from page 14 of *Good Doctors, Safer Patients,* DH, 2006.
[19] *Standards for Better Health,* Department of Health, 21 July 2004.

contract for GPs in April 2005 and in the standard consultant contract in June 2005. Finally, in April 2001, the National Clinical Assessment Service was set up to support and advise the NHS, and doctors, and to help deal with failing doctors.

In November 2006 The BMA referred to these changes when it responded to the Chief Medical Officer for England's report, *Good Doctors, Safer Patients,*[20] emphasising that the medical profession had become one of the most regulated in the country. The CMO's report made some controversial proposals: the move from the criminal to the civil standard of proof when adjudicating upon concerns about a doctor's performance, health or conduct; the creation of local GMC 'affiliates', who should be authorised to deal with some fitness to practise cases locally; the creation of a body separate from the GMC to adjudicate in fitness to practise cases; the introduction of 'student registration' with the GMC; and the proposal that appointments to the GMC should be made by the Public Appointments Commission. The report also had much to say on revalidation (*see section below*).

In its comprehensive response to *Good Doctors, Safer Patients* the BMA rejected outright the proposals to change the standard of proof and to move the GMC's adjudication function to another body. It also argued that, in order to maintain professional credibility, the medical members of the GMC had to be elected by the profession. These two proposals caused the greatest consternation to the BMA and its members, and appeared to signal the end of professional self-regulation. Yet despite the BMA's protests, these proposals and others emerged once again in the white paper, *Trust, Assurance and Safety – The Regulation of Health Professionals in the 21st Century'*, published in February 2007.[21]

The ARM in 2007 reacted with alarm, passing a motion demanding that medical members of the GMC must be in a majority and elected by the profession and that the GMC President must be a doctor elected by the Council. If these criteria were not applied the profession 'will decline to meet the cost of medical regulation'. The following year a similar sentiment was passed as a reference, though the ARM did pull back from demanding that the new GMC, being 'neither led nor controlled by the profession' should be funded by government.

[20] *Good Doctors, Safer Patients* DH, 2006.
[21] *Trust, Assurance and Safety – The Regulation of Health Professionals in the 21st Century,* presented to Parliament by the Secretary of State for Health by command of Her Majesty, February 2007.

Doctors felt strongly that, as they no longer had any way of electing their peers to the GMC, they should no longer be expected to pay for the GMC's activities. It took some persuasive speeches to convince the Representative Body that the profession must pay for its regulatory body unless it wanted to see its activities subsumed into government machinery.

The implications of the 2007 white paper were brought to the attention of the profession by a letter to all members of the BMA from the Chairman of Council, Hamish Meldrum, in September 2007: 'Many of these changes are very far reaching and, when taken together, could add up to the effective loss of professionally-led medical regulation.' The question was: what was the BMA going to do about them? One difficulty was the position taken by the GMC itself which, with a reforming zeal, had expressed strong support for the white paper. Dr Meldrum had said in his letter to the profession that the BMA would do all that it could 'to mitigate the effects of this assault on our profession' and this included lobbying to ensure the continuation of election to the GMC, the maintenance of the criminal standard of proof, and questioning the need for a separate adjudicator. The GMC, however, was in favour of moving to the civil standard of proof and was already consulting on this change. It had welcomed the publication of the Health and Social Care Bill, published on 16 November 2007, as a step towards implementation of the proposals in *Trust, Assurance and Safety*. It had also emphasised that the major changes being proposed in the bill should engender patient trust, together with confidence among doctors that they were being treated fairly.[22] From the GMC's reaction to the white paper and subsequent bill it was felt that the BMA could not expect support from the regulatory body as it fought to maintain what it saw as the essentials of professional self-regulation.

From autumn 2007 until the 2008 Health and Social Care Act received Royal Assent in July of that year, the BMA lobbied hard, holding meetings with Department of Health officials, peers and MPs, issuing parliamentary briefings and seeking alliances with other organisations. The Chairman of Council, Hamish Meldrum, and Chairman of the GMC Working Party, Laurence Buckman, also appeared before the Public Bill Committee in January 2008 to express the BMA's deep reservations about many aspects of the bill. In briefings the BMA

---

[22] Paper presented to GMC Council on 5 December 2007, entitled *Taking Forward the White Paper: The Health and Social Care Bill* (page 2). Accessed on GMC's website on 16 March 2011.

emphasised that a regulatory system should protect patients and support doctors with 'performance difficulties'. It admitted that some improvements to regulation were needed, but held that any reform must not only be practicable but also have the confidence of both public and doctors that it would be fair and just.

BMA members expressed particularly strong opposition to the requirement for all the health professional regulatory bodies and the proposed Office of the Health Professions Adjudicator (the new body to adjudicate on fitness to practise cases) to use the civil standard of proof (the balance of probabilities) in fitness to practise proceedings. The GMC was using the criminal standard (beyond reasonable doubt) but wanted to move to the civil standard on the grounds that its fitness to practise panels were not criminal courts applying the criminal law and that it would allow panels to be more flexible.[23] The BMA did not believe that a 'flexible approach' would be fair to doctors at all, and issued a detailed brief to peers on the bill's second reading in the Lords in March 2008. The BMA's main point was that it would be unjust to remove a doctor's livelihood based on the lower standard of proof. It also argued (as did the Medical Defence Union) that the criminal standard gave greater clarity. The BMA reminded peers that any restriction on practice, even under limited conditions, could seriously affect a doctor's career and his or her full-time employment.

Leaving aside the legal points and the flexibility of the proposed new standard, many doctors believed that the change would make it easier to prove allegations of impairment of fitness to practise. The 2008 ARM showed its concern by passing two resolutions. The first opposed the introduction of a civil standard of proof 'as it could lead to the victimisation of doctors.' The second warned the UK government that introducing a civil standard would lead to a more defensive style of medical practice, a huge increase in the costs of the UK health service (with clinicians being less willing to take or accept risk), a 'very likely' increase in referrals to secondary care, and a 'likely' increase in unnecessary investigations and prescribing.' These points about defensive medicine were made to MPs and peers in parliamentary briefings, as were related arguments that doctors could be less willing to admit mistakes (by them or their colleagues) if they thought that the consequences of doing so would not result in fair and proportionate treatment.

---

[23] GMC Parliamentary briefing for the Health and Social Care Bill, second reading, House of Commons – 26 November 2007.

Another controversial proposal in the bill was the creation of the Office of the Health Professions Adjudicator (OHPA). This body was expected to take over the adjudication of fitness to practise cases from, initially, the GMC and the General Optical Council and would eventually adjudicate on all fitness to practise cases for all healthcare professionals. There was sufficient unease about the GMC's current fitness to practise arrangements expressed in ARM and conference resolutions for the BMA not to oppose the proposal, but it did question the structure of the new body, its method of working and funding. It also signalled that the proposed changes mostly reflected the way the GMC had been functioning since 2004 when it had separated its investigation and adjudication functions. The BMA's main priority with regard to OHPA was, of course, to ensure that its operation guaranteed robust and fair adjudication processes for doctors.

The medical majority on the General Medical Council was also under threat as the bill proposed, as a minimum, equal numbers of medical and non-medical members. This was reflected in a piece of legislation which was consulted upon in early 2008.[24] The BMA had long argued that a medical majority, which did not need to be large, was essential in order to maintain the profession's confidence in its regulator. In its response to the 2008 Miscellaneous Amendments Order, the BMA reiterated that electing medical members to the GMC also ensured credibility. Further concerns came from a proposal that would allow the Privy Council to appoint the GMC's chair and treasurer. 'Doctors will begin to wonder why they will be expected to pay for something to which they cannot elect, which will not have a medical majority and which cannot elect its own officers', was the BMA's response. The GMC was also concerned on this issue: it was advised that the wording in the order allowed for the two positions to be either elected or appointed, and it received written assurances from the Department that the subsequent constitution order would deliver the GMC's preferred model.[25] Nevertheless, the profession's right to elect the GMC's medical members would be replaced by appointment by the Privy Council with the process being run by the Appointments Commission.

The BMA fought hard against the changes to the GMC's constitution and to the standard of proof, but it ultimately failed. The government had been resolute and the two main opposition parties gave little or no support to the BMA's position. Once the legislation had

---

[24] Healthcare and Associated Professions (Miscellaneous Amendments) Order 2008.

[25] Paper to GMC Council, 5 February 2008 on governance (paragraphs 23–26).

been passed there was little more that the BMA could do other than to encourage doctors to put their names forward to be considered as one of the 12 medical council members (they were appointed for a four year term of office beginning in January 2009), and to monitor fitness to practise cases in the context of the changed standard of proof.

One of the central planks of the bill had been the creation of the OHPA but this did not survive the incoming coalition's 'bonfire of the quangos'. In August 2010 a consultation document detailed 'fundamental' changes at the GMC, both with regard to its governance and its fitness to practise procedures, since the publication of the fifth report of the Shipman inquiry.[26] It suggested that the GMC could improve its procedures so that the OHPA would no longer be needed.[27] The BMA and others were asked for their views on three options: proceed with the OHPA as planned; draw back from the OHPA and improve existing processes at the GMC; or draw back from the OHPA and carry on as before. The BMA had been impartial about the establishment of OHPA and decided to support the second option. This led to the establishment of the Medical Practitioners Tribunal Service (MPTS) in June 2012. The service adjudicates in fitness to practise cases and has the power to remove doctors from the medical register or restrict their practice. It is accountable to Parliament and operates separately from the GMC, although the GMC continues to investigate and prosecute cases. The BMA backed the new service as long as it maintained public confidence in medical regulation and acted in a way which was fair and proportionate towards doctors. The BMA was worried, though, that fitness to practise hearings were no longer to be held in London, but all in the Tribunal's Manchester office. It thought that this would cause difficulties for doctors in the south of the country and also questioned how proceedings could be speeded up if the rooms used for hearings in London were to be closed.

Towards the middle of 2008, another battleground had opened up, this time over the GMC's decision to withdraw the exemption from payment of the annual retention fee (ARF) for doctors over the age of 65 from 1 November that year. Until then, doctors over the age of 65 had been permitted to remain on the medical register without the

---

[26] Page 11 of *Fitness to Practise Adjudication for Health Professionals: Assessing Different Mechanisms for Delivery. A Paper for Consultation*. Department of Health, 9 August 2010.

[27] 'Page 18 of *Fitness to Practise Adjudication for Health Professionals: Assessing Different Mechanisms for Delivery. A paper for Consultation*. Department of Health, 9 August 2010.

payment of the fee and, although many had ceased to practise, they attached great importance to remaining on the medical register as a mark of their continued membership of the profession. Therefore, the news that their names would be removed from the medical register if they did not pay the fee came as a shock, and some regarded it as tantamount to being 'struck off'. The GMC had taken the action on the advice of leading counsel that the maintenance of the exemption was contrary to age discrimination legislation. The BMA's retired members were furious and demanded that the GMC be challenged on this matter, pointing out that they had paid a professional lifetime's fees to the GMC. The BMA had received legal advice that a challenge to the GMC was unlikely to be successful, but took action anyway as feelings among retired doctors were running high and it wished to demonstrate to them that it took their views seriously. It pressed ahead with an application for judicial review of the GMC's decision, which was duly denied in October 2008 when the High Court upheld the GMC's decision as lawful. But, as the Chairman of Council, Hamish Meldrum, said, 'We felt it necessary to pursue this case on behalf of the thousands of retired doctors who have given years of service to the NHS and felt let down by the changes to the ARF by the GMC.'

By 2011, it appeared that professional self regulation was going to survive. Despite many changes, not all of them welcome, the central principle that the medical profession should regulate its own had been maintained and the GMC had survived, albeit fundamentally altered.[28] The BMA's position throughout had been to emphasise that most doctors were diligent and hard-working and presented no threat, while at the same time making it clear that there could be no hiding place for doctors who deviated from providing good medical practice. The BMA put out this message consistently and, judging from successive surveys, patient confidence in doctors continued to be high. At the same time, the BMA had had to defend rigorously the principle of professional self regulation, notwithstanding serious doubts about the GMC's fitness for purpose. At the end of a decade of turbulence, the BMA could look back with some equanimity on past events. There would always be tensions between doctors' professional and regulatory bodies, but relations between the two were back on an even keel. The GMC had been

---

[28] The size of the GMC's Council had been reduced in 2009 to 24 members, with equality of lay and medical members, all appointed by the NHS Appointments Commission, and was further reduced to 12 (6 medical and 6 lay) from January 2013.

transformed and the BMA could take credit for fighting for the rights of doctors to regulate themselves.

Revalidation

The future of the specialist register and the possibility of a comparable generalist register for GPs was the subject of a letter in July 1998 from the President of the General Medical Council, Sir Donald Irvine, to the Chairman of BMA Council, Ian Bogle. Enclosed was an earlier letter from Sir Donald to the Chairman of the Academy of Medical Royal Colleges, Professor Rodney MacSween, in which Sir Donald had raised two significant questions: 'Can it be sufficient . . . that a doctor, once admitted to the specialist register, remains on it indefinitely, subject only to remaining on the medical register itself? Alternatively, what assurance does the specialist register offer patients and employers other than that, at a point in time, the doctor, perhaps many years before, gained a CCST or held a consultant appointment? The answer is none, in the present form.'[29] His letter had gone on to suggest that a doctor's continuation on the specialist register should be conditional on revalidation at, say, five year intervals. This revalidation might depend on some quality assurance arrangements made by the appropriate college or colleges. Thus began 14 years of debate on revalidation.

The idea of doctors having to reaccredit or revalidate was not new. In 1975 the Merrison Committee[30] had discussed the fact that continued registration with the GMC did not guarantee competence. The committee believed that this matter was outside its terms of reference and passed the information to a BMA committee under the Chairmanship of Sir Anthony Alment, a distinguished obstetrician, who would go on to become honorary secretary and then president of the Royal College of Obstetricians and Gynaecologists.[31] His report in 1976 concluded that there was no evidence to justify compulsory re-licensure, but it recommended that doctors should be encouraged to keep up to date voluntarily.[32] Nearly two decades later, in

---

[29] Letter dated 15 July 1998 to Ian Bogle from Sir Donald Irvine and letter dated 30 June 1998 to Professor Rodney MacSween from Sir Donald Irvine.
[30] The Merrison Committee reported in 1975 and presented a number of proposals on registration, education and fitness to practise.
[31] Committee of Inquiry set up for the medical profession in the United Kingdom chaired by Sir Anthony Alment.
[32] *Competence to Practise*, report of a committee chaired by Sir Anthony Alment, published 1976.

1995, the GMSC proposed reaccreditation but, although welcomed by the LMC Conference, it foundered due to lack of government funding.

Sir Donald Irvine's 1998 proposals were made in the aftermath of the GMC's hearings into the conduct of the doctors involved in paediatric cardiac surgery at the Bristol Royal Infirmary and his letter was debated by BMA Council on 22 July 1998. Council was receptive, but wanted to know more; it agreed that the Chairman of Council should meet Sir Donald to discuss revalidation. As the years passed and the original proposals were refined, developed, consulted upon, nearly implemented, then withdrawn and reconsidered, the BMA's position remained remarkably consistent with its first reaction: supportive of the principles, but questioning how revalidation would work in practice.

On 27 August 1998 a meeting of the leaders of the profession took place and seven BMA representatives attended. The GMC's press release after the meeting confirmed that consultants and GPs had agreed that they 'should be prepared to demonstrate to people using their professional services that they are right up-to-date and providing a good standard of patient care'.[33] The press release also noted that 'as far as possible use should be made of information already available and used for other purposes'. In October BMA Council considered a report of that meeting and members agreed that a number of questions had to be answered on the practical aspects of revalidation's introduction and operation before proceeding further. Later, in February 1999, the GMC held a special conference and received 'strong backing to introduce a system of revalidation for all registered doctors'.[34] Ian Bogle, Chairman of Council, said in a press statement that the medical profession had sent out a clear message: 'That message is that doctors want to provide the highest possible standards of care for all their patients and that they are committed to showing that, if they are on the register of the GMC, it means that they are competent to practise.'

The BMA had nailed its colours to the mast and it is difficult to see what other line it could have taken at this early stage in the development of the proposals when the tragedy of the events at the Bristol Royal Infirmary was fresh in the public's mind. Indeed, its support for

---

[33] GMC news release, *GMC hosts meeting to discuss Specialist and Generalist Registration*, issued 27 August 1998.
[34] BMA press statement: *BMA gives strong backing to revalidation*, issued 10 February 1999.

the principles never wavered, but the time would come when principles would develop into practicalities, details would begin to emerge – and doctors would start to have reservations about how revalidation would affect their working lives and their relationships with patients. After the February 1999 conference the March BMA Council had a long debate, during which members asked searching questions about the need for revalidation, how it would work for doctors not on the specialist register (junior, career grade and retired doctors), and the effectiveness of the procedures and resources proposed. A few months later, at the 1999 ARM, more uncertainties surfaced. One resolution called for the revalidation process to 'take doctors' working environments into account.' Another expressed 'considerable concerns' over the cost in time and resources, the lack of clearly defined extra funding, and the 'lack of a clear ability of the GMC or the colleges to deliver on its proposals'. The motion called on Council to 'ensure that revalidation is not bought at doctors' expense.'

In May 2000 the GMC put its proposals out to consultation.[35] Just before the GMC's document was published, BMA Council committed to introducing a system of regularly proving to the public that they are fit to practise and that patients are safe in their hands. Both the Chairman of Council, Ian Bogle, and the Chairman of the BMA's Working Party on the GMC, James Johnson, emphasised the need for a system that was simple and workable, would identify problems where they existed and would be concerned with patient safety. Mr Johnson said clearly: 'The BMA is absolutely supportive of the concept of revalidation, but it has to be do-able.' Unfortunately, the proposals did not appear to be so.

The consultation document described a three-stage process. First, doctors would describe in a 'revalidation folder' their practice which would contain information to show how well they were practising. This folder would be reviewed regularly (probably annually), with any deficiencies identified and remedial action taken. For doctors working in the NHS, this would be done through appraisal. Then every five years the folders would be assessed independently by a 'revalidation group', of registered doctors and lay people. This group would have to recommend to the GMC whether or not the doctor remained fit to practise. The GMC would usually revalidate the registration but, in a minority of cases, would investigate the doctor's fitness to practise.

---

[35] *Revalidating Doctors: Ensuring Standards, Securing the Future*, General Medical Council, 2000.

The BMA considered the proposals at length and after internal consultation produced an 18-page response in September 2000. The BMA continued to support the concept of revalidation, but had several criticisms, including the lack of costings. It also felt that it was unrealistic to make doctors show that 'the competence which secured their initial registration is maintained throughout their professional life',[36] arguing that, for example, orthopaedic surgeons would not be expected to show that they still had a graduate level of competence in managing diabetes. The BMA thought that the process outlined would be bureaucratic and time intensive and the function of the 'revalidation folder' was unclear. And it had serious reservations about the proposal to include comments from patients and colleagues within the folder.

The GMC spent much of the following year, 2001, considering the responses, testing its proposals with pilot schemes and undertaking a cost benefit analysis. It also had to deal with some tough questioning from the BMA about the practicalities. Formal appraisal for NHS consultants began in April 2001 (GPs started a year later) and, on 4 April 2001, the Chairman of the Central Consultants and Specialists Committee (CCSC), Peter Hawker, wrote to Sir Donald Irvine to advise him that, at its meeting on 22 March 2001, the CCSC 'had reiterated its support for the appraisal process as the essential mechanism for senior hospital doctors to demonstrate their continuing competence, and regretted that the GMC did not seem to be accepting their view. Fears were expressed that if the GMC's revalidation process were introduced requiring additional layers of information gathering and assessment it would fail.'[37] Sir Donald assured Dr Hawker in a letter dated 25 May 2001 that 'I confirm our agreement with your statement that for senior hospital doctors working in the NHS the requirements of revalidation should be met for the most part by the outputs of appraisal. We are as keen as you are to avoid complexity and duplication; and we wish to work with the BMA and the Departments of Health to achieve this in practice.'[38] Letters continued to be exchanged between the BMA and the GMC and a number of meetings were held. But the BMA remained

---

[36] Page 4, paragraph 5 of *Revalidating Doctors: Ensuring Standards, Securing the Future*, General Medical Council, 2000.

[37] Letter dated 4 April 2001 to Sir Donald Irvine, President of the General Medical Council, from Peter Hawker, Chairman of the Central Consultants and Specialists Committee.

[38] Letter dated 25 May 2001 to Peter Hawker, Chairman of the Central Consultants and Specialists Committee from Sir Donald Irvine, President of the General Medical Council.

deeply concerned about whether revalidation could be made to work and in October the Chairman of BMA Council told the President of the GMC that BMA Council members had expressed their 'deepest reservations yet on the proposals'. He added: 'this cannot convey the sense of frustration and anxiety that was apparent during two heated debates when the conduct of the GMC itself came under attack.'[39] A high-level meeting was held soon after and, when the Chairman of Council reported back to the December 2001 Council, members were pleased to see that 'encouraging progress' had been made.

Significantly, the link between appraisal and revalidation had been agreed and an 'historic collaboration' was announced in April 2002 between the GMC and the Department of Health which would support the introduction of appraisal and revalidation for all doctors.[40] The material published at this time emphasised that appraisal and revalidation were separate processes with separate outcomes, but would be based largely on the same sources of information, with appraisal summaries informing revalidation. Doctors' leaders were quoted as endorsing this approach: the Chairman of BMA Council, Ian Bogle, said: 'revalidation is an important part of doctors' accountability to patients and the wider public. By building revalidation onto the process of appraisal, doctors will also gain from the process. They will have both a regular review of their own professional development and confirmation of their professional good standing.'[41] That year the BMA's GPs committee collaborated with the Royal College of General Practitioners to produce *Good Medical Practice for General Practitioners*[42] to guide GPs on the expectations of their peers and the public on standards of care and behaviour.

Most now agreed that it was sensible to link appraisal and revalidation, but doubts about the quality of the appraisal remained. Two years later, in September 2002, Dr Bogle wrote to the President of the GMC, Sir Graeme Catto, that a recent meeting between them had made it clear that the introduction of robust appraisal mechanisms had been, at best, inconsistent throughout the country. For general

---

[39] Letter dated 12 October 2001 to Sir Donald Irvine, President of the General Medical Council, from Ian Bogle, Chairman of BMA Council.

[40] Joint GMC/Department of Health press release issued in April 2002 entitled *Appraisal and Revalidation: Department of Health and General Medical Council Join Forces*.

[41] Quotation from information sent to doctors in April 2002 headed *Appraisal and Revalidation: Department of Health and General Medical Council Join Forces*.

[42] *Good Medical Practice for General Practitioners*, BMA/RCGP September 2002.

practice there were still insufficient resources to support appraisal and no arrangements in place for non-principals. He added: 'We are agreed that the introduction of a successful revalidation process depends, for the majority of doctors, on the foundation of a robust and effectively implemented appraisal system and we are concerned that unless the current gaps in the appraisal system are addressed, revalidation may falter.'[43] Dr Bogle also referred to a recent study that had shown that for most of the cases examined, the appraisal summary did not provide sufficient information to recommend whether a doctor should be revalidated or not.[44] The GMC was aware of this problem and Sir Graeme replied that improving the quality of appraisal summaries for all doctors was a priority, and that the GMC would undertake pilot studies before the first formal revalidations were carried out.[45]

The GMC was clearly confident that basing revalidation on appraisal for the majority of doctors would work because in April 2003 it issued detailed information to doctors on how revalidation would operate in a booklet *A Licence to Practise and Revalidation*.[46] This advised that there would be two routes to revalidation: the 'appraisal route' and the 'independent route'. Those taking the appraisal route were advised that if they were working within a managed system, already subject to annual appraisal, and expected to remain in that environment, the GMC suggested that the appraisal route would be the most practical and convenient route for them. Doctors should not have to collect any data for revalidation over and above that which they would be required to record and keep for appraisal, and other local systems.[47] Sir Graeme Catto was even clearer in his covering letter: 'My message is therefore straightforward. Make appraisal work for you, and your licence to practise will be secure.[48]

Under the GMC's original proposals, a 'revalidation group' was to examine the doctor's revalidation folder and then recommend to the GMC whether the doctor remained fit to practise. By the time that the information booklet was published the idea of the revalidation group had been dropped. Instead, it appeared that doctors would have to

---

[43] Letter dated 24 September 2002 to Sir Graeme Catto from Ian Bogle.

[44] This referred to the GMC's second revalidation pilot study, undertaken by its Revalidation Technical Group, which reported in September 2002.

[45] Letter dated 26 September 2002 to Ian Bogle from Sir Graeme Catto.

[46] *A Licence to Practise and Revalidation*, GMC, April 2003.

[47] Page 8 of *A Licence to Practise and Revalidation*, GMC, April 2003.

[48] Letter dated April 2003 from Sir Graeme Catto sent to all doctors with *A Licence to Practise and Revalidation*, GMC, April 2003.

communicate directly with the GMC. The profession, having become accustomed to the proposals for revalidation as originally put forward, was feeling uneasy at these changes and the 2004 ARM urged the GMC, 'in view of deepening anxieties over its wavering approach to revalidation, to promote greater clarity in terms of the revalidating process and the relationship between revalidation and annual appraisal.'

There was little opportunity for the GMC to provide the 'greater clarity' that was sought before the whole process was brought clattering to a halt in December 2004 when the report of the fifth Shipman Inquiry criticised the proposals so comprehensively that it was clear to all concerned that they could not possibly be implemented as they stood. The report stated that ' . . . if the GMC intends that revalidation should give the public a reassurance of real, as opposed to illusory, value it must accept that its present proposals are not adequate and must develop a system of revalidation which, at its first stage, entails a summative evaluation of each individual doctor's fitness to practise.'[49]

Within days the Department of Health halted the plans for revalidation and asked the Chief Medical Officer for England, Sir Liam Donaldson, to review all matters relating to doctors' performance raised in the report. James Johnson, Chairman of BMA Council, said: 'We can understand why it's necessary to do this, as we wouldn't want to see two different forms of revalidation. But we would want the delay to be a short one. It is important both doctors and patients have confidence in the revalidation system and that includes whether it is workable.'[50] His views were echoed in a resolution from the 2005 ARM that called for the revalidation process to be robust, practical and affordable and would not detract from delivery of patient care. It also called for it to be developed in consultation with interested and relevant professional groups. It believed that appraisal and clinical governance could be adapted to inform revalidation, and expressed serious concerns over diverting time and resources away from direct patient care to any revalidation process without an evidence base to justify it.

The Chief Medical Officer published his report in 2006[51] and drew attention to the meaning of revalidation as defined in an amendment to the Medical Act 1983: 'the evaluation of a medical practitioner's

---

[49] Paragraph 26.205 of the fifth report of the Shipman Inquiry (December 2004).

[50] Quotation from BBC News On-line article, *Doctor testing plans face review*, 16 December 2004 (accessed 29 March 2011).

[51] Chief Medical Officer. *Good Doctors, Safer Patients. Proposals to Strengthen the System to Assure and Improve the Performance of Doctors and to Protect the Safety of Patients.* London: DoH, 2006.

fitness to practise'.[52] He agreed with Dame Janet Smith, Chair of the Shipman Inquiry, when he said that 'revalidation as proposed by the General Medical Council fails to provide an objective evaluation, because it is based largely on the current model of NHS appraisal. Furthermore, the term revalidation does not distinguish between doctors working independently in specialist areas of practice and others: rather it assumes that an appraisal process will be sufficiently sophisticated to take account of this fundamental difference.'[53] He went on to say that the terms 're-licensure' and 're-certification' were more meaningful as the first related to the renewal of full registration and the second to renewal of a doctor's specialist certification; 'revalidation' could remain as an umbrella term for the two processes, and he made recommendations to this effect. He also recommended the creation of a medically qualified GMC 'affiliate' within each organisation or group of organisations providing healthcare.[54] The affiliate would be authorised to deal locally with some fitness to practise cases and to refer the more serious ones to the GMC.

The BMA's immediate reaction was guarded, particularly on the potential for the medical royal colleges to have a major role in assessing doctors' ability to remain on the specialist and GP registers. 'Very careful consideration and negotiation will be needed about how this would happen,' said the Chairman of Council, James Johnson. He also raised questions about the GMC affiliates, saying that, as it would place a huge responsibility on one person, it was unlikely many people would want to take on such a burden.

There was a long consultation within the BMA on the CMO's proposals and a response was submitted in November 2006. The BMA said that the affiliate function should not be for individuals: 'the idea of creating a single affiliate and lay pairing in each institution is half-hearted, impractical and an ineffective use of resources. It would create the wrong culture, offer the prospect of patronage and capricious threat to individual doctors and lead to a more defensive and less open

[52] In December 2002, the Medical Act 1983 was amended by the addition of new sections 29A to 29J. Revalidation was defined in the Act as an 'evaluation of a medical practitioner's fitness to practise'.
[53] Paragraph 65 of Chief Medical Officer. *Good Doctors, Safer Patients. Proposals to Strengthen the System to Assure and Improve the Performance of Doctors and to Protect the Safety of Patients.* London: DoH, 2006.
[54] Recommendation 2 in Chief Medical Officer. *Good Doctors, Safer Patients. Proposals to Strengthen the System to Assure and Improve the Performance of Doctors and to Protect the Safety of Patients.* London: DoH, 2006.

workplace.' The BMA also noted that because revalidation would apply to all doctors (not just those on specialist registers), it should be a single process applied equitably to all doctors. It pointed out that there were doctors with significant responsibilities not on the specialist register, but who would require revalidation. The BMA said that the recertification process would duplicate a great deal of the appraisal process, and that 'no clear benefits appear to arise from creating these two similar functions and we believe that the profession and the public will be confused by them'.

The two-stage process was in the white paper *Trust, Assurance and Safety* published in February 2007.[55] But it had been scrapped by the time that the GMC's seminal consultation document *Revalidation: The Way Ahead* was published in March 2010[56]: 'We have concluded that revalidation will be simpler, more effective and more efficient if it operates as a single set of processes rather than as the two separate strands of relicensing and recertification that were originally envisaged.'[57] Instead, revalidation 'will be based on a local evaluation of doctors' performance against national generic and specialty standards approved by the GMC.'[58]

Between the publication of *Trust, Assurance and Safety* and the launch of the consultation in March 2010, the BMA had been keeping members up to date on the development of proposals for revalidation in a series of quarterly 'Revalidation updates', which began in May 2009, and via regular articles in *BMA News*. Also, discussions were taking place on how the BMA could help doctors to prepare for revalidation. The CCSC and the Staff and Associate Specialists Committee (SASC) produced guidance setting out the likely assessment methods and how consultants and staff and associate doctors could meet the requirements of revalidation. *BMJ Learning* also gave advice on how to prepare for revalidation. The BMA regularly met the English Department of Health's revalidation support team and the emerging role of the 'responsible officer' (the proposed GMC affiliate had been abandoned) became a matter for concern: the BMA believed that medical directors should be responsible for this function but had major reservations about whether PCT medical directors would have the time

[55] *Trust, Assurance and Safety – the Regulation of Health Professionals in the 21st Century*, presented to Parliament by the Secretary of State for Health by command of Her Majesty, February 2007.
[56] *Revalidation: The Way Ahead – Consultation Document*, GMC, 1 March 2010.
[57] Paragraph 44 of *The Way Ahead – Consultation Document*, GMC, 1 March 2010.
[58] Paragraph 54 of *The Way Ahead – Consultation Document*, GMC, 1 March 2010.

to do so. Eventually, guidance on the role of responsible officers was strengthened, and doctors were given the option of having their revalidation overseen by an alternative officer once mediation procedures had taken place.

Discussions within the BMA on revalidation had resulted in the publication of its seven principles on 17 March 2010:

'1. There must be a clear mechanism for dealing with conflicts of interest with responsible officers, including an appeals process with an independent scrutineer.

2. Remediation must be fully funded to ensure equality across branches of practice.

3. Medical royal college standards for recertification must be equitable, fair and proportionate.

4. Knowledge tests should form no part in assessing fitness to practise, whether as part of the GMC's generic standards for relicensing or in college standards for recertification; any multisource feedback system must be validated.

5. The introduction of revalidation must be cost-effective and not put undue strain on the NHS.

6. Pilots must run independently and be fully evaluated, with the results published and fed into subsequent pilot stages.

7. There must be equality of opportunity to revalidate.'

These principles would inform the BMA's response to *The Way Ahead* consultation, which was made public on 28 May 2010. The BMA was pleased that the dual process of 'relicensure' and 'recertification' had been discarded, but found there was little else to like in the consultation document. Its press statement on the response said: 'Doctors' leaders today called on the General Medical Council (GMC) to go back to the drawing board and rethink the revalidation proposals for all UK doctors.' Hamish Meldrum, the Chairman of Council, was quoted as stating that the BMA would resist 'overly bureaucratic and cumbersome' proposals that would take doctors away from treating patients: 'It is essential that any system we have in place is fair for *all* doctors across the board,' he said.

The BMA submitted a 26 page response and its main concerns were as follows:

- Many of the specialist standards set by the medical royal colleges were too complex. The GMC would have to be proactive in revising many of these standards to ensure that the process would be proportionate and workable.

- Further work was needed to show how revalidation would apply to doctors in non-mainstream and non-clinical roles, and to those not working in the NHS.
- The document said nothing about the potential direct and indirect costs of revalidation.
- Revalidation should only be introduced after the lessons from the pilot studies had been incorporated into the plans for the national roll-out – and after an agreement that the plans would be fit for purpose.

Shortly after the BMA submitted its comments on the consultation document, the new Secretary of State for Health, Andrew Lansley, wrote to the Chair of the GMC, Professor Peter Rubin, in June 2010 to say that he intended 'to extend the piloting period for a further year to enable us to develop a clearer understanding of the costs, benefits and practicalities of implementation so that it can be paced in a way that is affordable, supports high quality care and makes effective use of doctors' time.' This announcement came partly as a result of BMA pressure on the UK Revalidation Programme Board and elsewhere. As it had stated in its response to the GMC's proposals, the BMA thought that the complex system being pilot-tested would not allow ordinary doctors to prove their excellence. The year's breathing space, which pushed the start of revalidation from the end of 2011 to the end of 2012, gave time for the development of the Medical Appraisal Guide (eventually published in March 2012), in which doctors could have far more confidence.

The GMC received more than 940 written responses to its discussion document[59] and issued its response in October which, with the support of the various government chief medical officers,[60] consisted of a statement of intent. It said that the over-riding message from the consultation was that revalidation was the right way forward, but that it must be straightforward and proportionate and not place excessive burdens on doctors or employers. The system should be cost effective and the GMC would analyse costs and benefits before the process was rolled out. It was committed to further pilots and would evaluate the results of these before continuing. The statement said the GMC hoped to launch revalidation in late 2012, if local systems were in place. The UK Revalidation Programme Board (whose members included

---

[59] Figure quoted in paragraph 1 of *Revalidation: The Way Ahead – Response to our Revalidation Consultation*, GMC, October 2010.
[60] *Revalidation: A Statement of Intent*, GMC, October 2010.

the four health departments, the BMA, the Academy of Medical Royal Colleges, the GMC and employer representatives) would continue to oversee the implementation of revalidation.

The Chairman of Council, Hamish Meldrum, welcomed the positive response to many of the BMA's key concerns but pointed out that the GMC still needed to work with partner organisations on how the improvements could be achieved: 'The commitment to a revalidation system that is cost-effective, streamlined, flexible, proportionate and meaningful to all doctors is to be welcomed. But the lack of detail means a significant degree of uncertainty remains.' The BMA looked forward to continuing as part of the UK Revalidation Programme Board and insisted that the extended pilot tests in England were fully evaluated before any launch.

But as late as March 2011, the BMA was having serious doubts that revalidation could be implemented in 2012[61] and Hamish Meldrum said that 'considerable difficulties' remained.[62] This was in response to a report from the House of Commons Health Select Committee in which MPs had said that there should be no further delay to the plans to implement revalidation. In the meantime, the GMC was advising doctors: 'Revalidation will be based on a local evaluation of doctors' performance through appraisal. Doctors will be expected to participate in annual appraisal in the workplace and will need to maintain a folder or portfolio of supporting information to bring to their appraisals as a basis for discussion. There will be some types of supporting information that all doctors will be expected to provide at appraisal over a revalidation cycle.'[63] This, in a nutshell, was how it was anticipated that revalidation procedures would work when introduced at the end of 2012, with the responsible officer recommending to the GMC whether doctors should be revalidated or not, taking into account the doctor's appraisals over the previous five years and other information drawn from the employer's clinical governance systems. The BMA warned in the summer of 2012 that revalidation was 'not a done deal' because some key issues needed resolving, including the question of 'remediation' and the cost-effectiveness of the process. The GMC was

---

[61] The consultants had already lost patience and the 2010 Consultants Conference made the following resolution: 'That this conference calls on the BMA: i) to actively oppose the current plans for revalidation; ii) to campaign for the replacement of current plans for revalidation with plans focusing not on individual doctors but on strengthened and effective systems of clinical governance by all healthcare providers.'
[62] *Government defends revalidation timetable*, BMA News, 30 March 2011.
[63] From FAQs on the GMC's website, accessed 31 March 2011.

confident, however, that it would meet its long-awaited assurance that 'registration should become an up-to-date statement of each doctor's fitness to practise'.[64]

Revalidation was finally introduced on 3 December 2012, with the Chair of the GMC, Professor Peter Rubin, becoming the first doctor to be revalidated. The BMA vowed to monitor its implementation to ensure that it is fair for all doctors and to continue to lobby on outstanding issues. The BMA's role over the 14 years of negotiation and discussion has been vital in helping to shape a system which, while not perfect, is finally operational. After having prepared for so long, doctors could now begin to participate with some confidence in the new process.

NHS complaints

A chapter on the regulation of doctors would not be complete without mentioning the complaints system which patients may use if they are dissatisfied with their care, either by individual doctors or by a health care organisation. By 1993, the complex, fragmented and inefficient NHS complaints system was in dire need of reform and the government appointed Professor Alan Wilson, Vice-Chancellor of Leeds University, to review it. The BMA was among the first to agree that the current arrangements needed an overhaul because they seemed to leave both those making complaints and those being complained about feeling aggrieved and dissatisfied. The BMA set up a working group to compile its submission chaired by David Pickersgill, a GP from Norfolk and future Treasurer, who was well versed in the minutiae of NHS regulations as he also chaired the GMSC's Statutes and Regulations Subcommittee.

In its evidence the BMA proposed a single body, independent of NHS management, through which all NHS complaints should initially be channelled. It supported the wider use of informal procedures and suggested that clinical complaints against GPs should be dealt with separately from contractual matters, and that the investigation of all complaints should be completely separate from any disciplinary action. The BMA suggested a new three-stage procedure for all complaints: an in-house, informal procedure; conciliation, reinvestigation and explanation; then, if necessary, escalation to formal procedures. The BMA believed that many complainants wanted an explanation and/or

---

[64] Paragraph 5 of *Revalidating Doctors: Ensuring Standards, Securing the Future*, GMC, 2000.

an apology rather than a lengthy formal procedure, so it emphasised the first two stages.

The report of the Wilson Committee, *Being Heard,*[65] was published in May 1994. The BMA welcomed the proposals for a common system for complaints by NHS patients and that the investigation of these complaints should be kept apart from any subsequent disciplinary action. Professor Wilson's team also recommended a quick and informal response with the intention of investigating and resolving most complaints promptly. (In fact the GMSC was already advising GPs to set up in-house complaints procedures in their own practice.) But the BMA did not approve of all the recommendations. The CCSC criticised the report for only superficially addressing the relationship between any new procedures and potential litigation and for not identifying the grounds on which complaints could go forward to the final 'independent' review stage. The consultants had been largely content with the informal clinical complaints system in operation since the early 1980s and were worried about the formality and potential legal hazards of the suggested new arrangements. The BMA was united though in its call to the government to respond to the report as it was keen to discuss any new procedures.

The government finally published its response in *Acting on Complaints* which appeared in March 1995; the new complaints procedures began in April 1996. The government's aims were broadly in line with those of Professor Wilson and his team and the NHS was set for a major change in the way in which complaints were managed. But although the new procedures were a radical improvement on what had preceded them, they were far from perfect: an evaluation in 2001 showed widespread dissatisfaction.[66] Patients felt that the procedures were insufficiently independent and not responsive to their needs. There were also reports that the local resolution stage was not working well because of unhelpful NHS staff, poor communication and a lack of support and information. The evaluation made 27 recommendations and the BMA welcomed in particular the proposal for increased use of mediation. It felt that this would prevent the growth of 'defensive medicine' where doctors felt inhibited from providing the care which

---

[65] *Being Heard: The Report of a Review Committee on NHS Complaints Procedures,* May 1994.
[66] The evaluation report, *NHS Complaints Procedures National Evaluation,* and the Government's response, *Reforming the NHS Complaints Procedure – a Listening Document* were both published on 3 September 2001.

their judgement and experience suggested would be most effective by the fear of legal action. The BMA response also pointed out some underlying problems: the complaints system had failed to meet expectations of greater accessibility, openness and quicker resolution – and a large number of complaints were still being made. The BMA felt that the public's perception of expected treatment had become unrealistic, with the NHS unable to keep up with expectations and demands.

Although the Department of Health for England appeared to be planning changes, events intervened. First came the report of the public inquiry into children's heart surgery at the Bristol Royal Infirmary[67] which led the Department to promise a new NHS complaints procedure before the end of 2002. But it did not do so and in April 2003 it published *NHS Complaints Reform: Making Things Right*, which described a visionary new complaints procedure. In truth, it was little different to September 2001's *Listening Document*, although it had taken subsequent developments into account and now placed responsibility for independent review with the new Commission for Healthcare Audit and Inspection (later to become the Healthcare Commission).

In December 2003, draft regulations for new NHS complaints procedures were issued for consultation, with the intention of implementing them on 1 June 2004. But by then the inquiry into the conduct of Harold Shipman was deep into its work and appeared likely to make recommendations on handling complaints; other inquiries into doctors' misconduct seemed likely to do the same. Pending the publication of these reports, the government laid abbreviated regulations before Parliament which came into force on 30 July 2004. These left the local resolution stage largely unchanged, but strengthened the statutory requirements for local resolution by NHS bodies and introduced a reformed independent review stage to be carried out by the Healthcare Commission. The current procedures in England are governed by the Local Authority Social Services and National Health Service Complaints (England) Regulations 2009 and were intended to achieve a more flexible system, an improved local resolution stage (to help avoid escalation), reform of the independent review stage (by placing responsibility with the Commission for Healthcare Audit) and generally encouraging a learning culture that helps to improve standards of care. Each of the UK countries has slightly different complaints systems, though all of them aim to resolve complaints at local level with

---

[67] *The Report of the Public Inquiry into Children's Heart Surgery at the Bristol Royal Infirmary 1984–1995* Learning from Bristol, July 2001.

provision for independent review if they are not. The BMA's aim has been to ensure that the systems are fair to all concerned, and to ensure (through guidance notes) that doctors are clear about their roles.

Chapter 8

The IT revolution

Introduction

The world wide web was launched on 6 August 1991 when the first page was posted by Sir Tim Berners-Lee. When the web went live, he said: 'We are very interested in spreading the web to other areas . . . Collaborators welcome.'[1] Collaborators joined in their millions and websites sprung up, with health and healthcare receiving extensive online coverage. The web and other technological advances changed how patients accessed healthcare information, how doctors worked and how the BMA communicated with its members and with the world at large. This chapter will look at this information revolution and its impact on the BMA and its members.

Access to personal healthcare information

Computers were first used in medicine as far back as the early 1950s. In 1982 the government-backed 'micros for GPs' scheme was heavily oversubscribed and showed GPs' enthusiasm for new technology. It also provided the commercial sector with a better understanding of computing needs in general practice.[2] At around the same time it had become clear that the NHS was unable to produce adequate information about its own operations and in 1980 a steering group[3] was established to agree and implement a new information system. It was chaired by Edith (later Dame Edith) Körner, a former vice-chairman of the South Western Regional Health Authority. The President of the Royal College of Physicians noted that the inquiry seemed to focus on management information,[4] whereas doctors would have preferred a greater emphasis on information on individual patients and on the monitoring of their needs. Data transmission was vital and the 1981–82 annual

---

[1] *Many happy returns. world wide web celebrates its 20th birthday. Daily Mail* 7 August 2011.

[2] For an evaluation of the micros for GPs scheme, see F P Howath *Micros for GPs, BMJ* 1 February 1986. vol 292, page 307.

[3] The Steering Group on Health Services Information.

[4] Douglas Black, President of the Royal College of Physicians, *BMJ*, vol 285, 30 October 1982.

report of Council noted that the Körner Committee had supported the development of a standard protocol for data transmission. Council agreed that there should be common pathways for collecting and disseminating information electronically. The following annual report noted that the BMA had set up an inter-professional working group to consider a national code of practice on access to personal health information (*see also Chapter 10 for other issues surrounding patient confidentiality*). Even in those early days, doctors were deeply concerned about the electronic transmission of sensitive patient information, and it would become a recurring theme during the BMA's discussions on technological issues.

In 1992, the NHS Management Executive (NHSME)[5] launched an information strategy costing an estimated £152 million[6] to ensure that all information, including that held electronically, was better managed. The proposals were to give every patient an identification number so that their records could be found more easily, electronic records developed and electronic patient information transferred between GPs and health authorities. The following year the BMA warned that the plans to transfer patient information and to link all NHS computer systems seemed to be driven more by the needs of management than those of patients. It argued that insufficient resources had been devoted to protecting confidentiality. Sensing correctly that this would become a major issue, the BMA set up an Information Technology Working Party to monitor developments. In November 1993 it brought together doctors, lawyers and patient representatives for a workshop on privacy, confidentiality and NHS networking. Participants agreed that the Association should take a lead in educating the profession, other healthcare workers and the public on these issues with a view to 'determining an appropriate balance between the benefits and dangers of information technology'.

Throughout the 1990s, as technology evolved and the Department of Health consulted on how the NHS network might function, the BMA kept up its pressure to maintain the privacy of personal health information; after all, doctors were ultimately responsible for the security and confidentiality of all identifiable patient data. The BMA was represented on the NHS Executive's information management group where it raised its anxieties about the NHS number replacement

---

[5] *Getting Better with Information*, NHS Management Executive, 1992.
[6] *The 1992 and 1998 Information Management & Technology Strategies of the NHS Executive*, National Audit Office, London, 28 April 1999.

programme and the importance of keeping patient identifiers and other personal details secure. In October 1995, Council agreed to suspend co-operation on the NHS's network project until it could be shown to meet the technical demands of the healthcare professionals for effective protection of identifiable patient data. The Association said: 'This is an issue which strikes at the heart of the doctor-patient relationship and the individual's right to personal privacy'. The BMA commissioned Ross Anderson from Cambridge University's Computer Laboratory to draft a security policy for clinical information systems and also end-user guidelines to protect patients and support healthcare professionals. The Chairman of Council, Alexander (later Sir Alexander) Macara, wrote to the Secretary of State for Health setting out the BMA's strong views on the subject. The BMA wanted collaboration rather than confrontation with the Department of Health so that both sides could marry the established principle of the confidentiality of personal healthcare information with the benefits of the new technologies. To that end, in January 1996, a top-level BMA/Health Department Group (chaired jointly by the Chairman of Council, Alexander Macara, and the Chief Medical Officer, Sir Kenneth Calman) was established to try to resolve a number of issues relating to the privacy of personal health care information and the phased introduction of the networking of IT systems. The group, whose work was divided into a number of separate work-streams, made good progress and one year later the chairmen signed a letter to trusts setting out the progress that had been made and where further work was needed. Unfortunately, despite this collaboration and the goodwill on both sides, the BMA's anxieties about the network remained deep and unresolved.

Two years later, in September 1998, the publication of the NHS Executive's *Information Strategy for the NHS*[7] gave new impetus to the use of information technology. The then Prime Minister, Tony Blair, was quoted in this document as saying, 'The challenge for the NHS is to harness the information revolution and use it to benefit patients'.[8] Whether this challenge was subsequently met remains open for debate, but the 1998 strategy did deal with the problems that had been apparent since the Körner work, and tried to move the emphasis from the administrative to the clinical. As the publication said, the

[7] *Information for Health: An Information Strategy for the Modern NHS 1998–2005.* NHS Executive, 1998.
[8] Originally a quote from Tony Blair from speech given at All Our Tomorrow's Conference on 2 July 1998.

previous strategy, published in 1992, was 'over-concerned with management information, and failed to address the real needs of the NHS for information to help clinicians and managers deliver more effective healthcare and improve population health'.[9] The Secretary of State for Health, Frank Dobson, put it more simply: 'For the first time ever, IT in the NHS will be geared towards helping doctors, nurses and other health professionals treat patients, rather than churning out figures to support the internal market.'[10] The BMA agreed and the Chairman of its Information Technology Committee, Kenneth Robertson, said in a press statement: 'The Government needs to be congratulated for hauling the whole focus of NHS IT away from management and finance towards patient care. This is a total change of direction and one which promises a dramatically better prospect for the future.'

The 1998 strategy was one of several NHS strategies published by a new and enthusiastic government, still glowing from its landslide victory the year before. It became clear that its plans to improve and modernise the NHS and public health depended on high quality information and that the strategy in *Information for Health* was a vital part of its agenda. The whole point of the strategy was 'to ensure that information is used to help patients receive the best possible care'[11] and it promised:

- life-long electronic health records for everyone,
- 24-hour online access to patient records and information about best clinical practice for all NHS clinicians,
- 'seamless care' for patients through the NHS with all aspects of the service sharing information across what was termed the 'NHS information highway', and
- care through online information services and telemedicine.

Although the 1998 strategy was an improvement on that of 1992, much remained to be done. The National Audit Office said that the objectives and targets should be measurable and called for business cases to clarify how the various individual projects would link up.[12] There was more criticism in April 2002 in the Wanless report[13] which said: 'The

---

[9] Para 1.33 of *Information for Health,* 1998.

[10] Department of Health press release, *Frank Dobson announces £1 billion modernisation of NHS information system,* 24 September 1998.

[11] Para 1.2 of *Information for Health,* 1998.

[12] *The 1992 and 1998 Information Management & Technology Strategies of the NHS Executive,* National Audit Office, London, 28 April 1999.

[13] *Securing our Future Health: Taking a Long-term View – the Wanless Report,* Department of Health, London, 2002. This review was chaired by Sir Derek Wanless and assessed the long-term resource requirements for the health service in the UK.

health service makes very poor use of ICT [information and communication technology]. There are examples of successful use of ICT at local level, but systems have typically been developed and installed in a piecemeal fashion. This prevents the effective integration and sharing of information across a wide range of health care providers.'[14] Even the Department of Health acknowledged that it needed to do more and admitted: 'Since the advent of IFH ['Information for Health'], there have been improvements in the level of IT funding and in the uses that are made at local, regional and national levels. However, there remain a number of critical barriers to the effective use of IT as a strategic tool in the delivery of healthcare by the NHS.'[15] The problems that it identified were low levels of local investment, a lack of a cohesive and nationally-led IT architecture for data and system standards, inadequate coordination of IT resources and procurement and low levels of secure high-bandwidth connectivity for NHS staff.

These failings were set out in yet another strategic document, published in July 2002. This time it appeared that an unprecedented programme of investment would give NHS IT in England a new start. Given that one of the problems already identified was the lack of a national picture, the 2002 plans left readers in no doubt where its emphasis would be: 'The core of our strategy is to take greater central control over the specification, procurement, resource management, performance management and delivery of the information and IT agenda. We will improve the leadership and direction given to IT, and combine it with national and local implementation that are based on ruthless standardisation.'[16] A new NHS IT Programme Director, Richard Granger,[17] was appointed that year to ensure that the national components of the programme were delivered and that there was coordinated local implementation.

Within two years, however, the BMA was commenting publicly that there had been too little involvement in the programme by the very clinicians who would be using it. Although the Association broadly supported the national programme to improve the IT infrastructure

---

[14] Para 2.24 of *Securing our Future Health: Taking a Long-term View* by Sir Derek Wanless, April 2002.
[15] Para 2.1.2 of *Delivering 21st Century IT Support for the NHS: National Strategic Programme*, Department of Health, July 2002.
[16] Para 1.2.1 of *Delivering 21st Century IT Support for the NHS: National Strategic Programme*, Department of Health, July 2002.
[17] Richard Granger had successfully delivered the system for the London congestion charging scheme.

of the NHS, it was obviously keen that the resulting systems would be of use to doctors and other healthcare workers. This message was repeated later that year by the Chairman of the BMA's IT Committee, John Powell: 'The national programme must learn the lessons of other high profile public sector IT projects such as the passport office fiasco of 1999. Large-scale public IT projects do not have a good track record in the UK and so it is paramount that the NHS learns the lessons of history and engages with the frontline staff who will be using the new systems. So far the level of engagement and consultation with the medical profession has been wholly inadequate.'

By coincidence in that same year of 2004 there had been a government review of 'arm's length bodies', and one outcome was to create a new body to deliver the NHS IT programme in England. This was NHS Connecting for Health, formed on 1 April 2005 as a Directorate of the Department of Health. Its primary role was to deliver the National Programme for IT (NPfIT), which included:

- The NHS Care Records Service, which would produce an individual electronic record for each NHS patient.
- Choose and Book, which was an electronic system for booking hospital appointments and would allow patients to choose the time and place of their appointment.
- Electronic Transfer of Prescriptions through the Electronic Prescription Service, for example, from the GP direct to the pharmacy.
- Picture Archiving and Communications Systems, which would enable digital images such as scans and x-rays, to be captured, distributed, stored and displayed electronically.
- NHSmail, the NHS email and directory service.[18]
- N3, the broadband network infrastructure to support the programme.

The BMA reacted by improving its internal processes for dealing with NHS IT. It created a new secretariat post to help develop BMA policy on the programme and also set up a high-level working group with representation from a wide range of BMA committees. To underline the importance of the matters to be considered, the new group was chaired by the Chairman of Council. Externally, the BMA increased its links with NHS Connecting for Health via cross-representation on

---

[18] The BMA and Connecting for Health issued joint guidance in July 2009 on the use of NHSmail and in April 2008 the two bodies issued joint guidance on protecting electronic patient information.

working groups and liaison with the NHS Care Records Development Board clinical leads, Gillian Braunold and Simon Eccles, both of whom already had links with the BMA (Simon Eccles was a recent Chair of the Junior Doctors Committee and Gillian Braunold was a member of the GPC with a special interest in matters relating to IT).

Broadly, the BMA welcomed the benefits to patients, but consistently warned over delays to implementation, the growing costs of the systems and their reliability and usability. When things went seriously wrong, the BMA did not hesitate to say so publicly and always monitored the potential of the new innovations to complicate the working lives of doctors. As in the 1990s, the discussions were long and complex, but both the BMA and the agencies that were responsible for the IT revolution in the NHS made great efforts to bring about a satisfactory outcome. This was not a contract negotiation, but a genuine attempt to introduce a new and better way of working to the NHS in England. This can be seen from the exceptionally high level of BMA involvement in the various groups set up over the years by Connecting for Health and the Department of Health, by the numbers of meetings between the bodies and by the joint conferences, workshops and guidance notes. The BMA's interventions and suggestions were generally listened to and often acted upon. For example, a letter from the Chairman of Council, Hamish Meldrum, to the Minister of State for Health Services, Ben Bradshaw, in August 2007 made a number of recommendations about the future of the National Programme for IT. As a result, the BMA and Connecting for Health set up together a number of roadshows to update secondary care clinicians and to listen to their concerns. The BMA also worked with Connecting for Health to target areas where systems were not working well, especially where this was due to PCT or trust interference, and to share best practice.

The BMA spent many hours debating the various elements of Connecting for Health and two areas dominated: the Choose and Book system and the arrangements for the Summary Care Record (SCR). Choose and Book was introduced from 2004 and the 2005–6 annual report of Council noted that it was causing concern. Consultants were worried how referrals would reach them and GPs that the system would not work. Both groups were trying to understand how the system would operate in reality and what effect it would have on their clinical practice and working lives. The BMA's official line on Choose and Book was that it 'can benefit both patients and clinicians, but that doctors' views of the system are mixed'.

The BMA supported the principle of a technological solution to paper-based referrals, which could be slow and risked sensitive letters being lost. Lost appointment letters were difficult to trace, so patients could face major delays to their treatment if one went astray. The proposed system would improve patient choice as it would allow them to choose the time and place of their outpatient appointment; it would also allow referrals to be tracked. The BMA's optimism, however, was tempered by its suspicions that the new system had been 'hijacked by a political agenda'. It felt that Choose and Book was being used to allow greater involvement by the independent sector with a subsequent loss of funding to the NHS as a consequence of Payment by Results.[19] Choose and Book could also be used to deal with capacity issues by removing waiting lists deemed too long from the choice menu and referring patients to shorter lists, thus reducing the choices available and preventing GPs from referring to the department, clinic or clinician that they felt would be best for a particular patient. There was also an issue of devolution: Choose and Book was an England-only initiative which meant that patients living on the borders would have their choices reduced. Political concerns were matched by frustration at the technological failings and the whole implementation was one where reality rarely matched the enormous potential.

GPs soon began to comment that the system was slowing down the referral process and a joint committee of the General Practitioners Committee and Royal College of General Practitioners collaborated on a plan to improve the system and make it more acceptable to the profession. This plan was given to Connecting for Health. The joint committee, together with the consultants committee, secured representation on the Choose and Book National Clinical Reference Panel and the Design Steering Group so that they continued to work with the organisations overseeing the implementation and operation of the system to suggest improvements. The BMA had been enthusiastic about the aims of Choose and Book and so was disappointed when it initially failed to live up to expectations. It therefore continued to offer constructive criticism aimed at ensuring that it would be suitable for doctors and their patients.

Despite good intentions on all sides, things had not improved by 2009 when the BMA reported the results of a small set of interviews

---

[19] Payment by Results (PbR) in England pays hospitals for the work that they do by paying a standard national price (Tariff) for each episode of treatment given. It replaces the old block contracts. The system was introduced incrementally from 2003.

with doctors about Choose and Book. These made it clear that GPs were still struggling with the reliability of the computerised bookings system, even though 13 million referrals had been made in England since 2004. Hospital consultants said that Choose and Book had had little impact on their working practices and the few who had used it to review appointments reported that it was slow, and that they had had insufficient time to use it, particularly during a busy clinic. As a result the BMA recommended improvements, including greater collaboration between primary and secondary care and naming a troubleshooter in each primary care and hospital trust. It also recommended addressing capacity issues by local analyses of demand. As a result of the research and subsequent discussions, the Department of Health in England published a guidance document[20] 'to help organisations understand the importance of using Choose and Book correctly.' Requirements included promoting rather than mandating the use of Choose and Book, allowing electronic referrals to named clinicians if paper based referrals to named clinicians are accepted and encouraging clinicians to initiate and review referrals themselves online. In June 2010, the Chairman of the GPC was including Choose and Book on his list of things that needed to be cut or reviewed and it was reported that, while many practices found the e-booking element useful, the 'choose' part was 'laboriously bureaucratic' and the 'system is now regularly used to ration demand and meet the 18 week waiting time target by PCTs. In practical terms it is often difficult for patients to exercise real choice.' Choose and Book continued to come under attack at GP conferences and annual meetings and GPs were exasperated when the English Minister for Health suggested that it was GPs themselves who were to blame for the low take-up of Choose and Book. The Minister was given a brisk reminder at the 2009 LMC Conference that 'GPs have a history of using new technology as soon as it is fit for purpose and offers benefits to patients and practices'. Choose and Book did become an established referral system in England with its own website for patients, but doctors continued to have their reservations.

While Choose and Book caused unease among doctors as a result of its political overtones and technological flaws, their problems with the summary care record (SCR), another fundamental aspect of the National Programme for IT in England, were to go much deeper. In particular it went to the core of the relationship between doctors

---

[20] *Responsibilities and Operational Requirements for the Correct Use of Choose and Book*, BMA and Department of Health, December 2009.

and their patients and threatened to damage that most sacrosanct of principles – medical confidentiality. Doctors also had deep reservations that, in the rush to get the SCR up and running, too little time and attention had been given to informing patients of its implications and, most importantly, of their rights.

Connecting for Health was responsible for delivering the NHS Care Records Service which was to have two components: the summary care record (SCR – held nationally) and the detailed care record (DCR – held locally). The summary care record became the subject of much debate. The Prime Minister, Tony Blair, had said in 1997: 'If you live in Birmingham and you have an accident while you are, for example, in Bradford, it should be possible for your records to be instantly available to the doctors treating you.'[21] The SRC was to be the vehicle for this instant access because it contained the core elements of a patient's health information (their medication, allergies and known adverse reactions to drugs) and would be uploaded onto a central 'spine' which could be accessed from urgent or emergency care settings anywhere in England. Access controls would be put in place to ensure that only registered NHS staff could read an SCR and access rights determined by the role of each staff member. In addition, patients would, if they were well enough, be asked for permission before their record was accessed. The first SCRs were uploaded in October 2007 in Bolton and then five other 'early adopter' sites. Opinions varied on the most appropriate consent model to be used, an opt-in or an opt-out one, and there was some disagreement within the BMA on this. The view of the GPC for an opt-in model prevailed and this was confirmed at the 2006 ARM. GPs felt strongly about their role as keeper of patients' records and believed that this was fundamental to maintaining confidentiality.

There was a flurry of activity in early 2008 when 'The Big Opt Out Campaign' began. This was not a BMA campaign and its literature was highly emotive, but it had received widespread media coverage and there were concerns that patients were making decisions based on media reports and that the BMA was being associated with the campaign (some individual members were supporting it). The BMA did not advocate an opt-out from the record, but merely pressed the Department of Health to make it clear to patients that they had the right to opt out if they wished.

---

[21] Quoted in BMA paper *Update on the Summary Care Record*, presented to the Board of the Directorate of Professional Activities in February 2010.

It was the BMA's perception of the poor quality of communication to patients about the implications of the SCR and their right to opt out of it which led to strong criticism of the Department of Health from the BMA. In December 2009, the Department of Health in England announced a sudden and unexpected acceleration of the roll-out of the SCR, which was condemned by the BMA as a 'rushed implementation' with patients being given insufficient information about their rights to opt-out of having a record created and GPs having too little time in which to support patients in making an informed choice. The reason was financial: extra funding for public information programmes had been announced in December 2009 and primary care trusts had until March 2010 to spend it. A strongly worded letter from the Chairman of Council, Hamish Meldrum, the Chairman of the GPC, Laurence Buckman, and the Chair of the BMA's Working Party on NHS IT, Dame Deirdre Hine, was sent to the Health Minister, Mike O'Brien. It set out clearly the BMA's view that the roll-out should be halted in areas which had not yet started their public information programmes. It also called for an opt-out form to be sent to patients in their information packs and for the withdrawal of BMA comment from the Connecting for Health's promotional video because it misrepresented the current BMA position. The letter said that the SCR pilot schemes had not had sufficient independent evaluation and that the BMA had been given to understand that there would be no further roll-out until a second report from University College, London (UCL) had been published. Not only was the roll-out occurring ahead of the second report, but the recommendations of the first, published two years before,[22] had not been fully implemented. The letter ended by reminding the Minister that the 'BMA and GPC have tried to be helpful in its engagement with NHS Connecting for Health to ensure appropriate implementation of SCRs . . . We are deeply disappointed that the current national roll-out has bypassed the BMA's views and ignored our goodwill which we have provided up until now'.

The BMA's intervention worked. Just over a month later the Department of Health in England told the GPC that the upload of patients' records to the national database would be suspended in areas where the roll-out had been accelerated and would not restart until

---

[22] *Summary Care Record Early Adopter Programme: An Independent Evaluation by University College London*, T Greenhalgh, K Stramer, T Bratan, E Byrne, J Russell, Y Mohammad, G Wood, Shinder.

there was greater public and professional awareness. This was followed in June by the second UCL report[23] which found 'little evidence that the record achieves any of the benefits hoped for'.[24] Responding to the report's publication, the Chairman of the GPC, Laurence Buckman, reiterated that the BMA did not in principle oppose shared electronic patient records, but that the implementation had been at fault. He gave an assurance that 'the BMA is happy to engage with the government to find a way forward that has the confidence of both patients and professionals.'

In 2010, ARM policy was refined in favour of explicit patient consent for the upload rather than for the access. The Representative Body stopped short of adopting a motion advocating withdrawal of co-operation with a system based on implied consent, but it did pass a motion on this as a reference.[25] A BMA media briefing paper stated in January 2011: 'The BMA has consistently stated that greater sharing of healthcare information has the potential to improve patient care. Its concerns about the summary care record were not about the principle of shared records, but about the programme's implementation, which failed to adequately inform patients of their choices, and in some areas made it too difficult to opt out. The BMA believes patients must have an informed choice as to whether or not their health information is kept on the system, and be sure they know who will be able to access their details.'

The saga concluded in October when a government-led review concluded that the content of future SCRs would be limited to patients' demographic details, medications, allergies and adverse reactions, with more information added only with the patient's explicit consent. The SCR would only be used in urgent or emergency situations and the patient information programme would be improved, with all patients sent an opt-out form. The BMA remained concerned, however, that while hospitals awaited the delivery of their all-inclusive 'NPfIT' computers, many of their systems still failed to communicate with each other.

---

[23] *Adoption and Non-adoption of a Shared Electronic Summary Record in England: A Mixed-method Case Study'*, Trish Greenhalgh, Katja Stramer, Tanja Bratan, Emma Byrne, Jill Russell, Henry W W Potts, *BMJ* 2010, 340, published 16 June 2010.

[24] *Future of NHS Summary care record hangs in the balance*, *BMJ* 2010; 340:c3230, 17 June 2010.

[25] Passing an ARM motion as 'a reference' means that it does not become BMA policy, but is instead referred to the relevant BMA committee to take the most appropriate course of action in the interests of the Association.

The delivery of both the summary care record (SCR) and detailed care record (DCR) were delayed. The SCR was eventually implemented, but the DCR turned out to be more complicated than initially thought. There were delays in software development, problems with applying a standard system across the NHS in England, and a multitude of contractual issues (one supplier left the programme and another's contract was terminated). The National Audit Office concluded in May 2011: 'Although some care records systems are in place, progress against plans has fallen far below expectations and the Department has not delivered care records systems across the NHS, or with anywhere near the completeness of functionality that will enable it to achieve the original aspirations of the programme . . . we conclude that the £2.7 billion spent on care records systems so far does not represent value for money, and we do not find grounds for confidence that the remaining planned spend of £4.3 billion will be different.'[26] The multibillion pound scheme to create a full electronic patient record across the NHS in England was doomed and the death blow finally came in September 2011 when Andrew Lansley, the Secretary of State for Health in England, admitted defeat and decided to discontinue the NHS Programme for IT. He put the blame on the previous Labour administration for a programme which 'wasted taxpayers' money by imposing a top-down IT system on the local NHS which didn't fit their needs'.[27] In fact, the Department of Health had concluded that a centralised and national approach was no longer required and that a locally-led, plural system should operate. The BMA commented: 'Giving NHS organisations more choice of IT systems makes sense, but we also need to be aware of the problems that could arise from a more local approach. The provision and experience of IT for clinicians on the ground is likely to vary according to the level of support and resources available locally. It is important that successful national IT initiatives are not lost, and that innovation is not stifled.'[28] Indeed, much of what NPfIT had achieved for patients would remain: the summary care record, Choose and Book, some of the electronic prescription service and the NHSmail confidential email systems. Also surviving was Connecting for Health, the body which was to continue to oversee NHS IT.

---

[26] Para 27 of the summary of *The National Programme for IT in the NHS: An Update on the Delivery of Detailed Care Record Systems,* National Audit Office, 18 May 2011.
[27] *NHS told to abandon delayed IT project, The Guardian,* 22 September 2011.
[28] Quote from Chaand Nagpaul, quoted on BBC News online, 9 September 2011.

Devolved nations

The story of the National Programme for IT was relevant only to England: the devolved nations had separate programmes and these continued while the story of NPfIT played out. The BMA's Working Party on NHS IT had observers from the devolved nations and their reports were included on all working party agendas and sent to both the Political Board and the Board of the Directorate of Professional Activities. Scotland had an ambitious e-health programme which aimed 'to improve patient care through advances in technology, resulting in better access to health information, quicker test results for clinicians and joined-up GP and hospital services.'[29]

The English summary care record (SCR) had counterparts in all three devolved nations. In Wales the individual health record was a summary of a patient's record held by the GP which could be accessed by those working in the local out-of-hours service. The NHS in Wales made a rather pointed distinction: 'The record that is being introduced in Wales does not form part of the English electronic summary care health record. In Wales, we have a different approach.'[30] In Northern Ireland, the emergency care summary record was introduced to GP out-of-hours services, emergency departments and hospital pharmacies and included a patient's current medication and any known allergies. It could only be accessed with the patient's explicit consent. Scotland had its emergency care summary, which was a summary of demographic, allergy and medication information. Unlike the English version it held a palliative care summary, and also information on resuscitation, patients' wishes and place of care. The emergency care summary enabled out-of-hours services, A&E services, the Scottish Ambulance Service and acute receiving clinicians to access important patient information in an emergency. The BMA suggested that the Scottish emergency care summary, which preceded the English SCR, should be used to inform the development of the English version. In particular they should look at the number of patients who had opted out, the perceived value of the summary record to doctors in Scotland, and the views of patients and doctors on the amount and type of information in the summary.

Scotland also had the general practice administration system for Scotland (GPASS), designed to help the efficient operation of GP

---

[29] From the Scottish e-health website, accessed 17 October 2011.
[30] From wales.nhs.uk website, accessed 17 October 2011.

practices and thus patient care. This had been designed by Scottish
GPs to meet the requirements of Connecting for Health and to ensure
that they were working within the government's eHealth Strategy.
It was due to be retired in 2012.[31] In September 2011, the Scottish
Government published a new eHealth Strategy[32] which was to 'switch
its focus from new technology projects, to the benefits and outcomes
they deliver to healthcare professionals in helping them redesign and
improve services.'[33] A key priority was the use of electronic information portals by all health boards to provide essential information to
frontline staff. Another was that information should be shared between
health and social care workers and that the two services should become
more integrated. In Wales, a 'clinical portal' was developed to link hospital computers so that staff would have better access to different systems and paper records. In Northern Ireland a 10-year Information
and Communication Programme was launched in March 2005. This
was an ambitious programme which included a project to connect all
general practices to the Department of Health, Social Services and
Public Safety system to make available secure internet access and email
and an electronic referral management system.

The world wide web

The dangers and benefits of information technology which the BMA
had raised in 1993 (in relation to the confidentiality of personal health
information) came to the fore once again a few years later when the
world wide web began to take off. Almost at once thousands of pages
of health-related information, of variable quality, become available.
People no longer needed to go to their GP with a set of symptoms,
but could type them into a search engine on the web. By 2011, a survey of 2001 people in the UK reported that 70% of them had used
the internet to access health information.[34] This development had the
power both to inform and terrify. It enabled patients who had been
properly diagnosed to find out more about their condition, but it also
could cause great harm to those who eschewed medical advice in favour
of online self-diagnosis. Meanwhile the dynamic of the doctor-patient

---

[31] From the Scottish National Information Systems Group website, accessed 17
October 2011.
[32] *eHealth Strategy 2011–2017*, published by the Scottish Government and NHS
Scotland on 12 September 2011.
[33] *Scotland publishes new eHealth strategy*, *The Guardian*, 12 September 2011.
[34] Page 17 of *BUPA Health Pulse 2011: International Healthcare Survey – Global
Trends, Attitudes and Influences*, BUPA, London, 2011.

relationship had changed: anyone could now claim to be an authority on virtually any condition, medication or treatment after a few mouse clicks. Doctors, while welcoming a well-informed public, sometimes found themselves having to deal not only with raised expectations following patients' web searches, but also correcting misinformed and inaccurate information that patients had acquired from biased web reports. Websites were developed in an attempt to counter this and to harness the undoubted benefits of information technology, and the BMA's website started to show links to some of them and also started to give advice on how to assess healthcare websites. The BMJ Group contributed its *BestTreatments* (and latterly *BestHealth*) webpages which were aimed at the public and give clear evidence-based advice. The information is based on the same research used to write *Clinical Evidence* for doctors *(see chapter 15)*.

Another hazard thrown up by the internet was that of patients buying online prescription medicines, some of which were counterfeit. Council discussed the issue in 2007–8 and a press release urged patients to obtain medicines from their doctor and not to self-diagnose and self-prescribe. The Chairman of Council, Hamish Meldrum, said: 'One of the messages we are trying to get over to the public is of the dangers of doing that. We want patients to be aware and to be protected and to seek appropriate advice to get proper diagnosis, and treatment.' The BMA also approached the World Health Organisation and the UK's Medicines and Healthcare Products Regulatory Agency (MHRA), and detailed warnings about internet purchases now appear on the MHRA's website.

The web also started to allow patients to check-up on individual doctors, hospitals and practices and post reviews about them. Such information ranged from the respected Dr Foster site, the UK's main provider of comparative data on health services, to sites similar to those used by consumers to review hotels and holidays. The NHS Choices website legitimised reviews of the services provided by GPs, hospitals, dentists and pharmacists in England. Officially, the BMA said that it was in favour of 'any information, advice and support that could help patients improve and better manage their health' and it welcomed 'meaningful and facilitative patient feedback where it can help to improve patients' health and experiences'. Nevertheless, this new development was hard for doctors. Local gossip about them and their services was one thing, but online reviews moved the doctor-patient relationship to a new level: good and bad reviews were in writing for all to see and there was nothing they could do to stop it. The BMA had to be careful in its public reaction so as not to make it appear that doctors were afraid of consumer comments, but nevertheless to make it clear that reviewing online the provision of healthcare was not, and never could be, the same as reviewing a hotel or restaurant.

The BMA's policy was to try to limit the damage and the GPC was closely involved when NHS Choices was being established to try to ensure that the GP rating and comment facility on the site would work effectively for both patients and GPs. There was a justifiable concern that the site's feedback facility might be used maliciously by individuals or groups to target practices and GPs. Therefore, the committee worked hard with the Department of Health to develop effective rules to prevent feedback being misused. Its intervention led to a system to highlight comments judged to be unfair or inappropriate. The committee also took part in developing realistic training scenarios for moderators and helped to develop a contacts database so that practices would be alerted when a comment was made so that they could respond. The BMA had to engage with NHS Choices, but it maintained its belief that practices themselves were 'best placed to collect patient feedback and gauge patient opinion, as they have established relationships with their patients and knowledge of the needs of the local population.' The Chairman of Council personally met the owner of a review site in 2008 to relay to him the deep concern expressed by Council members about the accuracy of the site's database, the potential for defamation, the use of anonymised postings, the lack of redress to malicious postings, the effect of false accusations on a doctor's career and the lack of clarity with regard to the site's moderation process. The site's owner promised to look at the technical and practical issues relating to these, but made it clear that he had no intention of closing the site.

The new world of online communications also provided another type of 'review' facility: allowing doctors to have their say on every aspect of the BMA's activities through external forums such as doctors.net.uk and others. The BMA had no influence over them, other than having its point put across by individual members. This was particularly important during contract negotiations when members of the negotiating teams had to spend many hours correcting facts and answering questions. The potential of these sites to spread misinformation was huge and it was essential that the BMA engaged with them to attempt to contain any possible damage. But the sites did provide valuable feedback on doctors' views, which were not always the same as those gleaned from BMA surveys and focus groups.

New technology and services to BMA members

It was noted in the 1987–8 annual report of Council that, by 1988, the services of the library would be fully automated and an online catalogue (note an early use of the word 'online') produced that would be immediately accessible from four terminals in the library. At first this information would be accessible only to those in the library, but it was anticipated that online public access would be available within two years. In the late 1980s, such services were very forward-looking and show that the BMA was committed early on to using technology to enhance its services to members. The 1987–8 annual report went on to say that 'new technology for the organisation and retrieval of information is in a stage of rapid development and the BMA library fully intends to lead the development of medical information in the UK.'

Medline started in June 1993, providing an index to much of the world's medical literature. When it started, eight incoming telephone lines were dedicated to it as part of 24 lines devoted to the networked information service as a whole. This service was one of the first of its type to be offered by a professional organisation. The library continued to exploit the new technology, and by the end of the 1990s, reported that more than 150 members had been logging on to its Medline Plus service simultaneously at peak times, putting huge strain on a system designed for only 40 users. The servers were replaced. All of the library catalogues were by this time accessible from the website and members could reserve loan items online. The BMA library has continued to be in the forefront of the BMA's technological innovations and by 2012 electronic journals in more than a dozen specialties and more than 1,100 books could be accessed via the BMA's website without needing additional usernames and passwords. Electronic books were also available and, with the advent of smart-phones and tablet computers, the library offered its *Library anywhere* app which gave details of library services to members.

The BMA first appeared on the world wide web in 1996 when it launched a site with about 150 pages of information. The site was continually reviewed and rebuilt over the next few years as the web changed and developed, and more information was obtained about what members expected and needed from their website. The BMA was aware that doctors were already overloaded with information and would need a website which enabled them to be selective. A relaunch in March 2002 provided a more individual service, giving members access to information relevant to their country and their branch of practice. Members were also able to create their own BMA homepage by bookmarking their favourite areas of the site. Individual departments within the BMA were given more control over their content and could develop it quickly and flexibly, while an overall web team was responsible for the look and feel of the website as a whole. The number of members registering with the site grew rapidly and visitor numbers continued to increase. The site became more complex and more sophisticated. From its start as a repository of information, it had developed by 2002 into an interactive facility that allowed members to calculate their pension payments, set up email alerts and join discussion forums. Further upgrades to the website were made in 2008 and 2012. The ability to keep up a constant, and cost-effective, stream of news alerts on the website was important in times of contract negotiations and these were used to good effect for the first time during the GP and consultant contract negotiations in 2003–4. The website also enabled the introduction of the weekly electronic newsletter (initially pilot-tested in the spring of 2008). This is a weekly round-up of news, tailored to a member's country and branch of practice, which goes straight into a member's inbox and has links so that the member can click through for further details if they wish.

By 2008 the BMA was ready to exploit the burgeoning social media sites that had appeared on the web and designed the annual report of Council as a web-based document with only a few print copies. The BMA set up BMAtv, its own page on YouTube, which had video-clips of senior elected members answering questions of interest. Improved video technology allowed the BMA to broadcast events live: the Annual Representative Meeting was an obvious candidate for such 'webcasting', and the facility was also used for seminars, conference sessions and, in 2008, the series of Westminster Lectures featuring the key health spokespeople from the three main political parties which had been organised by the BMA. Podcasts are also used. The BMA started to have a presence on Facebook and Twitter, led by medical students and junior doctors. While the BMA was developing its website, the BMJ Publishing Group was innovating in its use of technology *(see Chapter 15)*.

Doctors in their thousands also began to engage personally with social media, with their own Facebook pages and Twitter accounts and as members of professional forums such as doctors.net.uk. However, they have to take special care as guidance from the medical ethics department in May 2011 made clear: 'While many medical professionals use social media without encountering any difficulties, media interest and research into examples of unprofessional behaviour online have raised concerns that some doctors and medical students may be unknowingly exposing themselves to risk in the way they are using . . . applications and uploading personal material onto the internet. Although medical professionals should be free to take advantage of the many personal and professional benefits that social media can offer, it is important that they are aware of the potential risks involved.'[35]

The guidance gave practical and ethical advice on the issues that doctors and medical students might face when using social media. As well as advice on practical issues such as privacy settings, the guidance tried to sum up the difference between the use of social media by doctors and by those who do not have the special place that doctors have in society: 'Although the way medical professionals use social media in their private lives is a matter for their own personal judgment, doctors and medical students should consider whether the content they upload onto the internet could compromise public confidence in the medical profession.'

Listservers and paperless committees

A negative side of electronic communications showed itself within the BMA with the development of email groups or listservers. They were set up to allow members of internal groups, such as committees or Councils, to 'talk' among themselves between meetings. Posts on listservers went straight into the email inboxes of all on the listserver and members no longer had to visit a forum to send and receive posts from colleagues. This allowed for the rapid dissemination of information, the opportunity to discuss matters of interest before committee meetings and the occasional joke. When properly used, as they usually were, they were an effective way of enabling members to keep in touch between meetings. Regrettably, the facility started to become a burden. First, there was the sheer number of posts. In-boxes began to overflow and some committee chairmen spent hours dealing with them. More worrying was the tone of some of the posts: some listservers degenerated into attack vehicles with unpleasant and personal postings. At

---

[35] *Using Social Media: Practical and Ethical Guidance for Doctors and Medical Students,* BMA Medical Ethics Department, May 2011.

times they became effectively hijacked by a small minority of members who posted incessantly, with other members reluctant to get involved in the facility, thus losing out when important information was disseminated. In January 2009 Council, some of whose members were themselves guilty of such misuse, agreed a set of principles for BMA listservers. Before this the legal department had drawn up terms and conditions for listserver use and any member who wished to use a listserver had to sign up to them before being given access.

The BMA's committees had long engaged in robust debate, so it is difficult to explain why the listserver took disagreements to a new and damaging level. The impersonal nature of email can make it an ideal forum for conflict and the speed of the communication might also account for some problems. There was also a stark contrast between the initial absence of policy for listserver communications and the extensive rules of debate for meetings which have been built up over many years and which moderate face to face exchanges and encourage polite behaviour. In addition, when sentiments are expressed in a letter there is a built-in cooling-off period. Quick-fire email exchanges can soon get out of hand when tempers are heated and passions high. Guidelines and terms and conditions help to a large extent, but it appears to be impossible to eradicate such behaviour completely.

On a more positive note, more and more business could be conducted electronically between meetings and some electronic working groups began to replace face-to-face meetings, saving considerable sums in travel and subsistence expenses. Another innovation was the use of telephone and video-conferencing. Video-conferencing took some time to become established and endless patience was shown both by committee chairmen and those (often from the devolved nations) who tried to link into a meeting. But the benefits became clear: the BMA saved in expenses and members suffered far less disruption to their working day.

All organisations found the rapid growth of technology during this period unsettling and challenging, being obliged to set up websites, replace paper communications and generally do business in an unpredictable and often uncomfortable environment. To some extent, they had to make it up as they went along: few in 1991 could have forecast the all-embracing reach of the internet, the functionality and power of the websites that now use it, and the expectation that it should be possible to do virtually everything online (including booking an appointment with a GP). Doctors probably adapted better than many during this information revolution: as the LMC Conference reminded the Health Minister in 2009, they had always been comfortable with new technology and their work makes them natural innovators. Their problems, however, sprang from the forced changes to their working lives and to their relationships with their patients, and from the political overtones of some innovations. Throughout the constant change the BMA, while recognising new technology's benefits to members, defended patient confidentiality and stuck to the principle that technological innovations must not be used for political ends or for controlling doctors.

Chapter 9

The health of the public

The BMA is not only a trade union but also a professional association, with professional activities encompassing the health of the public, science, medical ethics, international activities, NHS IT and the BMA Library. These activities provide valuable services to members and show the outside world that the BMA's interests and concerns go beyond the narrow confines of doctors' pay and conditions. Committee chairmen 'on the political side' have sometimes commented on how useful these activities have been for keeping lines of communication with the government open when relations in other spheres were poor. On a more subtle level, even hard-headed government negotiators are aware of the good that the BMA's professional work does for its image and credibility among MPs and the general public, so that it becomes harder for them to dismiss the BMA as 'just another trade union'. The establishment of the professional, scientific and international affairs division by John Dawson in 1981 marked the beginning of increased activity in these areas and the media at that time recognised that he and John Havard, the Secretary of the Association, 'were determined that the BMA should win headlines as the patients' friend, not the doctors' "money-bagger"'.[1]

It would be a mistake, though, to regard the work of the professional activities directorate as merely window-dressing. A number of solid achievements were made in the period covered by this book and there is a genuine belief within the Association that it must use its influence and expertise both to effect improvements in public health and to guide doctors throughout their professional lives. BMA members want to do their best for their patients and communities and they recognise the need for their Association to be active in influencing policy and legislation in the interests of patients. They also expect the BMA to lead the scientific debate and speak out when the health of the public is in danger of being compromised. Areas in which members of the professional committees and their secretariats, working closely with

---

[1] Page 14 of *Promoting the Medical and Allied Sciences: A Short History of Science at the BMA*. BMA, London, 1995.

the BMA's parliamentary unit, influenced legislation during this time ranged from medical confidentiality to human rights. On an individual level, advice on ethical dilemmas has been available from the BMA's wide range of paper and electronic publications or direct from experts in the medical ethics department and this service is held in high regard at all levels of the profession.

The members and staff who work on the BMA's professional activities have their work rooted in the day-to-day-concerns of doctors' working lives. Policies often originate from individual members, sometimes through motions at annual meetings, and there is daily contact with members who bring real-life dilemmas to the BMA for solution. This enables guidance notes from the BMA to reflect the reality of medical practice. All this is achieved surprisingly economically: only £4 million of the BMA's total £48 million spend on services to members in 2010 was spent on professional activities.

The primary 'object' for which the Association was established was 'To promote the medical and allied sciences, to maintain the honour and interests of the medical profession and to promote the achievement of high quality health care.' This places promotion of scientific activities and the health of the public at the heart of the BMA's activities and this obligation has always been taken seriously by the Association. The Board of Science and Education became the main interface on matters of science and public health between the medical profession, the government and the public. Its work ranged from huge issues with an international dimension to those of interest mainly to scientists, and for many years it led the BMA's campaigns against the use of tobacco. The board's reports often attracted media and public interest, particularly when the public was seeking a rational and authoritative view on an anxiety-inducing subject, such as AIDS. The body of work undertaken by the Board of Science was enormous and the full list of reports issued over this period is attached (*see page 269*). This chapter will focus on a selection of four major issues relating to the health of the public: smoking, alcohol misuse, nutrition health and body image and health inequalities, and conclude with a summary of other BMA campaigns.

Smoking

Any account of the work that the BMA has undertaken to improve the health of the public must begin with its unrelenting battle against the use of tobacco, which led to the ban on smoking in all public places in the UK in 2007.

At the beginning of the 1980s, the hazards of smoking were already well-known. Professors Sir Richard Doll and Sir Austin Bradford Hill had established the link between smoking and lung cancer in an article published in the *British Medical Journal* in 1950.[2] Sir Richard Doll went on to show that smoking also caused heart disease and peptic ulcers and that passive and second-hand smoke was carcinogenic to humans. In the early 1980s the BMA maintained pressure on the government to revise its policies on smoking taxation, advertising and sponsorship. The Association was aware that simply presenting scientific evidence was not the best way to discourage smokers, so it sent out a leaflet to a number of organisations suggesting that stop-smoking groups should be set up within companies.

The first national No Smoking Day was on 29 February 1984[3] and the BMA was part of a co-ordinating committee which included Action on Smoking and Health (ASH), the British Heart Foundation, the Health Education Council, the Cancer Research Campaign, the Chest, Heart and Stroke Association and the National Society of Non-Smokers. In the face of a wealthy and obviously hostile tobacco industry, the Association's work to discourage smoking had to be done with other bodies: there was strength in numbers and these long-lasting alliances were to prove vital in later victories.

Tobacco advertising and sponsorship

After a 1984 ARM resolution calling upon the government to reduce the dangers of smoking by banning the advertising of tobacco products, the BMA's campaign to ban tobacco advertising, tobacco firms' sponsorship of sporting events and, most radical of all, smoking in public places, became relentless. As it had to find new ways of keeping this campaign alive, the BMA's press office managed to find inventive ways of keeping the dangers of smoking in the news once the core message that smoking was lethal had found its way into the public consciousness. From the beginning the BMA and its partners were up against a tobacco industry that was well-funded, well-organised, well-connected and determined to protect itself and its profits.

The BMA's early attempts to seek a ban on tobacco advertising did not bode well for the future. In 1984 a BMA deputation met

---

[2] Richard Doll and A Bradford Hill *Smoking and Carcinoma of the Lung, BMJ* 1950;2:739 (published 30 September 1950).
[3] The ARM banned smoking at all BMA meetings in the same year and, in January 1992, smoking was banned on all BMA premises.

the Minister for Sport, Neil MacFarlane, and drew to his attention research showing that sports sponsorship by the tobacco industry acted as cigarette advertising to children. As most smokers had started when children, the BMA asked for legislation to phase out sponsorship of sporting events by the tobacco industry. The Minister did not accept the need for legislation. Clearly the tobacco companies had to continue to recruit new smokers and it was inevitable that they would fight any attempt to prevent them reaching new consumers. The BMA hit back by producing a pamphlet countering the tobacco industry's arguments for advertising and sent it to members of both houses of Parliament and the press. The BMA kept links with the all-party parliamentary group on action on smoking and health and, in a clever piece of publicity, distributed 17,000 black-edged cards for doctors to send to their MPs each time a patient died from a smoking-related disease. In the meantime, the BMA urged the Chancellor of the Exchequer to provide an economic disincentive to smokers by increasing substantially the tax on tobacco products.

The tobacco industry defended its advertising on the grounds that it did not encourage people to begin smoking, but merely persuaded them to change brands. The BMA argued the opposite: advertising tobacco products as desirable would encourage children and young people to become smokers. By the end of the 1990s, it was estimated that 450 teenagers started smoking every day in the UK and that nearly one in three 15-year-olds was a regular smoker. In the mid-1980s, there was merely a voluntary advertising code for tobacco companies and in August 1985 the BMA urged the government to ensure that any new voluntary agreement should introduce tight controls on, for instance, advertising near sites where children spent much of their time, such as school playgrounds. Five months later the BMA was invited to submit its views to the Department of the Environment on possible changes to the sponsorship of sporting events by the industry, the first time that the Association had been invited to submit its views on this subject. It asked for greater compliance with the rules by the tobacco companies, which had become adept in finding loopholes in the current agreement. Despite this promising development, the Sports Minister refused to meet representatives of the BMA while the new agreement was being prepared and the new voluntary code on sports sponsorship, announced in January 1987, was disappointing as it failed to provide what the BMA judged to be satisfactory safeguards against the 'highly sophisticated promotional activities of tobacco companies.'

The BMA prepared a joint exercise in the mid-1980s with the Health Education Council which was known as The Big Kill, which conveyed the scale of mortality from tobacco smoking to opinion formers throughout the UK. They prepared figures for each parliamentary constituency showing the expected annual death rate and hospital admissions from lung cancer, heart disease, bronchitis and emphysema. The report also showed the cost to the NHS and the number of bed days taken up by people suffering from these diseases. The publication of The Big Kill report was marked by the release of 200 black balloons from the courtyard of BMA House in London.

In 1985 the BMA published two documents: *Cigarette Advertising and Smoking: a Review of the Evidence* and *When Smoke Gets In Your Eyes*. In the following year a new voluntary agreement on tobacco advertising and the Protection of Children (Tobacco) Act was passed. In 1987 the annual meeting called for an increase in tobacco tax and the BMA held joint press conferences with bodies such as the Medical Research Council. Every MP was sent a leaflet on the case for increased taxation, published by the BMA, ASH and the Health Education Authority. Another initiative encouraged couples about to get married to give up smoking together. The idea received widespread publicity after the Director of the Cancer Research Campaign, Ann Charlton, spoke at a press conference of studies she had carried out on the influence that parents who smoked had on their children. The BMA also took the lead in a European initiative to encourage doctors to help their patients stop smoking and with the World Health Organisation, International Union Against Cancer and the Imperial Cancer Research Fund, produced a leaflet that was sent to all GPs. In 1989 the BMA affirmed its policy for a ban against smoking in public places, emphasising that non-smokers had the right to air free from tobacco smoke.

The BMA kept up its pressure on the UK government to stop the advertising of tobacco and to ban smoking in public places, but for much of the 1980s and 1990s, it achieved little because successive governments chose not to act. It was not until May 1997, when the new Labour government came to power with a strong commitment to improve public health, that the BMA felt that firm action could be taken. Within a month, the new government had committed to ending tobacco sponsorship of sporting activities and in December the EU Council of Ministers voted to ban tobacco advertising, sponsorship and promotion. The stage appeared to be set for a UK ban and the

BMA celebrated. But disappointment soon followed when it appeared that the British government wanted to exempt Formula One motor racing. The Chairman of Council, Alexander (later Sir Alexander) Macara, led a delegation to Downing Street to impress upon the Prime Minister the importance of the ban in the light of new evidence showing that tobacco sponsorship of motor sports was influencing young people. The government later announced that motor sports would be given an eight-year exemption.

The government published the UK Tobacco White Paper *Smoking Kills* on 10 December 1998. This set out measures aimed at reducing smoking among children and young people, helping adults to give up, and also offering practical help to pregnant women who smoked. As the BMA said in the annual report, this saw 'the fruits of decades of campaigning by the BMA'. It led to huge relief throughout BMA House when it became clear that government had at last embraced much of what it had been calling for since 1984. But the BMA did not stop putting pressure on the government to do what it had promised. In the press statement welcoming the White Paper, the Chairman of Council, Ian Bogle, said: 'The Government has taken an historic first step against the tobacco industry, but its approach is more tentative and less courageous than doctors hoped for.' The BMA was disappointed that the government was sticking to the 'leisurely pace' of the EU advertising directive and urged it to hurry so that the country could 'start the new millennium free from the billboards and glossy inducements to smoke'.

Passive smoking

The BMA continued to campaign for restrictions on smoking in public places and for bans on tobacco advertising and promotion. In December 1999 it gave evidence to the House of Commons Health Select Committee Inquiry into the response of the tobacco industry to the harmful effects of smoking. In 2000 it published a booklet on smoking and male sexual impotence. The BMA's Tobacco Control Resource Centre (TCRC), which was funded by the BMA and the EU, was instrumental in the battle to ban smoking in public places and it worked in partnership with medical associations across Europe. It also encouraged doctors to stop smoking. The TCRC published an action manual, *Doctors and Tobacco*, which was made available in six European languages and campaigned for tobacco legislation and regulation at European level. The work of the centre later received an award from the World Health Organisation for its outstanding contribution to tobacco control.

In November 2002, the Board of Science and the Tobacco Control Resource Centre published *Towards Smoke-Free Public Places*. This report said that a thousand people died each year as a result of passive smoking and called for a total ban on smoking in all public places. Two years later the BMA published a report on the damage that smoking had on the reproductive health of men and women and on the harm caused to infants by exposure to second-hand smoke.[4] This was the first time that this particular aspect of the damage caused to health by smoking had been examined and the report carried some stark warnings to the public: smoking was linked to impotency in about 120,000 men between 30 and 50, implicated in about 1,200 cases of malignant cervical cancer each year, and linked to about 3–5,000 miscarriages each year.[5] Among the report's recommendations was a renewed call to make enclosed public places smoke-free. Linking the report with the BMA's concerns about health inequalities, the Chairman of Council, James Johnson, said that the BMA welcomed the government's recognition that smoking was a key factor in health inequalities and poverty, but warned against complacency: 'We need more action to tackle the devastation that smoking wreaks on families – especially in our most disadvantaged communities. Health inequalities are a key government concern, yet they continue to pursue a softly, softly approach to smoking in public places. They must act on the evidence and introduce legislation to make all enclosed public places smoke free.'

A major international development occurred five months later in May 2003 when the World Health Assembly adopted the World Health Organisation's Framework Convention on Tobacco Control. The BMA and the TCRC had given oral evidence at the preceding WHO hearings, held in response to the global tobacco epidemic. A total of 168 nations, including the UK, signed up to the convention and its implementation date of 16 March 2005. This committed

---

[4] *Smoking and Reproductive Life: the Impact of Smoking on Sexual, Reproductive and Child Health*, BMA, February 2004.
[5] Figures quoted in a press release issued by the BMA on 11 February 2004 to launch *Smoking and Reproductive Life: the Impact of Smoking on Sexual, Reproductive and Child Health*. The figures were estimates of the impact on selected aspects of sexual and reproductive health in the UK and were made by the BMA Tobacco Control Resource Centre. The press release stated that 'These figures should not be regarded as precise measures. However they do provide a reasonable indication of the magnitude of the burden of smoking on reproductive life.'

them to take firm action on tobacco-related illness and death, and the BMA was determined not to let the British government forget its pledge.

In 2004, the BMA asked members to write to the Prime Minister with their patients' experiences of passive smoking. There was a huge response, with 2,500 letters arriving within 24 hours and another 2,000 letters arriving within three weeks. The receipt of so many tragic stories allowed the BMA once again to push home the message that this was something that doctors cared passionately about and that it was imperative to ban smoking in public places to help save lives. The Deputy Chairman of Council, Sam Everington, and the Deputy Chairman of the Board of Science, Peter Maguire, arrived in Whitehall carrying an enormous replica cigarette packet with the messages: 'Passive smoking kills' and 'Smokefree workplaces save lives'. They then handed in to No 10 Downing Street the 4,500 letters from doctors. This powerful image and message generated enormous press interest and ensured that the BMA's call for a smoking ban remained in the public eye. Later, extracts from the doctors' letters were included in a BMA report, *The Human Cost of Tobacco*, as testimony to the tragedy wreaked by smoking. In the foreword the Chairman of Council, James Johnson, wrote that the report 'moves away from the numbers game and provides a snapshot of individual case studies. As doctors we see these every day because we are the ones telling patients that they have cancer or heart disease. We are the ones who witness their worlds falling apart.'

The BMA had been calling for smoking to be banned in public places for almost 20 years and, finally in May 2005, the end of the battle appeared to be in sight. In the Queen's speech that year the government announced a Health Bill. This would contain clauses on a partial smoking ban in public places and opened the door to a more widespread ban. This announcement had been preceded by intense lobbying from the BMA and other organisations such as ASH. During the general election the BMA had sent briefing material to parliamentary candidates explaining why the BMA was supporting a total ban on smoking in enclosed public places. This pressure probably led to a proposal for a partial ban being included by the Labour government in its manifesto. However, not all members of the government agreed and press reports indicated that the Prime Minister, Tony Blair, was not in favour of a total ban. But the momentum was becoming overwhelming and the BMA went all out to achieve its aim. Soon afterwards the government conducted a three-month consultation which was followed by weeks of Cabinet-level discussions. During this time the BMA had many meetings with ministers, MPs and peers. It signed up to letters to the Prime Minister and Health Secretary and took part in a fringe meeting at the Labour Party's annual conference. The BMA also worked closely with the Health Select Committee during its inquiry into smoke-free public places and submitted written evidence. The committee came out strongly in support of comprehensive legislation and the committee's MPs later tabled an amendment to the Health Bill, with assistance on drafting from the BMA's parliamentary unit.

The BMA's aim of smoke-free public places in England needed one last push. It issued another report, *Booze, Fags and Food,* which made a nonsense of the government's proposals for all pubs and bars that prepared or served food to be smoke-free after 2008. The BMA showed that in some areas over 80% of pubs did not prepare or serve food so would still allow smoking. In June 2005 the BMA's health policy and economic research unit helped to develop questions for a MORI poll which showed that 68% of the UK public believed that the health of pub staff should be protected from second-hand smoke at work. The same month the BMA responded to the Government's consultation to ban smoking in enclosed public places in England and in November the BMA joined forces with Cancer Relief UK and Asthma UK on a conference on the subject. A press conference six months later in the House of Commons united the BMA, incongruously, with the British Beer and Pub Association, Business in Sport and Leisure, and Kevin Barron MP, Chair of the Commons Health Select Committee, a long-time anti-smoking campaigner. They agreed that a partial smoking ban would be unworkable, unethical and illogical. The final step came on 14 February 2006 when, in a free vote in the House of Commons, MPs voted by a margin of 200 votes for a total ban on smoking in public places.

Considering its vigorous campaigning on the smoking ban, the BMA's reaction to the news was strangely muted and contained in a six-line press statement issued the following morning. It expressed the BMA's delight at the news but contained a reminder of the mountain still to climb, 'Every day around 30 people die in the UK as a result of second-hand smoke. Yesterday's vote will mean the beginning of the end to these frightening statistics.' Other bodies were more effusive: Professor Alex Markham, Chief Executive of Cancer Research UK, said: 'This is the most important advance in public health since

Sir Richard Doll identified that smoking causes lung cancer 50 years ago. Today's vote will protect thousands of workers and save many lives.' Deborah Arnott, director of ASH, said: 'MPs will rarely get the chance to cast a vote that does so much good, at such little cost, in such a short time. This is the best news for public health for more than 30 years.' The ban was also welcomed by the Trades Union Congress, the British Heart Foundation, the British Beer and Pub Association and the Local Government Association.[6] It came into effect on 1 July 2007.

England was the last of the four UK countries to ban smoking in enclosed public spaces. The ban in Scotland came into effect in March 2006. Wales and Northern Ireland followed in April 2007 and England in July. BMA Scotland's *Breathe Better in Scotland* campaign relied on a single message: passive smoking can kill. A ban on passive smoking in Scotland had been announced in 2004 and this decision by the Scottish Government gave added impetus to the BMA's campaigns elsewhere in the UK. The BMA in Northern Ireland, encouraged by the smoking ban in the Irish Republic, held seminars to brief the media and others. It followed this by delivering 500 letters from members in the province to the Secretary of State for Northern Ireland setting out the dangers of passive smoking and calling for immediate steps to introduce a ban. BMA Cymru Wales urged the Welsh Assembly Government to *Let the Dragon Breathe* and a ban on smoking in public places was a major focus.

Other tobacco-related campaigns

The BMA continues to work towards a 'tobacco-free society'. In 2008, it published a report on the effect of smoking imagery on encouraging young people to begin smoking[7] and recommended reducing young people's exposure to 'positive' images of smoking. Bearing in mind that the majority of smokers begin before the age of 18, and virtually all by 25, the importance of limiting the exposure of young people to the many images that appeared to make smoking a glamorous pastime was stressed. In 2011, the BMA called on the UK governments to extend smoke-free legislation to include a ban on smoking in private vehicles.[8] This attracted widespread publicity and exasperation from those smokers who felt that measures to restrict them had gone far

---

[6] Source: BBC News on-line 14 February 2006.
[7] *Forever Cool: The Influence of Smoking Imagery on Young People*, BMA Board of Science, July 2008.
[8] *Smoking in Vehicles: A Briefing from the Board of Science*, November 2011.

enough. The research compiled by the BMA was compelling: there was strong evidence that the restrictive internal environment in motor vehicles could expose drivers and passengers to toxins up to 11 times greater than in a smoky bar. This put children and other vulnerable individuals, such as the elderly, at risk.

A ban on smoking in cars might sound unachievable and unrealistic, but the BMA was determined; after all a ban on smoking in public places would have been regarded with the same sense of incredulity in 1980. The BMA might also like to take some comfort in the advice that Bertrand Russell gave to his students, 'Do not fear to be eccentric in opinion, for every opinion now accepted was once eccentric.' The Labour Government, elected in 1997, may have needed constant coaxing by the BMA and others to legislate, but its intentions on tobacco control were sincere and it effected long-standing change between 1997 and 2010. The coalition government has followed and in March 2011 announced that it had decided to implement a ban on tobacco displays in shops. Public attitudes towards smoking have changed and the BMA can take satisfaction in the revolution that it has helped to bring about. It is impossible to know how much the BMA's campaigning to ban smoking in public places led to the eventual legislation, but ministers said at the time that it had come about largely as a result of pressure from the BMA and others.[9] The efforts to bring about the ban had also taught the BMA the value of loose alliances with like-minded bodies, and it would make use of similar alliances again.

Alcohol

The BMA's campaigns on sensible drinking had to have a different emphasis from its campaigns on smoking. The anti-smoking message was simple because there was no 'safe' level of tobacco consumption. The arguments about alcohol were not so cut and dried: certainly alcohol can cause enormous damage when misused, but sensible drinking is largely safe. The BMA acknowledged this in 2008 when a report from the Board of Science said that it aimed 'to tackle alcohol misuse and not to assail those who enjoy consuming alcohol sensibly . . . [and to] promote a culture where alcohol is enjoyed safely.' Nevertheless, the BMA has never been afraid to emphasise the massive harm that misuse of alcohol can cause to the individual, their family and society and has emphasised that alcohol is a highly addictive drug.

---

[9] Author's interview with Vivienne Nathanson, BMA Director of Professional Activities, 8 March 2012.

Early on, the ARM realised that a ban on the advertising and promotion of alcohol was probably unachievable and, in 1986, the annual meeting changed its policy from a ban on advertising and promoting to supporting a policy of sensible drinking. It recognised that a total ban would be impractical but urged the government to require alcohol advertisements to include warnings against excessive consumption. The pros and cons of a ban were regularly debated within the BMA as opinions swung back and forth. In 2003, the annual meeting called on the government to ban advertising alcohol as it had done for cigarettes. Eight years later a proposal to ban alcohol advertising was agreed only as a reference,[10] not because the meeting disagreed with it, but because attitudes had hardened and the motion being debated did not go far enough and propose banning advertising of alcohol at the point of sale. Meanwhile the BMA continued to work to reduce alcohol-related harm, stressing the damage that alcohol can do and advocating measures such as restricting its availability and reducing drink-driving.

In 1981, the Association met the Trades Union Congress and the Medical Council on Alcoholism to find areas of common interest. The BMA had sought the view of the British Multiple Retailers Association and the Advertising Association on the effects of alcohol advertising in supermarkets. It brought together a number of groups for a symposium on alcohol abuse. The impact of alcohol abuse on young people was of particular concern to those at the symposium and the BMA began preparing a report on the alcohol problems of young people. It also started work on the risks of alcohol misuse during pregnancy and in 1984 distributed a leaflet warning of the effects of alcohol on an unborn baby; it even managed to persuade the Brewers' Society to meet the costs. In 1988 it published *The Drinking Driver*, which examined the evidence on drink-driving and proposed measures aimed at persistent offenders, who were likely to have an underlying drink problem, and at social drinkers who offended. The following year *The BMA Guide to Alcohol and Accidents* provided information on alcohol as a cause of accidents and also practical advice on finding out how much alcohol those attending accident and emergency departments had consumed.

As with smoking, much of the BMA's work on alcohol was targeted towards young people. In May 1986, a Board of Science report *Young*

---

[10] Passing an ARM motion as 'a reference' means that it does not become BMA policy, but is instead referred to the relevant BMA committee to take the most appropriate course of action in the interests of the Association.

People and Alcohol found that alcohol consumption had risen substantially in the UK in the preceding two decades and that people were starting to drink at a younger age. Young people had started to drink large quantities of alcohol in a single sitting leaving them susceptible to physical injury, particularly from road traffic accidents. Not surprisingly, the report recommended efforts to promote safe and responsible drinking among young people through education and controls on the purchase and consumption of alcohol. This report was updated 13 years later when it addressed a number of ARM resolutions calling for action to protect children from the dangers of alcohol. This report was considered by the ministerial group reviewing under-age drinking. Three years before, the BMA had examined the evidence on recommended daily limits and advocated a 'sensible drinking' message with clear guidelines on limits. It also recommended increasing the cost of drinking since the evidence had shown that this would have a greater effect than education and health promotion in reducing drinking. In 2005 the BMA published a web resource on the new phenomenon of 'binge drinking'[11] (when a large amount of alcohol was consumed in one sitting with drunkenness the aim of the exercise). This provided a hub for information on binge drinking, summarised the recommended drinking guidelines and suggested sources of further information.

In 2003 the Licensing Act was passed. This brought together fragmented pieces of legislation and introduced flexible opening hours for licensed premises, with the potential for 24-hour opening, seven days a week. The BMA was dismayed that public health had not been taken into account. It warned that 24-hour opening would be a disaster for social as well as health reasons, and was roundly condemned by the government who saw the new licensing laws ushering in a new 'cafe culture' and discouraging binge drinking. The BMA was later vindicated when a 2007 Home Office report indicated that, after the introduction of the act, offences of all types (criminal damage, harassment, assault with no injury, less serious wounding, serious violent crime) between 3am and 6am had increased. The report concluded that the probable factors were the change to opening hours of licensed premises and the increased numbers of people in a public place at these times.

The harm that drinking could do to unborn children was set out in a 2007 report.[12] Maternal alcohol consumption during pregnancy

---

[11] *Binge Drinking*, BMA, 2005.
[12] *Fetal Alcohol Spectrum Disorders – A Guide for Healthcare Professionals*, BMA, 2007.

could lead to mental and physical birth defects and the report aimed to raise awareness of these disorders. The report was intended for health-care professionals and bodies involved with public health and health promotion, and it outlined the responsibilities of healthcare profes-sionals and the wider medical community. It was compiled in associa-tion with charities devoted to increasing the awareness of fetal alco-hol spectrum disorders and, rather like the report on the devastating effects of passive smoking, included moving vignettes highlighting the life-long effects of even low levels of neurocognitive deficits.

Over time, the BMA developed a multi-strand approach to tack-ling excessive drinking and redressing what it termed 'the excessively pro-alcohol social norms in the UK'. In 2008 a comprehensive report, *Alcohol Misuse: Tackling the UK Epidemic*, called for reducing licens-ing hours, increasing and rationalising taxation and taking the local density of licensed premises into account when considering any plan-ning and licensing applications. The report also called for existing leg-islation to be strictly enforced. In addition there should be a compre-hensive ban on all alcohol marketing communications and legislation to prevent irresponsible promotional activities in public houses and off licences as well as minimum prices. Alcohol education and health pro-motion would be vital and the BMA recommended that educational programmes should be used only when part of a wider evidence-based strategy. It also wanted legislation to enforce standard labels clearly stating the alcohol content in units, the recommended daily UK guide-lines for alcohol consumption and a warning over exceeding these guidelines. Those selling alcohol should display notices with the same information wherever alcohol was on sale. Finally, the report proposed measures to reduce drink-driving and to establish early intervention and treatment services.

The BMA sensed that the area where it might have the most suc-cess, and that which would have the greatest impact on the social cost of excessive drinking, would be the cost of alcohol. By the millennium strong alcohol was cheap and readily available. There was no minimum price, allowing shops to sell it at a loss to lure in customers; a prac-tice which the BMA condemned. BMA Scotland led the way with a report in September 2009 setting out some facts: alcohol consumption in the UK had more than doubled over the 40 years to 2009 and latest survey estimates revealed that 40% of men and 33% of women were drinking twice the daily limits. In Western Europe, alcohol consump-tion was decreasing at a time when Scotland's consumption rates were increasing. Scotland had one of the fastest growing mortality rates from chronic liver disease in the world and alcohol-related death rates were twice those of England and Wales. In Scotland, alcohol was a factor in one death every three hours.

There was a strong relationship between the price of alcohol and consumption. When prices fell consumption increased, so the BMA suggested that drinks which were cheap but with a high alcohol content should be subject to minimum pricing, ie, the more units of pure alcohol a drink contained the more expensive it should be to buy. This would mean that there would be a minimum price for one unit of pure alcohol, below which it could not be sold, thus targeting the cheapest drinks which were popular with young people and heavy drinkers. In November 2011 the Scottish Government published its landmark Alcohol (Minimum Pricing) (Scotland) Bill, which sought to introduce a minimum price per unit of alcohol. Retailers were no longer able to sell alcoholic drink more cheaply than alcohol-free fizzy drinks.

The BMA was wary of the willingness of the drinks industry to regulate itself since the industry's main concern was to make a profit by selling as much alcohol as possible. The BMA suspected that governments chose to listen to industry rather than to health organisations and in May 2011 the Chairman of Council, Hamish Meldrum, said so publicly: 'Unfortunately the government has often ignored the advice of health organisations on how to tackle alcohol misuse and obesity, preferring to listen to and rely on the views of industries which have a vested interest in selling unhealthy products.' The BMA has never been afraid of upsetting vested interests such as those in the tobacco, alcohol or food industries, arguing that its own vested interest is in a healthier population. Two months earlier the BMA and five other health organisations[13] had decided not to sign up to the Public Health Responsibility Deal. This had been a partnership between the Department of Health, industry and the health community covering alcohol, food, physical activity and health at work. The six bodies said that they could not sign up for a number of reasons, including the fact that the drinks industry's pledges were not specific or measurable, and did not state what would be evidence of success. They also felt that the process had failed to consider alternative pledges put forward by the health community and that the policy objective, to 'foster a culture

---

[13] The other organisations were Alcohol Concern, British Association for the Study of the Liver, British Liver Trust, Institute of Alcohol Studies, and the Royal College of Physicians.

of responsible drinking' and did not address adequately the need to reduce alcohol-related mortality and morbidity.

The BMA made clear its impatience with the government, saying that it had relied on the wrong people – the drinks industry – to develop policies. Its statement continued: 'We are not sure how much evidence the government needs to see before it has the courage to act. If it really wants to tackle alcohol misuse it must develop a comprehensive strategy that will work across government departments and focus on affordability, availability and promotion. These policies will not be popular with the alcohol industry. But the government must show that it cares more for reducing the number of lives ruined by alcohol misuse than it does for keeping the industry happy.'[14] The BMA had wanted to work with various government departments to explore evidence-based policies that could turn the tide against harm caused by alcohol. At the end of this period, led by BMA Scotland, it was focusing its efforts on minimum pricing and, as with the ban on smoking in public places, perhaps positive action in one of the UK nations may shame the others into action.

Nutrition, health and body image

The importance of diet and health was discussed at the 1984 ARM when members of the Board of Science made clear their belief that information had to be given to the public on the use of additives in food. They also said that the government should encourage the marketing of healthy foodstuffs to, as the BMA delicately put it, 'sections of the population who, for reasons such as poverty or lack of knowledge, tend to eat inappropriate or harmful foods.' In response to these concerns, in 1986 the BMA published *Diet, Nutrition and Health*.[15] It set out comprehensive, practical national dietary goals and explained how many organisations and individuals could help to improve the nation's diet.

The message is as relevant in 2012 as it was in 1986: less refined sugar, fats, salt and alcohol and more poultry, fish, fruit and vegetables. Some groups, however, have on the whole remained stubbornly indifferent to these healthy eating messages, though the BMA tried hard over the years to persuade the nation to change its eating habits.

---

[14] The BMA quoted in a press release issued by the Royal College of Physicians, *Key health organisations do not sign responsibility deal*, 14 March 2011.
[15] *Diet, Nutrition and Health: Report of the Board of Science and Education*, BMA, 1986.

Towards the end of the period under study it called on the governments to promote healthy eating and physical exercise. The prevalence of obesity had more than doubled in the UK between 1985 and 2010 and over half of the UK population could be obese by 2050. In cash terms, the BMA said, the health and social care costs associated with treatment for obesity and the costs to the wider economy arising from chronic ill health was costing England an estimated £7 billion annually. So when in 2011 the English government disbanded its expert advisory group on obesity, the Association condemned it as a retrograde step. As with its battles over alcohol misuse, the BMA suspected that the food and drinks industry had the ear of the government: 'It is more evidence that the government is listening to big business rather than public health experts on matters of national public health importance.'

As with smoking and excessive alcohol consumption, individual doctors had to deal with the disastrous health and social consequences of over-eating and obesity. The Association focused on pressing the UK governments to take action at the national levels. It has promoted the benefits of food labelling, believing that consistency was vital in helping the consumer to make properly informed choices. It therefore called on the food and drink industry to use the 'traffic light' approach recommended by the Food Standards Agency.

Obesity was implicated in the soaring rate of diabetes in a report published in February 2004.[16] It made clear that the 'global explosion' in diabetes was largely due to social and behavioural changes, with studies showing that lack of exercise and high fat intake could result in insulin resistance. Obesity was a key factor in the increased incidence of non-insulin dependent (type 2) diabetes in the young. As with smoking and drinking, the BMA concentrated much of its efforts on the young, with two reports: *Growing Up in Britain: Ensuring a Healthy Future for our Children* (1999) and *Adolescent Health* (2003). A third report in 2005 looked at preventing childhood obesity[17] and was written as a guide for GPs and other healthcare professionals: it reminded them that there were about 1 million people under 16 who were obese. The BMA then went further back in the life-cycle with its 2009 report *Early Life Nutrition and Lifelong Health* which provided information for health care professionals about how to improve early life nutrition and underlined the importance of fetal and early life nutrition to lifelong health.

[16] *Diabetes Mellitus: An Update for Healthcare Professionals*, BMA, February 2004.
[17] *Preventing Childhood Obesity*, BMA, 2005.

Another story ran parallel to that of the obesity epidemic: the growth of eating disorders. This subject received considerable media coverage when it was debated at the 1998 ARM and even more when the Board of Science published a report on the subject in May 2000, especially as the media, particularly magazines aimed at young women, was the target of doctors' concern.[18] Fashion models were becoming thinner while women were becoming heavier, leading to a gap between the media's 'ideal' body shape and reality. The report acknowledged that eating disorders were caused by 'a complex interplay between genetics, family history, and the cultural environment', but maintained that the influence of the media was enormous and urged television programme makers and magazine publishers to adopt a 'more responsible editorial attitude towards the depiction of extremely thin women as role models, and . . . portray a more realistic range of body images'.

Although the report had contained other recommendations, the main story was predictably the link between eating disorders and 'skinny models'.[19] Equally predictable was the defence by magazine editors who argued that the issue had been over-simplified by the BMA. The editor of *Elle* magazine said: 'It insults readers of glossy magazines to hear that women should be treated as fragile neurotics; that we are not intelligent enough to make a simple distinction between fantasy and reality.'[20] The editor of *Vogue* claimed: 'All we are doing is showing images of women we regard as interesting or beautiful or fashionable. But we are not actually saying you have to be like this.'[21] On the other hand the BMA's report was warmly welcomed by the Eating Disorders Association which, along with the BMA and representatives of the advertising and fashion industry, attended a 'summit' in Downing Street to discuss the ways in which body image could affect young girls' self-esteem, and the increasing prevalence of disorders like anorexia and bulimia. The summit was hosted by Women's Minister, Tessa Jowell, who backed the idea of a new voluntary code regulating media images of women. Unfortunately, thin models continue to be the norm and it is newsworthy when magazines feature models with a normal body shape. Eating disorders continue to proliferate and the debate continues on the link between these disorders and the ideal body image purveyed by the media.

---

[18] *Eating Disorders, Body Image and the Media*, published 30 May 2000.
[19] *Skinny models 'send unhealthy message'*, The Guardian 31 May 2000.
[20] *Glossies hit out at BMA*, Media Week, 1 June 2000.
[21] *Models link to teenage anorexia*, BBC on-line article, 30 May 2000.

Health inequalities

Inequalities in health is a subject with a chequered history and one over which the BMA has campaigned for many years. The BMA's reports on childhood nutrition and obesity highlighted environmental issues and in particular parental socio-economic status. The 2005 report stated clearly:

> 'Those [children] from low socio-economic backgrounds have a greater risk of obesity than children in more affluent households. There is evidence that inequalities exist in the consumption of fruit and vegetables, with lower consumption among children from lower socio-economic households . . . Low income may also restrict access to food retailers where healthy food is available, and deny access to the equipment necessary for food storage and preparation. Food deserts (areas of relative exclusion where people experience physical and economic barriers to accessing healthy food) are more likely to be found in areas of socio-economic deprivation. Opportunities to exercise may also be limited in such environments; for example, there may be nowhere safe to play, no facilities for physical activities outside school and shortage of money to participate in such activities.'

The history in the UK of examining statistics to help explain the causes of social inequalities in health goes back to the 1830s and in 1980 a seminal report was published by Sir Douglas Black, then President of the Royal College of Physicians.[22] This showed that inequalities in Britain persisted, despite the great improvements in health in the twentieth century, and that social class gradients were present for many different causes of morbidity and mortality. Sir Douglas also concluded that, although the NHS offered free universal health care, it could not respond to the challenge posed by the relationship between wide social inequalities and health. The circumstances surrounding the publication of the Black report contributed to its renown. It had been commissioned in 1977 by the Labour Health Minister, David Ennals, and was ready for publication in the spring of 1979, but was delayed due to the impending general election. The new Conservative government did not publish it until 1980, choosing to do so on the August bank holiday and on the day making only about 260 press copies available. This aroused suspicions of a cover-up of an uncomfortable read, but did not stop the report having a huge impact.

---

[22] Black D, Morris J, Smith C *et al* (1980). *Inequalities in Health: Report of a Research Working Group*. London: Department of Health and Social Security.

The BMA wanted to find out how it could support the report and the 1985 annual meeting agreed that the BMA should campaign for its implementation. Council set up a working group to identify areas for further investigation and, as a sign of the importance that the BMA attached to this subject, other groups sprang up within the Association to consider the report. One of these was set up by the Board of Science, now chaired by Sir Douglas Black, to consider evidence for a relationship between deprivation and disease. The Board's working party reported in 1987 and confirmed that social disadvantage made an important contribution to ill health.[23] It recommended that:

- preventative services and education, especially outreach and community initiatives, should be improved;
- the standards and availability of housing should be raised;
- financial support for those on low incomes should be reviewed; and
- the relationship between social circumstances and health should be further studied to help with planning health and local government services.

Health inequalities in the UK did not decline, of course, and, eight years later, the Board of Science and Education warned again that the wealth and health gap was widening and that health education and promotion were insufficient on their own.[24] The report urged the government to 'provide a social and economic environment in which health education and promotion strategies can succeed'.

There was one topic on which the BMA was especially vociferous: 'water poverty'. In 1994 its publication *Water – a Vital Resource*[25] called for a halt to the practice of disconnecting water supplies to those who had not paid their bills. This prompted an editorial in *The Lancet* and was used by organisations attempting to influence water company policy. The number of disconnections of domestic customers went down. The BMA also gave evidence to the House of Commons Environment Committee arguing that water metering should not be used as a means of conserving water supplies.

The new Labour administration, elected in May 1997, appeared to take health inequalities more seriously than its predecessor governments and asked the former Chief Medical Officer, Sir Donald

---

[23] *Deprivation and Ill-Health*, BMA, 1987.
[24] *Inequalities in health: An Occasional Paper from the Board of Science and Education* published in 1995.
[25] *Water – A Vital Resource*, BMA, 1994.

Acheson, to chair an inquiry. Sir Donald and his team, which included Sir Michael Marmot, the author of ground-breaking work on the social determinants of health, reported in November 1998[26] and their message was stark. Average mortality had fallen over the previous 50 years but 'unacceptable' inequalities in health persisted: 'For many measures of health, inequalities have either remained the same or have widened in recent decades.' The report continued that the scientific evidence the group had gathered supported a socioeconomic explanation of health inequalities which traced 'the roots of ill health to such determinants as income, education and employment as well as to the material environment and lifestyle'. These inequalities affected the whole of society and people at all stages of life. The BMA welcomed the publication of this report and its recommendations that involved every government department in closing the gap between the health of the rich and poor. Severe problems persisted and in 2003 the BMA drew attention to the fact that 'the most socially and economically deprived are also those who suffer the worst health.'

Poor housing remained a great concern to doctors and the BMA contacted the Secretary of State for the Environment about this during the passage of the Housing Bill in 1988. The Association said that rented housing should be geared towards the needs of the poorest families, especially the homeless. Many homeless families at that time lived in unsuitable and unhealthy bed and breakfast accommodation with high levels of gastroenteritis, skin disorders and chest infections. The 2000 ARM asked the Board of Science to produce a report that would set the minimum health requirements for housing. When it was published three years later[27] it noted that there had been a steady decline in political interest in poor housing in the second half of the twentieth century and that this was in spite of overwhelming evidence of growing social inequalities in society and wide-spread recognition of the health consequences of poor housing. The report examined evidence on health and housing, suggested strategies for ensuring that everyone had good quality housing, and proposed ways of moving forward. The main recommendation was for a Healthy Housing Taskforce. By 2003, when the BMA's report on health and housing was published, public attention had already been drawn to the importance of improving insulation and heating systems in new and existing buildings in the

---

[26] Acheson D, *Independent Inquiry in Inequalities in Health*, November 1998.

[27] *Housing and Health: Building for the Future*, May 2003.

Acheson report.[28] The government's 1999 white paper, *Saving Lives: Our Healthier Nation*, expressly recognised housing as a key health determinant, as did a number of Scottish Office publications. The 2002 Spending Review had recommended that housing should be a focus of programmes and resources.

It was one thing for the BMA to draw attention to the damaging effect of social class on health, but what was it doing to improve the situation? Its work in this area was given an enormous boost in June 2010 when it elected Sir Michael Marmot as its President for a year. Sir Michael's reputation in the area of health inequalities and social determinants of health was unrivalled and his Presidential address on the subject will never be forgotten by those who heard it. Sir Michael's passion for his subject and his call for action to be taken to address an iniquitous situation that was condemning swathes of people to ill-health and early death led to a spontaneous standing ovation – the first that had ever occurred in the rarefied atmosphere of the installation of the president ceremony. The Association therefore decided to encourage doctors to take action. The subsequent report *Social Determinants of Health: What Doctors Can Do*, encouraged doctors to be community leaders as well as clinicians and to 'work to raise the understanding of the impact of social determinants of health, and to reduce that impact by tailored interventions.' The BMA started to post examples of effective actions on its website and urged the World Medical Association to collect examples world-wide. The Association continued to press the UK governments to assess the impact of all policies on health inequalities and for the effects of social determinants to be included in some medical examination syllabuses. In November 2011, the University College London Institute of Health Equality was established to build on the work of Professor Sir Michael Marmot and was supported by University College London, the Department of Health and the BMA.

Other issues

Weapons and warfare

In 1981, when armed conflict between the nuclear superpowers remained a strong possibility, the ARM asked the Board of Science and Education to review the medical effects of nuclear war and the value of civil defence. At the time doctors were being asked to work with local authorities on stocking nuclear shelters. After a marathon

---

[28] Acheson D, *Independent Inquiry in Inequalities in Health*, November 1998.

evidence-collecting exercise,[29] the report was published in early 1983[30] and Council held two heart-searching debates that spring on whether its entry into this area was compromising its political neutrality. Council wanted to make clear that the views in the report were not BMA policy and that it was certainly not the intention of the BMA to adopt any stance on the question of nuclear weapons. The report spoke for itself, however, and it made a terrifying read with its devastating account of the immediate effects on civilian populations of the blast, the delayed clinical effects and the impact on the ability of the NHS to function. It became something of a best-seller: by the beginning of 1984 it had sold more than 10,000 copies and sales were continuing at about 500 a month. The report had been uncompromising in its assertion that a nuclear attack would cause medical services to collapse and therefore planning was futile. As a result of its report, the BMA was invited to a meeting with ministers at the Home Office and Health Departments on redrafting the circular dealing with the operation of the NHS in times of war. Rarely has a single BMA report been so influential. It was followed up in 1986 by *The Long-term Environmental and Medical Effects of Nuclear War*. Both reports were published before the Chernobyl disaster and the Chairman of the Board of Science at that time, Professor Peter Quilliam, later said that it was interesting to compare the reports' predicted effects of a local nuclear strike on the medical care of victims with what actually happened at Chernobyl, 'which produced both expected and unexpected effects.'[31]

These works were followed by a report on the criteria to be applied when selecting casualties for treatment following a nuclear attack,[32] which had been called for by the 1986 ARM. This report aroused much public and press interest. It detailed the extreme situation where medical equipment would be in short supply with no more being available, and made clear that its conclusions should be seen as a starting point for public debate. Two more related reports followed: *Medical Implications of Biological and Chemical Warfare* (1987) and *Biotechnology, Weapons*

---

[29] The 1982–83 Annual Report of Council records that written evidence was received from over 60 organisations, including the Home Office, the Ministry of Defence and the Department of Health and Social Services. Oral evidence was also taken.

[30] *The Medical Effects of Nuclear War: Report by the Board of Science and Education*, 1983.

[31] Page 36 of *Promoting the Medical and Allied Sciences: A Short History of Science at the BMA*. BMA, London, 1995.

[32] *Nuclear Attack: Ethics and Casualty Selection*, BMA Board of Science and Education, 1988.

and Humanity (1998). This latter report formed the basis of a television documentary.

Acquired Immune Deficiency Syndrome (AIDS)

During the first half of the 1980s the advent of Acquired Immune Deficiency Syndrome (AIDS) was causing widespread public alarm and the BMA was receiving many calls about it from worried individuals. A number of initiatives were taken by the BMA, led by John Dawson, the head of Association's professional, scientific and international affairs division. In 1985 the BMA produced guidance for the medical profession, with a summary for the public.[33] As knowledge about AIDS advanced rapidly, the Board of Science convened experts to review the guidance and, by the end of 1986, the Association had issued its third statement on AIDS. There was a background of public fear and prejudice against those with HIV infection or AIDS and, given the context, the BMA's advice was sensible, measured and compassionate. The Association said:

- consent was needed before testing for HIV antibodies if the patients were identifiable;
- the population as a whole did not need to be screened for the disease;
- members of 'at risk' groups should not be screened without their consent, but should be encouraged to undergo voluntary testing;
- antibody testing should always be accompanied by counselling;
- AIDS and HIV should not be made notifiable diseases[34];
- AIDS sufferers should not be subject to compulsory isolation; except in the rare and extreme circumstances provided for in regulations.[35]

Importantly for those with HIV infection, the BMA made the following statements: discrimination against them in employment or non-sexual social contact was both unnecessary and unjustified and that there should be no circumstances in which a person should be refused necessary treatment because of HIV infection and the traditional confidentiality of the doctor-patient relationship should be upheld in the cases of patients with HIV or AIDS.

---

[33] BMA Statement on AIDS, BMA Board of Science, March 1985.

[34] A 'notifiable disease' is one which must by law be reported to an appropriate authority. These are normally diseases which could spread rapidly, are difficult to treat or cure and potentially life-threatening.

[35] The relevant regulations in 1986 were the Public Health (Infectious Diseases) Regulations 1985.

A problem did occur, however, when the 1987 annual meeting passed a resolution stating that testing for HIV antibodies 'should be at the discretion of the patient's doctor and should not necessarily require the consent of the patient'. Some doctors had become worried that the AIDS virus could be transmitted to healthcare workers and wanted to be clear about the status of their patient. But the resolution presented the BMA with ethical, scientific and political dilemmas. Council sought legal advice which stated that taking a blood sample for the predominant purpose of testing for HIV antibodies without patient consent could, except in the most exceptional circumstances, constitute battery – or leave the doctor open to a negligence claim for failing to make clear to the patient the nature of the test and the possible consequences of a positive result. The Central Committee for Hospital Medical Services sought further legal advice which agreed with that obtained by Council. In view of this, Council had little choice other than to invoke the constitutional instrument by which it can disregard ARM policy in the interests of the Association. A full report went to the Norwich ARM the following year in a meeting which was dominated by heated exchanges on the Association's stance on testing for AIDS and the subject threatened to tear the meeting apart. David Bolt, the President, in an impressive display of diplomacy, brought the warring sides together to draft a motion which most could agree on. The motion was passed and the Association's policy was now 'That HIV testing should only be performed on clinical grounds and with the specific consent of the patient. There may be individual clinical circumstances where a doctor believes that in the best interests of a particular patient it is necessary to depart from this general rule, but if the doctor does so, he or she must be prepared to justify this action before the courts and the General Medical Council. This does not preclude the BMA from supporting anonymous prevalence screening for HIV without specific consent.' David Bolt's shuttle diplomacy was a highly unusual, and probably unique, example of the BMA President becoming closely involved in a political issue.

The BMA was active in providing public education on HIV prevention, producing a well-received booklet *AIDS and You* and producing videos for GPs on caring for HIV patients. At a time when AIDS and its transmission was causing enormous public concern, often based on misinformation, the BMA was a voice of reason. Copies of the *Third Statement on AIDS* were in great demand and the document had a major influence in establishing public policy. The *AIDS and You* booklet received professional acclaim and huge demand following its publication in March 1987 when 30,000 copies were sent to doctors. It was reprinted for the third time in July 1988 and within a year 80,000 copies had been distributed and it had been established as a standard educational and counselling booklet. It was also translated into Portuguese, German and Japanese. A second edition appeared in 1991 and was again widely distributed.

The BMA Foundation for AIDS was set up as a charity in 1988 and work was transferred to this from the BMA secretariat. The name was changed in 2002 to the Medical Foundation for AIDS and Sexual Health to reflect its extended role. The Foundation soon got down to the important work of providing guidance to doctors and produced a series of videos and booklets for GPs and their practice staff. The videos gave much needed practical advice, explaining appropriate control of infection procedures and showing how patients could be counselled before and after HIV testing. Other videos were made for senior and junior hospital staff. The foundation summarised the legal and ethical opinions that had begun to appear in *HIV Infection and AIDS Ethical Considerations for the Medical Profession (1988)*. This was exactly the sort of practical help that doctors had been calling for and the Association made sure that it continued to offer support and advice to the profession while not neglecting the important work on human rights and UK-wide policy.

Transport, health and the environment

The BMA has long been interested in the effect of environmental factors on health and produced a number of policy documents looking at the environment and pollution. In 1987 it published *Living with Risk*[36] which considered environmental risks as part of its study into how people dealt with risk in their daily lives. *Hazardous Waste and Human Health*[37] followed in 1991 and gave an overview of the available evidence on hazardous waste and regulations governing its disposal. As with most of the Board of Science's reports, it was written to help doctors in their daily lives and, specifically, to give them the information that they might need when patients came to them with concerns about, for example, local waste disposal facilities. The report addressed the role that doctors could play in increasing public knowledge of potential

---

[36] *Living With Risk*, BMA 1987. This publication was reissued by Penguin Books in 1990 as *The BMA Guide to Living with Risk*.
[37] *Hazardous Waste and Human Health*, BMA, 1991, published by Oxford University Press.

risk factors. It was produced partly in response to anecdotal evidence from GPs worried about patients with symptoms that might have been related to exposure to hazardous wastes. Doctors themselves produce hazardous waste and the BMA also issued advice on how to dispose of it properly.[38]

Transport is clearly of interest to doctors as different modes of transport can impact on health, for example through air pollution, and also because transport safety is an important issue. In 1982 the Association called for lead to be removed from petrol unless scientific evidence could be produced to prove that it posed no risk to health. The Association was doubtful that such evidence could be produced because its information showed that lead in petrol contributed substantially to the total lead load carried by an individual. This concern was, in the early 1980s, ahead of its time. The Association also saw the dangers of travelling unrestrained in moving motor vehicles and had long advocated the use of seat belts in the front seats of cars. This became a legal requirement in 1983 after a 10-year campaign by the BMA. Once this had been achieved, the BMA began to press for the compulsory use of rear seat belts also. It welcomed regulations requiring rear seat belts or child restraints to be installed in all new cars from 1 October 1985 and for those first registered from 1 April 1987. It took two years before compulsory wearing of back seatbelts was introduced for children and another two for adults.

The BMA continued to develop policy on transport and, in September 1997, it published *Road Transport and Health* which assessed the scientific evidence for the impact of vehicle emissions, traffic noise, increased congestion and the social isolation resulting from poor public transport. The report recommended that government and local authorities at the macro-level, and employers and hospital trusts at the micro-level, should act to improve the health of their workforce. The BMA submitted detailed written evidence to the government's integrated transport policy and the transport white paper published the following year, and issued a press statement highlighting its concerns about air pollution and the need for a reduction in road traffic.

In 1995 the ARM called for harmonising the drink-drive limit throughout Europe and for legislation on the effect of drugs on driving. For many years the BMA's policy had been to reduce the drink-drive

---

[38] *A Code of Practice for Sterilisation of Medical Instruments and Control of Cross-infection* (June 1989). *A Code Of Practice For The Safe Use And Disposal Of Sharps* (1990).

limit from the 1967 level of 80 milligrams of alcohol in 100 millilitres of blood to no more than 50 milligrams. Its argument was that the relative risk of a driver being involved in traffic accidents increased significantly at that point. Despite some success in drawing attention to this issue, the original 1967 level has not been reduced. The 2011 annual meeting reiterated the Association's condemnation at the refusal of the then coalition government to make a change in the light of recommendations made by Sir Peter North in his expert report[39] and said 'a further 168 people will die needlessly on our roads this year and in every subsequent year.' The government had argued that better enforcement would have more impact on the most dangerous drink-drivers and it would not be an effective use of resources to lower the limit.'[40] Lobbying by the BMA did have one important result, however: a new law came into effect on 1 October 2002 allowing blood samples to be taken from unconscious drivers involved in road traffic accidents. The specimen may be tested if the driver recovers and agrees.

With the increased interest in cycling, the 1989 ARM asked for a study of cycling safety and the Board of Science established a group to look at bicycle usage and the risks associated with it. This work generated much public interest and the BMA set up a steering group with UK and European cycling organisations. In February 1992 it published a report *Cycling Towards Health and Safety* and this had to manoeuvre a careful line between advocating the health benefits of regular cycling and acknowledging the risks of dangerous road conditions. The report recommended measures to increase cycling and also to increase greater safety for all road users through reducing speed limits in urban areas and introducing cycle networks. The report was followed by a campaign launched in general practices to promote the health benefits of cycling and to encourage GPs to discuss physical activity with their patients. The BMA was 'delighted' when the government announced a national cycling strategy, particularly since the government acknowledged that the BMA's report had been influential.

As well as its work on the benefits of cycling, the BMA had a prolonged, and somewhat esoteric, internal debate on whether or not to recommend the compulsory wearing of cycle helmets. This matter was not one in which the majority of members had a great deal of interest, but it still commanded time at annual meetings. In 1998 came a call for

---

[39] *Report of the Review of Drink and Drug Driving Law*, published on 16 June 2010.
[40] *The Government's Response to the Reports by Sir Peter North CBE QC and the Transport Select Committee on Drink and Drug Driving*, March 2011.

a campaign to promote the wearing of cycle helmets and the Board of Science then wrote a report sent to all health authorities with a BMA safety poster for displaying in schools. The report strongly recommended cycle helmets, but did not call for them to be compulsory. However, five years later the BMA's Board of the Directorate of Professional Activities, taking into account a review of evidence which had emerged since 1999, changed this policy by recommending the compulsory wearing of cycle helmets by both adults and children. The ARM affirmed this policy in 2005, but there has been no legislation on this.

During the period covered by this book the BMA has acted to show doctors how they can play an effective part in helping to manage the environment. This was made clear in the 1998 report *Health and Environmental Impact Assessment: an Integrated Approach*,[41] which led to the BMA being consulted by the British government, the European Commission and the World Health Organisation. In its report the BMA had called for human health to be at the heart of the planning process and recommended that all major policies should be assessed in advance to see if they would have health benefits or unintended adverse consequences.

By the mid-1990s, public concern was growing about the potential dangers of genetically modified food. As with other subjects which had caused public anxiety, the BMA's report, published in 1999,[42] generated great interest. The publication was followed by a round-table meeting which the BMA hosted and which included major interest groups. The BMA had acknowledged that the issues around GM foods were moving fast and had concluded that the safest course of action would be a moratorium on planting GM crops. It expressed deep concerns about the long-term impact of GM foods on health and called a halt until trials could be assessed for environmental contamination and ecological impact.

Concerns about climate change continued to grow, and the BMA received a reminder from the Representative Body that its reaction had so far been 'muted at best'[43] and it was urged to increase awareness of the issue, lobby the UK governments on appropriate action and highlight the enormous carbon footprint of the NHS. The BMA, working with the sustainability consultants Best Foot Forward, took a close look

---

[41] *Health and Environmental Impact Assessment: an Integrated Approach*, BMA, 1998, published by Earthscan.
[42] *The Impact of Genetic Modification on Agriculture, Food and Health*, BMA, 1999.
[43] ARM resolution 2009.

at its own carbon footprint and set up an internal staff group to examine ways of reducing it. It joined the Climate and Health Council, part of the BMJ Publishing Group and an international body established specifically to encourage healthcare professionals to take action to help limit climate change. The major refurbishment of BMA House which was completed in 2008 used low energy lighting and heating. The BMA also took a lead role in developing the 2009 World Medical Association declaration on health and climate change which encouraged doctors 'to act within their professional settings (clinics, hospitals, laboratories etc.) to reduce the environmental impact of medical activities, and to develop environmentally sustainable professional settings . . . to act to minimize their impact on the environment, reduce their carbon footprint and encourage those around them to do so.'[44]

The BMA put information on its website advising doctors on what they could do on climate change, pointing out that it would be good for their patients' health. Those who walked or cycled more, for instance, would improve their health and decrease their carbon emissions. Encouraging people to eat less red meat would reduce the carbon emissions associated with livestock farming and provide health benefits through an improved diet. The BMA emphasised that doctors, as trusted influential professionals, were well placed to take action on climate change and urged them to make changes in their own workplace and in their community. It asked them to inform their patients and the public about climate change and encouraged them to lead by example by ensuring that their own life-styles were climate friendly. All of this was accompanied by information on how doctors could take practical steps to achieve all of these things. The BMA had realised that climate change was of fundamental importance to doctors as a result of its effects on health, but was aware that there was only so much that it could do on an organisational level and, once it had lobbied government and joined forces with international bodies, it had to come up with some practical measures that doctors could adopt in their professional and personal lives to help make a difference on an individual level. Therefore, as with its advice to doctors on what they could do as individuals about health inequalities, it took its information on climate change down to the personal level to encourage action in the face of a potentially overwhelming problem that the individual could feel powerless to affect.

---

[44] Points 1.3 and 1.4 of *WMA Declaration of Delhi on Health and Climate Change*, Adopted by the 60th WMA General Assembly, New Delhi, India, October 2009.

Risk

The Board of Science's report on risk[45] (1987) attracted outstanding reviews, extensive media coverage and excellent sales. It was also awarded the first Science Book Prize by the Science Museum and the Committee on the Public Understanding of Science. The report had stated that in a complex and technological world all activities carried some risk to health and no-one could be assured of safety. It concluded with sections on the perception, acceptability and management of risk. The report explored methods used to estimate and evaluate risk, such as cost-benefit and cost-effectiveness analyses, and concluded that limited resources were best spent where the most reduction was likely to be achieved. The report was popular and a second edition was published in the spring of 1990.

The 2010 ARM asked the Board of Science to update this important work to reflect the understanding of risk in the 21st century. *Risk: What's Your Perspective?* was published in February 2012 to give doctors an overview of the major health risks faced by people in Britain and to provide practical advice on communicating these risks to patients. The 2012 document focused more specifically on health risks, whether they were public health issues (such as pandemic influenza or natural disasters) or those associated with life-style (smoking, obesity or alcohol). As the report said: 'Doctors will be familiar with the risks, benefits, and uncertainties surrounding the common procedures and treatments of their chosen specialty', but just as important as the statistics behind the various health risks were associated social and psychological factors and the communication of these to patients was vital.

Boxing

The 1982 ARM passed a motion calling for boxing to be abolished in view of the resulting and proven damage to eyes and brain. This became a difficult subject for the BMA over the years as, despite the clarity of ARM resolutions, the profession disagreed over the wisdom of calling for abolition. On the one hand, boxing is the only professional sport where the deliberate infliction of injury is the whole point of the exercise; but, on the other, boxing clubs are attended by some young people who might otherwise vent their aggression in less controlled environments elsewhere. Nevertheless, the BMA took its concerns to

---

[45] *Living with Risk*, BMA 1987, reprinted by Penguin Books in 1990 as *The BMA Guide to Living with Risk*.

the top, and when the World Boxing Council visited London, drew the attention of its President to the fact that medical associations in many countries had advocated a ban.

Following its report on boxing in 1984,[46] the BMA continued to press home the message that boxing could cause enormous harm and promulgated the evidence for this. The Association provided speakers at a number of meetings, including one at the Cambridge Union and the annual meeting of the Amateur Boxing Association. In 1986 the BBC invited the BMA to take part in a programme based on the argument that 'boxing is unacceptably dangerous and should be banned'. The BMA retained editorial control and the programme was critically acclaimed. In 1991 the House of Lords discussed a bill sponsored by Lord Taylor of Gryfe to abolish 'boxing for profit' and the BMA's views were widely reported during the debate. The bill was lost by two votes.

Meanwhile there had been developments within the control of boxing, changes in attitudes towards it, and advances in medicine which enabled early detection of damage to the brain. In the light of these the BMA published in June 1993 *The Boxing Debate* to review the evidence on acute and chronic injuries resulting from boxing. It attracted widespread public attention. BMA policy on boxing had strengthened as the 1992 annual meeting had called for a total ban on amateur and professional boxing. More importantly, the BMA had been given information showing that since 1984 eight boxers had died and a further six survived only after surgery for intra-cranial haemorrhage. Since 1988, three boxers had suffered detached retinas and two had had to stop boxing. The BMA said in 1993: 'Over the ten years of the [BMA's] campaign there has been a notable change in media coverage of boxing. It is now commonplace for the media to report on the ongoing debate regarding the safety of boxing and the BMA's views have been reported by sports journalists and medical journalists alike . . . The BMA's campaign has therefore been successful in achieving this apparent change in attitude towards boxing and the damage that it may cause.' *Where's the Sport in Boxing?*, a short film made by the BMA and funded by advertising and film executives, was shown in cinemas in 1996–97.

In May 1998 the boxer Spencer Oliver was seriously injured in a title fight. The BMA reiterated its call for a ban and said that none of the safety measures introduced over the past 10 years could have

---

[46] *Boxing*, BMA, 1984.

any effect as long as the head remained a target. Serious brain injury and eye damage would continue. However, some doctors dissented and an article in the March 1998 edition of the *Journal of Medical Ethics* (itself a *BMJ* publication) claimed that the BMA's policy was 'inconsistent, paternalistic and too weak to justify a change to criminal law'.[47] Nevertheless, the BMA said it was optimistic that the tide was turning in its favour and its spokesperson said, 'I've no doubt we will see further change over the next number of years.'[48]

Alternative and complementary therapy

Alternative and complementary therapies have long been popular in the UK and doctors have viewed them with varying amounts of scepticism. Some see them as harmful, while others practise them. The 1983–84 annual report noted that there was 'increasing public interest' in alternative therapies and reported that, encouraged by the Prince of Wales who was President of the Association in 1982–83, a working party had been set up to assess the value of the different therapies and clarify the BMA's policy. More than 600 written submissions were received on more than 60 different therapies and, as was wearily reported at the time, the task of dealing with the mass of material had delayed the report. It was finally approved by Council in May 1986,[49] and concluded that the fundamental difference between orthodox and alternative medicine was that orthodox medicine was based on scientific principles. If unorthodox methods were to be accepted, they had to be evaluated scientifically. The report also noted that part of the appeal of alternative medicine was that its practitioners were able to offer patients time and compassion, which orthodox practitioners were often too busy to do.

The Board of Science continued to work on complementary and alternative therapy as public interest in this area of treatment grew and in 1990 set up a working party to consider developments since the 1986 report. The working party commissioned a survey of bodies representing the major therapies in the UK to seek their views on training, qualifications, practice, organisation and research. It also invited ministries of health and medical associations in Europe to submit information on the practice and control of non-conventional therapies. The report, published in June 1993,[50] considered in particular the process by which

---

[47] Quoted in *BMA renews call for boxing ban*, BBC News on-line, 3 May 1998.
[48] Quoted in *BMA renews call for boxing ban*, BBC News on-line, 3 May 1998.
[49] *Alternative Therapy*, BMA Board of Science, 1986.
[50] *Complementary Medicine, New Approaches to Good Practice*, Oxford University Press, June 1993.

care was transferred between medical practitioners and therapists and considered models of good practice in control of various therapies. It topped the best seller list in the *BMJ* bookshop for September 1993 and many complementary medicine organisations supported its findings.

Seven years later a BMA press release reported that up to 5 million people in the UK had consulted a practitioner in complementary and alternative medicine. The press release was part of the launch of *Acupuncture, Efficacy, Safety and Practice* (2000). The BMA had found that almost half of GPs had referred their patients for acupuncture and forty-six per cent wanted to be trained in the therapy. On the crucial question of efficacy, the BMA concluded that acupuncture appeared to be more effective than control interventions for nausea and vomiting (particularly for post-operative symptoms in adults), back pain, dental pain and migraine. The evidence was unclear, however, on whether it was effective in treating osteoarthritis, neck pain, recovery from stroke, tension headache, fibromyalgia and certain joint dysfunctions.

At the end of that year the House of Lords Science and Technology Committee produced its report on complementary medicine. The BMA had submitted oral and written evidence and the final report reflected BMA policy, in particular the need for a single regulatory body for each of the main therapies.

Doctors were divided over the validity of complementary and alternative therapies, but their patients used them and still needed information about them. In 2009 the Board of Science published a web resource, *Complementary and Alternative Medicine: What Your Patients May be Using*. Although the report was approved by Council in March, a number of sceptics successfully insisted that a summary box should be added highlighting the lack of evidence and stating that the BMA did not endorse their use. The sometimes considerable disagreement among doctors over these therapies had made this a difficult subject for the BMA.[51] The BMA's work in relation to complementary and alternative medicine is, though, a good example of its willingness to engage with a difficult subject where there is a lack of consensus in the medical profession and look at it from the perspective of individual doctors trying to advise their patients.

---

[51] Not to mention complaints from witches when homeopathy was compared to witchcraft at the Junior Doctors Conference in 2010.

APPENDIX

Reports from the Board of Science 1983–2011

1983
The Medical Effects Of Nuclear War

1984
Boxing

1985
Board Of Science And Education Working Party Report On Air Transportation Of The Sick & Injured
Board Of Science And Education Working Party Report On Notifiable Diseases
Cigarette Advertising And Smoking: A Review Of The Evidence
First Statement On Acquired Immune Deficiency Syndrome (AIDS)
Report on investment in the UK Tobacco Industry
When Smoke Gets In Your Eyes – Cigarette Advertising Policy And Coverage Of Smoking And Health In Women's Magazines

1986
All Our Tomorrows: Growing Old In Britain
Alternative Therapy
Cervical Cancer And Screening In Great Britain
Diet, Nutrition And Health
Second Statement On Acquired Immune Deficiency Syndrome (AIDS)
The Long-Term Environmental And Medical Effects Of Nuclear War
Third Statement On Acquired Immune Deficiency Syndrome (AIDS)
Young People And Alcohol

1987
AIDS And You – An Illustrated Guide
Deprivation And Ill-Health
Immunisation Against Hepatitis B
Irradiation Of Foodstuffs
Living With Risk
Medical Implications Of Biological And Chemical Warfare
Medical Libraries – A Users Guide
Surrogate Motherhood

1988

Casualty Selection After Nuclear Attack
HIV infection and AIDS
Medicines In Developing Countries
The Drinking Driver

1989

A Code Of Practice For Sterilisation Of Instruments And Control Of Cross Infection
AIDS And You: Educational Game
Infection Control: The BMA Illustrated Guide
The BMA Guide To Alcohol And Accidents

1990

A Code Of Practice For The Safe Use And Disposal Of Sharps
BMA Guide To Living With Risk
The Future Of Medical Scientific Research

1991

AIDS And You – An Illustrated Guide
Hazardous Waste And Human Health
Helping Harry Educational Video Package

1992

A Stressful Shift Educational Video Package
Chemicals, Pesticides & Human Health
Cycling: Towards Health And Safety
Preventing Cancer Educational Video Package
Stress And The Medical Profession

1993

Complementary Medicine, New Approaches To Good Practice
Hyperbaric Medicine Facilities In The UK
Immediate Care Schemes
Living With Risk: Educational Game
The Boxing Debate
The Morbidity And Mortality Of The Medical Profession

1994

Age Of Consent For Homosexual Men: A Scientific And Medical Perspective
AIDS & You Game: Interactive Computer Version
Environmental And Occupational Risks Of Health Care
Water: A Vital Resource

1995

A Code Of Practice For Implementation Of The UK Hepatitis B
Alcohol: Guidelines On Sensible Drinking
Immunisation Guidelines For The Protection Of Patients And Staff
Inequalities In Health
Multicultural Health Care: Current Practice And Future Policy In Medical Education
Promoting The Medical And Allied Sciences. A Short History Of Science At The BMA
The BMA Guide To Rabies

1996

A Guide To Hepatitis C
Driving Impairment Through Alcohol And Other Drugs
Reporting Adverse Drug Reactions
Sport And Exercise Medicine: Policy And Provision
Strategies For National Renewal: A BMA Commentary On The Report Of The Commission On Social Justice

1997

Road Transport And Health
School Sex Education: Good Practice And Policy
The Misuse Of Drugs
Therapeutic Uses Of Cannabis

1998

Bloodborne Viruses And Infection Control: A Guide For Healthcare Professionals (Interactive CD-ROM)
Domestic Violence: A Health Care Issue?
Health And Environmental Impact Assessment: An Integrated Approach

1999

Alcohol And Young People
Biotechnology, Weapons And Humanity
Boxing Packs A Punch
Cycle Helmets
Growing Up In Britain: Ensuring A Healthy Future For Our Children
The Impact Of Genetic Modification On Agriculture, Food And Health

2000
Acupuncture: Efficacy, Safety And Practice
Clinical Indicators (League Tables) – A Discussion Document
Eating Disorders, Body Image and the Media

2001
Doctor's Assistance To Sports Clubs And Sporting Events
Healthy Ageing – Web Resource
Injury Prevention
Mobile Phones And Health, An Interim Report

2002
Drugs in Sport: the Pressure to Perform
Sexually Transmitted Infections
Asylum Seekers: Meeting Their Healthcare Needs
Effects of Sleep Deprivation on Doctors (web briefing)
Towards Smoke-Free Public Places
Clinical Trials (web source)

2003
Adolescent Health
Drugs in Sport: the Pressure to Perform
Housing and Health: Building for the Future
Sexually Transmitted Infections

2004
Diabetes Mellitus: an Update for Healthcare Professionals
Genetically Modified Foods and Health: a Second Interim Statement
Sunbeds (web briefing)
Smoking and Reproductive Health

2005
Hepatitis B Vaccination in Childhood
Population Screening and Genetic Testing
Preventing Childhood Obesity
Healthcare in a Rural Setting

2006
Child and Adolescent Mental Health – a Guide for Healthcare Professionals
Driving Under the Influence of Drugs (an update – 2006) (web briefing)
Emergency Planning Arrangements for the NHS in the UK – a collection of responses from the Board of Science (web briefing)

Healthcare Associated Infections – a Guide for Healthcare Professionals
Legalising Illicit Drugs: a Signposting Resource
Reporting Adverse Drug Reactions: A Guide for Healthcare Professionals
Sexual Health Clinics – Examples of Good Practice (web briefing)

2007
Breaking the Cycle of Children's Exposure to Tobacco Smoke
Clinical Trials Internet Resource
Domestic Abuse
Evidence-Based Prescribing
Fetal Alcohol Spectrum Disorders – A Guide for Healthcare Professionals
Gambling Addiction and its Treatment Within the NHS: A Guide for Healthcare Professionals
Healthcare Associated Infections – update to the BMA 2006 report (web briefing)
Over the Counter Medication
Prevention and Treatment of Viral Respiratory Disorders (web briefing)
The Use of Drugs as Weapons

2008
Alcohol Misuse: Tackling the UK Epidemic
Boxing (web briefing)
Cancer Genetics (web resource)
Forever Cool: the Influence of Smoking Imagery on Young People
Health and Ageing (web resource 2008 update)
Health Professionals Taking Action on Climate Change (web resource)
Promoting Safe Cycling (web briefing)
Sexually Transmitted Infections (STI) update (web briefing)

2009
Under the Influence – the Damaging Effect of Alcohol Marketing on Young People
Tackling Healthcare Associated Infections Through Effective Policy Action
Complementary and Alternative Medicine: What Your Patients May be Using (web resource)
Doctors Providing Medical Care at Sporting Events (2009 edition)
Driving Under the Influence of Drugs (web briefing)
Early Life Nutrition and Lifelong Health

Tuberculosis in the UK: What is Being Done? (web briefing)
Fluoridation of Water (web briefing)
Transport and Health

2010
The Health Effects of Working Unsocial Hours and Shift Work (web briefing)
Joint Statement on Direct-to-Consumer Screening
Violence and Health

2011
Doctors Providing Medical Care at Sporting Events (2011 edition)
Doctors Taking Action on Climate Change (web resource)
Sex Trafficking and Healthcare Services for Sex Workers (web briefing)
Psychological and Social Needs of Patients

Chapter 10
Medical ethics

Medical ethics grew enormously as a subject during the 30 years covered by this book and the BMA's Medical Ethics Committee[1] and department have played a pivotal role throughout this time. Scientific advances sometimes bring in their wake complicated ethical questions which did not exist in the past and it has been the task of the ethics committee and department to help guide doctors through the increasingly complicated ethical maze of modern medicine. Until the late 1980s, ethical guidance to doctors was thin on the ground and consisted mainly of the GMC's small 'Blue Book'[2] and an equally slim BMA book, mainly drawn up by Alexander Macara and Alan Rowe. There was little available guidance on the law. By the end of the period the BMA's ethics team was providing daily advice to members, giving lectures, on-line advice, producing a large number of guidance notes and publishing an ethical handbook *Medical Ethics Today*, which appeared in its third edition at the beginning of 2012.

Medical ethics varies from the science of medicine in that it is not evidence based, but relies instead on a consideration of moral principles, values and judgements. For this reason, a number of issues considered by the Medical Ethics Committee are controversial and generate heated debate within the Association, the medical community and the public. The composition of the committee means that it is well adapted to consider such issues from all angles as, in addition to a number of elected medical members, it includes philosophers, lawyers and religious leaders. These members are often chosen precisely because their views differ from those held by one another and from BMA policy, so the committee can be sure that all points of view have been considered and challenged. The elected medical members, meanwhile, keep discussions grounded in the reality of everyday practice.

---

[1] The Medical Ethics Committee was created at the 1988 ARM following a constitutional review. Prior to that, the committee was known as the Central Ethical Committee.
[2] *Professional Conduct and Discipline: Fitness to Practise,* General Medical Council, London.

Reproductive technology

In July 1978 Louise Brown was born. She was the first child conceived as a result of in-vitro fertilisation (IVF) and, from then on, developments in this field of reproductive technology were rapid. By the time that Louise celebrated her 30th birthday in 2008, some 3 million babies had been born around the world using IVF.[3] Perhaps not surprisingly, it is issues surrounding both the beginning and end of life that have led to some of the most difficult ethical dilemmas of recent years as they touch on the basic human questions of how our lives begin and end. While at one end of the spectrum, medical technology has allowed life to be extended, prompting questions about what is in the best interests of the patient, it has also made possible incredible advances in assisting reproduction, which bring with them a whole new set of ethical predicaments which simply did not exist in the past. Throughout, the basis of the BMA's policy has been that the welfare of any potential child created as a result of new technology has to be paramount. It has also been consistent in its rejection of applying inflexible rules on access to fertility treatment, believing that each application must be considered on its merits.

In 1981, IVF was still a new technique on which the BMA and other organisations had not had the opportunity to develop policy, so the Association established a working party to consider the present position and the future implications of IVF techniques. This working party was active at the same time as the government inquiry into IVF, which was being chaired by Dame Mary Warnock. This had been established in July 1982 'To consider recent and potential developments in medicine and science related to human fertilisation and embryology; to consider what policies and safeguards should be applied, including consideration of the social, ethical and legal implications of these developments; and to make recommendations'.[4] The BMA gave both written and oral evidence to the Warnock Inquiry and welcomed the recommendations in the committee's report which was published in June 1984.[5] The BMA was particularly pleased to see that it recommended the establishment of a statutory licensing

---

[3] The figure of 3 million quoted on BBC on-line report, *30th birthday for first IVF baby*, 14 July 2008.
[4] Paragraph 1.2 of *The Report of the Committee of Inquiry into Human Fertilisation and Embryology*, Department of Health and Social Security, June 1984.
[5] *The Report of the Committee of Inquiry into Human Fertilisation and Embryology*, Department of Health and Social Security, June 1984.

body to regulate both research and those infertility services which it recommended should be subject to control throughout the UK. From 1985 an interim body operated until the Human Fertilisation and Embryology Authority (HFEA) was set up in 1991, following the Human Fertilisation and Embryology Act 1990.

IVF raised the vexed questions of the storage and use of gametes and embryos, consent for their use and the payment of donors, and these were debates in which the BMA took a leading role. An especially difficult and public case arose in 1995 when Diane Blood wished to use stored sperm samples taken from her husband when he was hospitalised with meningitis. As Mr Blood had subsequently died it was impossible to obtain his consent for the use of these samples and it had not been possible to obtain consent before he died. Mrs Blood was denied the use of the sperm samples on the grounds that her husband had not given the written consent required by the Human Fertilisation and Embryology Act 1990. The HFEA refused to allow the sperm to be used either in the UK or exported for use in another European country.

The BMA, although very sympathetic to Mrs Blood's personal position, looked at the wider implications of subjecting an adult who was not mentally competent to any medical procedure from which they would obtain no personal benefit. In a consultation which followed the Blood case, the BMA said that it should be lawful to collect gametes without consent, but only in cases where the donor was likely to regain competence in the future. The logic for this argument was that the removal of gametes in such cases was in the patient's best interest as it would give them the option of parenthood in the future. The BMA did not initially support the posthumous use of gametes or embryos in any circumstances, even when the patient concerned had given consent but, during 2004, reviewed its position on this and in October that year changed its policy to one of support for the posthumous use of gametes and embryos where the deceased person had given prior explicit consent to their use after death.

Diane Blood's case eventually ended happily for her as the Court of Appeal, while upholding the decision of the HFEA that the sperm could not be used in the UK, decided that the authority had not taken sufficient account of Mrs Blood's right, under European law, to seek treatment in another country. On the basis of this, the HFEA withdrew its objection to the sperm being exported and Mrs Blood went on to have two children after treatment with the sperm outside the UK. The BMA welcomed the decision of the Court of Appeal in the Blood case as the court had upheld the importance of gaining valid consent before obtaining or using the sperm or eggs of an individual, but had also opened the way for the person at the centre of the case to use the sperm. In the BMA's press statement the Chairman of the Medical Ethics Committee, Stuart Horner, said that 'The issue on which the BMA has continually focused is the fundamental principle of individuals' valid and informed consent to the medical procedures to which they and their genetic material are subjected. This principle is central to medical ethics and is particularly important in relation to the use of genetic material which we believe to be distinct from the use of other body tissue.'

Towards the end of the 1990s, concerns began to surface about the future supply of gametes for IVF and whether it was necessary to consider paying donors to ensure sufficient supplies for the future. In 1998, the HFEA reversed its policy and announced that payment in money and other benefits should be permitted, although it stressed its commitment to altruistic donation. The BMA's Medical Ethics Committee said that gamete and embryo donation should be a gift 'freely and voluntarily given' but concluded that it did not oppose egg sharing on the basis that any risks taken by the woman were for her own benefit not for the recipient's. Also, the motivation of the donor was not commercial, but to receive a health benefit herself. It also agreed that it was unreasonable to expect donors to lose out financially and so expenses should be paid. By the end of the period covered by this book (2012) the HFEA was allowing donors to claim reasonable expenses for travel and compensation for loss of earnings, though with maximum limits.

The anonymity of donors was another controversial issue – an area where principles and pragmatism can be seen to conflict, according to the BMA. The Association had great difficulty with the issue and the RB eventually resolved in 2002 to oppose removal of anonymity. Within two years, however, legislation removed donor anonymity by allowing details about egg and sperm donors registered after 1 April 2005 to be passed on to offspring, including the name and last address of the donor.[6]

Combined with the developments in IVF was the rise in surrogate motherhood and this was a matter with which the Association struggled for some years. Council considered doctors' obligations towards this new

[6] Human Fertilisation and Embryology Authority (Disclosure of Donor Information) Regulations 2004/1511.

phenomenon in 1983 and its initial advice was for doctors to steer clear of it, given the 'difficulties, anxieties and uncertainties to all the individuals concerned, [Council] considers that it is unethical for a doctor to become involved in techniques and procedures leading to surrogate motherhood'. The BMA welcomed the Warnock report's recommendation that it should be a criminal offence to set up agencies to recruit women for surrogate pregnancy or to help those looking for a surrogate. In 1985, however, BMA policy changed when the RB came out in favour of surrogacy in selected cases, while adding that doctors should not take part until a future ARM had agreed appropriate ethical controls. A Council working party was set up to consider these safeguards and its remit was extended to cover human fertility services in general. This would enable it to prepare the BMA's response to a DHSS white paper, *Human Fertilisation and Embryology: A Framework for Legislation.*

In 1995 the BMA updated its guidance on surrogacy in a new book, *Changing Conceptions of Motherhood: the Practice of Surrogacy in Britain.* This was accompanied by an information leaflet for patients produced jointly with the Human Fertilisation and Embryology Authority.[7] The book stated that BMA policy was that 'surrogacy is an acceptable option of last resort where it is impossible or highly undesirable for medical reasons for the intended mother to carry a child herself. In all cases the interests of the potential child must be paramount and the risks to the surrogate mother must be kept to a minimum.' This has remained the position of the Association on surrogacy.

Abortion

The debate about abortion, ranging as it does all the way from whether it should be permitted at all to relaxation of the current legislation, has been one of the most sensitive in which the BMA has been engaged. BMA policy since the passing of the Abortion Act in 1967, has, though, remained consistent and the act has been viewed by the Association as a practical and humane piece of legislation and the BMA has continually called for its extension to Northern Ireland. It has been Association policy since 1968, when the RB made a resolution on the matter, that doctors should have the right, on the grounds of conscientious objection, to refuse to perform or facilitate an abortion. It was the case, however, that such doctors also had an ethical obligation to patients seeking an abortion to refer them promptly to another doctor.

---

[7] *Considering Surrogacy? Your Questions Answered.* BMA and Human Fertilisation and Embryology Authority, 1996.

The interpretation of the right to conscientious objection was called into question in 1988 by the House of Lords judgment in the case of *Janaway v Salford Health Authority*.[8] The Association acted quickly to issue a full policy statement on the matter to help clear up any confusion in doctors' minds and stated that doctors did not have an ethical duty to sign the statutory form, but they did have an ethical duty to refer the patient to another doctor quickly and that any unreasonable delay in making a referral would be contrary to good practice.

In the 1988–89 session, Council adopted a recommendation from the Medical Ethics Committee that the 28-week upper time limit for terminations (as specified in the 1929 Infant Life Preservation Act) should be changed to 24 weeks. The RB agreed at the 1988 ARM stating that 'other than [in] the most extreme cases, 24 weeks should be the upper limit for termination of pregnancy, and the figures show that this has already been achieved.' The 24 week limit was adopted in 1990 when the Human Fertilisation and Embryology Act was passed, with the proviso that there would be no upper time limit if the pregnancy had to be prematurely terminated to save the mother's life, if there were serious fetal handicap or the risk of grave permanent injury to the mother.

The BMA's 24 week policy remained for some years and then was challenged at the 2005, 2007 and 2011 ARMs, where, on each occasion, motions to decrease the legal limit to 20 weeks were heavily defeated. The current time limit had been questioned as improvements in medical technology meant that the survival chances of very premature babies had improved, although those who did survive almost always suffered from severe disabilities. At the 2011 ARM, representatives were urged not to change the Association's position by both the Chairman of Council, Hamish Meldrum, and the Chairman of the Medical Ethics Committee, Tony Calland. Pro-choice and anti-abortion groups had followed the debate with interest and its eventual conclusion was greeted with relief by pro-choice groups and with inevitable disappointment by anti-abortion groups, one of which had accused the BMA of 'institutional bias' on the issue.[9]

---

[8] In this case a doctor's secretary (Janaway) refused to type the referral letter for an abortion, claiming conscientious objection under the Abortion Act. The House of Lords decided that, in order to make such a claim, the person concerned had to be obliged to take part in administering treatment and this did not apply to Janaway.

[9] From an article entitled *BMA attempts to skew debate on abortion upper time limit* posted on cmfblog.co.uk, the official blog of the Christian Medical Fellowship on 26 June 2011 by Peter Saunders and accessed on 20 March 2012.

The BMA courted further controversy at the 2007 ARM when the following motion appeared on the agenda:

'That this Meeting calls for legislation to be amended so that:

(i) first trimester abortion would be available on the same basis of informed consent as other treatment and therefore without the need for two doctors' signatures;

(ii) first trimester abortion could be carried out by suitable trained healthcare professionals including midwives and nurses;

(iii) the current rules in relation to 'approved premises' are relaxed with regard to first trimester abortions.'

The Medical Ethics Committee supported the motion, writing in a briefing paper that clinical advances in inducing abortion meant that the safeguards, set out in the Abortion Act, were no longer necessary. There were also the more philosophical arguments around whether it was still appropriate for access to abortion being reliant upon two doctors' approval of the woman's reasons for ending her pregnancy and whether legislation drafted 40 years earlier was still wholly appropriate and relevant. The Royal College of Obstetricians and Gynaecologists (RCOG), while welcoming the BMA's briefing paper, disagreed that changes needed to be made on the grounds that the 1967 act 'meets the need and does not inhibit access to abortion services in this country.'[10] The ARM did not pass the parts of the motion which called for abortions to be carried out by healthcare professionals other than doctors and for relaxing the rule on premises. It did, though, agree that first trimester abortion no longer needed signatures from two doctors. Legislators have yet to catch up with the views of doctors and the complete requirements of the 1967 act remain, despite the attempts of the BMA and others to use the opportunity of the 2007 Human Fertilisation and Embryology Bill to push for changes.

Human genetics

Advances in the understanding of human genetics are transforming the diagnosis and management of hereditary diseases, allowing those who may be at risk from particular conditions to be screened for them and for treatment to be designed to work at the genetic or cellular level. The BMA made its first major public statement about the developing technology in 1998 with the publication of its book, *Human Genetics: Choice and Responsibility*. This aimed to provide an accessible and comprehensive

---

[10] *RCOG Statement on the BMA Medical Ethics Committee Briefing on First Trimester Abortions*, RCOG, 5 June 2007.

guide to the ethical dilemmas posed by developments in human genetics. It provided a lay person's introduction to genetics and went on to debate and make recommendations on the testing of adults and children, pre-natal screening and diagnosis, carrier testing, the medical and social uses of genetic information, employment and insurance issues.

As the book acknowledged, developments in genetic testing had taken into new areas the debates about confidentiality, individual choice and the importance of respecting patients' decisions. Decisions by individuals to discover whether they carried a genetic disease could have enormous implications for their relatives and the book concluded that individuals had moral obligations to others but that these could not be enforced or regulated. Michael Wilks, Chairman of the Medical Ethics Committee, summed up the dilemma when he said, 'For some people, knowledge brings peace of mind and the ability to face the future. Other people prefer to remain in ignorance of what destiny holds for them. But do any of us have the absolute right to decide whether to be tested or not, without considering the often vital impli-cations of that decision for our families?'

In fact, in the view of the BMA, many of the ethical problems that arose in the sphere of genetics were the same as those that arose in other areas of medicine as they centred on the traditional duties of health professionals to act in the best interests of the patient and to avoid harm. The BMA said that 'These common areas of ethical debate may be seen from a different angle when applied to genetic technology, but the usual imperatives of maximising benefit and minimising harm still apply.' The Association began from this starting point when address-ing the issues that arose along with the new developments.

In 2000, scientists with the International Human Genome Project released a draft of the human genome to the public and this news was welcomed by the BMA as 'an extraordinary moment in the history of science and medicine' which might 'be the beginning of the end to huge areas of human suffering'. One of the areas which had huge potential for ending human suffering was that of stem cell research[11] and the BMA had long been in favour of research using human embryonic stem cells. As it said in 2000, it was hoped that these cells could be used to develop into tissue for transplantation and repair to treat Parkinson's and other degenerative diseases, leukaemia, damaged hearts and skin for burns victims.

---

[11] In 1998 stem cells from human embryos were isolated and cultured in a laboratory for the first time.

Stem cell research is an extremely sensitive area and research using human embryonic stem cells especially so as some believe that life begins at conception and therefore that embryos should be given the status of human beings and not be used, under any circumstances, for research purposes. The opposite argument is that embryos are no more than a collection of cells. The BMA was cognisant of both of these points of view and of the huge ethical complexities, but eventually reported that it agreed with the Warnock Committee which had said in 1984 that 'though the human embryo is entitled to some added measure of respect beyond that accorded to other animal subjects, that respect cannot be absolute, and may be weighted against the benefits arising from research'.[12] Parliament had reached the same conclusion in 1990. But many doctors felt that embryonic stem cells should be treated differently to those from adults and that adult cells should be used where possible. This sentiment was reflected at the 2002 ARM which resolved that the BMA should strongly campaign for the increased funding of research into the use of adult stem cells.

The BMA's voice has been heard throughout the long debates on the ethics of stem cell research which have continued to the present. In 2002, it gave evidence to, and welcomed the decision of, the House of Lords that research should continue on both adult and embryonic stem cells.[13] Two years later it told the House of Commons Science and Technology Committee that research on human embryos should be extended but that adult, rather than embryonic, stem cells should be used wherever possible. The BMA has always seen the potential for life-saving and life-enhancing treatments that could emerge from stem cell research and has continually emphasised the important potential of this. It said in its evidence to the House of Commons Science and Technology Committee that, 'Given the BMA's long-standing support for embryo research, the BMA believes that there are very strong grounds for extending the areas of research that should be permitted to offer the greatest hope to people who suffer from life-threatening and very debilitating conditions.'[14] The BMA also took the view that the current safeguards were adequate and allowed research to progress in a safe and regulated environment. It reiterated its support for stem cell research in May 2008 in a brief to MPs during the passage of the

---

[12] BMA Parliamentary Briefing, issued on 16 November 2000.
[13] *Report of the House of Lords Stem Cell Research Select Committee*, published 13 February 2002.
[14] *BMA calls for more stem cell research*, The Guardian, 27 October 2004.

Human Fertilisation and Embryology Bill, drawing attention to the fact that, in the seven years since embryonic stem cell research had been legalised, it had already advanced understanding of early human development and the processes involved in diseases such as Parkinson's and motor neurone disease and it could, in future, lead to the development of new, cell-based therapies for these conditions.

Confidentiality

Confidentiality of medical records and the privacy that a patient can expect in discussion with their doctor are at the heart of the trust that is inbuilt into the relationship between doctor and patient. It may be for this reason, or as a result of the legal and ethical complications that surround it, that the BMA's ethics department receives more questions about confidentiality than about any other single subject. The BMA has always carefully scrutinised any proposed laws that could compromise confidentiality and as early as 1981 it was reporting publicly that Home Office plans for data protection were inadequate. It also stated that the Home Office was the wrong body to be undertaking this work and that the proposed voluntary code of practice would be insufficient to safeguard the confidentiality of medical information.

In November 1982 a row erupted between the BMA and the government over the Police and Criminal Evidence Bill. Under the bill, police officers believing that a 'serious arrestable offence' had been committed could ask a circuit judge for confidential information to be disclosed. Previously such information could only be disclosed after someone had been charged and a doctor subpoenaed to attend court with the medical records. A BMA delegation, led by the Chairman of Council, Anthony Grabham, met the Home Secretary, William Whitelaw, to ask for medical records to be exempt on the basis of the special relationship which existed between doctor and patient and the importance of keeping the trust of patients. The Home Secretary was prepared to amend the bill to enable a doctor to go before the circuit judge and state his or her reasons for objecting to the disclosure of medical records before the order was made. He also gave assurances that medical evidence would be destroyed as soon as the police no longer needed it. The BMA felt that this fell well short of what was necessary and continued to campaign against the offending clauses of the bill. This campaign, which many doctors supported, led to the bill being amended after the 1983 general election so that confidential personal records relating to the work of the health and caring professions were exempt from the provisions on powers of entry, search and seizure.

The BMA and the government also clashed over the 1984 Data Protection Act. The BMA's over-riding concern in relation to this piece of legislation was to ensure that it adequately protected individual patient records. Just before the bill was reintroduced to Parliament in October 1983, the Association had set up an Interprofessional Working Group on Access to Personal Information under the chairmanship of Sir Douglas Black, a former chief scientific adviser to the Department of Health. Representatives of the group met the Home Secretary, Leon Brittan, in November 1983 to relay concerns that the bill would allow anybody registered as a 'data user' to disclose or transfer information without the knowledge of patients or their doctors. The representations secured a commitment from the Under Secretary of State that the DHSS would produce, in conjunction with the BMA group, a statutory code of guidance on the disclosure of automatically processed personal health information and which would be enforceable under the 1977 NHS Act. This guidance never saw the light of day: first, a complication arose over personal data held outside the NHS, then nurses and midwives made objections (though these were subsequently resolved). Differences also arose inside the BMA, with the BMA's consultants' committee saying that it did not see an urgent need for a statutory code as it had been given an undertaking that medical records would only be used subject to the ethics of the medical profession. During these high-level policy discussions, the BMA did not lose sight of the fact that doctors needed guidance on the implementation of the act and it held sessions throughout the country to explain its implications. The GPs committee issued guidance for doctors on registration with the Data Protection Registrar, a legal requirement under the act for those who held personal data.

The BMA held a major conference on the subject of a statutory code in May 1989 when it was agreed that a code was necessary and this was followed by another round of consultation that summer. The Department of Health then decided that a statutory code was unnecessary and promised instead to publish a guidance note on the use and disclosure of NHS information, but publication was delayed several times. The BMA continued to warn that personal health information was being insufficiently protected and in the mid-1990s launched several initiatives to protect patients' confidentiality. The Interprofessional Working Group was re-established to review the need for legislation on confidentiality (the group had been suspended following the Department of Health's refusal to publish the agreed code on confidentiality in favour of its own guidance).

In November 1993, the BMA hosted a workshop on privacy, confidentiality and NHS information networks for members, lawyers and patient representatives. Those present agreed that the BMA should take the lead in educating health professionals and the public about the need to balance the benefits of information technology with its dangers. In 1996 a draft bill was introduced into the House of Lords on the collection, use and disclosure of personal health information, and guidance was published. The BMA issued its own advice on its website, which dealt with the disclosure of anonymous and identifiable information, consent to disclosure and reasons for breaching confidentiality 'in the public interest'.

It was announced in the Queen's Speech in May 1997 that the 1984 Data Protection Act would be strengthened and the BMA welcomed this. The new act would regulate how personal information about living people would be stored and processed. As a result of the new act, which came into force in March 2000, and the Criminal Procedure and Investigations Act, which came into force a year earlier, the BMA issued comprehensive ethical guidance in October 1999 on confidentiality and the circumstances in which it was permissible to disclose information about individual patients. The GPC issued an updated code of practice for GPs as a result of the new data protection legislation in September 2000.

The BMA's ethics department issued a number of guidance notes about confidentiality over the years as the law and ethics of the subject have evolved. In 2009 it compiled an innovative set of guidance in the form of a 'tool kit', which turned out to be a neat guide to a fiendishly complicated subject. As the introductory page on the website stated, its purpose was not to provide definitive answers for every situation, but to identify the key factors which needed to be taken into account when making decisions about confidentiality.

Consent and capacity

Patient consent, like confidentiality, is a fundamental tenet of the doctor-patient relationship. Just as the patient needs to have the assurance that the consultation with the doctor will not be disclosed, he or she also has to have confidence that the best treatment option will be arrived at. Given the importance of consent to medical practice, it has been the subject of many debates in the Medical Ethics Committee and a number of guidance notes have been made available to members. It was an area of concern with the Police and Criminal Evidence Bill in 1982 because it stated that intimate body searches should be carried out by a doctor or by a person of the same sex as the person being searched. The BMA maintained that only doctors should carry out such searches and only with the valid (ie, free and sufficiently informed), consent of the suspect. The only exceptions might be in rare circumstances, such as during terrorist activities, to save a life or to prevent serious injury. There was also a problem with taking intimate body samples. Before the bill, written consent from the suspect was required and the doctor had to be satisfied that this consent was valid. The BMA was worried that doctors would be pressurised into taking samples on the basis of written consent alone. As a result of the BMA's campaign against certain sections of the bill, the clause relating to intimate body searches being carried out for the purpose of providing evidence was eventually deleted from it.

The subject of consent to treatment, and especially the rights of young people under the age of 16, became a huge public interest story in the mid-1980s as a result of a legal challenge launched by Victoria Gillick in December 1982 and the BMA became embroiled in this. Mrs Gillick had failed to obtain assurances from her local health authority, West Norfolk and Wisbech, that her daughters would not be prescribed contraceptives without her knowledge or consent. The health authority had refused to give these assurances as it relied on the guidelines in a 1980 DHSS circular.[15] These guidelines recommended that only in exceptional circumstances should contraceptive advice be given to those under the age of 16 without parental consent, but recognised that some parents were not willing to support their children and it was the young women from such families who appeared to be most at risk of an unplanned pregnancy. If the young woman was not willing to involve her parents, then it was up to the doctor to use his/her clinical judgement and maintain the rules of confidentiality. Mrs Gillick lost her case at the High Court before Mr Justice Woolf, but took it to the Court of Appeal, which, in December 1984, reversed the High Court decision. It ruled that the 1980 DHSS guidance was unlawful, but allowed for the provision of advice in an emergency, without defining what it meant by 'an emergency'.

---

[15] DHSS circular HN(80)46.

The BMA condemned the Court of Appeal's ruling in the Gillick case. Its guidance on consent to treatment co-incided with that of the General Medical Council and acknowledged that a person's ability to consent depended upon their ability to understand the nature of the treatment proposed by their doctor and its consequences once these had been fully explained by the doctor. Prior to Mrs Gillick's action, there had been other calls for the law to be changed so that no person under the age of 16 should be given medical treatment without the consent of their parent or guardian and this was also in the context of the prescribing of contraceptives to young women under 16. The BMA opposed these petitions to change the law, arguing that guidelines on this matter issued by the GMC and BMA, together with the 1980 DHSS circular, emphasised the importance of involving the young woman's parents, wherever possible, before prescribing contraceptives. Unfortunately, the BMA's defence of the current position was interpreted by some as its advocating a lowering of the age of consent, which it emphatically was not. It was dragged into a public dispute about this when Mrs Gillick said that 'the BMA has allowed itself to be led by the nose by those other fringe minority organisations who have for years been advocating sexual liberty for school children and the abolition of the protective age of consent.'[16] This accusation was again levelled at the BMA when it spoke out against the Court of Appeal's ruling in the Gillick case.

The DHSS appealed the Appeal Court decision to the House of Lords which, in October 1985, decided in favour of Lord Woolf's original judgment.[17] The Lords clarified the right of doctors to help their young patients within the law and to follow the BMA's existing guidelines. The BMA was relieved that its existing advice was still relevant, but was then plunged into new uncertainty after the GMC published new guidance four months later. The GMC had been advised by its lawyers that the Court of Appeal's judgment indicated that, if a young person were not mature enough to understand the full implications of a request for treatment, then a doctor-patient relationship did not exist and, crucially, nor did the legal obligation upon doctors to maintain confidentiality. This horrified the BMA because it meant in effect that young people could not be sure in advance whether a consultation with

---

[16] *Contraception and Under-16s: Why the British Medical Association Supports the Existing Department of Health and Social Security (DHSS) Guidelines*, BMA, 1984.
[17] *Gillick v West Norfolk & Wisbech Area Health Authority* [1985] UKHL 7 (17 October 1985).

the doctor would remain confidential. The BMA was aware that the GMC meant that disclosure would only occur in exceptional circumstances, but its guidance had muddied the waters and the BMA was concerned that it would discourage young people from seeking medical advice if they could not be assured of confidentiality.

One concern of doctors throughout this long-running saga was that giving advice to people under 16 would risk them being accused of aiding and abetting unlawful sexual intercourse. The 1984 edition of the *Handbook of Medical Ethics* (reaffirmed in March 1986) advised: 'if the doctor acts in good faith in protecting the girl against the potentially harmful effects of intercourse, he would not be acting unlawfully'. As for confidentiality, the BMA advised that doctors could not provide treatment if they felt that the young person was insufficiently mature to understand the consequences of her actions, because her consent would not be valid. However, the BMA was clear that, regardless of the outcome of the consultation, both the fact that it had taken place and the matters discussed had to remain confidential. The BMA made strong representations to the GMC's standards committee to reconsider, but it declined. The BMA continued to advise doctors that the fact and content of consultations with young people should remain confidential and the ARM affirmed this position at the 1986 meeting.

In 1993, the BMA joined with the Royal College of General Practitioners, the Brook Advisory Centres, the Family Planning Association and the Health Education Authority to produce a guidance note for doctors and other healthcare professionals on the law and ethics of confidentiality as it affected people under 16, with particular regard to contraception. The Health Education Authority paid for this to be sent to all GPs and family planning clinics. The organisations concerned felt it was important to continue to stress to young people that their confidentiality would be respected by their GP. The BMA's work on consent and young people was later consolidated in *Consent, Rights and Choices in Healthcare for Children and Young People,* published in 2000 which gave advice on the ethics and the law on treating people below the age of 18, covering day to day issues and exceptional cases.

The law on capacity to consent is complicated and the BMA has to react swiftly whenever the law changes. It issued interim guidance when, in a 1989 judgment in the case of 'F',[18] the House of Lords

---

[18] *F v West Berkshire Area Health Authority* (1989) 4 BMLR 1.

established the law on the non-emergency treatment of adults unable to give valid consent. In 1994, the BMA and the Law Society issued guidance for doctors and lawyers on the assessment of mental capacity, which aimed to clarify what lawyers needed from doctors in their assessment and what the law laid down as standards for different types of assessment. The BMA published a report on consent in 2000, along with a 'tool kit' focusing on who should seek consent, communication with patients, and consent as a process. With financial support from GlaxoSmithKline, about 4,000 copies of the report were sent to clinical and medical directors of trusts throughout the UK and about 70,000 tool kits distributed free to hospital doctors.

Consent with regard to young people and those who may lack the capacity to give valid consent has been a major preoccupation of the BMA and it has continued to undertake a large amount of work over the years on consent and capacity to consent, thankfully without the media circus that surrounded the Gillick case.[19] In 2002, the BMA began to lobby for the introduction of legislation in England and Wales on mental incapacity (Scotland already had such legislation, introduced in 2000 and in Northern Ireland the common law position prevailed). It worked both with the Law Society and directly with the Department for Constitutional Affairs on the draft bill for England ensuring that the bill included clarification of issues such as providing for proxy decision making on behalf of incapacitated adults and putting advance directives into law. The Mental Capacity Act 2005 came into force in two stages in 2007 and the work of the Medical Ethics Department with the bill team paid enormous dividends as the BMA had ensured that doctors' views were reflected in the bill itself and in its code of practice. At the same time, work was also being undertaken on a draft English Mental Health Bill which raised a number of ethical questions (Scotland already had the Mental Health (Care and Treatment)

---

[19] The BMA has published a large number of guidance notes on capacity to consent to medical treatment, for example: *Consent, Rights and Choices in Health Care for Children and Young People* (2000), *Advance Decisions and Proxy Decision-making in Medical Treatment and Research* (November 2007), *Mental Capacity Act Tool Kit* (September 2008), *The Mental Capacity Act 2005: Guidance for Health Professionals* (September 2009), *Consent Tool Kit* (5th edition, December 2009), *Parental Responsibility: Guidance from the Ethics Department* (February 2009), *Taking Blood Specimens from Incapacitated Drivers: Joint Guidelines from the British Medical Association and the Faculty of Forensic and Legal Medicine* (July 2010), *Guidance on Statutory Advocacy Services* (September 2010), *Children and Young People Toolkit* (January 2011), *Assessment of Mental Capacity – A Practical Guide for Doctors and Lawyers* (3rd edition, March 2011) written in conjunction with the Law Society.

(Scotland) Act 2003). These questions related to whether it was appropriate to use legislation to manage individuals who presented a risk to others, but for whom no therapeutic intervention was available. The BMA set up a network of experts to consider the draft legislation and propose amendments as it progressed through Parliament.

Another issue was consent by patients for insurance companies to access their medical records. It was common practice in the 1980s for companies to advise the doctor that their client had consented without forwarding a statement of consent. Doctors doubted whether this consent was truly informed and that highly sensitive information could be released. Doctors were reluctant to challenge the insurance companies because patients sometimes felt that their doctor was making difficulties for no good reason. The BMA received many letters from doctors about this and met the Association of British Insurers (ABI) to ask for copies of consent forms to be sent to doctors as a matter of course. The ABI refused and later withdrew from a planned meeting with the BMA on the grounds that an 'open and public' meeting was unacceptable to them (the BMA had hoped to make a public statement after the meeting). The RB was not impressed and at the 1987 meeting advised doctors to refuse to complete a medical report for insurance purposes unless satisfied that:

- written informed consent had been given;
- a separate copy of the consent was provided for the reporting doctor to keep;
- the form of words used was acceptable to Council; and
- that requests for medical information came from, and were returned to, the company's chief medical officer.

More discussions were held but the insurance industry refused to accept that the ethics of the doctor-patient relationship extended to the provision of information for insurance purposes. Meanwhile complaints from doctors about industry practices continued to pour into the BMA. In the new era of AIDS, doctors objected particularly to questions speculating on their patients' lifestyles. Other practices they objected to included asking for judgements on risk factors and precluding the doctor from discussing the forms with patients. The BMA eventually persuaded the industry to agree that lifestyle queries should be sent to the patient and not the doctor. The insurance companies, however, were still asking for HIV tests to be carried out on some patients and the BMA produced a guidance note setting out their obligations in terms of pre and post-test counselling and other matters.

Discussions between the BMA and the ABI continued and were mainly centred on the consent forms to be used when individuals authorised their doctors to release personal health information. In 2002 they agreed that doctors did not need to disclose incidents of sexually transmitted infections providing that there were no long-term health implications. The two bodies then developed a standard GP report package which became available in 2003 and included a covering letter from insurers, an overview of the different types of information needed, a standard GP report form and a standard consent declaration for patients.[20]

Human rights

One area where the BMA can be proud of its work is that of human rights, where it has campaigned on a number of fronts: to draw attention to human rights abuses throughout the world (not flinching from highlighting doctors' involvement where it occurs), to supporting individual members of the profession and medical organisations targeted by repressive regimes and to speak out on behalf of refugees who come to the UK.

The 1975 Declaration of Tokyo had set down doctors' obligations not to take part in torture or degrading treatment and in 1981 the ARM unequivocally condemned the 'usage of medical personnel in enforcement of inhuman laws and degrading measures.' Council later reaffirmed that the BMA would support any national or state medical organisations which protested to their governments about torture and in 1984 it was asked to investigate claims that doctors in many countries were co-operating with the use of torture. It set up a working party which in 1986 reported its shock and distress at the revelation of 'incontrovertible evidence of doctors' involvement in planning and assisting in torture, not only under duress but also voluntarily'. It recommended that there should be a proper distance between the state and the medical profession and did not hold back from criticising how detainees in Northern Ireland were being brutally interrogated. The BMA was the first medical organisation to take an honest look at doctors' involvement in human rights abuses and from that point on became a focus for work on this disturbing issue.

---

[20] New information was issued in March 2010, *Medical Information and Insurance: Joint Guidelines from the British Medical Association and the Association of British Insurers.*

In 1990 the BMA began examining new evidence of abuse of medical skills in relation to prisoners and sought advice and evidence from medical associations and other bodies worldwide. This led in 1992 to one of the BMA's most widely read and influential publications: *Medicine Betrayed*. It made uncomfortable reading as it detailed clear evidence that doctors around the world were involved in detaining healthy people in psychiatric facilities, maltreating detainees, and being involved in punishments such as flogging, amputation and the death penalty. It was translated into several languages and became a basic reference book for all doctors working in the field on behalf of the International Committee of the Red Cross. Those involved in producing the book were invited to various international meetings: for instance the head of the ethics department, Ann Sommerville, was invited to go to Washington, DC to give a lecture on medical involvement in torture at the US Holocaust Museum in 1996 on the 50th anniversary of the Nuremberg trials. This was at a major conference tracing medical involvement in human rights abuses from the 1930s to the present. The conference was largely funded by the film director, Steven Spielberg. Another result of the book was the BMA involvement in opposing a practice in China whereby organs from executed prisoners were used for transplantation, even to the extent of prisoners being shot on demand when their organs matched a patient waiting for a donor organ. A long-running campaign led eventually to some legal changes in China, but not necessarily to the end of the practice.

The two BMA reports led to a flood of correspondence from doctors and medical students from around the world documenting human rights abuses. But, as the BMA acknowledged, as a professional organisation it was unable to provide immediate and practical solutions. The publication in 2001 of *The Medical Profession and Human Rights: Handbook for a Changing Agenda* moved the debate forward by setting out practical ways of implementing change by doctors taking steps to prevent, detect, deter and publicise abuse. It covered human rights abuses at home and overseas, citing abuses in prison medicine, forensic medicine, the care and examination of asylum seekers, domestic abuse and detection of abuse in residential homes. This work involved the BMA in key international initiatives. Ann Sommerville wrote several sections of the United Nations ground-breaking 1999 *Manual on the Effective Investigation and Documentation of Torture and Other Cruel, Inhuman or Degrading Treatment or Punishment* (known as the Istanbul Protocol) which is used by doctors and others throughout the world.

While some doctors were clearly involved in administering torture and judicial punishments, others were the recipients of harsh punishment. These were the doctors working in countries run by oppressive regimes who spoke out against human rights abuses or who were themselves victims of such abuses. The BMA has always shown solidarity with those doctors. In 1983 the BMA received reports that the President of the Turkish Medical Association and a medical professor at the University of Istanbul were being held in degrading conditions in prison. The BMA asked the Turkish Embassy to justify the sentences, but received no reply. Around the same time, the BMA supported the Nigerian Medical Association which had been banned, and its leader imprisoned, by the military government after it had called for improvements in health care. Chile was also under a military government in the 1980s and in January 1986 the Secretary of the BMA wrote to the Chilean Ambassador in the UK about the disappearance of an eminent Chilean dermatologist. Such cases were to become depressingly familiar as the years progressed. *The Medical Profession and Human Rights: Handbook for a Changing Agenda* noted that the civil conflicts in Croatia, Kashmir, Kosovo and Chechnya had shown that military leaders often planned systematic attacks on health facilities as part of their war strategy. Such attacks could not be countered by individual doctors (courageous though they often were) but required political action by the international medical community.

Clearly, oppressive regimes that regularly abuse human rights are unlikely to heed a faraway organisation like the BMA and the BMA realises the limits of its actions and influence. What it can do is highlight human rights abuses and publicise the names of detained doctors, which it has done in countries such as Nigeria. Much more recently, the BMA has been vociferous on behalf of 20 Bahrani healthcare workers who were sentenced to imprisonment in September 2011 following civil unrest in Bahrain. It sent letters to ministers in the country, had a letter published in *The Guardian* newspaper in the UK and published an editorial in the *BMJ*. *The Guardian* letter led to an invitation from the Bahraini Embassy in the UK to outline the Association's concerns. This was quickly taken up by the BMA which emphasised to officials the importance of the detainees receiving a fair trial. By helping to keep the Bahraini healthcare workers in the public eye, it is less likely that their detention will fall from public consciousness. The importance of international publicity was clearly shown in October 2000 when a BMA delegation attended a meeting in Izmir in Turkey to discuss

HRH The Princess of Wales, accompanied by John Marks, Chairman of Council, opening the New Nuffield Library in BMA House, London, on 20 February 1986.

The *BMJ* editors, Richard Smith (left, who edited the journal from 1991 until 2004), and Stephen Lock (editor from 1975 until 1991) pictured in 1991.

HRH The Princess Royal opening the refurbished BMA House on 28 November 2008. Hamish Meldrum, Chairman of Council, is also pictured.

The 2011 ARM in session in Cardiff.

Vinod Tohani, Chairman of the Northern Ireland Public Health Committee, and Brian Patterson, Chairman of NI Council, holding a replica cigarette packet at Stormont during the campaign to ban smoking in public places. Also pictured are members of the legislative assembly and the BMA NI Secretary, Brian Best (at the back of the group).

Pictured left to right are Graeme Eunson, Chairman of the Scottish Junior Doctors Committee, Peter Terry, Chairman of Scottish Council, and David Love, Joint Chairman of the Scottish General Practitioners Committee, during the *Breathe Better in Scotland* campaign against smoking in public places.

Pictured left to right are the Chairman of Welsh Council, Tony Calland, Julie Morgan, member of the Welsh Assembly, and the Welsh Secretary, Richard Lewis, campaigning in Westminster about the dangers of passive smoking.

David Pickersgill, BMA Treasurer, 2002-11.

Prince's Room, BMA House, London.

Council Chamber, BMA House, London, which was constructed during the 2007-08 refurbishment.

Café and Garden Room, BMA House, London. This was previously the Council Chamber before refurbishment in 2007-08.

The Great Hall, BMA House, London, set (above) for a formal dinner and (below) for a conference. This was previously the Library before refurbishment in 2007-08.

A selection of publications by the Board of Science and the Medical Ethics Committee.

Publications and electronic products from the BMJ Publishing Group.

The new Library, BMA House, London.

The no. 30 bus destroyed by a bomb outside BMA House, Tavistock Square, London on 7 July 2005. (Photo by Press Association.)

Sir Douglas Black, President, 1984-85

Parveen Kumar, President, 2006-07

Jeremy Lee-Potter, Chairman of Council, 1990-93

James Johnson, Chairman of Council, 2003-07

Mark Porter, Chairman of Council, 2012-

John Havard, Secretary, 1980-89

Ian Field, Secretary, 1989-93

Ernest McAlpine Armstrong, Secretary, 1993-2000

Jeremy Strachan, Secretary, 2001-04

Tony Bourne, Chief Executive/Secretary, 2005-

human rights and healthcare for prisoners. The Turkish police were also in attendance and insisted on filming the meeting and intimidating participants, which meant that the Turkish activists due to speak were reluctant to do so. There was stalemate: the security forces would not leave, the speakers would not speak, and the conference could not go ahead. The BMA representatives, who were the director of professional activities, Vivienne Nathanson, and Ann Sommerville, contacted the BMA's press office in London which issued a press statement deploring the situation. The news was also picked up by the media and attracted international attention. The conference did go ahead, but in a more low key and isolated setting.

The BMA has long spoken up for the rights of the victims of torture and Council supported the Charter 87 movement which pressed for safeguards for asylum seekers. The number of refugees seeking medical help grew during the 1980s and 1990s and some of these had been tortured. UK doctors then became alarmed at the effect that the procedures for seeking asylum were having: some asylum seekers did not know whether they might be returned to their country of origin to be tortured and even killed. The BMA used the publication of *The Medical Profession and Human Rights: Handbook for a Changing Agenda* to issue a strongly worded press release deploring the hardening of attitudes towards asylum seekers in the UK. It was especially critical of the way in which the dispersal of asylum seekers had been managed and pointed out that a number of them had been cut off from support from refugee community groups and doctors were struggling to cope with the needs of these vulnerable people. This was especially so with the survivors of trauma and torture with whom doctors needed to build up trust. Aside from the political issues, doctors needed advice from the BMA on the entitlement to healthcare of asylum seekers as there was some uncertainty about this and this advice was provided by the BMA in *Access to Healthcare for Asylum Seekers and Refused Asylum Seekers* which was published in January 2012.

Organ donation and transplantation

By the end of the 1980s the success of organ transplantation and immunosuppressant drugs meant that the numbers of transplant operations were beginning to rise. The main limitation was the number of donor organs and new ethical dilemmas arose around the techniques being used to acquire organs. In 1991 the BMA considered the technique of keeping patients on ventilators, without their prior consent, for the purpose of organ donation. The legal situation was unclear as consent from the patient's relatives was not considered valid. The BMA concluded that elective ventilation was acceptable as long as each unit that practised this had a comprehensive protocol in place. In 1995, the BMA confirmed its view, and the current legal position, that an organ donor card should be considered as binding and which could not be vetoed by relatives. It was common for doctors to seek the views of relatives even when it was clear that a deceased person wished to donate their organs after death and a refusal by relatives to donate organs frequently over-rode the deceased person's wishes as set out on their donor card.

As late as 1998, the BMA was not prepared to advocate a change in the law to allow an opt-out system[21] with regard to cadaveric organ donation and a motion to this effect put to Council by the Medical Ethics Committee was narrowly lost at the Council meeting on 9 December 1998. Six months later, however, the 1999 ARM came out in favour. The Medical Ethics Committee worked to stimulate debate about the issue and in 2000 published *Organ Donation in the 21st Century – Time for a Consolidated Approach*. This report emphasised that an opt-out system would have to be accompanied by a radical review with new legislation and major changes in the infrastructure. While it was undertaking work on this report, the BMA became aware that a number of other organisations were also calling for changes to be made to the current arrangements but on an individual basis with little co-operation, co-ordination or impact. Therefore, the BMA established the Transplant Partnership in 2000, an alliance of 18 professional and patient groups which aimed to campaign for a radical review of the organ donation system. In February 2001 it sent all MPs a 'have a heart' Valentine's card encouraging them to sign an early day motion supporting the campaign. The BMA also met UK Transplant,

---

[21] With regard to terminology, the BMA said in its 13 February 2012 press release to launch its report, *Building on Progress: Where Next for Organ Donation Policy in the UK?* that 'An opt-out system is often referred to as 'presumed consent' however this has caused some controversy as people argue that 'presumed consent' does not constitute 'consent'. There is a risk that the debate becomes focused on the terminology rather than on the issues themselves, therefore the BMA's preferred terminology is 'opt-out with safeguards'. Under an opt-out system everyone would be assumed to want to donate organs after their death unless, having received information about the system, they chose to opt out of donation during their lifetime. Before the new system is introduced there would be extensive and high profile publicity to ensure all members of society were aware of the forthcoming change and to encourage them to consider their own wishes about donation after their death.'

the Department of Health and other bodies to look at improving the transplant infrastructure. In July 2001 the Department of Health published a consultation document, *Human Bodies, Human Choices*, which proposed an opt-out system with safeguards in the form promoted by the BMA.

In November 2003, the Scottish Independent Review Group on Retention of Organs at Post-mortem published a report on its work and for England, Wales and Northern Ireland the government published the draft Human Tissue Bill. The BMA continued to respond to new proposals, especially on the need for codes of practice and the establishment of the new Human Tissue Authority. Discussion was also ongoing with the Retained Organs Commission and other medical organisations about measures to rebuild public confidence in pathology and related services following the scandal at Alder Hey Hospital. The BMA's campaign to improve organ donation rates for transplantation continued. Many of its main aims in relation to the legislation on organ and tissue donation were met by amendments to the Human Tissue Bill as it made its way through Parliament, showing that its close work with the team preparing the bill had paid off.

These amendments would allow human tissue samples to be used for education and training without explicit consent from the individual from whom they were taken. The BMA also welcomed an amendment to introduce regulations allowing tissue to be used for specific purposes from those who lacked mental capacity. Despite its considerable achievements in securing significant changes to the bill, the BMA was unable to hide its disappointment that the government had not taken the opportunity of the Human Tissue Bill to include an opt-out system for organ donation in the legislation. Its frustration that people continued to die while usable organs were wasted was shown in its press statement: 'What is now needed is a full-scale public information campaign to raise awareness about the need to improve the system for organ donation in this country. Every day someone on the waiting list dies because they can't find a donor. We know that the majority of the public support a system of presumed consent as one way of increasing the number of donors available. The BMA calls on MP's voting on this issue to put dying patients' interests first.' The Association also called for an informed public debate on this issue confident that 'the Government will see that there is support for such a change'.

Despite its disappointment at the lack of movement towards an opt-out system, the BMA could report in early 2012 that a good deal of progress in improving the organ donation infrastructure had been made since its 2000 report. The legislative changes brought in by the Human Tissue Act 2004 and the Human Tissue (Scotland) Act 2006 provided a clear legal framework in which organ donation could increase and the Organ Donation Taskforce (established in 2006) had recommended far-reaching improvements to the infrastructure which had not only been accepted by all four UK governments, but they had also agreed to provide the funding needed to make the recommended changes. The Taskforce was confident that these changes could increase donation rates by fifty per cent by 2013.

The Organ Donation Taskforce had also undertaken a review of the impact of introducing an opt-out system in the UK. After a thorough examination of the evidence it reported in its 2008 document[22] that it would not be recommending such a shift at that time, for various reasons including the belief that the recommendations it had already made could make such a shift unnecessary. It suggested that the issue should be reviewed again in the future if necessary. There was even a challenge to the long-established policy on an opt-out system at the 2011 ARM. During a debate challenging the policy, some representatives said that it could damage patient trust in doctors if people felt that doctors treating patients in intensive care were unduly interested in harvesting their organs. The motion was, however, lost, and the BMA's policy in favour of an opt-out system remained in place.

Early in 2012, the BMA published a major report, asking the awkward questions about where organ donation in the UK was heading.[23] Despite the welcome advances made since 2006, people were still dying needlessly while on waiting lists for donor organs and even if the Organ Donation Taskforce's aim of increasing the number of donors by fifty per cent by 2013 was achieved, this would not meet demand for organs and patients in need would continue to die. The Chairman of the Medical Ethics Committee, Tony Calland, said that, 'We are at a crossroads in terms of public policy. As a society we need to decide whether we should accept that we have done all we can or whether we should move forward, cautiously, and look at other options for increasing the number of donors. It is important that society discusses them openly in a reassuring way. The aim here is to save lives while at the

---

[22] *Organs for Transplants. A report from the Organ Donation Taskforce.* Department of Health, London, 2008.
[23] *Building on Progress: Where Next for Organ Donation Policy in the UK?*, BMA, February 2012.

same time protecting individual rights and autonomy.' The report went on to consider a number of options for increasing the number of donor organs, including using organs from older people, paying the funeral expenses of those who signed the Organ Donor Register and went on to donate organs, and keeping brain-dead patients alive on ventilators so that their organs could be used. The BMA maintained that an opt-out system with safeguards was the best way in which to improve donation rates, but said that this would only work if these safeguards were adequate and the system had public support. Therefore, more public debate was necessary and the BMA hoped that its report would help to stimulate and facilitate that debate. One immediate effect from the publicity surrounding the report was a sudden increase in the number of people signing up to the organ donation register. As with other initiatives, such as anti-smoking legislation and the introduction of a minimum price for alcohol, it is one of the devolved administrations, this time in Wales, which has led the way with the publication in June 2012 of a draft bill introducing an opt-out system for adults.

End of life issues

Human life is, without question, the most important value which the law sets out to protect. In criminal law, acts which end life, or seek to end life, are dealt with severely and this reflects the attachment of most ethical systems to the preservation of human life. The sanctity of human life and the importance placed on its preservation has caused the courts many difficulties when patients have wished to end their lives. In such circumstances the sanctity of human life has to be squared with the right to self-determination which, in some cases, will lead to suicide and the ending of life prematurely when the quality of a person's life has deteriorated to the extent that they no longer wish to remain alive. The BMA has remained opposed to assisted dying and euthanasia (with one temporary change to a neutral position on assisted dying in 2005), but it has had to deal, over recent years, with related issues. These include when it is acceptable to withhold or withdraw treatment from a patient with no prospect of recovery and how far a patient's self-determination at the end of life affects medical decisions.

Physician assisted suicide and euthanasia

In discussions about these issues the terms 'euthanasia', 'assisted suicide' and 'physician assisted suicide' are sometimes used interchangeably, with some drawing a clear moral difference between them while others believing that there is, essentially, no difference. The BMA's view is that distinctions can be drawn as euthanasia occurs when a doctor, or other person, actively terminates someone's life and assisted suicide happens where a doctor, or some other person, provides the patient with the means to commit suicide, but does not undertake the act.[24] It is not illegal to commit, or attempt to commit, suicide[25] and a competent patient who refuses life-saving treatment is not committing suicide.[26] However, it is a criminal offence to assist a suicide or a suicide attempt.[27] This means that a person who wishes to end his/her life, but lacks the physical capacity to do so, cannot ask for another person to help them without that person facing criminal charges.

Apart from a short-lived change to policy in 2005, the BMA has been clearly opposed to euthanasia and assisted suicide since the Representative Body rejected the concept of euthanasia in 1950. There are a number of reasons why individual doctors oppose euthanasia and assisted suicide: some object on religious grounds, others believe that their role in caring for patients is incompatible with helping them to end their lives, some are convinced that, should assisted suicide become legal, then some, especially older, patients will be pressurised into ending their own lives and other doctors feel that the practical objections to legalising assisted suicide are too complicated to be overcome. The BMA's objection stems from the harmful effects it believes legalisation would have on society as a whole. In the second edition of *Medical Ethics Today*, published in 2004, the BMA states: 'The key principle underpinning the BMA's views on euthanasia and physician-assisted suicide is that this is an area where it is unacceptable for individuals' choices to impinge pejoratively on others. The impact of a general lifting of the ban on intentional killing by doctors would have detrimental effects on society and medical practice that outweigh the benefits to the small number of patients who would use these types of legal provision.'[28] This is a difficult argument to put across to the public, many of whom believe that allowing terminally ill people to end their

---

[24] The distinctions are set out in *Medical Ethics Today*, 2nd edition, 2004.

[25] Section 1 Suicide Act 1961.

[26] Lord Goff said in *Bland*: '. . . there is no question of the patient having committed suicide, nor therefore of the doctor having aided or abetted him in so doing. It is simply that the patient has, as he is entitled to do, declined to consent to treatment which might or could have the effect of prolonging his life, and the doctor has, in accordance with his duty, complied with his patient's wishes.'

[27] Section 2(1) Suicide Act 1961.

[28] Page 394 of *Medical Ethics Today*, 2nd edition, 2004.

lives is a compassionate and civilised way for society to behave. Many doctors agree, though polls have shown that far more doctors approve of assisted dying than would be prepared to assist it.

The issue often produces heated debates in Parliament and in the media. In the 1997–98 session both Parliament and the courts tried unsuccessfully to change the law on physician assisted suicide. In January 2000 Ann Winterton MP published the Medical Treatment (Prevention of Euthanasia) Bill and between 2003 and 2006 Lord Joffe made several attempts to introduce bills which would have legalised voluntary euthanasia. None of these made it on to the statute books, but they did reignite the debate and the opinion of the BMA was sought by parliamentarians, the press and the public.

In spite of its opposition to assisted suicide and euthanasia, the BMA recognised that it was a subject which would continue to arouse passionate views on both sides and was one which needed to be fully discussed. In April 1998 it circulated a discussion paper on the moral differences between assisted suicide and euthanasia.[29] Later that year, the ARM asked the BMA to hold a major conference on physician assisted suicide in order to develop a consensus. A year later, the BMA launched a global debate through its website in an attempt to inform a conference on physician assisted suicide which was held in March 2000. This conference decided against any moves to change the law and in 2000 the ARM welcomed the conclusion of the BMA consensus conference 'rejecting any moves to change the law on physician assisted suicide.' The BMA's position had been settled, for the time being.

This position was controversially turned on its head at the 2005 ARM. The ARM had started to experiment with open debates, in which a subject was discussed in open session without the formality of speaking for or against a motion. These open debates sometimes led to motions being drafted for debate later in the meeting and this happened at the 2005 meeting after an open debate on assisted dying. The RB was presented with three motions and asked to vote on these in sequence, noting that if one motion passed then the motions following it would automatically fall. The first motion reaffirmed the RB's opposition to assisted suicide and euthanasia, the second stated that the matter was one for society and Parliament to decide and the third was in favour of assisted dying in exceptional cases. The third option, which was voted on first, was rejected by the RB, but option two was carried

---

[29] *Euthanasia and Physician Assisted Suicide – Do the Moral Arguments Differ? A Discussion Paper From the BMA's Medical Ethics Department*, BMA, April 1998.

by a majority of 53% in favour to 47% against. Option 1 was not put to the meeting as the Chairman ruled that it had automatically fallen with option 2 being accepted. Therefore, the Association found itself, for the first time in its history, in the extraordinary position of having a neutral stance on assisted dying as the resolution which the RB passed read as follows: 'That this Meeting believes that the question of the criminal law in relation to assisted dying is primarily a matter for society and for Parliament. The BMA should not oppose legislation which alters the criminal law but should press for robust safeguards both for patients and for doctors who do not wish to be involved in such procedures.'

The narrowness of the vote showed that a spectrum of views remained within the BMA and there was strong resistance among some members to the change in policy. Motions were submitted by them to the next ARM to overturn the 2005 policy and it was changed so that there could be no doubt about the BMA's stance:

'That this Meeting

- (i)   believes that the ongoing improvement in palliative care allows patients to die with dignity;
- (ii)   insists that physician-assisted suicide should not be made legal in the UK;
- (iii)   insists that voluntary euthanasia should not be made legal in the UK;
- (iv)   insists that non-voluntary euthanasia should not be made legal in the UK;
- (v)   insists that if euthanasia were legalised there should be a clear demarcation between those doctors who would be involved and those who would not.'

The BMA's opposition to euthanasia and assisted suicide has held since the 2006 ARM (and was restated in 2009 and 2012), but remains a matter for passionate and heartfelt debate within the profession as opinions continue to differ and challenges to the law on assisted dying continue to be made.

Since 1998, when the charity Dignitas began operating, some people travelled to Switzerland to take advantage of that country's liberal laws on assisted suicide to end their lives.[30] Travelling abroad to

---

[30] In 2009 it was estimated that around 110 people from the UK had travelled to Switzerland to end their lives. Figure quoted on BBC News on-line in an article entitled *Dignitas: Swiss suicide helpers* which was posted on 14 July 2009 and accessed on 7 March 2012.

commit suicide was not illegal in the UK, but facilitating suicide, which could include helping someone to receive assisted suicide abroad, was a criminal offence. This meant that some people travelled abroad to commit suicide earlier in the course of their illness than they wished as they feared that, if they later became dependent on a relative or friend to make the journey, that person could face prosecution upon their return to the UK. It was this point that was at the heart of the case that Diane Pretty brought to the House of Lords in 2001. Mrs Pretty, who was paralysed from the neck downwards due to motor neurone disease, wished her husband to help her commit suicide at an unspecified date in the future as she was unable to take her own life. Her husband agreed and sought an undertaking from the Director of Public Prosecutions (DPP) that he would not be charged under section 2(1) of the Suicide Act 1961. The Lords dismissed the case and held that the European Convention on Human Rights did not oblige a state to legalise assisted suicide.[31] In a press statement the BMA said it believed that the House of Lords had made the right decision. Its reasoning was that although Diane Pretty's condition was debilitating it was rare and would not justify a change in the law that would affect many more people. Diane Pretty died the following year, a few days after losing a challenge to the ruling in the European Court of Human Rights.[32]

Contrast Diane Pretty's case with that which Debbie Purdey brought before the House of Lords eight years later in July 2009.[33] The Lords ruled that Debbie Purdey, who was suffering from multiple sclerosis, had the right to know the circumstances under which her husband would be prosecuted if he helped her to travel abroad to die and instructed the DPP to specify when a person might face prosecution under the 1961 Suicide Act. Two months later the DPP set out draft advice to prosecutors citing a range of factors to be considered. The BMA sought clarification of the role of doctors and emphasised its opposition to weakening the existing prohibition on assisted suicide, but concluded that the suggested factors to be considered by prosecutors appeared reasonable. Its response was no doubt coloured by the decision of the 2009 ARM to vote against legal immunity for people who accompany patients to an assisted death abroad.

---

[31] *Pretty v Director of Public Prosecutions* [2001] 3 WLR 1598; [2002] 1 All ER 1; [2001] UKHL 61.
[32] *Pretty v United Kingdom* (2002) 35 EHRR 1.
[33] *R (on the application of Debbie Purdy) (Appellant) v DPP (Respondent) & Omar Puente (Interested Party) & Society for the Protection of Unborn Children* [HL] [2009] UKHL 45.

The final rules for prosecutors were published in February 2010 by the DPP for England and Wales and the DPP for Northern Ireland.[34] Someone acting out of compassion to help a terminally ill person with a 'clear, settled and informed wish to die' would be unlikely to be prosecuted, but anyone who persuaded or pressured a person would be likely to be prosecuted. The DPP for England and Wales, Keir Starmer QC, said the new rules did not open the door for euthanasia but provided a clear framework for prosecutors to decide which cases should proceed to court and which should not. He stressed that the decision on whether to prosecute would involve considering each case on its own facts.[35] The BMA followed this with its own guidance to doctors.[36] It advised them to avoid all actions that might be interpreted as assisting, facilitating or encouraging a suicide attempt. It also said that doctors should not provide medical reports if they thought that they would be used to obtain assisted suicide because this could be seen as facilitating that process. Similarly, they should not accompany a patient going abroad for assisted dying.

Withholding and withdrawing treatment

Prior to the judgment in the case of Tony Bland in 1992,[37] there was confusion among doctors about when and if medical treatment could be withdrawn in the best interests of the patient and whether artificial hydration and nutrition could be considered medical treatment. Some coroners were inclined to take no action when they felt that the circumstances had justified withdrawing treatment but others, including the coroner consulted by Tony Bland's doctors, warned that a murder or medical negligence charge could follow if treatment were withdrawn.

Tony Bland had sustained serious brain injury in the Hillsborough Football Stadium disaster in April 1989 and had lapsed into a persistent vegetative state. In September 1992 his family and medical team sought a declaration that they might lawfully discontinue all life-sustaining treatment and medical support measures, including

---

[34] *Policy for Prosecutors in Respect of Cases of Encouraging or Assisting Suicide*, issued by the Director of Public Prosecutions in February 2010. No separate advice has yet been issued by the Lord Advocate in Scotland.

[35] *DPP publishes assisted suicide policy*, Crown Prosecution Service press release, 25 February 2010.

[36] *Responding to Patient Requests Relating to Assisted Suicide: Guidance for Doctors in England, Wales and Northern Ireland*, BMA, July 2010.

[37] *Airedale NHS Trust v Bland* [1993] AC 789.

ventilation and artificial nutrition and hydration. The case was of huge legal and ethical importance because at that time there was no case law nor any published guidance either about the treatment of patients in PVS or about treatment withdrawal more generally. The BMA was heavily involved in the case from the beginning. Tony Bland's medical team originally contacted the BMA seeking advice as they had been told by the coroner locally that they would be prosecuted if they failed to continue treatment for him, despite their and Tony Bland's family's belief that continuation of treatment would not be in his best interests. It appeared from the coroner's warning, however, that doctors had no choice other than to continue treating him.

There were doubts that the UK courts would be willing to create case law on such a controversial issue, but the BMA was convinced of the merits of the case and of the need for a clear judgment on the matter in order to move the law forward. Therefore, working with the Official Solicitor's Office, it was instrumental in bringing the Bland case as a test case to court. It eventually went to the House of Lords and their Lordships decided unanimously that the discontinuing of Tony Bland's nasogastric feeding tube would be an omission by the doctors treating him, not an act. This decision was justified on the basis that the withdrawal of artificial nutrition and hydration was in the patient's best interests. These interests were not being met by continuing to treat him, simply to prolong his life when that life had no benefit to him. This judgment changed the law in the UK. In addition to its influential role in bringing the Bland case to court, BMA guidance on withholding and withdrawing medical treatment (necessarily based, pre-Bland, on American cases in the absence of any British ones) was quoted at various stages in the Bland hearings. As a result of the case, the BMA's guidance was refined and finalised, completing a circular process.

The ethics department continued to receive enquiries about how to asses a patient's best interests if the patient were mentally incapacitated and their previously expressed wishes unknown. In July 1998 the BMA launched a major public consultation on the ethics of withdrawing and withholding treatment from patients who had no prospect of recovery. More than 2,000 responses were received. The consultation process revealed anxiety and uncertainty about the existing legal position and a strong desire for practical guidance to help doctors and their colleagues take decisions that were clinically appropriate, ethically sound and legally robust. The consultation resulted in new guidance published by the BMA in June 1999, *Withholding and Withdrawing Life-Prolonging Medical Treatment* and this was the first comprehensive statement of the principles which should apply to all decisions to withhold or withdraw life-prolonging treatment. It confirmed that doctors should not routinely be obliged to seek court approval before withdrawing artificial nutrition and hydration from patients with no prospect of recovery but should seek an independent review by a senior clinician from outside the treatment team. Decisions to withdraw or withhold life-prolonging treatment should follow good practice and doctors should seek a wide consensus on the best interests of the patient. The main focus of the new guidance was on decisions about patients who were likely to live for weeks, months, or possibly years, if treatment was provided but who, without treatment, would or may die earlier. Clearly, where patients were competent, they would be able to judge what represented an acceptable level of burden or risk to them. In those cases where patients were unable to express their wishes, doctors, in consultation with relatives and other carers, had to decide whether providing life-prolonging treatment would be in their best interests.

As with many of the pieces of guidance from the Medical Ethics Committee, this guide took an extremely emotive subject and approached it from a practical point of view, taking into account the enquiries which the ethics department received from members to produce a book which gave practical advice to those faced with making some of the most difficult decisions doctors ever have to take. The guidance received formal support from a number of organisations, including the ethics committees of the Royal College of Physicians, the Royal College of General Practitioners, the Royal College of Nursing, the Association of Palliative Medicine and the Alzheimer's Society. In Scotland, meanwhile, issues around withholding and withdrawing treatment had been brought to the fore by contentious new legislation on adults with incapacity, which included proposals for a 'welfare attorney' empowered to make medical decisions on behalf of patients.

In 2002, the General Medical Council published new guidance on withholding and withdrawing medical treatment at the end of life.[38] This was issued to address the dilemmas that were occurring where medical technology could prolong life, but did not always have the ability to restore health or functioning. As some patients were

---

[38] *Withholding and Withdrawing Life-prolonging Treatment: Good Practice and Decision Making*, General Medical Council, August 2002.

concerned that their life would be prolonged with no benefit to them, they were making living wills or advance directives to refuse treatment. Therefore, to ensure that decisions were made properly and to allay fears about both over and under treatment at the end of life, the BMA and GMC had issued guidance setting out the process and criteria for stopping active interventions. While some patients wished to die at a time of their own choosing, others were worried that their life may be ended prematurely against their wishes. This was the fear of Leslie Burke.[39] He had spinal-cerebellar ataxia which would lead eventually to his losing physical functions, including the ability to swallow, though he would maintain cognitive functions until the end of his life. He was deeply concerned because he believed that the GMC's guidance gave doctors the discretion to withdraw artificial nutrition and hydration (ANH) even if his death were not imminent.[40] He challenged the guidance, claiming that it was incompatible with the European Convention on Human Rights. In July 2004 Mr Justice Munby upheld the challenge, ruling that some parts of the GMC's guidance were not compatible with the Human Rights Act.

The GMC immediately appealed and the BMA gave a witness statement in support of the regulator's position. The Association said it was worried that the ruling left unclear some crucial aspects of law, such as when doctors could cease active interventions for dying patients. Without clear guidance patients' relatives and doctors would have to go to court more frequently to obtain rulings in individual cases even, in some cases, where they all agreed. The Court of Appeal overturned Mr Justice Munby's judgment in July 2005, stating there was never any question of Mr Burke not receiving ANH towards the end of his life and that he did not need to go to court to ensure this because he had always made it clear that he would like to continue to receive ANH treatment when he was no longer able to express his wishes. The BMA was relieved that the situation had been clarified and reviewed its own code of practice. Put simply, the BMA's position was that a doctor could withdraw or withhold life-prolonging treatment if that treatment was not benefiting the patient and therefore not in their best interests.[41]

---

[39] *R (on the application of Burke) v General Medical Council* [2005] EWCA Civ 1003.
[40] It had been determined in the case of Tony Bland that the provision of artificial feeding was medical treatment (*Airedale NHS Trust v Bland* [1993] AC 789).
[41] As set out on page 391 of the second edition of *Medical Ethics Today*, BMJ Books, 2004.

Advance directives

Some people, anticipating a time when they may not be able to make their wishes known, wished to have advance directives or living wills. The purpose of living wills is to enable patients to shape the treatment they receive after they have become incapable of expressing their wishes. Such documents are not without their own problems,[42] but can nevertheless provide at least an indication of the patient's wishes. The BMA's policy has changed completely since Council first considered the concept in its 1983–84 session and concluded at that time that there was a danger that such statements could acquire quasi-legal status which could lead to elderly people fearing that they might be 'encouraged' to sign such statements against their will. Council concluded at that time that 'it would be undesirable for a model declaration to be prepared for use by patients who may, as has been the case in the past, make their wishes known to their general medical practitioner.'

BMA policy began to change in the early 1990s, after an ARM resolution asked the Association to re-examine its stance. Council subsequently supported the principle of advance directives. They should not be given legal force, but, in the absence of any contrary evidence, they had to be regarded as the patient's wishes. However, case law confirmed that if a competent adult signed an advance directive refusing treatment it was legally binding.[43] In January 1994 Council agreed to endorse the view of the Law Commission that limited legislation should be introduced to allow for specific refusals of treatment. But following a House of Lords select committee report[44] recommending a code of practice developed by the healthcare professionals would be preferable to legislation, the BMA, working with the Royal College of Nursing and the Medical Royal Colleges, published a code of practice on advance directives for healthcare professionals in 1995.[45] Furthermore, at its March 1995 meeting, Council approved a statement on advance directives which said that 'although not binding on health

---

[42] Problems can occur when the statements are badly worded and can be misinterpreted or implemented in ways that the patient had not foreseen. It is also the case that the way healthy people feel about illness before they have experienced it may be quite different to how they might feel when it happens. This discussion summarised from chapter 10 of *Medical Ethics Today*, British Medical Association, London, 2004.

[43] *Airedale NHS Trust v Bland* [1993], *Re C (adult: refusal of medical treatment)* [1994], *Re T (adult: refusal of medical treatment)* [1992].

[44] *Report of the Select Committee on Medical Ethics*: [199:3–1994]: House of Lords Papers: 3–1994.

[45] *Advance Statements About Medical Treatment: A Code of Practice*, BMA, Royal College of Nursing and Royal College of Physicians, April 1995.

professionals, advance statements deserve thorough consideration and respect' and 'where valid and applicable, advance directives (refusals) must be followed'. Four years later the BMA reported that the government did not propose to include legislation on advance directives as it believed that case law, together with the BMA's code of practice (which was on the website) provided sufficient clarity. This confidence in the BMA's guidance was welcome, but the BMA had already concluded that legislation in England and Wales was needed, and its lobbying culminated in the 2005 Mental Capacity Act.

Chapter 11

The BMA's international work

From a small office in Bloomsbury, the BMA's international influence reaches surprising widely. It campaigns on global healthcare, lobbies European institutions, supports refugee doctors in the UK, advises those from overseas who wish to come to the UK to work or study and has a voice in a number of international and European medical groupings. The Association is seen as a respected 'elder statesman' by many other national medical associations, impressed with its influence both within the UK and abroad. The scope of the BMA's international work, coupled with its human rights activities (covered in the medical ethics chapter, Chapter 10), brings credit to the BMA.

The BMA was involved in European affairs long before the UK joined the European Community in 1973 and, with the steady encroachment into the UK of European law and influence, has strengthened its structures to deal with these. Over the years a number of changes have taken place to the BMA's European and international committees, leading to the creation of the current International Committee in 1996 which today (2012) is a thriving committee leading the BMA's work on matters as diverse as immigration rules and ethical supply of surgical instruments. An International Department had already been created in 1993 and this and the International Committee consolidated all work and activities relating to overseas activities including input into European and international bodies and providing secretariat support to the European Forum.[1] This committee and department have been served by some quite extraordinarily dedicated members and chairs and foremost among them has been Alan Rowe. He was for very many years the BMA's eyes and ears on a number of European bodies, he was hugely knowledgeable on European and international affairs and had a truly global perspective on medicine.

---

[1] The European Forum was established by the BMA in 1993 and meets twice yearly. Unlike the BMA's European Committee, which was focused on the BMA's interests, the European Forum had representation from other medical bodies and the Department of Health and its purpose was to help the profession in the UK to present a united front in Europe.

The BMA's local UK bodies are known as divisions, its overseas ones as branches. There had been an extensive network of these for a number of years but, over time, the work of the branches declined and their contact with the BMA in the UK became minimal and many of the branches themselves became moribund. The branches, although operating very much at arm's length from the BMA centrally, were still entitled to use the BMA's name with very little accountability to the BMA, carrying the risk that they could become dominated by individuals or certain interest groups. Therefore, a decision was made by Council in May 1996 to close the majority of the overseas branches, retaining only those in Cyprus, Gibraltar, Hong Kong and Malta.

European institutions

In view of the impact of European institutions and legislation on the practice of medicine in the UK, Europe has been the main focus of the BMA's international work during this period. The Association has contributed to the European Union of Medical Specialists (UEMS), the European Union of General Practitioners (UEMO), the Permanent Working Group of European Junior Hospital Doctors (PWG) and the Standing Committee of Doctors of the European Community or *Comité Permanent des Médicins Européens* (CP). In 1994, the BMA opened a small office in Brussels to provide a link between the Association and the various European institutions and to allow swift delivery of BMA messages on EU policy and legislation and on-the-spot liaison with MEPs and others. It also provided an early warning system to the BMA on proposed policy initiatives in Europe. This was important because EU law supersedes UK law in many policy areas such as employment law (European Working Time Directive) and internal market (free movement of doctors). There was a brief falling out with the standing committee (CP) in November 1995 when the BMA's contingent left the plenary meeting after its leaders had failed to take a vote on the need for audited accounts. The BMA withheld its subscription for a year, but hostilities were suspended once the standing committee agreed to audit its accounts and reduce its costs.

One of the BMA's main objectives was to try to achieve the same standards of training and practice for doctors throughout Europe. The body which oversaw medical training in Europe was the Advisory Committee on Medical Training (ACMT), and its remit was to 'help ensure a comparably demanding standard of medical training in the community'; it had two nominees from the BMA. Although under-resourced, it set up working groups to study continuing medical education and new subjects for undergraduates. The BMA lobbied the Department of Health over its concern that European doctors could move freely among the member states but specialist training varied so much that there was a strong case to update and extend relevant legislation. It also wanted member states to limit access to medical studies: some states, such as Italy and Belgium, were substantially overproducing doctors and this was distorting medical staffing planning and employment in other states.

By 1994 there was deep anxiety that the ACMT had been so starved of resources and support that it would be unable to function as its members were finding it impossible to fulfil their remit to achieve comparable standards of medical training. The BMA, and other European medical organisations, lobbied their governments to strengthen the committee. By the following year the outlook was more encouraging: the committee had met again and set up more working groups (to consider GP and specialist training) and had also elected a member of the BMA's Central Consultants and Specialists Committee, Len Harvey, as its President. It produced a training charter for medical specialists. Meanwhile the BMA hosted the European specialists' group (UEMS) annual meeting and members discussed the committee's remit and resources, the co-ordination and dissemination of information to delegates and to doctors in the UK and the potential for streamlining the committee.

The BMA's involvement at the European level was especially important during the tortuous discussions on specific training for general practice. A directive on this was adopted in September 1986, after 16 years of campaigning by UEMO and the Standing Committee of Doctors of the EEC.[2] They had been concerned for a long time that inconsistencies across Europe in the training of GPs meant that in some countries general practice was not a specialty but a career option for less competent doctors. The directive laid down that each member state had to establish at least two years' specific training in general practice. The directive also specified that, from the beginning of 1995, no GP would be able to practise in the publicly-funded health service of any member state unless he/she had undergone this training. The

---

[2] The directive was Directive (86/457/EEC) on specific training for general practice.

BMA continued to lobby for GP training to be increased from two to three years and this was achieved through a consolidating directive in 2005.[3] Thanks in part to loud objections from the BMA, the final version of the directive dropped a draft clause which would have allowed doctors to practise in any EEA state without having to register in the state where they wished to work.

The BMA was less enamoured of a proposed directive on the recognition of higher education diplomas. This had been agreed by the European Council in 1984 in an attempt to speed up the process of enabling all professionals to work in all member states, but there was widespread opposition. The BMA argued that healthcare professions should be excluded from the directive because there was no mechanism to guarantee standards of training other than for doctors, dentists, nurses and midwives, so it was possible that doctors in the UK would have to work with health workers from Europe who were not trained to the standards of their UK-qualified counterparts. As a result of pressure from the BMA and others, the European Commission revised the directive. If applicants from the paramedical professions without their own directives wanted to work in a member state other than where they had qualified, they would have to take an aptitude test or undergo a three-year period of adaptation.

Immigration

The BMA had long-standing policy that all UK nationals fully registered with the General Medical Council but who had qualified outside Europe should enjoy the right to practise freely within the EEC and this was reinforced at the 1981 ARM. Responding to this policy, representatives of the BMA met the Minister for Health in the autumn of 1981 and proposed that the Council of Ministers be asked to recommend that such doctors be allowed to practise in member states and the Minister agreed to pursue the matter. Despite this agreement and the BMA's constant pressure, the issue was not to be resolved for many years. The coming into existence of the European Economic Area (EEA) on 1 January 1994 did not address the problem. European legislation on free movement and the mutual recognition of medical qualifications had been extended to other countries (Austria, Finland, Iceland, Norway and Sweden) but did not extend the right to free movement to those who were EEC citizens but whose primary medical

---

[3] This was Directive 2005/36/EC.

qualification was from a 'third', non-member country. The BMA continued to campaign on this throughout the rest of the 1990s and only began to see some positive moves towards the end of the decade when, following hard BMA lobbying, proposed European legislation came forward which would commit registration bodies to take into account the experience of doctors who were registered and practising in the EEA but who had obtained their primary medical qualifications elsewhere. This eventually came into force in a directive consolidating and simplifying European law on the mutual recognition of professional qualifications in 2005.[4] The events had shown that little could change at European level without a huge amount of patience, lobbying and time passing.

A linked issue was the UK immigration status of doctors from outside Europe. The BMA has always considered that an important part of its international role was helping overseas doctors who wanted to come to the UK to train and work. It responded quickly to changes to immigration rules that would make it harder for them to do this. Problems began in 1993 and the BMA pressurised the government for clarity: it emerged that the government was reviewing the immigration status of overseas doctors training in the UK. During the consultation process the BMA emphasised the importance of effective information about the new rules. It also called for better supervision so that overseas doctors would gain useful experience while in the UK. A circular was expected in 1994 to summarise the application of immigration rules to overseas doctors and dentists training in the UK, but this failed to materialise, partly due to continuing discussions on the Calman report on specialist training.[5] The result was that the Home Office started to enforce more rigorously its four-year permit-free period allowed in hospital training. It also applied more strictly its 'no switching' policy from permit-free to work-permit employment, despite evidence from the Department of Employment that there was a service need. The Department of Health consistently failed to come up with any guidance, leading to great uncertainty for many BMA members. European doctors also had problems because they had to deal with changes in arrangements for specialist certification from 1995–96. The replacement of the UK certificate of specialist training with a certificate of completion of specialist training affected doctors from other EU

---

[4] Directive 2005/36/EC.
[5] *Hospital Doctors: Training for the Future. The Report of the Working Group on Specialist Medical Training.* Department of Health, London, 1993.

countries who had done their training for the old certificate. The BMA intervened on their behalf, but the government refused to introduce transitional arrangements to help them.

The BMA embarked on a bitter battle with the government in March 2006 when the government suddenly changed the rules on permit-free training for non-EEA doctors without UK residency. Doctors on training schemes without a work permit would need to acquire one, thus changing retrospectively rules that had promised permanent residence after four years. The Department of Health announced that hospitals had to prove that they were unable to recruit junior doctors from the UK or the EU before short-listing candidates from other countries. The BMA accused the government of scapegoating overseas doctors in the fall-out from the chaos of the new applications system for training posts, which was partly due to the increased number of trainees in the system. The Chairman of Council, Hamish Meldrum, outlined the BMA's case in a letter to the Secretary of State for Health, Alan Johnson sent in December 2007: 'The NHS owes an incalculable debt to international medical graduates. In the past we have failed to train sufficient numbers of medical graduates and without the large-scale immigration of doctors, the health service would have failed decades ago. Recent immigrant doctors came to the UK on the understanding that there was a virtual guarantee of their entitlement to training opportunities. To change the rules when these doctors have committed themselves to this country is unacceptable.' The Department of Health's guidance was challenged by the British Association of Physicians of Indian Origin and eventually ruled unlawful by the House of Lords in April 2008. Throughout the period, the BMA continued to lobby hard for fair treatment for international medical graduates and co-ordinated an International Doctors Action Group which looked at future challenges and possible solutions.

A further challenge occurred in March 2009 when the government announced another change to immigration rules: individuals had to score a minimum number of points within each of five tiers to be allowed to enter or remain within the UK. Tier 1 was the 'highly skilled worker category', but those applying for it needed at least a master's degree, while a medical degree was classified only as a bachelor's degree. Many medical students and junior doctors would have to leave the country, although they had been studying in the UK for up to seven years: five years' of undergraduate study followed by the two-year foundation programme. The consequences would be devastating to those concerned, who saw their career plans and lives thrown into chaos. It would also be damaging for NHS workforce planning because these people had been included in statistics projecting the future numbers of doctors. The BMA protested loudly, with the Chairman of Council writing in May 2009 to the Immigration Minister, Phil Woolas, and the Secretary of State for Health, Alan Johnson. He pointed out that the immigration rule changes, along with the impact of the European Working Time Directive on junior doctors' hours, would be likely to exacerbate rota gaps and put patient safety at greater risk.

The points-based immigration system was not enacted through legislation, which meant that the UK government could change the system regularly, which it did. Towards the end of 2010 the Home Secretary announced changes to tiers 1 and 2 in order to cut immigration still further, bringing bewildering changes to an already complex system. By the middle of the 2000s, staff from the BMA's International Department had permission from the Office of the Immigration Services Commissioner to provide basic immigration advice to BMA members in matters relating to their employment in the UK.[6] This was provided by the BMA's immigration advisers who receive internal and external training in relevant aspects of immigration law. The BMA also tried to protect members who were subject to visa rules by talking to the relevant authorities and making them aware of the impact that the changes were having on individual doctors and on the NHS. In 2011, the BMA responded to five consultations from the government and the migration advisory committee on proposed changes to the immigration rules. It also wrote to ministers, held meetings with government and other related bodies while working towards 'a smooth transition through the immigration system for our members'.

The group of overseas doctors most in need of the BMA's help were those who had come to the UK as refugees and the BMA has consistently supported these doctors. The BMA began its work with refugee doctors in a modest way towards the end of the 1990s by publicising the problems that they encountered when trying to find work in the UK. It urged the Department of Health to help support refugee doctors and worked with the NHS Executive to develop an improved

---

[6] Under the Immigration and Asylum Act 1999, the provision of immigration advice is restricted to individuals and organisations registered, or exempt from registration, with the Office of the Immigration Services Commissioner (OISC), an independent public body. The BMA has been granted exemption to provide basic immigration advice to BMA members in matters relating to their employment in the UK.

communications strategy for all overseas doctors. The Association worked with a wide range of organisations to help refugee doctors to resume their medical careers in the UK and representatives of the BMA met government officials to discuss the problems of this group of vulnerable doctors. The government eventually pledged £500,000 in 2000 for projects to help refugee health professionals.

While it continued to press government agencies to help refugee doctors, the BMA began to look at what it could do as an organisation for this group of colleagues and, over time, developed a strategy to assist them. Its main priority was to help refugee doctors to reestablish their careers in the UK, especially supporting those who were ready to enter the medical workforce. The BMA's first step was to work with the Refugee Council on a voluntary database for refugee doctors and the Association also supported a mentoring scheme for these doctors which was run by the Refugee Education and Training Advisory Service and the World University Service. The refugee doctors' database was a project jointly set up by the BMA and the Refugee Council and collected information on refugee doctors in the UK, and used this to help ensure that appropriate help was offered in the right areas. On registering, doctors received a regular newsletter providing information on forthcoming activities and events. They were also sent information on relevant schemes and other projects or services. By 2003, the voluntary database had 800 members, rising to 1,000 a year later. The BMA then set about compiling a package of benefits for refugee doctors who were preparing for registration in the UK, but who were not eligible for full BMA membership.[7] It also established a refugee doctor liaison group and BMA representatives spoke around the country at meetings to highlight refugee doctor issues.

International medical associations

The BMA has membership of a number of medical organisations which bring together doctors from around the world and, although liaison with fellow professionals can be rewarding, it is fair to say that the BMA's relations with some of these bodies have not always been happy.

---

[7] The package of BMA membership benefits for refugee doctors included free weekly subscription to the *BMJ* (including the BMJ Careers supplement), free weekly subscription to *BMA News*, the use of the BMA library, including access to the Medline Plus search facility via the internet or on computers at the library, guidance notes and reports on a wide range of subjects, local BMA support and access to a confidential 24-hour telephone counselling service for refugee doctors and their families for personal, emotional, work or study related problems.

There have been serious disputes with the World Medical Association (WMA) which led to the BMA breaking off relations with it for a ten-year period from 1984. This was especially sad as the BMA had been instrumental in establishing the WMA in 1947. Tensions arose in 1977 when, following the killing of Steve Biko in South Africa (then under apartheid rule) and the failure of the Medical Association of South Africa (MASA) to properly address the failings of Biko's doctors to protect him, the MASA was welcomed back into membership of the WMA. This prompted the immediate departure of the majority of African nations and was one of the factors that led to the BMA's leaving.

The BMA was also increasingly concerned about the constitution of the WMA. As a result, Council decided in early 1982 that, unless radical changes were made to the constitution by the 1985 biennial assembly, the BMA should leave the WMA. In the interim period, the BMA continued to state publicly that it believed in the importance of an international forum for the exchange of medical opinion and worked to seek reforms to the WMA's constitution 'which would lead to a more acceptable and representative association'. The BMA proposed a change to the current weighted voting system and was supported in this by a majority of other member associations, but the proposal was defeated at the WMA's meeting in October 1983, opposed by those countries who were benefitting from the prevailing undemocratic voting arrangements. The Representative Body had already agreed that 'unless there is an alteration in the constitution of the World Medical Association which would lead to a fairer voting structure, the BMA should cease to be associated.' Following the WMA's failure to effect reform at its October 1983 meeting, BMA Council agreed in January 1984 that the BMA should withdraw at once from the WMA. At this meeting, Council reiterated its belief in the importance of there being an effective international representative body for doctors to allow discussion of professional and ethical issues and it remained willing to make a full contribution to any international body which would allow such issues to be discussed on a fully representative basis. This included rejoining the WMA if it reformed itself.

The WMA was slow to reform, so in February 1985, the BMA convened a two-day meeting, and medical representatives came from the Canadian, Danish, Finnish, Dutch, Norwegian and Swedish Medical Associations and the Irish Medical Organisation. Those associations unhappy with the WMA eventually formed themselves into a loose alliance known as the 'Toronto Group', which focused on professional and ethical issues. They maintained contact with the WMA and tried to persuade it to make constitutional changes so that they could rejoin. But they did not want to become an alternative international medical association and after seven years some of them rejoined the World Medical Association. The BMA was not yet ready for re-entry and held out until it believed that the requisite constitutional changes had been made before rejoining in 1994. Since that time the BMA has been a diligent contributor to WMA work, but relations between the BMA and the WMA have veered from the strained (for example, in 1999 when the BMA was publicly critical of the WMA's proposed amendments to the Declaration of Helsinki on the ethics of research on humans) to the friendly (James Appleyard, former Treasurer of the BMA, was elected President of the WMA in 2002). The BMA's engagement with the WMA did, though, allow it to have a say over important issues and the BMA was careful to seek and put forward the views of UK doctors. As a result of its work in the WMA, the BMA was invited in 1996 to give evidence to a United Nations review on the control of biological weapons – the first time that a national medical association had made a presentation to such a UN committee according to the 1996–97 annual report of Council. The UN policy was amended, reinforcing a ban on genetic weapons.

The BMA's relations with the Commonwealth Medical Association (CMA) were also rocky at times. The CMA had been founded in 1962 at the instigation of the BMA, and its members were national medical associations. By the middle of the 1980s, support for the CMA was declining and there was concern about its future. The BMA offered to provide the secretariat for a council meeting to be held in Cyprus in October 1986. The two-day meeting was attended by 17 delegates representing six countries and the BMA agreed to continue to provide the CMA's secretariat for the period leading up to the next Council meeting in London three years later. The Cyprus meeting also discussed healthcare and a forthcoming conference of Commonwealth health ministers. The BMA had undertaken a large volume of work preparing for the health ministers' meeting and the CMA Council agreed to make its reports – on financing of health services, the contribution of women to health, and the economics of alcohol and tobacco – available at that meeting.

In addition to its provision of secretariat support, the BMA also provided a regular subscription to the CMA and the BMA's Council agreed to continue funding the body at least until its meeting planned for July 1989. Another 15 medical associations had given a firm commitment to support the CMA and it was hoped that an acceptable system for levying subscriptions could be established. The meeting held in London in July 1989 was a success: more than 20 medical associations in the Commonwealth sent representatives, a new constitution was agreed as was an arrangement whereby subscriptions were based on the size of each member association. The new constitution had at its heart the extension of technical advice and co-operation to medical associations in the Commonwealth's less developed countries. Elections were also held at the meeting with the result that the BMA left with its appointees occupying the major offices of the CMA: John Marks was its President, Alistair Riddell was its Treasurer and John Havard (who had just retired as BMA Secretary) was its Honorary Secretary.

Despite its funding and constitutional problems, the CMA continued to exert influence: during 1989–90, it secured observer status on the Commonwealth Health Ministers meetings and consultative status with the World Health Organisation and the United Nations. It had also established, with four other Commonwealth professional associations, the Commonwealth Human Rights Initiative. The BMA had been pivotal to seeing the CMA through its crisis in the mid-1980s and, following its reconstitution in July 1989, the CMA began to grow in strength, building upon its work with Commonwealth ministers and medical associations in the Commonwealth. By 1991, it had 25 member associations and a record number of 33 medical associations attended the CMA Council meeting in Jamaica in October 1992. At this meeting, the CMA's first female President, Margaret Green, commended the CMA for its renewed vigour following the adoption of its new constitution three years earlier. By 1994, the CMA had 38 subscribing national medical associations and the income from subscriptions, plus its grants from the Ford Foundation and the Overseas Development Agency, meant that it now had the means to open a small office in BMA House and to more effectively help to strengthen the capacity of national medical associations in less developed countries. As the 1990s progressed, the CMA expanded its international activities, especially with regard to human rights, AIDS and the health of women and young people.

The BMA continued regularly to pay its subscriptions and to support the work of the CMA but, by 2003, had lost patience with the way in which the organisation was being run. Many of its member medical associations had been in default with their subscriptions for a number of years and the CMA had consistently failed to attract the support of the medical associations in Australia, Canada, New Zealand or South Africa with the result that the BMA's contribution to the CMA now represented its core funding. The CMA had also decided to provide services through the staff of the Malta Medical Association and had made London and South Africa based staff redundant. Therefore, in June 2003, following a review of its membership of international associations, the BMA advised the CMA that it would resign its membership from October 2004. It subsequently rejoined a couple of years later but, this time, no subscription money changed hands and the BMA's contribution to the CMA's activities was desk space and IT support in BMA House in London.

Third world debt and international sanctions

Not all of the BMA's international development work was carried out with the WMA and CMA. Its individual contributions began in earnest towards the end of the 1990s when the Association made representations to the Department for International Development about reducing third world debt. Then, in March 1998, the Secretary of the Association, Mac Armstrong, wrote to the Chancellor of the Exchequer, Gordon Brown, about economic programmes imposed by the International Monetary Fund that were forcing governments to cut spending on health and education. The BMA also joined the Jubilee 2000 Coalition which campaigned for the burden of unpayable debt to be lifted from the poorest countries by the Millennium. The Chairman of Council, Alexander Macara, wrote to the Prime Minister, Chancellor and Secretary of State for International Development in May 1998 saying that: 'For every £1 spent on health in the so-called 'developing' world, £3 is paid in debt interest, thereby preventing the implementation of health and social development programmes. That is nothing short of scandalous.' The New Labour government, elected the previous year, did take these matters seriously and in March 1999 the Chancellor announced a plan to reduce the debt of the poorest countries. The BMA wanted it to be written off altogether and encouraged other medical associations to lobby their governments to cancel bilateral debt owed by the poorest countries.

The BMA also took up the cause of doctors and their patients in countries where international sanctions had been imposed. In 2001 it called for 'smarter' sanctions against Iraq: directed against the regime but avoiding damage to the health of innocent civilians. In a press statement it pointed out that the current policy helped Saddam Hussein and his supporters build 'palaces while his people starve'. The Association arranged for free *BMJ* subscriptions and medical books to be sent to the main medical libraries in Iraq to help overcome the professional isolation of Iraqi doctors. The BMA/BMJ Information Fund was established in 2000 and donated health-related information to institutions around the world.

In 2003 the BMA reached a landmark in its overseas work when it signed a strategic grant agreement with the Department for International Development. The government funded a project to help make BMA members more aware of the role that they could play in improving health and reducing poverty world-wide. The BMA surveyed doctors' experiences of working in developing countries, which captured much-needed information on what did and did not work, and in February 2005 it received the results of new research which it had commissioned, with MEDACT[8] and Save the Children on the migration of health professionals from developing nations to the developed world. These showed new ways of addressing this problem, which had the potential to help health care migration benefit both rich and poor countries. The BMA also liaised with the pharmaceutical policy R&D Group at the London School of Economics to look at tropical diseases that the pharmaceutical companies tended to neglect.

International health care and ethical procurement of medical equipment

The BMA's work to highlight the health needs of people in the world's poorest countries included funding a project called *Healthcare Information for All by 2015* (HIFA). The Association is a member of its national steering group. HIFA is present in 149 countries and its aim is for everyone in the world to have access to an informed healthcare provider by 2015. BMA members were encouraged to join its email forums and to contribute their expertise and ideas. The forums provided the means to share knowledge with others involved in the project who came from backgrounds such as medicine, publishing, IT, social science and journalism. In 2001 the BMA organised the Humanitarian

---

[8] MEDACT is, according to its website, 'a global health charity tackling issues at the centre of international policy debates. Led by its health professional membership it undertakes education, research and advocacy on the health implications of conflict, development and environmental change.' (Website accessed 19 November 2012).

Fund, which offered grants of up to £3,000 to current NHS employees for projects taking place in developing countries. The provisos were that the projects had to offer clear health benefits to the local population, had to involve at least one NHS employee and would have a sustainable impact. A BMA Information Fund has provided health information and educational materials to health-related organisations in the developing world.

In the same way that the BMA's publications on matters relating to the health of the public tended to take an enormous, and perhaps overwhelming, issue such as climate change, and explain how individual doctors could make a difference, so a similar approach was taken in a 2007 publication, *Improving Health for the World's Poor – What can Health Professionals do?* This aimed to inspire health professionals, and the organisations in which they worked, to play a powerful role in improving the health of the poorest. The report identified eight barriers to the improvement of health for the world's poor: health systems, water power, climate change, fair trade, hunger and obesity, tobacco control, poverty and health leadership. On each issue discussion was followed by recommendations for action by health professionals and their organisations.

The BMA also encouraged its members to act over the fair and ethical procurement of medical equipment. As it pointed out in 2007 in *Improving Health for the World's Poor*, the NHS purchased millions of pounds worth of medical equipment every month. Much of the medical equipment was manufactured in developing countries where international reports had found that working conditions in surgical instrument factories could be dangerous and unhealthy. There was particular concern about the use of child labour. The BMA called on the NHS to develop ethical purchasing guidelines and in February 2009 launched a campaign to promote fair trade in medical supplies. It set up a Fair Medical and Ethical Trade Group, which encouraged doctors to ask their chief executives to adopt an ethical procurement policy, to ask healthcare suppliers where they produced their goods and to form ethical trade interest groups within their trusts. The BMA's campaigning on this little-known issue bore some fruit in May 2011 with the launch of *Ethical Procurement for Health*, a practical online tool kit to help UK health organisations improve the working conditions for those making equipment for the NHS. This had been organised with the Department of Health in England and the Ethical Trading Initiative, an alliance of companies, trade unions and voluntary organisations whose members worked in partnership to improve the working lives of poor and vulnerable people in supply chains.

Other international work

The BMA has a long tradition of helping members who want to work or study overseas. For many years the Commonwealth and International Medical Advisory Bureau advised UK-based doctors wishing to work abroad and kept information on regulations for visiting or working in other countries. It also advised each year up to 4,000 doctors wanting to enter the country.[9] In 1994 the Bureau was incorporated into the International Department, which started to run 'working abroad' seminars around the UK. These seminars enabled the BMA to form links with major aid agencies which provided medical help worldwide. The advice given to doctors wanting to work abroad included making sure it could be incorporated into their training, that they had the correct visas and would be eligible for registration in their chosen country.

---

[9] For example, according to the 1982–83 Annual Report of Council, during 1982 the Bureau dealt with 2,000 enquiries and sent 4,000 written replies to enquiries from doctors living overseas.

Chapter 12

The BMA and its members

Between 1981 and 2012 the number of BMA members in the UK more than doubled, from 59,000 to 150,000 (with 22,200 student members). Sixty seven per cent of the target group were members. During this time the membership department transformed from a Dickensian office with a card index and a few clerks (some of whose time was devoted until the 1980s to maintaining the armed forces medical reserve list for the Ministry of Defence) to a thrusting team of marketing professionals with targets to reach and computer metrics at their fingertips.

Many factors play in the recruitment and retention of members. In a changing world, doctors' decisions about whether to join the BMA are affected by some external factors: the gradual shift from societal to individual values, for instance, has made people less likely to join organisations for fellowship and solidarity, and more likely to be looking for personal benefits. This trend has been compounded by the declining influence and membership of trade unions. The current junior doctors – generation 'Y' in marketing terms – are less likely to attend meetings, use electronic media to get their information and are confident about choosing services from a variety of suppliers. Changes in the medical profession have given doctors different expectations: the communal life of hospitals that was part of training, with its hardships and shared experiences, has largely disappeared so that doctors now focus earlier on their domestic life and are less likely to perceive their profession as a brotherhood or club. The proportion of women doctors has increased substantially: in England for example it has reached 43% in 2012.[1] Women doctors are more likely to have career breaks and to juggle domestic and professional responsibilities, which makes them more organised about their expectations from a membership organisation. They are less likely to join committees and more likely to look for practical and focused advice.

Membership levels are mostly influenced by doctors' perceptions of how effectively the BMA represents them, and of what services it

---

[1] DDRB 40th Report 2012.

provides and how well. The BMA measures these perceptions in regular surveys of members and non-members. In 1979, 91% of members said the most important reason for being a member was 'national negotiations', while in 2012 they gave a much broader spread of reasons, with trade union representation, employment and careers advice, access to the *BMJ*, and the BMA website also figuring highly. The Association can respond to members' perceptions in three main ways: providing services to individual members, enabling members to influence and feel well represented in the development of policy, and setting up effective channels of communication – in both directions – between the BMA and its members. These will be dealt with in the rest of this chapter.

Regional services

The BMA first set up an employment advice and representation service in 1978, after a working party chaired by Alastair Clark, recently retired as Chairman of the Representative Body, said that the Association, following its registration under the 1974 Trade Union and Labour Relations Act, needed to develop its functions as a trade union. This was the forerunner of the BMA's regional services, which moved from a small team of generalists, working largely in isolation, to a sophisticated and highly organised service. It became one of the BMA's key assets, with a unique knowledge base and experience of doctors' contracts and other employment issues.

One of Alastair Clark's main proposals was a network of Place of Work Accredited Representatives (Powars), BMA members who could act as a point of contact for their workplace colleagues. Another was to appoint Industrial Relations Officers (IROs) to deal with members' employment problems. By 1981 these changes were well under way, building on the existing network of regional offices that had been providing a mainly secretarial function to divisions and local committees. They were overseen by provincial medical secretaries, who had been appointed in the expectation that the BMA would start to provide medical indemnity cover, a development which was shelved as being too expensive and not what members wanted.

The new regional services were not considered significant enough to be mentioned when the second volume of the BMA's history was written in 1981, but were growing fast. Norman Ellis, the experienced former general secretary of the First Division Association, the union for senior civil servants, was appointed to oversee their development. Working closely with two imaginative and iconoclastic provincial medical secretaries, Francis Piggott and Ian McKim Thompson (who was already providing an informal advice service to members from his Birmingham base), he pressed ahead with new appointments. Norman Ellis had been surprised to find how far behind other unions the BMA lagged in offering individual services to members – all its efforts had been concentrated on national negotiations – but, with recent contractual changes having been introduced for hospital doctors, take-up of the new services was rapid.

Workplace services

By 1984, 17 IROs were in place, one for each NHS region and nation, and more than 500 Powars represented employed senior, junior and academic doctors. They provided advice on contracts, removal expenses, study leave and starting salaries, as well as – unexpectedly – advice to GPs on staff employment and partnership issues. Members valued the service, which was promoted through visits to mess meetings, where attendances were boosted by hospitality from pharmaceutical companies (then an accepted part of medical life). Overcoming internal resistance, Norman Ellis and Ian McKim Thompson introduced direct debit for subscriptions; these developments were reflected in a 20% increase in members over the first four years.[2]

Regional services grew steadily over the next 20 years and became a core element of what the BMA could offer members. The first IROs were recruited from trade union, NHS or BMA backgrounds, and they became expert in industrial relations skills (such as representing doctors at disciplinary hearings or tribunals), and wider medico-political issues. They were well known figures in their region, both among doctors and among employers. As the original cohort of provincial medical secretaries disappeared and Norman Ellis moved to the central secretariat, Ian McKim Thompson took over responsibility for managing regional services in England; IROs in Scotland, Wales and Northern Ireland reported to their national secretaries. He resolutely remained in Birmingham, developing the IROs' expertise and cultivating for his empire a fierce independence from 'that central lot', similar to the relationship between the headquarters of a commercial firm and its sales team in the field.

---

[2] N Ellis *The BMA's trade union structure – four years on. BMJ* vol 285, 3 July 1982.

The superimposition of a new, dynamic and managed group on an already complex representative structure created inevitable tensions. Strategic reviews in 1984[3] and in 1989[4] looked at the role of the divisions, which were feeling excluded by the increasing focus on workplace representation, and also of the regional councils, which were seen to have a vital function in co-ordinating medico-political activity throughout the region. Both recommended better sharing of information and more cross-representation. They also reflected members' appreciation of regional services by reaffirming their value, as a result of which they were strengthened and expanded.

By the mid-1990s the workload of IROs had grown to the extent that Scotland and some larger regions had more than one. A degree of rivalry had grown up between regional and central staff, which at times led to reluctance to exchange information. But the shared experience of the Association's campaign against the 1989 white paper built enough mutual respect and understanding to enable a big co-operative exercise in 1990 that established local negotiating committees (LNCs). These were to become a key aspect of regional services' work.

The strategy behind LNCs (*see Chapter 1*) was worked out by central and regional staff. The job of setting up the new committees fell to IROs, who needed skills of persuasion and organisation – and a great deal of commitment. Local doctors were often sceptical about the value of LNCs in trusts where they saw management as all-powerful, and understandably they were hesitant to commit time to them. The IROs stuck to their guns, and within two years had established LNCs in most trusts. As already described (*page 50*) and despite the much vaunted freedoms of trusts, their early tasks were less about discussing local contracts than about implementing national agreements. These tasks were important in establishing the value of LNCs in the eyes of trust managers and local doctors, some of whom had not seen the BMA at work at close hand before and were impressed by the IROs' expertise.

The BMA then put considerable effort into supporting and developing LNCs, with training courses and briefing material for members, and a new network of communications to enable the local committees to share information and experience. Servicing LNCs provided a new focus for regional services, and by increasing the BMA's local visibility at a time when doctors were fearful about their terms and conditions of

---

[3] *Review of the role and functions of the division, regional council and POWAR*. 1984.
[4] *Ten Years On*: report of the working party on regional services 1989. (Chairman JA Ford.)

service, it drove up membership levels among employed senior doctors to peaks of over 90% during the 1990s.

LNCs have plenty of routine negotiating tasks to do, but from time to time they have flagged and the effort of keeping them going has been questioned. But the growth in foundation trusts (ever more focused on financial bottom lines) and the pressures of severe cost savings have once again highlighted the need for a recognised interface between doctors and managers in each workplace. Many trusts are seeking to erode existing contracts and LNCs have a vital role in insisting that new working patterns are properly negotiated. Good managers recognise that buy-in to change is best achieved by discussion, while poor managers who avoid engaging with staff representatives need to be challenged and held to account. LNCs, supported by their IROs, are strongly placed to do this. The fragmentation of NHS provision, continuing financial pressures and renewed impetus for local solutions, which foundation trusts with their business ethos are increasingly empowered to deliver, are bringing immense challenges. But the BMA's original decision to establish LNCs, and the effort it has put into supporting and developing them, has given doctors a mechanism for responding effectively to these challenges.

As the LNCs became established, the network of Powars became increasingly anomalous. They had been a successful innovation, enhancing the BMA's profile locally, raising doctors' awareness of trade union issues, and enabling active and enthusiastic members to become involved in a new way. For many years the Powars were well supported with training courses, a detailed handbook and regular briefing material. This was co-ordinated through a central department led by the redoubtable and highly efficient Thelma Mills, who made it her business to ensure that mailing lists and documentation were constantly updated. After she had retired, as Powars moved on and were not replaced, and as IROs began to supplant them as the first point of contact for members with queries, the network began to lapse. LNC members were being appointed instead of and alongside Powars and to end the confusion the role was dropped and LNC members became accredited as the recognised BMA local representatives.

The growing demand for advice

It had been understood from the outset that the development of regional services would require a major investment. In the late 1970s UK membership had dipped to below 50,000 and significant expenditure was a big risk. The Treasurer, Jack Miller, was supportive but there were sceptical voices. Nevertheless the gamble paid off as membership increased, regional services continued to grow, and escalating costs were accepted as the justified price for a popular service.

By 2002 the cost of regional services was close to £6 million a year, and 28 IROs were in post in England, handling 46,000 new enquiries a year. The overall configuration of regional services had not altered since the start, though the services they provided had gradually changed. Bill Mayers, a manager with a health service background, had modernised the staffing structure, appointing employment advisers and senior employment advisers to handle the more straightforward queries and cases, leaving the IROs more time to concentrate on LNCs and more complex casework, and also assume a managerial role in the regional offices. An advocacy unit was set up to deal with cases that required representation at tribunals or other legal proceedings, and extended opening hours for some regional offices were trialled, using call centre technology.

In 2001 the BMA had recognised that as its finances grew and became more complex, it needed more rigorous business disciplines. The Council appointed the first non-medical Secretary and Chief Executive, Jeremy Strachan, a lawyer with a business background. He saw that regional services, as a major area of expenditure, was a priority and, with the retirement of Bill Mayers and of Michael Lowe, who had taken overall responsibility for regional services after Ian McKim Thompson, a new manager, Chris Darke, was appointed. He had been general secretary of the airline pilots' trade union Balpa, and arrived with a brief to modernise service delivery while preserving and enhancing the reputation of regional services as the 'jewel in the crown' of the BMA.

Over the next three years, the service was reorganised so that members would use a single point of contact and be quickly referred to the most appropriate staff to deal with their problem – from straightforward queries to the most complex legal cases. The system relies on updated technology to record and track cases, and on identifying and training staff with the right expertise for each type of response.

Some members may have seen such changes as leading to a more impersonal service, and on the rare occasions when the system fails the experience can feel like the worst kind of call centre nightmare – familiar from other areas of modern life but not acceptable in an organisation owned by its members and existing to provide them with high quality services tailored to the needs of busy professionals. But the modernisation of member services has enabled the BMA to handle the hugely increasing volumes of calls and queries (105,000 contacts in 2011), to make the most effective use of the specialist expertise of different types of staff, and to monitor and improve the quality and timeliness of responses. Satisfaction rates with the service provided have been running at over 90% for the past five years and are higher than they were with the previous arrangements, though there is no place for complacency.

The first stage was a change in the provision of legal support. An additional driver here was a case brought by a member against the BMA, which had highlighted weaknesses in the processes for handling complex cases. Rajendra Chaudhary, a urologist, alleged that the BMA had racially discriminated against him by failing to give him adequate support. He had fallen foul of the changes in specialist training during 1996/97 when entry to the new specialist registrar grade was determined by an assessment of the applicant's previous training. Mr Chaudhary was denied entry to the new grade – clearly a major blow to his career prospects – and he embarked on a long series of appeals and challenges. He received extensive help over several years with advice from different BMA staff members. But after several unsuccessful attempts to get the decisions changed, the BMA decided that the case could be taken no further. In March 2000 Mr Chaudhary took the Association to an employment tribunal.

The tribunal's decision came as a major shock to the BMA, which like other trade unions had been active in opposing discrimination. Although his claim of direct discrimination was not upheld, the tribunal concluded that the BMA had been guilty of indirect discrimination and awarded Mr Chaudhary nearly £900,000. The award was thought at the time to have been the largest ever made in a race discrimination case. In 2004 the Employment Appeal Tribunal upheld the original decision, but in July 2007 the Court of Appeal overturned it, finding that Mr Chaudhary had not been discriminated against and that there was no evidence that the BMA's processes had a discriminatory effect on members from ethnic minorities. But the case had hung over the Association for seven years, prompting a vigorous review of the issues raised.

One immediate action was to enhance the role of the BMA's Equal Opportunities Committee, encouraging it to root out any practices that might give rise to a perception of discrimination, and also to promote truly inclusive policies and practices. The review then looked at the way legal support was provided to members. Members looking for legal solutions to their problems increasingly expected that advice would come from legal professionals rather than specialist members of staff who mostly were not qualified lawyers. The BMA decided to contract an external law firm, as many other unions were doing, to provide legal advice and representation for members. This would offer a professional service and also, since decisions on the merits of each case would be taken externally, the Association would be protected against the financial risk that had become apparent. The work went out to tender and in 2003 the law firm Irwin Mitchell was contracted to handle members' cases and provide a training service and advice helpline on employment law to BMA regional services staff.

The advocacy unit was discontinued and the BMA's role changed to managing the contract with the lawyers to ensure value for money and high quality. After the first term, the two parties were unable to agree on costs so the business was moved to Halliwells, which was then taken over by another firm, HBJ Gateley Wareing, though with a smooth transfer of staff and ongoing cases. In 2011 the service covered about 400 legal cases and cost almost £1.2 million. Members see legal advice and support – though most will fortunately not need to use it – as one of the key benefits of BMA membership.

Joining the call centre revolution

The other major change was to the stock-in-trade of regional services – individual employment advice to members. It was important to improve the existing arrangements in which a member might have to make several calls to track down the right office and the appropriate person. The first stage had been a pilot scheme in some regions for extended office hours using staff at an external call-centre, Essentia in Glasgow. Take-up much outside normal office hours was low, but the Essentia staff proved to be of high calibre, keen to learn and well managed, and their call handling technology worked well with the BMA's systems.

By the time the pilots were evaluated, Chris Darke was in post and was starting to explore more radical options for using regional services staff. He developed a proposal for schemes in three regions (including Glasgow) to 'bottom slice' the first level of member queries so that they could be dealt with by Essentia staff with appropriate guidance documents. Between two-thirds to three-quarters of calls were estimated to come into this category. The BMA would train Essentia staff to receive the calls and answer these queries, and protocols would be developed for passing on the more complex queries to BMA staff, who would have more time to deal with them.

The trials were successful. The centre staff dealt with more than 30,000 calls of which over 75% were resolved without onward referral, and members receiving the new service gave good feedback. The relationship with Essentia worked well and systems were quickly developed to ensure that their staff were included in the briefings given to BMA staff. In 2004 Chris Darke and the BMA's senior managers introduced a new service, to be called askBMA. It relied on a heavily publicised single contact number, and was rolled out first in England and soon afterwards in the devolved nations. This involved a significant investment of £0.75 million and the business case was carefully scrutinised by the Finance Committee. They agreed that it would be a catalyst for new ways of working that would focus directly on members' needs, and recommended that it should be partly financed by efficiencies elsewhere in regional services. Such savings were not to be found through reducing the number of IROs and employment advisers whose contribution was highly valued and vociferously supported by members, who regularly generated Annual Representative Meeting (ARM) resolutions calling for more of them. Early indications were that, despite the top slicing of legal work and the bottom-slicing of basic queries, their workload was still increasing, through LNC duties, the implementation of new contracts, banding appeals for juniors and the growing appetite of trusts to use formal disciplinary procedures against doctors.

One major area where efficiencies might be generated without impacting on members was in the use of the BMA's 15 local offices, which existed in addition to national offices in Edinburgh, Cardiff and Belfast. This was to prove much more contentious. Most local offices had opened during the 1980s and 1990s and were usually leased, often under a joint arrangement with Professional Affinity Group Services (PAGS) who ran BMA Services (see below) and had locally-based staff. Some of these offices were in city centres, others in suburban business parks. They provided a comfortable working environment for small numbers of BMA staff, but members rarely visited, some had no large meeting rooms, and most IROs went to see members in the workplace.

Expenditure on these office premises (excluding staff costs) was substantial: over £600,000 in 2003, and for some time senior managers had questioned whether closing an office might release money for better services. There had been piecemeal attempts to do so, for example when the lease of the Liverpool office came up for renewal in the late 1990s. But these had been met with fierce opposition from influential local members (several of whom were leading members of Council), and managers quickly backed off. This time, however, there were both operational and strategic reasons to review the role of the offices more thoroughly: several leases were due for renewal and the PAGS, like many commercial organisations, had decided in 2003 to introduce home-working for its sales force. This meant it would no longer need local offices. In addition, the electronic revolution had changed dramatically the role of the office as a postal hub and askBMA was dealing with many of the basic queries formerly handled by staff in these offices.

So a plan was developed for another big change. The local offices in England would be rationalised with the creation of five major centres – in Liverpool, Birmingham, Bristol, Purley and Leeds – and the gradual closure of the remaining offices as leases expired. Similar but smaller changes were proposed for Scotland. Regional staff, other than administrative staff in those centres, would be asked to move to home working. An opportunity to try these ideas out had arisen in the north west, where the lease of the Manchester office was about to expire in 2003, and the need to make new arrangements was urgent. Staff were invited to trial homeworking or work in Liverpool, where the office was refurbished and redesignated as the north west centre. With little time for consultation over this unexpected decision, local committees responded angrily, many staff were unenthusiastic, and when the move went ahead there was a backlash. So it was with some trepidation that managers worked up a full plan over the summer of 2004. Offices would need refurbishment, new technology would need to be installed and staff trained to use it, and there would have to be a programme of change management. There would be a few redundancies, mainly among local secretarial and administrative staff. It was clearly important that the staff concerned should learn of the proposals from their managers rather than through rumours (as had happened in Manchester), and they had to be given proper rights of consultation. On the other hand it would be a major development and therefore needed the support of the Finance Committee, Council and BMA members. But it was feared that circulating the proposal to staff or to Council members could lead to leaks.

The tactic adopted to get over this difficulty was to table the proposals at a Council meeting (in Edinburgh) in September while managers simultaneously briefed their staff in the local offices. It proved disastrous. Both Council members and staff were shocked and offended at being presented so precipitately with changes of this order, and they reacted badly. The ill-tempered Council meeting that followed was the first overt expression of an erosion of trust and understanding between Council members and the BMA's senior managers that had been spreading beneath the surface for some time and had come close to erupting at the 2003 ARM. An increasingly professional senior management team, some brought in specifically from business backgrounds, saw it as their role to develop challenging business strategies. Those used to working with boards of directors expected tough accountability, but with a presumption of support from the board, and they found it difficult to understand the instinct of many Council members to act as representatives rather than directors. Some members felt the managers were being high-handed: strategy should be determined by Council itself, albeit with staff advice, and they expected to be involved in developing plans, not just approving them. Furthermore, there was a tendency for the cultural suspicion of managers' motives and competence that is common among NHS doctors to spill over into their perception of BMA managers and some saw the plan as an exercise in 'cost-cutting', riding roughshod over members' interests and a mistreatment of employees (many of whom they worked with closely and felt responsible for).

Tensions between managers and elected members exist in all organisations with a representative structure. In the BMA it was something that staff had learnt to work around, recognising that the elected members had the real power, even though they relied heavily on the knowledge, experience and advice of staff. Under previous Secretaries there had been skirmishes over such parochial matters as the application of a management edict banning sun-blinds from offices, when the elected members of the GPs committee, lobbied by staff, simply leaned heavily on the Secretary to allow the rule to be overridden. But as the senior management team grew, and with the appointment of the first non-medical Secretary, Jeremy Strachan (who often chose to express his powerful analyses in robust, even confrontational language), the tension became more serious, and was to flare up again in the coming years.

At the Edinburgh Council meeting there was an eruption of anger against the senior managers who had drawn up the plans, and also against the Council Chairman, James Johnson, who was seen as complicit in the way the issue had been handled. A long battle ensued with many tense exchanges. Some staff were enthusiastic about home working but others were not. Managers put much effort into discussing with staff the many practical implications – from telephone systems and furniture to mechanisms to avoid isolation. A similar effort went into consulting with members, particularly the local committees who looked to regional offices for support, and service level agreements were drawn up to reassure them. Gradually the ideas gained acceptance – though it was by no means universal – and in December 2004 Council approved a revised version of the plan. The office closures could begin, the new centres be developed and the change management programme go ahead. Those made redundant were helped to find new work, and special arrangements were made for those few for whom home working was not practicable. In time, even those who had been sceptical recognised the advantages of not having to commute. Staff said that they worked harder at home, and this was supported by the observations of their managers, and by outside research on the productivity gains that 'telework' can make.[5] Nevertheless, a few local representatives still felt bitter: there was affection in some medical communities for the local BMA office and the focus it provided for medico-political activity, and they thought this had been too readily dispensed with. But on the whole members recognised that keeping pace with the changing world sometimes brings difficult choices.

A more recent development for regional services has been a separate service for GPs in their capacity as employers. The BMA always gave advice to this group but it became clear that their cases should be more clearly differentiated from advice to employees. New legislation has led to more complex employer responsibilities, requiring BMA staff to develop special areas of expertise. The number of salaried or sessional GPs, many employed by other GPs, has grown, requiring 'Chinese Walls' to be developed so that all BMA members – both employers and employees – can be supported by their union. Finally, the BMA's services to GP principals were not widely known, with many GP members looking first to their Local Medical Committee for advice and support. So in 2009 the BMA launched its Employer Advisory Service, staffed by specialist advisers. Within two years it had eight members of staff and dealt with close to 4,000 cases in 2011.

---

[5] *The shifting nature of work in the UK* – Telework Research Network 2011.

Feedback from members and advances in technology have brought other changes, such as online training for LNC members and greater choice over how to receive advice, including webcams, instant messaging and web chat. The askBMA service has been rebranded as First Point of Call in order to show that it is part of a seamless range of support. For instance, staff from the Glasgow call centre, now provided by The Listening Company (which took over Essentia and was bought by Serco in 2011), cover maternity and other absences among the BMA's own employment advisers. By 2011 regional services employed 132 staff in England and another 21, separately managed but part of an integrated UK service, in the devolved nations (in addition to the national office staff). The total cost of the English regional services, including the First Point of Call and legal services contracts, was about £10 million a year. About one third of members use these services each year, and BMA research shows that it is one of the main reasons why doctors join and stay.

Financial and other services

The greater range of benefits and services compared with 30 years ago reflects the greater diversity of needs within the profession and today's competitive market for all kinds of services. Two other important member benefits are the BMA library and the *British Medical Journal (BMJ)*, which is provided free to every member and which offers access to products and services such as the *Student BMJ*, BMJ Learning, BMJ Careers, BMJ Masterclasses and the BMJ Evidence Centre *(see Chapter 15)*.

The library had two transformations during this period. In 1986 it was moved from dark premises at the back of BMA House to the grandly refurbished Great Hall, opened by the Princess of Wales, where it benefited from more light and space and better IT facilities. Over time, however, it suffered from the revolution in electronic publishing as fewer members visited in person, preferring to access documents electronically. The library responded by developing new services, particularly the Medline-plus service giving members free access to this database. Although the services were well used it became clear that members no longer needed the huge numbers of books that were stored there. In 2007 there was a major refurbishment of BMA House and as the first stage the library moved again to smaller but more welcoming accommodation with access direct from the building's main entrance. The opportunity was taken by the go-ahead Librarian, Jacky Berry, to revamp the library's services for the 21st century and to market them more positively to members. It now offers a range of e-journals and e-books, catalogue searches, an inter-library service, courses on online searching and a smartphone app for members to browse services and items. Since the new premises opened, visitor numbers have increased by three-quarters (these include many medical students) and use of the postal service for books and other items has doubled *(for more details of the library's involvement with IT developments see Chapter 8)*.

Other member services include advice and guidance in areas other than employment, such as pensions, medical ethics, immigration and partnership. Doctors for Doctors is a small unit offering counselling and advice on personal and professional problems and BMA Law offers a discounted service to practices seeking advice on matters such as corporate structures, bidding and tendering, and data protection. Careers guidance and exam revision courses are available at special rates to members.

For 20 years the BMA engaged in an ambitious enterprise to offer financial services to members, either at preferential rates or involving products that were particularly tailored to doctors: BMA Services which was established in 1982 as a joint venture with an established insurance company Jardine Glanville. There were reputational risks for the BMA in committing to a sector in which it had no expertise or experience, but the financial risks were largely borne by Jardine, and the corporate structure that was put in place proved to be sound. Sir Anthony Grabham, a former negotiator and chairman of Council and later chairman of the *BMJ*, who was a pioneer of the venture having seen a similar scheme operating to the benefit of the Canadian Medical Association, chaired the Board of Directors throughout. BMAS offered insurance and financial products that members seemed to like, with over 50% choosing a BMAS product during the 1990s. It generated substantial profits: about £15 million a year by 2000, half of which went directly to the BMA. In 1999, as financial services boomed, BMA Services became Professional Affinity Group Services Limited, embracing wider markets (though still trading as BMAS for BMA members) but by 2002 the growth of online services had started to change the insurance sector. The BMA astutely made use of an opportunity to buy out Jardine Glanville at a reasonable price, and then sold the business a year later at a substantial profit to Wesleyan. After a few years Wesleyan decided to sell its own financial products only. The BMA believed that its members wanted independent financial advice and therefore arranged for tailored financial products to be available to members through other reputable providers.

Much less successful was the attempt in 1996 to establish a parallel venture, known as BMA Professional Services (BMAPS), which was to provide accountancy services to members by negotiating preferential rates with established accountancy firms. It was set up as a BMA company, but its governance and management were less robust than in the case of BMAS and critically the business model was flawed: doctors were generally well served by existing medical accountants and the BMAPS offer was not sufficiently attractive.

The company grew initially, establishing several local offices and employing staff, but it soon started to lose money. Board members became worried and took steps to reduce the losses, but in 1999 a report commissioned by the BMA's new Audit Committee persuaded the Finance Committee to bring the venture to an end. The episode ended with bad feeling between the board and Council, and the BMAPS venture now stands in the corporate memory as a cautionary tale for whenever bright ideas are put forward that might tempt the BMA to venture into areas too far removed from its core activities.

Local structures and communications

While many of the BMA's high profile activities are performed by a relatively small group of members at national level, they depend on the input, feedback, participation and support of the thousands of ordinary members on whose behalf they are carried out. Members can make their views known in a variety of ways, and the BMA is constantly trying to help them by improving its representative structures and methods of communication.

Many members are introduced to the BMA through its local structures, yet these structures are complex and can be off-putting, particularly when meetings are dominated by procedural issues or personal agendas. The basic unit is the division, comprising all members living in the area. Their strength is their inclusiveness but their weakness is their lack of formal links to the local representative committees discussing employment, pay and conditions. Activities in the divisions vary. Some meet rarely and are poorly attended, while others meet regularly and make sure that their views are vigorously represented at the ARM and other meetings. The BMA makes frequent efforts to invigorate the divisions, most recently by providing divisional honorary secretaries with web pages they can use to post items of local interest and by helping them send regular e-mails to division members. But the divisions rely heavily on the commitment of enthusiastic individuals, and their effectiveness fluctuates accordingly.

Local committees representing the different branches of practice attract more consistent involvement, but are more narrowly focused. There has been a long-standing network of regional committees for consultants, specialty doctors and associate specialists, public health doctors, juniors, and committees at university level for medical students and academic staff. There is also a network of Local Medical Committees which, though independent from the Association, send GP representatives and motions to various BMA national meetings. To these have been added more recently the network of workplace-based local negotiating committees. All these groups communicate directly with their national branch of practice committees, but have a less direct relationship with the BMA Council or with each other. In the devolved nations, similar structures are in place but the smaller numbers involved and the absence of a regional tier enables the local bodies to feel more closely involved with the centre.

The observation that this machinery is less than integrated is not a new one and it is a matter of concern that the BMA is missing an important trick by not providing an effective mechanism to bring together at local level the most engaged medico-political activists from the different branches of practice. This would greatly enhance the ability of doctors to join together and ensure that medical values are to the fore when local services are under consideration. The BMA is the natural organisation to do this, since it represents all branches of practice. It has sometimes been able to provide support when doctors have joined together locally on their own initiative, but this has not become the norm.

Two initiatives tried to address this issue. The first was the establishment in England of BMA regional councils, which was first attempted in 1976, given new impetus after the 1984 and 1989 reviews of local functions, and relaunched in 2009. The rationale was to co-ordinate all medico-political activity in a region. There were some encouraging periods when, through a combination of able and enthusiastic officers and genuine regional issues to address (for example Sir Ara Darzi's proposals for London in 2007), some regional councils flourished. But overall the initiative has had only patchy success. Perhaps regions are too far removed from the issues that capture local interest; perhaps constitutional questions have been too contentious and too difficult to resolve; perhaps an additional tier of representation merely adds further complication.

A more recent initiative has been the appointment since 2009 of BMA regional co-ordinators, of whom there were six in 2012. These are senior and experienced members of staff whose job is to facilitate and co-ordinate activity between the various local committees and elected representatives. Their work complements that of the IROs and other regional staff who focus on employment advice, and they have helped to improve links between LMCs and hospital based-doctors, and in establishing relationships with strategic health authorities and primary care trusts before their abolition. This initiative applies only to England; in the devolved nations staff in the national office can carry out this role.

Many doctors lack the time or inclination to sit on representative committees, but nevertheless take an interest in developments and want to have a voice in formulating BMA policy over matters that may affect their terms and conditions of service or their working environment. These members, probably a majority, depend heavily on the BMA's various methods of communication to receive information and express their views. In the past 30 years, communication has been one aspect of the BMA's work that has changed fundamentally, and the impact of this has been significant.

Until well into the 1990s all communication was by post. Doctors relied for their medico-political news on the weekly *BMJ* (which still carried reports from BMA committees), on the monthly magazine *BMA News Review,* and on newsletters and other mailings sent out from various BMA departments. They also had the less authoritative but more entertaining accounts in the medical 'comics' such as *Pulse, GP, Doctor* and *Hospital Doctor,* which had no trouble in finding committee members to give them information. Paper communication permitted a more stately process for decision making than is now possible. Committee chairmen could fit their BMA duties around an only partly reduced clinical timetable, while members were usually content to wait a week or more for a considered response to a letter.

Now communication is much more diverse and people expect immediate and interactive responses. Although some things are still sent through the post – including *BMA News,* now a weekly tabloid and the Association's main organ of communication – most communication is electronic. *BMA News* is also available electronically, and the BMA also issues a weekly e-mail update to members, tailored to their individual preferences for subject matter and pulling together branch of practice and local stories. Increasingly members prefer on-demand services through the BMA website, where news is constantly updated, linked to background information and allows feedback and discussion. The tone of communications has altered with the growing diversity and less formal ethos of the medical profession. Communications must reflect the reality that members may increasingly work part-time, will have different ethnic and religious backgrounds, and will work under differing circumstances as devolution gathers pace, so will have widely varying needs and preferences. Communications have become more concise, with added links to more detailed information.

The BMA's website is thus central to its communications strategy. Since it was established in 1996, mainly as a repository for the volumes of guidance produced, it has undergone three major redevelopments. But the new technology offers even greater possibilities, and the latest revamp, launched in the summer of 2012, changed the whole architecture of the site and promises to revolutionise members' interface with their organisation.

The substantial growth in the Association's membership over the past 30 years has required major organisational changes. In the process the BMA has become less clubby and more service-orientated, more professional in its interactions with members and less stuffy in tone. Membership figures are still growing – the target of 150,000 was reached during 2012 – which suggests that doctors seem to approve of these changes and feel that they want to be part of the BMA. But the Association will face more challenges. One is the relatively low level of membership among junior doctors, which has declined from more than two thirds to just over half of the target group (though the recruitment of medical students has been healthy in recent years and the hope is that many will remain in membership). Possible explanations are the continuing negative impact of the MTAS crisis of 2007 *(see Chapter 3)*, disillusionment with the current employment contract, and – more worryingly – a preference among younger people to obtain services from different sources rather than from belonging to an organisation. Whatever the reason, junior doctors are the Association's future, and the BMA will have to find new ways to attract them in larger numbers if it is to maintain the momentum of the past 30 years.

Chapter 13
The BMA's constitution and governance

Throughout the period covered by this book the BMA has been adapting its constitution to meet the demands of national legislation and of its members. This has not always been an easy journey. There have been some bitter disagreements and these surfaced at several ARMs in the 2000s. But there were also many positive efforts to improve what remains a labyrinthine structure. These efforts followed a long tradition within the BMA of examining its constitutional arrangements for fitness for purpose, inclusivity and 'representativeness'. Not all members find such matters fascinating, but the BMA has been admirably served by a succession of doctors who got to grips with the minutiae of the constitution to try to ensure that all members can take part in the decision-making processes and that the democratic machinery changes with the times.

Trade Union Act 1984 and changes to Council

The Association faced huge challenges in the early 1970s. Edward Heath's Conservative government's 1971 Industrial Relations Act and Harold Wilson's Labour government's 1974 Trade Union and Labour Relations Act both threatened the status of the BMA. But it managed to emerge listed as a trade union under the 1974 Act, while keeping its status as a company registered under the Companies Act and as a 'special register body'.[1] The 1979 Conservative government, led by Margaret Thatcher, was determined to curtail the power of the trade unions and set about this with Employment Acts in 1980 and 1982 and, after the government's 1983 landslide, the 1984 Trade Union Act. Although the legislation was aimed primarily at the powerful industrial

---

[1] The following background information on Special Register Bodies is included in *Governance, a confidential brief* issued to Council on 23 July 2008 by the BMA's Director of Legal Services, Jonathan Waters: 'Under the Industrial Relations Act 1971, a Special Register was established for the registration of those limited companies (mainly professional bodies) which took part in collective bargaining on behalf of their members. The Trade Union and Labour Relations Act 1974 subsequently provided that trade unions could no longer be limited companies. It did, however, provide an exception for those bodies, such as the BMA, which were already on the Register. There are only 13 Special Register Bodies.'

unions, the BMA found itself obliged to make some unwelcome changes.

The 1984 Trade Union Act required all trade unions to elect their principal executive committee by secret ballot of all their voting members. This directly affected the BMA because the Act prevented election by any intermediate body and the BMA had been electing voting members of Council (then and now the BMA's principal executive committee under trade union law) from members of the Representative Body (RB) and of the committees representing doctors in various branches of practice. The BMA bridled at this change and the Chairman of Council, Sir Anthony Grabham, wrote in the 1983–84 annual report of Council: 'The BMA has traditionally been organised on a highly democratic basis so I am somewhat saddened to find that the Association may be obliged to change the method of electing the Council to meet the requirements of trade union legislation now going through Parliament which are supposedly aimed at strengthening democracy in unions. I, and some senior colleagues, have met the minister responsible but so far we have obtained no concessions.' The Secretary of the Association had written a long and complicated letter to the Secretary of State for Employment, Tom King, in December 1983 setting out in detail how the proposals would upset the Association's constitutional arrangements and this was followed up by a meeting with the Minister of State for employment, John Selwyn Gummer, on 11 January 1984. He listened politely to the high-level deputation from the BMA but did not make any changes to the Bill as a result. The BMA, along with all other trade unions, had to consider constitutional changes to comply with the new law.

The Organisation Committee was asked to advise and reported that, as the legislation did not prevent election by geographical or 'craft'[2] constituencies, the regional members of Council could be elected by all members in their regions and the craft representatives by all BMA members in that craft. The four members elected by the RB could be elected by all members of the Association. The *ex officio* members, of whom there were 23 when the legislation was proposed, could only vote if they also held a voting seat.

The Trade Union Act came into effect on 1 October 1985. The election of Council for 1985–86 could proceed as before, but

---

[2] The term 'craft' or 'craft committee' was used within the BMA for many years, but never defined in the Association's articles and bye-laws. The 2005 governance reforms introduced the term 'branch of practice' and 'branch of practice committee' and this is now used instead of 'craft'.

amendments to the articles and bye-laws would have to be approved at the 1985 ARM, with elections on the new basis operating for 1986–87. The new constitution of Council (*see appendix to this chapter*) was designed 'merely to bring the council within the terms of the Act with the minimum of change'. Nevertheless, the changes brought considerable upheaval and the report of the Organisation Committee, which appeared in the 1984–85 annual report of Council, anticipated a number of problems that recurred frequently in the following years. One problem was deciding which category doctors belonged to if they were engaged in more than one craft and this was true of both those standing for election and the electorate. Another problem was that *ex-officio* Council members had no voting rights. Among these were the Chairman of Council, and it was recommended to the 1985 ARM that 'in view of the considerable powers vested in the Chairman of Council . . . it is important that he should have been directly elected in the first instance and thus ensure that he has a vote.'

The constitution that was agreed at the 1986 ARM was modified over the years, but remained largely intact until the governance reforms of 2005. That is not to say that Council elections always ran smoothly. Following the 1986–87 election, the first run under the new arrangements, the annual report of Council stated: 'The cumbersome, expensive and time-consuming nature of the new elections led the Council to establish a working party to examine both the conduct of the elections and the constitution of the council. Careful consideration was given to alternative constituencies, voting systems and the ratio of places on the council to the members represented.' An important change was the decision to abandon the 'staging' of the elections which had allowed unsuccessful candidates in one constituency to stand in another. This had been possible when the elections were run at the ARM, but it lengthened the process considerably when all members were entitled to vote. Another change was to give voting members of Council two-year terms of office. Further changes were later made to the arrangements for electing regional representatives and to the numbers of members of the various crafts on Council.

Governance Committees 2001–4

One of the motivations behind the Trade Union Act of 1984 was to make unions more accountable to their members and more democratic. For the BMA this meant that every voting member could now vote in elections to their trade union's principal executive committee and any voting member could stand for election to Council without first having to be elected to the RB or to one of the craft committees. However, the arrangements for elections to Council or the role of Council did not meet with universal contentment and, in 2002, a major review of the 'governance' of the Association got under way. An earlier review of the constitution had taken place in 1995, but this had been a low-key exercise, concluding that the constitution of Council should not be reviewed until there is a demand by the 'grass roots' of the Association. There may not have been a 'demand by the grass roots' in 2002, but fundamental questions were coming to the fore and in July 2001 Council discussed whether to review the relationship between Council, the RB and the divisions. For the first time a governance project team was set up with substantial resources and it started to ask difficult questions about the BMA's ageing structures; these had not been fundamentally overhauled since 1902 when Council established the RB. The Governance Committee, chaired by Russell Walshaw, a GP from Scunthorpe who was also Chairman of the Organisation Committee, and with advice from external management consultants the Boston Consulting Group, diagnosed the following problems:

- The roles of Council and the RB overlapped, leading to a lack of clarity over which body was responsible for policy-making and when one body may over-rule the other.
- Council was too large and met too infrequently to manage day-to-day business and fulfil its executive functions.
- The BMA was run between Council meetings by an informal group, leading to dissatisfaction and lack of transparency.
- Council was disconnected from the grass-roots and its representativeness was in question, with no formal feedback mechanisms, low turn-out and uncontested elections.
- Council was preoccupied with operational matters at the expense of high-level strategy.
- The RB's legitimacy and representativeness was undermined by lack of divisional activity, falling attendance from divisions and patchy attendance at debates.
- The RB met too infrequently (once a year) to be an effective policy-making body.
- The ARM had too many narrow motions and placed too much emphasis on process.

In March 2003 the BMA sent a questionnaire to all members of the Association, and 20,000 members responded. This was considered a high response rate and put paid to the notion that governance and constitutional matters were of interest only to a fringe group. Dr Walshaw's committee then put forward some radical proposals as a consultation document in June 2003:

- The number of directly-elected Council members should increase to between 60 and 70, with a third of the seats turning over at annual elections.
- Council should separate its policy-making and executive functions.
- The role of Council would be to develop and set policy, informed by the views of the RB, members, committees and national councils.
- An executive board would be set up to oversee the implementation of policy and the management of the Association, and to discharge the functions of a board of directors.
- The RB would have fewer and more detailed debates, and discuss craft-specific business only under exceptional circumstances.

The proposals could, the Governance Committee believed, 'form the basis of a broad consensus within the Association.' It planned to consult for another year before putting final proposals to the ARM in 2004. Unfortunately, resentment of the Governance Committee had been brewing for some time among members of Council and the RB. There were genuine concerns that the establishment of the Governance Committee had not been democratic and that its members did not represent the wide range of views within the BMA. A report submitted to Council in May 2003 set out the background to the establishment of the committee, but suspicion lingered to the extent that the ARM called for the committee to be replaced. The motion stated:

'(i)   a review of the governance of the BMA is essential and urgent;

(ii) the current governance process is failing to produce a credible review of the BMA due to the lack of openness, transparency and accountability of the current Governance Committee and its unwillingness to produce a series of detailed and comprehensive options for the future of the BMA;

(iii) due to the hand-picked nature of the current Governance Committee, the credibility of the Governance Committee with BMA members is very low;

(iv) the current Governance Committee must be replaced with a new democratic and representative Governance Committee at the 2003 ARM of the BMA.'

The debate that preceded the passing of this motion was a difficult one and came during a demanding ARM. It was symptomatic of the problems that the Governance Committee was trying to address that the motion did not address the merits or content of the proposals (which had been sent to all members of the Association that month) or the ongoing consultations; it focused instead on process. The RB's views and instructions were clear, however, and the Organisation Committee, chaired by its then Deputy Chairman, Ian Wilson, met in hasty session to work out a way in which to deal with the resolution during ARM week. The committee suggested that the RB should elect a new Governance Committee. The meeting endorsed this and immediately held elections. The terms of reference for the new committee were 'to consider the relationship between Council, the Representative Body, local representative structures and members and to report on progress to the 2004 ARM.'

The RB had taken the unusual, but fully constitutional, step of setting up its own committee, to be known as the Governance Committee of the Representative Body. Its legitimacy could not be in doubt. The new chairman was John Canning, a GP from Middlesbrough and a member of the General Practitioners Committee (GPC) who was not only closely involved with constitutional changes to the GPC, but who, at the 2001 ARM, had called for an earlier set of BMA-wide governance changes to be sent back to the originating committee (see under *Changes to committees* below). His challenge was to re-establish credibility in the review process and to come up with proposals which would meet with general approval, for the problems identified by the previous Governance Committee still remained and their attempted solution had now been delayed by a further year. Much of the extensive background research carried out by the former Governance Committee could be used by the new group and the expertise of the Governance Project Team, led by Julie Coulson, was retained. The new committee, unbowed by the fate of its predecessor and confident of its validity in the eyes of the RB, looked afresh at the problems with the current constitutional arrangements and considered far-reaching options for reform. It took careful note of the difficulties that had been indentified with the current structure and dared to suggest that one solution might be to do away with the current RB/Council arrangement, which would remove at a stroke the long-standing predicament of two large policy making groups within the same organisation.

After extensive consultation, the Governance Committee of the Representative Body reported back to its parent body in 2004 with the following options for change;

Option 1   *Assembly:* 500–600 members meeting annually, elected from the local cross-craft structure and the main branches of practice, giving a 'policy steer' to the Senate.

Senate: 60–80 people meeting four times a year, elected nationally, making policy and acting as the BMA's national executive under trade union law.

Board: 12–20 people meeting monthly elected or appointed by the Senate acting as the directors and accountable to the Senate as the national executive.

Option 2   *Annual conference:* 500–600 members meeting annually, with representatives drawn from the local cross-craft structure and the main branches of practice, discussing 'profession-wide issues'.

Assembly: 200 members meeting quarterly, nationally elected, making policy and acting as the BMA's national executive under trade union law.

Board: 12–20 people meeting 8–12 times a year, elected or appointed by the Assembly, implementing policy and acting as directors, accountable to the Assembly.

Option 3   *Assembly* 500–600 members meeting annually, drawn from the local cross-craft structure and the main branches of practice, discussing profession-wide issues and giving a policy steer to the Board.

Board: 20–35 people directly elected by members, meeting 8–12 times a year, making and implementing policy, and acting as the national executive under trade union law and the board of directors.

Many people thought that it would be politically unacceptable to deny members the opportunity to vote in favour of the current arrangements, with all their problems. So the committee added a fourth option: retain the status quo. The committee set out the options, giving the advantages and disadvantages of each, but did not give the RB a steer in favour of any one of them. The 2004 RB held an open debate[3] on governance and then voted, using the alternative voting method on

---

[3] Open debates at the ARM occur when a subject is discussed in open session without the formality of speaking for or against a motion. These open debates sometimes, but not always, culminate in motions being drafted for debate later in the meeting.

the advice of Electoral Reform Services. The result was decisively in favour of the status quo.

Why did the RB choose not to make a firm break with the past and modernise the BMA's structures with all its associated problems? Perhaps the suggested changes were too radical and the RB felt that members would not accept such an upheaval. More likely they believed that the current flaws were not insurmountable, and that the constitutional machinery needed to be improved rather than replaced with something brand-new and untried. In fact, as was shown the following year, the RB had not set its face against all change, but was signalling that changing the Association's structures had to be slow and steady. That is probably why the RB also voted that year to keep divisions as the preferred model for the Association's local cross-craft structure, rather than set up local units based on government or primary care boundaries.

The modernisation project

At the same time as it voted for the status quo in 2004, the ARM asked the Organisation Committee to review the articles and bye-laws. The Organisation Committee, now chaired by Ian Wilson, an anaesthetist from Leeds with an encyclopaedic knowledge of the BMA's constitution, examined the constitutions of, and electoral processes for, Council and the RB. The Modernisation Project lasted a year and built upon the previous work, but with the new aim of trying to reform what was already there. The constitution of Council had changed little since 1985 and by 2005 elected members were coming from different constituencies with different electorates but with electoral boundaries based on outdated NHS structures. These no longer reflected a changed professional and political climate. According to a document sent later to BMA divisions, there were also inconsistencies and anomalies. The structure was inflexible and bore little relation to the membership of the Association. Low participation had also become an issue, with almost half of Council seats uncontested or unfilled, particularly in the regional elections where long-standing members were rarely opposed.

The Organisation Committee first proposed a single UK election. There would be no 'safe' seats: each member would have to appeal to a UK-wide electorate. But the notion of Council comprising only those who fared best in such an election, regardless of their craft and geographical location, was quickly abandoned: it would have been untenable for an organisation claiming to represent all doctors to risk having a Council with some groups not represented. The committee therefore devised a set of 'constraints' so that there would be at least one representative from each of 11 branches of practice and each of 10 geographical zones. Council would be smaller, with 34 elected members instead of 59, and fewer *ex-officio* members. The geographical zones were redrawn and based as far as possible on strategic health authority boundaries. These changes were complicated and Council held a special meeting to debate them in May 2005.

The committee also proposed reforms of the RB, aimed at improving access and ensuring that it better reflected the make-up of the profession. Each year the seats allocated to each craft would be adjusted to take account of the number of members in each group. There would be a two-stage appointment process to the RB, with unused divisional seats reallocated regionally. This would address the long-standing problem of unused seats being 'wasted', while members who wished to attend the RB being unable to do so if they lived or worked in an area covered by an inactive division or if their divisional seats had already been allocated. In 2004, for example, only 117 of the 202 divisions had sent representatives to the ARM. Regional fora were set up to allocate the unused divisional seats, but these were quickly abandoned following the revival of regional councils and the task given to these councils.

The 2005 ARM approved the proposals after a largely good-natured debate, a contrast to the stormy debates of the last few ARMs. Thanks to extensive consultation, members knew about the changes that they were being asked to consider, and knew also that the Organisation Committee was carrying out the RB's instructions to review the articles and bye-laws. However, implementing the changes would be complicated and there was a serious challenge in 2006/7. After the first elections to Council under the new rules, a candidate made a formal complaint which led to a hearing before the Certification Officer for Trade Unions. The complaint was not upheld, but this and subsequent experiences (for example, disputes about members' branches of practice) showed that the electoral procedure was particularly complicated and needed to be refined.

BMA Council

In 2005, the RB also found itself grappling with the fundamental question of which body was in control of the Association. The articles of Association stated: 'The general control and direction of the policy and affairs of the Association shall be vested in a body of representatives styled 'the Representative Body'. It was generally accepted that the RB, often referred to as the doctors' parliament, had ultimate control and that in many respects Council was subservient to it. These assumptions were challenged by the Audit Committee, which took the exceptional decision to qualify the Association's accounts in its 2003–4 report: 'The governance process within the Association is acknowledged by both Council and the ARM to be inadequate, a serious risk and in urgent need of reform . . . the operation of the second phase of the governance reform process, defining and codifying the fundamental issues of who is ultimately responsible to members for the conduct and affairs of the BMA, is unclear and unsatisfactory . . . the execution of the process leaves the Association exposed to reputational risk among its members and the world at large.'

In its report the following year the Audit Committee stated that it had asked the Organisation Committee how its modernisation project would 'address the fundamental . . . concerns previously expressed by both governing bodies of the Association. Without clarification of ultimate responsibilities, the governance of the Association will never be entirely satisfactory.' The 2005 RB asked for these concerns to be addressed in time for the following year's report. It now seems remarkable that it was not until the middle of the first decade of the twenty-first century before anyone sought to question who or what was in ultimate control of the Association. Advice was sought from Ian Gatt QC who concluded, in January 2006, that Council, not the RB, had overall responsibility for the affairs of the BMA. Mr Gatt based his view on four factors:

- Although the articles gave 'general control and direction of the policy and affairs of the Association' to the RB, Council was, in fact, far more involved in the operational and day-to-day running of the BMA.
- Council had the power to control the effect of RB resolutions and even to postpone or prevent their implementation.
- Council members were the directors of the BMA in its capacity as a registered company and Council therefore had collective responsibility for the BMA in the same way that the board of directors took responsibility for the running of a company.
- Council derived its legitimacy from being directly elected by members, in the same way as a board of directors derives its legitimacy from being elected by shareholders. The RB, by contrast, was partly elected and partly appointed.

This advice remains on the record but, at the time of writing, no formal changes have been made to the articles of Association to reflect Mr Gatt's opinion. Council retains its dual role as the principal executive committee of the BMA as a trade union and is its board of directors under company law. As a board of directors it is far too large but, as regards its trade union role, it is important for it to have representation from all branches of practice and regions of the UK, which means that it is sizeable. One of the reasons for the change to the constitution of Council in 2005 was to make it slightly smaller, but it was not possible to shrink it down to, say, 10 or 15 members, without compromising its 'representativeness'. One solution suggested during the governance exercises, and subsequently, was for Council to remain as the principal executive committee of the BMA as a trade union, but that a separate board of directors be created to carry out its functions under company law. Although this looked superficially attractive, it could create its own problems in that the BMA would have two governing bodies: Council and the board (not to mention the RB) which could create tension and conflict by separating the Association's political and business functions with the legal powers and responsibilities for the governance of the Association resting with the board of directors.

There is now a general acceptance that it is not possible to separate Council's trade union and company law responsibilities and it remains vitally important that those who stand for election to Council, or who are appointed to it by virtue of another office, are aware that they will become directors of the company and will assume the accompanying directors' duties and responsibilities. In recent years, this has been made clear to candidates and appointees, but this was not always the case in the past and it is fair to say that some members of Council were surprised, and concerned, that they had to assume unlooked-for duties. A director's primary responsibility is towards the company itself and not to a class of member, and, again, it is the case that some Council members had difficulty with this because, as medico-politicians, they quite naturally identified more with some groups than others and saw themselves as representatives of their constituents. It is the case, however, that a Council member's representative (trade union) role is inseparable from that of a director of the Association and this applies to both elected and *ex-officio* members, an issue of some concern to *ex-officio* members who are obliged to assume the responsibilities of directors without voting rights, an unsatisfactory situation which has worried successive generations of *ex-officio* members.

As a board of directors, Council now meets six times each year (until 2005, it met only four times each year) and although in recent years new methods of communication have made it easier for members to keep in touch between meetings, Council members' involvement in the nitty-gritty running of the Association is, necessarily, remote. These duties are instead assumed by the Senior Management Group (SMG) which comprises the Chief Executive/Secretary and the directors of the BMA's directorates. Its function is 'to act as the Association's senior executive management team with day to day operational responsibility for managing the Association'. Management, including the SMG, was held to account through the Supervisory Board of the Secretariat on behalf of Council. This body comprised the Chairman of Council, the Treasurer and the Chief Executive. The existence of the SMG and uncertainty about its functions and authority and its separation from the Council as the elected board of directors, has caused tensions in the past. These erupted into a serious dispute between the SMG and Council in the spring of 2008 which was provoked by the long-running problem about changes to the way in which BMA staff pay was structured and especially the introduction of performance-related pay. A staff strike to protest about this was planned for Thursday 22 May 2008. The Scottish Consultants Committee (SCC) reacted to the news of the strike by passing a motion of no confidence in the SMG which was posted on the electronic listserver[4] used by Council members and to which a large number of staff at all levels had access. This was followed by threats of legal action against the Association by the SMG who had felt badly let down by Council's initial failure to back them following the no confidence motion.

Relations between management and elected members had now reached their nadir. In retrospect, some said that 'the showdown' had been coming for years. Tension between senior managers and Council had been growing with Council members unwilling completely to surrender the management of the Association to the highly qualified people it employed to run it on the directors' behalf and the feeling among some managers that Council members tried to micromanage the Association. The perhaps unlikely issue of staff pay served to bring the friction to a head. Events were fast-moving and, in the thick of

---

[4] A listserver is an electronic email and discussion group which allows emails from members of it to go straight into the email in-boxes of fellow members, without the need to log on to a specific forum. The BMA has a large number of these listservers and virtually all committees have their own ones.

the conflict, were the Chairman of Council, Hamish Meldrum, the Treasurer, David Pickersgill, and the Chairman of the Representative Body, Peter Bennie. They had the difficult task of holding the ring between the aggrieved SMG and the shocked Council which learnt of the proposed legal action at its meeting on 22 May 2008. By then, the threatened staff strike due to take place that day had been averted. There was relief that the strike would no longer go ahead, but Council now had to deal with the damage that the prospect of it had caused. Although Council immediately dissociated itself from the SCC's motion, it did not give its unequivocal and explicit backing to the Association's senior managers which led to a deepening of the crisis. Both sides, the directors and the managers, sought independent legal advice and the predicament was discussed again at a special Council meeting held on Saturday 7 June 2008. This time, the required backing was forthcoming and the immediate threat of legal action was lifted. Council's public backing for the SMG took the heat out of the crisis, but an enormous amount of work needed to be done and goodwill summoned to rebuild the bridges between Council members and the SMG. Individuals were left feeling bruised by events, trust had almost completely broken down between the two bodies and a huge amount of energy, time and effort had been spent on the dispute to the detriment of the core work of both managers and Council. What had survived was the trust between some individual members of Council and some senior managers, who had worked together over many years, and who had been equally tormented by the turn of events. While there was a strong desire to move on and not dissect the bones of the crisis, measures clearly had to be taken both to re-establish cordial working relations between Council and the SMG and to put in place procedures to stop similar crises spinning out of control in the future.

In August 2008, the SMG and the Chairman of Council, Treasurer and Chairman of the RB sat down together and agreed a number of constructive steps to help build relations for the future. These were not especially radical and the fact that they had to be considered at all perhaps shows how bad relations had become, but goodwill was exhibited on both sides and, by the end of the year, the Chief Executive/Secretary and Chairman of Council were able to report solid progress in implementing these reforms. Council also wished to look again at governance structures and, while there was no desire for an expensive and time-consuming major exercise, given recent events, it was clear that there was at least a need to look at how the current structures could be adapted to work more efficiently. The outcome of these deliberations was the creation of a new body, the Oversight and Finance Committee which began to operate towards the end of 2010 and was formally established at the 2011 ARM. This body subsumed the duties and powers of the existing Finance Committee and Supervisory Board of the Secretariat (both of which were disbanded in 2011) and thus ensured that one body, with a majority of elected Council members, had responsibility for the Association's finances and for its oversight and supervision. Reports suggest that this body is functioning well, although is not appreciably different to its predecessor the Finance Committee and, like its predecessor, it retains virtually water-tight confidentiality which allows senior staff and members to discuss potentially controversial matters safe in the knowledge that leaks rarely occur.

With the passage of time and new personalities on the SMG and Council it is inevitable that the turmoil of spring 2008 is receding, as bad memories tend to do. It is impossible to say with certainty that such events will not recur again in the future as, despite the reforms made since 2008, there are unavoidable tensions in a membership organisation between the members themselves who have clear ideas about the running of their organisation and the senior staff who they employ who have equally strong ideas about the licence and authority that they need. Some of the difficulties surrounding staff pay remain unresolved and, in June and July 2012, staff members of the GMB finally carried out their threat to strike, this time over the level of the 2012 pay award, rather than the structure of the pay system. This time, though, an actual strike, rather than the threat of one, was not accompanied by the turbulence of 2008 and perhaps that is the most significant legacy of the reforms put in place and the re-establishment of trust over the four years since then.

Changes to committees

So far, this section has considered the structure of the Association in terms of its governing bodies of the RB and Council and has looked at the governance exercises which were established to examine these and suggest possible changes. Throughout the period from the early 1980s until 2011, an enormous number of important changes were made to the Association's structures below the level of RB and Council which have had a dramatic impact both on how the Association is organised and operates and on how it relates to its members. Close to the centre, Council established an Audit Committee in 1999. In the 1990s and following the 1992 Cadbury report,[5] subsequent reports and the resulting code on corporate governance,[6] companies were reforming their structures and setting up audit committees. Council agreed that, although the BMA was under no statutory obligation to have an Audit Committee, it would be sensible for it to have an internal body responsible for, among other things, considering the Association's procedures for approving investment in new commercial activities which would expose the BMA to significant cost or risk, or both. The Audit Committee would also consider the Association's systems of internal financial control, its risk assessment and management and its compliance with accounting standards. It also has a specific responsibility for monitoring the effectiveness of the governance processes within the BMA. Although its difficult questions and close scrutiny have challenged the medico-politicians and senior staff trying to manage governance processes and changes, the Audit Committee's chairs and members have been persistent in their determination to ensure that the BMA's governance is fit for purpose. From the beginning the Audit Committee has had strong expert lay (ie non-medical) involvement and, of its three chairmen so far, two have been lay people with no prior involvement with the BMA who have been able to bring to the Association external knowledge and perspective.

One of the Audit Committee's chairmen, John Bishop, was asked to chair a governance committee set up by the Finance and General Purposes Committee in 2000.[7] This exercise was put in train following a serious incident concerning the trial of the GP and mass murderer Harold Shipman at the beginning of 2000 when there had been an inadvertent disclosure by the BMA of briefing papers relating to the trial before its conclusion. The incident was investigated on the BMA's behalf by KPMG and one of its recommendations was that there should be a distinction between the respective roles and responsibilities of BMA Council and the secretariat. The Governance Committee's task was: 'to define and clarify the responsibilities of the Council and secretariat and to formulate the various guidelines. The group should comprise representatives of the Council and secretariat

---

[5] *The Report of the Committee on the Financial Aspects of Corporate Governance*, December 1992. The committee was chaired by Adrian Cadbury and established by the Financial Reporting Council.

[6] *The Combined Code on Corporate Governance*, issued by the Financial Reporting Council 1998.

[7] At the time when he chaired the 2000–1 Governance Committee, John Bishop was the lay member of the Audit Committee; he became its chairman later.

and its output should be approved by the Chairman of Council and Secretary.'

The committee's report, presented to the ARM in 2001, concluded that a root and branch upheaval was unnecessary and described its recommendations as an attempt to bring the Association into line with best practice. The committee defined the roles of all the main office-holders and proposed a new structure built around a representational and political activities directorate, a professional activities directorate and a new Finance Committee. The Executive Committee of Council would be abolished and most of its work transferred to the new Board of the Representational and Political Activities Directorate. The Association, it recommended, should draw up an annual plan that should be agreed by all relevant parties, each of whom would be accountable for delivering their parts of the plan. It recommended a new Supervisory Board of the Secretariat to oversee and control the infrastructure of the Association and the work of its staff (since merged with the Finance Committee at the 2011 ARM). Finally, a Nominations Committee would be created to recommend to Council suitable candidates for the new boards and the Finance Committee, as well as developing a group of elected members to fill future vacancies. The Nominations Committee, initially regarded with suspicion as its functions appeared to interfere with democratic processes, was abolished at the 2011 ARM on the grounds that it had added little value to the nominations procedure.

The 2001 ARM, presaging future governance debates, did not accept the proposed changes and a procedural device in the standing orders was invoked to send the report of the Governance Committee back to Council 'to allow for proper and appropriate consultation'. This took place and the recommendations were passed without incident at the 2002 ARM, the RB probably feeling that its instruction for further consultation had been carried out. The BMA now had an altered internal structure and three new and influential bodies: the Finance Committee, the Board of the Representational and Political Activities Directorate (later to be renamed the Political Board) and the Board of the Directorate of Professional Activities. The Finance Committee continued in most part the work of its predecessor, the Finance and General Purposes Committee, but was now augmented by two external experts. The two directorate boards were innovations and the BMA had to grapple with how best to use them. Reporting structures changed: previously, most committees had reported to Council but now they reported to one of the two new boards. Council was accustomed to receiving reports from influential committees such as the Medical Ethics Committee, the Board of Science and the International Committee, whose reports now went to the Board of the Directorate of Professional Activities. Considering the substantial amount of Council time that had been devoted to discussion of professional issues in the past, this sudden removal of professional matters from Council agendas caused little comment and there is general contentment with the way in which the Board of the Directorate of Professional Activities deals with such matters.

Political issues were another matter and, although the craft committees had reported to the Executive Committee of Council, important issues, especially those relating to contract negotiations, often made their way onto Council agendas. There was a feeling that allowing the Board of the Representational and Political Activities Directorate to authorise industrial action was a step too far and this power reverted to Council in 2008. It was also accepted that not all 'political' issues should be dealt with by the Board of the Representational and Political Activities Directorate (where would this have left Council?) and sometimes the same matters were debated both by the Board and by Council. This was not altogether a bad thing: some matters benefited from being discussed twice and sometimes circumstances had changed by the time they were discussed for the second time.

Throughout this period there were constant changes to committee constitutions by the dedicated constitutionalists on the Organisation Committee; most of the changes had to be approved both by Council and the RB. There were some significant developments. In 2001 the RB agreed that the Medical Students Committee be made a 'craft committee of equal standing with the other craft committees'. At the other end of the career spectrum, an annual Retired Members Forum (there had long been a Junior Members Forum) was established in 2003. In 2002 the Staff and Associate Specialists doctors gained craft status and the derogatory title of non-consultant career grade doctor, which had been used in the group's title, was banished. Patients and lay people were welcomed into the heart of the BMA's constitution with a change to the bye-laws in 2002 which allowed all committees to co-opt up to two lay people if they wished and the establishment in 2003 of the Patient Liaison Group, the function of which is to ensure that the patient voice is represented on matters being addressed by the BMA and to highlight areas of concern to patients and the public which the

BMA should consider. The group is now represented on key BMA committees and on Council itself.

As the demography of the medical profession has changed, so have the BMA committees set up to deal with the needs of doctors in minority groups. An Equality and Diversity Committee grew from committees and working groups for women doctors, those from ethnic minorities and those who are disabled, and it aims to promote, and provide advice on, equal opportunities. It also monitors and reviews equal opportunities issues raised by members, usually via local offices. The BMA has worked to shake off its old image of a club for white, middle-aged, middle-class men by working with committee secretariats to ensure that the representational structures reflect the make-up of the membership. The BMA has monitored the ethnic and gender composition of its committees for nearly a decade and has developed measures, such as 'shadowing' schemes, to introduce members to committee work. It has also introduced practical measures, such as the provision of crèche facilities and prayer rooms.

Devolution

Devolution has been one of the major constitutional challenges faced by the BMA (*see Chapter 3 for its impact on contract negotiations*). At the start of the period covered by this book, the BMA already had strong representative structures in all four nations of the UK, with national councils in Northern Ireland, Scotland and Wales. After devolution, the priority was to allow representatives in each country to consider devolved matters while ensuring that the BMA continued to function as a UK-wide organisation. There was a flurry of activity concerning the BMA's status as a UK-wide trade union, but legal advice quickly assured the Association that the 1957 Treaty of Rome enshrined the right of commercial and other bodies established in one state of the European Union to carry out their functions in another.

The Executive Committee of Council set up a working party in June 1997 to examine the implications of devolution, chaired by Jane Richards who was also Chairman of the Representative Body. The group took as its starting point a provision in the Association's bye-laws that BMA committees should take all reasonable steps to implement BMA policy and not take any action that might affect another part of the profession without consultation. Another guiding principle was that any changes to the BMA's constitution should allow as much flexibility as possible to cope with devolution as it developed. The group combed through the articles and bye-laws for nearly a year, identifying areas where amendments needed to be made and by the following May was ready to make a number of recommendations to Council.

The main sticking point proved to be the rules to be followed when one national branch of practice committee was in dispute with its counter-part in another country or when a national council disagreed with a UK-wide branch of practice committee. The working group suggested that such disputes should be referred straight to UK Council or its Executive Committee for resolution with the national councils being responsible for the resolution of differences between two branch of practice committees in the same country. However, some Council members felt that differences between branch of practice committees in different countries should not be settled by Council but by the appropriate UK committees. Council agreed to amend the proposed bye-law to this effect. The other recommendations went through Council relatively unscathed in May 1998 and were approved by the ARM later that year. They included the following:

- The UK Representative Body should remain the BMA's policy-making body for the whole of the UK.
- Each devolved nation would hold national branch of practice conferences.
- Members of UK Council should vote on all matters, regardless of whether they concerned their country.
- The committees representing GPs, senior and junior hospital staff, public health medicine and community health and medical academics should have full autonomy to negotiate on devolved matters. Committees for the other branches of practice (for example, the armed forces and occupational health) should continue to be organised at UK level.
- Ethical and scientific matters should continue to be dealt with on a UK basis, but the reports should identify national differences.

Council agreed in May 1998 that it was up to individual branch of practice committees to decide whether to have mechanisms to consider matters concerning their branch in England. Only the GPC took the need for an English committee seriously and set one up in 1999. This was not a success because the secretariat struggled to fill the agendas for the England-only meetings and in April 2000 the GPC UK decided that GPC England should become a dormant committee. Nevertheless, it had been a useful example to other UK committees. The Association never seriously considered an English Council, but it did re-establish the regional council network from the middle of the 2000s. Regional councils had always existed in the constitution, but most had dwindled. It is arguable now, in 2012, whether, following the establishment of clinical commissioning groups, the BMA should persevere with a regional structure, or whether a push to revive the division network in England would be more worthwhile. This emphasises the fact that getting devolved structures right in England is one with which the BMA is likely to continue to struggle.

The constitutional changes of 1998, when devolution was new, have proved to be robust and resilient and most are still in place. The national councils, as expected, changed their constitutions from divisional to branch of practice representation, and the provisions relating to the RB continue to work well, although some representatives from the devolved nations abstain from voting on motions relating purely to English matters.

The real test of the arrangements for devolution came as a battle raged over a new contract for the staff and associate specialist doctors. The Scottish SASC wanted the votes on any ballot to be counted separately in Scotland, but the UK SASC, sticking to the 2005 agreement which Scottish SASC had signed up to, wanted the ballot to be held on a UK basis. The constitution stated that such disputes were to be considered by the Board of the Directorate of Representational and Political Activities (BRPAD) and one of the first tasks of the newly-elected Chairman of Council, Hamish Meldrum, was to chair a specially convened meeting of BRPAD in July 2007 to try to resolve the dispute. This delicate issue got a thorough airing at the meeting, which eventually voted in favour of the Scottish SASC. The BMA's first devolution-related constitutional difficulty had been almost 10 years in coming, but the representative machinery had shown itself capable of dealing with it. While UK SASC might not have been happy that it had lost the argument, it could at least be content that the matter had been properly dealt with.

By 2008, the Organisation Committee decided that it was time to give a health check to the Association's constitutional, representational and political arrangements in relation to devolution. It wanted to see if they were still fit for purpose, or needed to be updated. Steve Hajioff, then the Deputy Chairman of the Representative Body, chaired the Devolution Working Group. It asked the national councils for their feedback and the national councils, as had been the case 10 years earlier, replied that they still made it a priority for the BMA to remain a

UK-wide organisation, with the devolved nations acting for members on national issues and UK Council maintaining ultimate executive control over the running of the Association. The one area of extensive debate, which had formed the basis of the 1998 working group's discussions, was the provision in the bye-laws that all BMA bodies should take 'all reasonable steps' to implement BMA policy and that none should take action which might materially affect another part of the profession without full consultation. The 2008 working group considered changing this provision to allow national councils to deviate from ARM policy when appropriate. This was dangerous ground: the working group suggested that ARM policy could only be overturned by a national council if it would adversely affect members in that country, since it was the responsibility of the national councils to act in the best interests of doctors in those nations. In any case Council would be the final arbiter, from which flowed the next question: in what circumstances, if any, should UK Council say 'no' to a devolved nation's Council? Again, this was thorny territory and the group approached the issue carefully, agreeing a framework in which deviation from ARM policy could only occur if the decision of a national council diverged substantially from the UK policy, or if it would threaten the interests of other BMA groups. Lawyers were asked to redraft the relevant bye-law and the RB later agreed an amended version that leaves no doubt that, while there are mechanisms for divergences of policy to be considered, Council's decision is binding on all of the BMA's constituent bodies throughout the UK.

In any highly political organisation, occasional tensions in the operation of the democratic machinery are inevitable and, in the mid-2000s, these took up a considerable amount of energy from elected members and staff. Issues of representation and democracy matter hugely to members, as can be seen from the astonishing response to the governance questionnaire in March 2003 and from the number of relevant motions appearing on ARM agendas. It is likely that matters relating to the structure and running of the Association will continue to be enthusiastically debated as they should be in an organisation with as healthy a democratic tradition as the BMA.

APPENDIX

CONSTITUTION OF COUNCIL AS RECOMMENDED TO THE 1985 ARM

Officers (all to be non-voting, unless directly elected in some other capacity)

President
Chairman of the Representative Body
Deputy Chairman of the Representative Body
Chairman of Council
Treasurer
(Plus, where appropriate, the immediate past Chairman of the Representative Body, Chairman of Council and Treasurer for one year after holding office)

Craft representation

Six members of the Association engaged wholly or mainly in NHS general practice, elected by members in the same category.
Four members of the Association employed wholly or mainly as senior hospital doctors, elected by members in the same category.
Five hospital doctors in the training grades who are members of the Association, elected by members in the same category.
Two members engaged wholly or mainly in community medicine or community health, elected by members in the same category.
Two members of the armed forces, elected by members in the armed forces.
Two members employed whole time in universities and in medical research, elected by members in the same category.
Two members employed wholly or mainly in occupational medicine elected by members in the same category.

Regional representation

One member representing each of the 14 NHS regions of England and two each representing Wales, Scotland and Northern Ireland elected by members in the same region/country.

National representation

Four 'other' members elected by all members of the Association.

Chairmen of 'non-craft' committees (all to be non-voting, unless directly elected in some other capacity)

The Chairmen of the following: Board of Science and Education, Central Ethical Committee, Charities Committee, Journal Committee, Junior Members Forum, Organisation Committee, Private Practice and Professional Fees Committee and Superannuation Committee.

Chapter 14
Inside the BMA

Finances

This book is being written at a time when the global economy is going through its longest and deepest recession since the 1930s; financial markets are volatile, interest rates are low and property markets are depressed. The BMA is not immune from the economic crisis, but has managed to weather the worst of the storms, reporting in 2010 that the year had been 'another good year for the Association's finances.' Over the past 30 or so years, the Association's finances have usually been healthy, despite economic downturns, property slumps, major out-goings on new technology, increases in staff numbers, the development of a regional network and national devolution.

The BMA has traditionally relied upon three main sources of income to fund its work: that from membership subscriptions, profits from the BMJ Publishing Group and investments and rental income from tenants in BMA House in London. At the start of this period members' services had been heavily subsidised, the Association's reserves were seriously depleted and the BMA's finances generally were in a sorry state. Tony Keable Elliott, who became Treasurer in mid-1981, recalls that virtually the first paper to cross his desk after taking up office proposed the sale of BMA House in London and a move to Birmingham, purely to save money. Stricter controls were introduced in 1983, with rental income to be used only for the upkeep of the buildings, income from investments and publishing to restore the reserves and revenue from subscriptions to be spent on services to members. This meant that subscription rates would have to be increased. 'An increase of 20% to £120 per year would permit further expansion of BMA activities in line with the wishes of the Representative Body (RB) and would enable a start to be made on building up the Association's reserves, which have fallen in recent years to a dangerously low level', reported Council. The RB agreed and for several years members' services were funded solely from members' subscriptions.

This fiscal discipline, along with realistic increases in subscriptions, allowed the BMA to rebuild its reserves and to embark on a major property development programme. In the mid-1980s the lower section of the great hall in BMA House was converted into a library and the upper section into a suite of committee rooms (*see Chapter 12*). This was followed by refurbishment of 35,000 square feet of run-down parts of the building, partly to increase rental income and also to make more efficient use of space. BMA Scotland moved to new premises in Hill Place in Edinburgh, allowing its previous building to be sold (it later moved again, this time to Queen Street). Earlier that year the Northern Ireland office had also moved and the old premises sold.

Towards the end of the 1980s costs started to rise. A number of factors were responsible for this but the main ones were as a result of a restructuring of staff salary scales to recruit and retain staff and the need to raise the Association's profile in the press and in Parliament. These additional costs were partially off-set by an increase in membership subscription income, but this was not so noticeable as in previous years as subscription rates had not been increased in 1987, the year that a new Treasurer, Alistair Riddell, a GP from Glasgow, took over. These factors meant that, for the first time in several years, there had been no surplus on members' services costs. From this point on, it became apparent and accepted that, in order to sustain high-quality membership services, it would not always be possible to fund these solely from subscription income; either services had to be reduced or subscriptions had to rise dramatically and Council was not willing to take either measure while income from the BMJ Publishing Group and other sources was available to plug the gap. The question would eventually be not whether the existence of a gap between membership income and expenditure was acceptable, but how large a gap would be prudent and reliably funded from these other sources.

The budget for 1989 forecast higher than usual levels of expenditure on the campaign to protect members' interests following the publication of the government's review of the NHS.[1] Added to this were the costs of improving services to members and the continuing need to pay competitive salaries to recruit and retain good quality staff. By the following year, the surplus had been almost totally wiped-out by the costs associated with opposing elements of the government's NHS review, which totalled £2.5m. On the positive side, increases in membership had continued and had been significant in 1988. Large profits had been made on the sale of a warehouse in St Albans and a residential

---

[1] Department of Health. *Working for Patients*. London: HMSO, 1989.

block of flats in London in early 1989. But wage inflation continued to run ahead of the retail price index and the Association's biggest item of expenditure was (and still remains) staff salaries.

No sooner had the unprecedented levels of expenditure on opposing government health reforms levelled-out than a recession hit the UK economy. For the Association, this meant that revenue from sources such as rents, dividends and publishing was adversely affected, leading to cut-backs in all internal budgets and services to members in order to protect the reserves, which were themselves being eroded by the effects of inflation (the Retail Prices Index reached nearly 11% in October 1990[2]). Council was aware of the seriousness of this for its own work, as the government's NHS changes would require the provision of greater support for members and it believed that the annual rate of subscriptions should be raised above the level of inflation. Encouragingly, membership numbers continued to grow and the increased income from subscriptions helped to ease the worst of the financial strain.

The BMA's investment policy had been constant for some years and this was to avoid speculative shares and concentrate instead on investing in sound companies with good underlying growth, This had paid off as, despite significant stock market falls in some sectors, the value of the BMA's stocks and shares had been protected in 1990–91 and the value of its investment portfolio had grown in this time. However, the recession in the property market meant that the 1990 budget for rental income had not been achieved, advertising income from BMA publications had fallen and there had been a downturn in journal and book sales. Overall, adverse developments had led to a budgeted surplus of £231,000 becoming a deficit of £68,000. Despite this depressing financial news, things were looking a little more cheerful the following year as, despite the continuing recession, the BMA's finances had performed well in the areas of membership subscriptions, rents, dividends, profits on sale of investments and publishing – all of which had exceeded budget estimates. On the strength of this, the opportunity was taken to enhance the regional network.

1992 turned out to be an outstanding year, with an unexpectedly large increase in the numbers of full-paying members, the return of some legal costs, a one-off boost to property income from a lease surrender, sales of investments while stock market values were high and

---

[2] Inflation rate source: Towers Watson UK % Annual Inflation Rates.

an expansion in journal advertising income. The surplus nearly doubled from £2.2 million in 1991 to £4.2 million in 1992. The BMA
could resume the expansion of its regional network, a priority for
the Association at a time of uncertainty for members as a result of
the changes taking place within the health service. Most of the new
expenditure was, of course, closely scrutinised by the sharp eyes of
the Treasurer Alistair Riddell. He frequently observed that new initiatives could have 'serious financial implications' and this became his
catch-phrase.

An on-going refurbishment programme in BMA House was fairly
low-key as the commercial property market remained depressed and
there were no takers for the BMA's surplus space, despite aggressive
marketing in 1992. One project that had to be done was a refurbishment of the Council Chamber which took place in 1994; its first major
upgrade since it had been built in 1925. New lighting, air-conditioning
and audio equipment were installed but, despite these improvements,
the Council Chamber remained mostly an unloved relic and difficult
to use.

After several years of depression, the commercial property sector
was showing some signs of recovery by 1996, which encouraged the
BMA to increase the refurbishment of BMA House to help generate
future rental income. A new Treasurer, Jim Appleyard, a consultant
paediatrician from Kent, was elected in mid-1996, at a time when the
Association was investing in a corporate communications network to
link local and national offices and in an electronic publishing system.
Council had been delighted at the increases in membership which had
taken place over the preceding few years and the priority for the rest
of the 1990s would be to consolidate the BMA's strength by investing to retain the current high levels of membership with the improvement of current services and the introduction of new ones. As time
progressed, these investments were increasingly driven by the need to
develop the Association's technology capability so that it could provide
members and others with the information that they required quickly.
Membership numbers and membership subscription continued to
grow, as did the contribution to BMA activities from the Publishing
Group and, by the end of the 1990s, there was a small increase in the
total income generated from investments and from tenants within BMA
House. The new demands of devolution led to the national offices in
Edinburgh, Cardiff and Belfast recruiting extra staff and investment
was made in larger premises for the BMA in the three national capitals.

The millennium opened with several major costs. There were some expensive campaigns: one supported junior doctors over their pay negotiations and another promoted a positive image of the medical profession to counter-balance a slew of stories about negligent and criminal doctors. A third campaign followed, over the proposed new contracts for hospital consultants and GPs. The major investment in 2001 was in the redevelopment and relaunch of the BMA's website which would provide for a new and better communication channel with members. In the same year the management of the BMA's investments was transferred to professional fund managers through a holding company, BMA Investments Limited, a wholly owned subsidiary of the Association.

From the middle of 2002, following constitutional changes agreed at the Annual Representative Meeting (ARM) that year, a new Finance Committee was established. This took over virtually the same functions as its predecessor, the Finance and General Purposes Committee, but its constitution included, for the first time, experts in business and finance who were not members of the Association. In addition, two key members of staff, the Chief Executive/Secretary and the Finance Director, became full voting members of the Finance Committee. The introduction of lay experts was an acknowledgement that the committee with responsibility for managing the finances of a large business such as the Association could no longer get by with a membership composed of those who joined it as a result of the vagaries of the electoral process; it needed the input of external financial specialists who had the detailed knowledge and expertise both to challenge the staff and doctor members and to contribute their professional skills. The first two lay members to be appointed were experts in marketing and investments respectively and contributed greatly to the management of the BMA's funds and initiatives to increase and maintain membership numbers.

That same year, in the middle of a world-wide slump in equity markets, the annual report highlighted a new problem: the potential liabilities of the defined benefit staff pension scheme. A new accounting rule (FRS 17) obliged all companies to state in full on their balance sheets their pension scheme's surplus or deficit. As a result of the financial slump the deficit in the Association's scheme had increased in one year from £5.7 million to £24 million. It looked unlikely that the losses would be recovered by an upturn in the markets and therefore the cost of the scheme would probably become significantly more expensive. The Finance Committee decided that from September 2003 new staff would join a new pension scheme which would have a defined contribution. It hoped that this would reduce the costs of staff pensions and make them less affected by fluctuations in investment performance. That same year the BMA made a special payment of nearly £10 million into the pension scheme, money that had come from the sale of Professional Affinity Group Services[3] (*see Chapter 12*).

While membership continued to grow, one or two potential difficulties were beginning to appear. David Pickersgill, a former Treasurer of the General Medical Services Defence Fund and a GP from Norfolk, took over from Jim Appleyard as BMA Treasurer in mid-2002. In his first report (2003) he warned of a 'growing risk of complacency' about the strength of the Association's finances. Expenditure had outstripped income, with the deficit on members' services up from £2 million in 1997 to £6.5 million in 2002. In the fast changing world of medical publishing, the high surpluses generated by the Publishing Group, which for many years had helped to fill the financial gap, could not be relied upon to continue indefinitely. Therefore, the emphasis of the Association's financial management would be to try to find ways in which to correct the imbalance between subscription income and expenditure on members' services. The objective would remain the provision of high quality support and services to BMA members and a strong voice in national negotiations, but expenditure could not be allowed to run out of control.

One of the reasons that the deficit had grown was that the increase in membership subscriptions had not kept pace with some of the annual increases in staff salaries. It was proposed to rectify this by recovering some of the deficit with an increase in subscription rates in October 2004. Changes had also been made to the way in which staff were paid by breaking the long-standing link between the annual increase in staff salaries and the increase in GPs' remuneration as recommended by the Doctors' and Dentists' Review Body. This gave the BMA greater control over its future employment costs, although the change caused considerable upheaval. The Association's senior managers had also been asked by the Finance Committee to identify ways in which high-quality services could continue to be delivered to members in more cost-effective ways.

---

[3] From 16 September 2002, Wesleyan Assurance Services had owned the business operations of BMA Services and had been granted a seven year licence from the Association for the business to continue to use the name 'BMA Services'.

The BMA's financial position remained strong as it entered the middle of the 2000s. In 2004, income from membership subscriptions grew by 7.8% as a result of increases in both membership numbers and subscription rates. The number of members had grown by 4,600 in 2004 and the total membership was now in the region of 133,000. Other good news was an increase in the surplus from publishing activities (despite difficult trading conditions) and a boost in the value of the Association's investments. There had also been some significant progress in managing the gap between income from membership subscriptions and expenditure on membership services as the deficit had fallen for the first time in a decade in 2004 by over £1.5 million. This had been better than expected and was being achieved more quickly than anticipated by a tight control being kept on costs. There was a similar positive picture at the end of 2005 and the reserves now totalled close to £80 million.

In 2006, however, there was a sharp fall in the surplus from publishing activities (£5.5 million lower than the previous year). This was due to two NHS contracts not being renewed and a decline in the advertising market for doctors' jobs. Despite this the Treasurer was able to report that the Association's balance sheet at the end of 2006 was even stronger than it had been at the end of the previous year and the deficit on membership services was continuing to fall. Funds were available to embark on a once in a generation refurbishment of BMA House in London (*see below*).

The global financial crisis began in 2007 and worsened in 2008. Notes of warning about BMA finances had been sounded already in 2007. Although the BMA's finances were still very sound at the end of 2007, there were some worrying developments: membership numbers had reduced slightly and the deficit from membership services was greater than in the previous year. This looked likely to grow and it was imperative that the small fall in membership numbers was to be reversed and investment made in those activities which made BMA membership an attractive proposition to doctors and medical students. Nevertheless, the BMA's finances were still in good shape to withstand the gathering economic storm: income from membership subscriptions had grown, the surplus from publishing activities had increased, there was a further increase in the value of the BMA's investments and a large decrease in the deficit of the pension scheme.

The turmoil in the global financial markets impacted upon the BMA mainly in relation to its investments, the value of which decreased by £34.1 million during 2008. The finances of the BMA Staff Pension Scheme suffered as it was also an investor in global financial markets. The BMA was the sponsor of the scheme and was therefore exposed to the funding consequences of the substantial falls in the value of the scheme's investments. The net pension deficit, calculated in accordance with FRS 17, was £28.3 million higher at the end of 2008 than it had been at the end of 2007. More positively, the BMA's financial position was not based upon its ability to raise money from the capital or credit markets and it had entered this period of unprecedented volatility with a very strong balance sheet. As a result of this, and thanks too to an exceptionally good year for the BMJ Publishing Group, investment in members' services was able to continue, the major project in 2008 being in an upgrade to the website. Additional employment advisers had been recruited and considerable investment had been made in surveying the needs of members and designing new services for them, as the Treasurer said: 'Those services which we know make a difference to, and are valued by members, will be the focus for our future investment.' One area where there was a call to invest was in support for regional activities in England and a number of new regional coordinator posts were created in response to this.

The continuing concern was the position of the BMA Staff Pension Scheme. It too had benefitted from the bounce in equity markets in 2009, but these had in no way made up for the significant increase in the value of the estimated liabilities of the scheme and the net deficit which, calculated in accordance with FRS 17, was £44.7 million at the end of 2009. Discussions opened with the Scheme Trustee to agree a recovery plan to fund the deficit. After a period of negotiation, a special payment of £27 million was paid into the scheme by the BMA in 2010 with further special contributions of £4.5 million to be paid in 2011 and 2012 and possibly in the two years following, depending on the actuarial valuation of the scheme at the end of March 2012. The £27 million payment cash injection had been funded by the sale or transfer of some of the Association's investment reserves and underlined the BMA's commitment to fulfil its obligations towards the scheme. The effect of this significant payment was to reduce the FRS 17 deficit to £10.2 million at the end of 2010, compared to £44.7 million a year earlier. Unfortunately, this improved position was to be short lived: by the end of 2011, the scheme was once more showing a significant deficit which had increased by £12.6 million, mainly caused by the effect of quantitative easing on gilts.

In 2011 Andrew Dearden, a GP from Cardiff and former Chairman of Welsh Council, took over from David Pickersgill as Treasurer. At the end of the year he reported that total income had grown by 5.5%, membership had grown by 2.2% and the BMJ Publishing Group had made a £9.7 million surplus. In the face of a national and international economic misery, this was positive news.

Payments to members

For many decades, employers and partners of committee members and office holders allowed them time off while continuing to pay salary or provide locum cover on the grounds that their work was good for the profession and for the NHS. The BMA paid expenses to all members and a small honorarium to some senior post holders. In addition, a Compensation Committee paid expenses to those, often consultants in private practice, who could provide evidence of loss of earnings. On the basis that they may need to pay for locums, members of the General Practitioners Committee (GPC) also received an honorarium through the General Practitioners Defence Fund, financed by a levy on practices to support the work of Local Medical Committees. But the majority of ordinary BMA committee members expected no financial reward from the BMA, making a personal choice to devote their time to committee work, be it for reasons of duty, passion for change, political aptitude and/or ambition, enjoyment or an escape from a humdrum clinical environment.

As the NHS changed and time away from work became more difficult to negotiate, pressure began to grow for the BMA more actively to facilitate members' involvement in BMA work, perhaps by recompensing employers for their time. When the matter was openly debated the lack of transparency surrounding the work of the Compensation Committee provoked criticism (despite the fact that payments to members were published yearly in the Annual Report of Council). In February 2004 a hard-hitting article in *Hospital Doctor* said that 'hundreds of thousands of members' pounds have been used to reimburse Council members for BMA work.'[4] The story questioned the appropriateness of compensating individuals for lost private practice income, though acknowledged that lost NHS income was also reimbursed.

The BMA's whole system of payments to members was already under review and the deliberations of the working party gave rise to

---

[4] Page 1, *Hospital Doctor*, 12 February 2004.

difficult debates in Council as members were obliged to set aside any personal interests they might have in the existing system and respond to the mounting unpopularity of compensation. This had been given added impetus by a *BMJ* article that summer by a former Deputy Chairman of the Junior Doctors Committee (JDC) and Central Consultants and Specialists Committee (CCSC), Nizam Mamode, who had questioned whether the BMA was a '21st century organisation'.[5] On a practical level, compensation was costly, volatile and difficult to budget for as payments varied depending on the earnings of office holders.

In October 2004, Council agreed to look instead at standard daily payments to all committee members who attended a certain number of meetings – a fundamental shift away from compensation for loss and towards reward for time spent. This was introduced in 2005, together with fixed annual payments for a group of BMA office holders.[6] Compensation was abolished. While this system met the need for greater transparency and fairness, it led to an inexorable and substantial rise in costs; by 2008 honoraria payments had risen to over £1.2 million a year (from £431,215 in 2005). Though the threshold for the number of eligible meetings has since been raised and efforts have been made to hold down the level of the honorarium, expenditure has continued to increase and the BMA, like other membership organisations, will need to keep under continual review the affordability, fairness and effectiveness of the arrangements for securing members' time.

BMA staff and departments

The number of BMA staff members grew steadily over the period covered by this book and currently stands at just over 500. One of the main changes has been their professionalisation, a process begun in the 1970s when the modernising secretary John Havard appointed the first 'personnel officer', and set about transforming the divided ranks of 'officials' and 'executive and clerical staff' into a unified and expert workforce with a range of professional skills and outside experience. More and more specialist staff have been needed in finance, information technology, legal services, estates management and human resources, but most are employed in providing services to members: employment

---

[5] *Is the BMA a 21st Century Organisation?* Nizam Mamode, *BMJ*, vol 329, 17 July 2004.
[6] This group comprised the President, Chairman of the RB, Chairman of Council, Treasurer and the chairs of the three national councils.

advice, local support, research and policy development, communications and marketing. On the one hand this expansion has inevitably led to a less friendly and cohesive and more protocol-driven organisation, where there is talk of 'silo mentalities', where communication is more by email and edict than by personal contact, and where in 2012 some staff resorted to industrial action over proposed changes to the pay structure and the staff pension scheme. On the other hand, staff who join the BMA from elsewhere are regularly struck by the ethos of high quality and service to members among staff, and those who overcome their frustration at the level of committee bureaucracy come to appreciate the depth of knowledge and experience in the organisation.

The make-up of the senior secretariat is notably different from 30 years ago when most of the key roles were filled by doctors, of whom there were eight on the staff in England in 1975.[7] Now there are two: Professor Vivienne Nathanson, director of professional activities, and Dr Michael Peters, who runs the doctors for doctors unit part-time. (Richard Lewis, the Welsh Secretary, is also a doctor). Some members bemoan this shift, and the preference of some doctors to deal with other doctors still lingers. But the less deferential working relationships are clearly better suited to the modern age, and the recruitment of professionals from other fields has invigorated the organisation.

Two functions in particular developed significantly over this period. The health policy and economic research unit (HPERU), established in its present form in 1994, was effectively launched with the appointment in 1976 of a young economist, Jon Ford – in 2012 more venerable but still its head, and probably the most knowledgeable person in the country about doctors' remuneration, the review body and a host of related subjects. The unit's early brief was to improve on a somewhat amateur approach to preparing evidence to the review body by providing sound economic and statistical data and robust analysis. It quickly grew, acquiring expertise in survey methodology, policy research and development, and providing input to negotiations and to collaborative research projects. It published a stream of briefings and discussion documents, in particular a long term cohort study of medical graduates which brought new insights into the factors influencing doctors' career choices.

Another department central to the BMA's effectiveness over this period is the communications directorate, previously known as the

---

[7] *World Medicine*, 7 May 1975.

public affairs division (Padiv), which manages all the Association's dealings with the press and media, the parliamentary unit, *BMA News*, the website and all of the BMA's communications. The press office was already well established in the 1970s under its genial head Tony Thistlethwaite, renowned for his generous parties as well as for his great knowledge and sound advice. His successor, Pamela Taylor, brought a hard-edged dynamism to the department, and during the campaign against Kenneth Clarke's white paper in 1989–90 (*see Chapter 1*) turned it into a formidable fighting machine. It gained the admiration of the health correspondents and became central to the Association's strategic activity. Media skills training became compulsory for senior committee members, and the organisation was schooled in the discipline of tailoring its outputs for press statements, soundbites and messages that would resonate with readers of the tabloids and broadsheets alike, within timescales dictated by press deadlines rather than committee schedules.

In the late 1970s Padiv set up a small unit to monitor *Hansard*, the parliamentary journal of record, for relevant material. The press officer who was given the task, Sue Marks, quickly saw the potential and with Pamela Taylor's encouragement, and support from the ARM, she was given a budget to develop a briefing service for MPs on health issues. This, it was felt, would enhance the BMA's reputation and create opportunities to promote BMA policy and influence legislation. Cutting her teeth on debates surrounding the Health, Mental Health, Abortion, Data Protection and Police and Criminal Evidence Acts, Sue Marks built the parliamentary unit into a highly professional operation. She established working relationships with MPs and their researchers across all parties, monitoring debates, scrutinising legislation, proposing amendments and facilitating meetings between doctors and MPs. Parliamentary activity of this kind is now routine for organisations wishing to exert influence, but the BMA was the first of the health bodies to set up its own parliamentary unit, and it became the model for others to follow.

Before long Sue Marks and her unit had become a prime source of information for MPs seeking briefings on health issues, and this stood the BMA in good stead during the heated exchanges over the 1989 white paper, when despite the fury of some back bench Conservative MPs over the BMA's campaign, relationships were maintained on non-political issues such as smoking. The parliamentary unit, now complemented by parallel functions in the devolved nations, went from strength to strength, sustained by Sue Marks' unfailing enthusiasm until her retirement in 2008. She was replaced by Rob Okunnu, who has been able to build on her reputation and establish his own authority. He led a thorough exercise over the complex Health and Social Care Bill in 2011 which contributed significantly to the pressure that led to the listening pause, the Future Forum and some important changes in the legislation.

In the early 1990s, following the high adrenalin ride of the white paper campaign, Pamela Taylor departed for new challenges (the BBC and later the water industry) and was succeeded by her deputy Nigel Duncan, formerly deputy editor of *Pulse*, who maintained Padiv's standards and made full use of his background to develop a strong network of media contacts. Since he retired in 2004, the department's role has been widened, and directors of communications Brian Butler (to 2010) and Michelle Dixon, with backgrounds in Whitehall and the King's Fund respectively, have added expertise in new media and corporate strategy.

The great strength of the BMA's public relations activity has always been its authoritative voice and campaigning stance (*see in particular Chapter 9*). Journalists greatly appreciate the information it provides on public health issues and much co-operative work is undertaken with politicians and government departments. Members have at times complained that the BMA is too preoccupied with this sort of activity at the expense of its trade union role, but the proportion of expenditure on those issues is small (about 8.5%) and the value, in terms of credibility, is high. Often strained relationships with government were repaired through a shared agenda on a health issue, or journalistic hostility to the BMA's stance on pay tempered by an understanding that the Association stands for more than its members' sectional interests.

Presidents

The BMA has four chief officers. Three of them – the Chairman of the Representative Body, the Chairman of Council and the Treasurer – normally climb their way up the BMA's medico-political tree over many years and wield considerable influence once at its top. Presidents, with one or two exceptions, are doctors who have distinguished themselves outside the BMA. Although they are technically 'elected' at the Annual Representative Meeting, they are, in practice, invited to take up the office after their names have been recommended to the RB by Council.

The Presidency is largely a ceremonial role, but the fact that it is normally occupied by an eminent doctor ensures that any observations the President may put forward are listened to with respect. The Presidents are great assets to the BMA and, as such high achievers, can often offer an extra dimension to debates. Some past Presidents have observed that their role is similar to that of the Queen: they may advise, encourage and warn, but not become embroiled in the detail of the Association's affairs; others have felt that they could have contributed more. The role remains undefined and there have been discussions about whether the term of office could be extended. This had not happened at the time of writing, although Presidents now have a more thorough induction at the start of their year. The BMA has also been able to retain the services of some Presidents beyond their presidential year by them agreeing to take on a subsequent office; the chairmanship of the Board of Science, in particular, has benefitted from this arrangement.

There were two royal Presidents in this period: the Prince of Wales in 1982–83 and the Princess Royal in 2007–8. They followed their father, the Duke of Edinburgh, who had been President in 1959–60, and their mother the Queen is the BMA's Patron. The Prince of Wales was President in the BMA's 150th anniversary year and, as a proponent of complementary and alternative medicine, he took the opportunity of his temporary position to challenge medical orthodoxy. The Princess Royal's term of office coincided with the BMA's 175th anniversary. The Princess Royal Trust for Carers is the largest provider of support services for care services in the UK and she gave her support to work for carers carried out by the BMA's Community Care Committee. Shortly after her Presidential year ended, she returned to BMA House to open the building formally following its major refurbishment.

Transformation of BMA House

In July 2005 Council agreed to an ambitious plan to make significant changes to the BMA's headquarters building in Tavistock Square, London. Earlier changes had led to the conversion of the Great Hall in 1985–86 to create a suite of meeting rooms above the Great Hall while the new Nuffield Library was created in the hall itself. In 2002–3, nine meeting rooms were updated and in 2006 the David Carter boardroom style meeting room was created, along with the Bloomsbury Room (a small private dining facility). The changes agreed in 2005, however, were on a much larger scale and were among the biggest made to BMA House since Sir Edwin Lutyens had designed the first three wings in 1911.

The BMA commissioned the property consultants, Drivers Jonas, and conservation architects, HOK International, to develop proposals for the 'state rooms': Hastings Room and members' dining room on the ground floor overlooking the court of honour, the great hall/library, the Council chamber in the basement and the Prince's Room, overlooking Tavistock Square on the first floor. These rooms were the most prestigious parts of BMA House. Some still had features from Sir Edwin's original designs, but there was a need to consider their usefulness in the 21st century. The members' dining room, for instance, provided a pleasant ambience, but was used mainly for committee lunches and on some days of the week was virtually empty. The Hastings Room, with its well-worn sofas, armchairs and occasional snoozing member, resembled a gentlemen's club. The Council chamber remained a gloomy subterranean room in which to spend long hours in Council and committee meetings. And for a high-profile organisation, the BMA lacked a welcoming reception area and a central 'hub' for staff, members and visitors.

In July 2005 Council members rejected the modest 'lick of paint' option and jumped at the chance of a radical remodelling. Members agreed that parts of the building looked tired and outdated and that facilities should be upgraded both for the BMA's core activities and to increase their attractiveness for external hire. The work would be disruptive and revenue from external room hire would be lost while the work was being done. Therefore, Council decided to have huge disruption, noise and dust for a short time, rather than have a slow, drawn-out building programme which would cause less disturbance day to day, but which would take much longer to complete. BMA staff, members and tenants gritted their teeth while, for 18 months from April 2007, they shared the building with dozens of builders with their jack-hammers and scaffolds.

The project was championed throughout by the Treasurer, David Pickersgill, who had a detailed knowledge of and affection for the building and whose enthusiasm never waned, even when potential disaster loomed as poor 1920s workmanship was uncovered, forcing one wing of the building to be propped up with steel girders. The Finance Director, Leigh Whittingham, also had a huge input to the work overseeing the project day-to-day and keeping a close eye on the costs.

The first part of the modernised building to be unveiled was the new library, now on the first floor near to the new reception area. In the modern IT-enabled age, members were referring less and less to books and printed journals and very few visited the physical old Library, preferring to interact with the Library over the internet. The new Library was light and airy, with excellent reference facilities and free scanning and printing. It was easily accessible from the new main entrance and reception area, which was spacious and welcoming, and which led to the new members' lounge. This provided a modern comfortable space for members to relax, read the newspapers or use the incorporated business centre. They could also make use of the new lockers to leave coats and luggage.

Next came an unexpected transformation as the dark wood-panelled Council chamber became a stylish and bright 'garden room' and cafe. This quickly developed into the hub of the building, used throughout the day by staff and members for informal meetings. The old great hall was renovated into a 300-seat conference hall with state-of-the-art audio-visual equipment and track mounted seats that could be rolled away under the stage to create space for formal dinners or trade fairs. The new 88-seat Council chamber was created out of office space above the old chamber and gave members more desk space and laptop facilities as well as more natural light.

Before the work, anyone wanting to cross from one wing to another on the ground floor had to go outside, regardless of the weather. Important parts of the project were to carve out a 'colonnade' alongside the former members' dining room and Hastings Room and add a lightweight, glass-sided bridge over the new basement cafe. This meant that people crossing from one wing to another on the ground floor would no longer have to brave the elements and go outside, but could walk from the new reception area, past the new members' lounge, across the bridge and through the colonnade right through to the meeting rooms on the far side of the courtyard. (Lutyens had envisaged a walkway around the central courtyard, so his vision was belatedly realised.) The members' dining room was decommissioned and converted into a sizeable meeting room while a new restaurant was set up for staff and members. The former Hastings Room, superseded by the members lounge, also became a committee room. Both of these rooms maintained original features and were attractive enough to be used or hired out for formal lunches and dinners. The new building was formally opened by HRH The Princess Royal on 28 November 2008.

The modernisation work came in on time and on its budget of about £12 million. It had been a significant investment and the BMA hoped to recoup some of it by hiring out its new facilities to outside individuals and companies. Unfortunately, the completion of the work coincided with the financial crisis and a sudden downturn in demand. Revenue from this source picked up in 2010, however, producing a profit of £500,000, though it dipped again in 2011. But the important part of the project was not to make money but to restore an historical building for the future and improve conditions for members using BMA House.

Terrorism reaches the BMA

Thursday 7 July 2005 was in the week following the ARM, a relatively quiet time in BMA House, though some meetings were scheduled. The morning was overcast, and staff and members making their routine journeys to the office were experiencing transport difficulties; many were seriously delayed. Tube stations had been closed and the streets were crowded with people while everywhere the sirens of emergency services could be heard. People told each other that there had been power surges on the underground. Later they learnt that three bombs had already exploded on tube trains near Edgware Road, Russell Square and Aldgate.

A fourth bomb was being carried by Islamist terrorist Habib Hussain on a number 30 bus, which because of the disruption had been diverted from its normal route and was heading through Tavistock Square. At 9.47, just as it was passing BMA House, the bomb detonated, killing thirteen members of the public and injuring 110. The sound was massive, and seemed to last an age, shaking the building; staff in upper offices saw the roof of the bus rise past their windows. In one of them Peter Corpe, secretary of the JDC, picked up the telephone and called the emergency services. The ensuing exchange was played back on the radio weeks later as the media reconstructed events.

First on the scene were passers by and people coming into BMA House, including Roger Chapman, a senior member of the GPs committee, who immediately went to help. Encountering gruesome scenes, he and others did what they could for the victims without equipment, supported very quickly by other doctors and staff who hurried unquestioningly from BMA House to help people off the bus. The front entrance was made of specially reinforced glass (following a terrorist threat to a neighbouring building some years earlier) and had not been damaged. People started to lead or carry those casualties who could be moved into the relative safety of the courtyards of BMA House, using table tops or whatever was to hand.

Sam Everington, deputy chairman of Council, was already in the building. He quickly made his way to the scene and began to co-ordinate first aid efforts among the various helpers; these were greatly facilitated when ambulance crews started to arrive after about 20 minutes, bringing fluids, oxygen and intravenous sets.

Among the GP negotiators who were meeting on the third floor was Peter Holden, an experienced emergency care practitioner, active with the East Midlands Ambulance Service (whose accreditation card he carried), and Honorary Secretary of the British Association for Immediate Care (Basics). Having established the nature of the incident, and following proper precautions in case of a secondary explosion, Peter Holden led his GP colleagues to the courtyard, where he took charge of activity, and started to put in place rudimentary triage and identification systems. Making himself known to the senior ambulance staff, he worked with them to establish clearing procedures, while supporting the willing but shaken group of GP negotiators, surgeons from the Staff and Associate Specialists Committee negotiating team, Professor Bill Dunlop (chairman of the Joint Consultants Committee and president of the Royal College of Obstetricians and Gynaecologists), doctors from the *BMJ* editorial staff and others who had happened to be on the spot and who were battling to help the injured in unfamiliar circumstances and with little equipment. Sam Everington marshalled resources within BMA House so that as the morning wore on, basic information was compiled on the casualties and what had been done for them and the team was regularly debriefed. The last casualties were taken to hospital shortly after midday. Sandwiches were then conjured up from the kitchen before the team eventually dispersed in the afternoon.

Immediately after the explosion, the hundreds of staff and tenants in BMA House were evacuated to the rear of the building, following an often-rehearsed fire drill. Few had seen the bus, but the sound of the explosion and the confused scenes in the courtyard, which was filling up with dazed figures with blackened faces, had frightened many. Once outside, staff, some shivering without jackets in the drizzle, waited for several hours as events were gradually pieced together, largely from television reports shown in the bar of the Lord John Russell pub in

Marchmont Street, which, like the local hotels in Cartwright Gardens, offered shelter to the stunned and anxious crowds. Mobile phone networks were closed down and there was a long queue at the only phone box as staff realised that they needed to reassure their relatives. Tony Bourne, BMA Secretary, who had been to an early morning meeting at the Law Society in Chancery Lane, arrived on foot and was let through into the building by police. From time to time an ambulance would emerge from the back entrance of BMA House with flashing lights and make its way, painfully slowly, through the cordoned-off streets as the watching staff fell silent.

By early afternoon rumours went round that staff would not be readmitted to the building and, since the central transport networks had closed down, most set off for home on foot. A few had left keys and wallets in their offices, and were eventually escorted back in by police to reclaim their belongings. Around mid afternoon a few senior staff were allowed to rejoin those inside who were making arrangements for the remaining doctors to get home. Some basic communications were put in place, such as a message on the BMA website and calls to the national and local offices to ensure that they could still be in touch with members, and a traumatised BMA House was then left in the hands of the police.

That Thursday evening and the next day managers established telephone contact with their staff, telling them to stay at home and to check the website for further instructions. The senior managers group held a long telephone meeting to put into place the existing business continuity plan and to consider other measures that would need to be taken. These teleconferences continued over the next week as the police were conducting meticulous forensic investigations of the site and needed longer access to the building than originally envisaged. Tony Bourne, in regular contact with the police officer in charge, negotiated escorted access to the building to retrieve key documents and equipment. After a few days, a small suite of offices at the rear of the building was opened from which a core group of staff could carry out essential tasks.

During this time staff stayed in contact with each other by telephone and email (though at that time only a small proportion had access to the BMA network) and many departments arranged to meet up, for mutual support as well as for work. Important functions were maintained, including a meeting of BMA Council hastily relocated to the nearby Bonnington hotel, and other meetings and activities were rescheduled as necessary. *BMA News* was published as normal with eyewitness reports of the incident, and the *BMJ*, temporarily relocated to the business continuity unit near Old Street which it had set up only a year earlier 'in what seemed at the time a fanciful precaution,'[8] overcame major technological problems to maintain its proud 165 year record of never missing an edition. A week after the bomb it carried frank personal accounts of their experiences by doctors who had helped to treat the casualties – Andrew Dearden of the BMA, Kieran Walsh and Graham Easton of the *BMJ*'s editorial staff, Alexander Wai Ying Chai, a specialist registrar working at University College Hospital nearby, and the *BMJ* Editor herself, Fiona Godlee.

The building reopened 12 days after the bomb. Remarkably little damage had been sustained to the robust Lutyens structure and fortunately no staff or members had been physically injured: luckily those with desks nearest to the explosion, where glass and debris had fired in, had been held up in the travel chaos. But some people present, particularly those involved in the efforts to help the injured and comfort the dying, suffered post-traumatic reactions and needed professional counselling, which was provided through the First Assist service and staff at the Tavistock Clinic. There was also a need for a general coming together to mark an event that all had experienced but few had come to terms with, and this was met by an act of remembrance in the main courtyard of BMA House, on Thursday 21 July, two weeks after the bomb. The ceremony was attended by staff, tenants and members, and also by surviving passengers, victims' families, the emergency services, the Secretary of State for Health and the NHS Chief Executive. There were prayers from the representatives of different religions (including the Bishop of Edmonton and the Rev Debbie Hodge of the organisation Churches Together in England, who had been present on the day of the bomb), and readings from the Chairman of Council, BMA Secretary, and Mary Church, a GP negotiator who had helped the injured. The soprano Lesley Garrett sang the *Pie Jesu* from Fauré's Requiem and led the singing of *Abide with Me*. Those present placed flowers in the fountain in memory of the victims. But later that day, as the BMA and the rest of London tried to get back to normality, news came through of four more terrorist attacks on London buses and trains, which brought the transport system to a halt once again, although the bombs failed to explode. This caused more weeks of

---

[8] Editorial. *BMJ* of 16/7/05 – *BMJ* 2005;331:0.8.

disruption and increased the general sense of unease and nervousness among Londoners.

Gradually the BMA resumed its normal activity, sustained by hundreds of messages of support from around the world. Through the police, the BMA remained in contact with the victims' families, and welcomed them when they wished to visit. It was already known that an official memorial was to be placed at the site, but staff and members were keen for the BMA to have its own tribute. A bronze sundial, commissioned from the artist Joanna Migdal, was erected in the BMA's private Council Garden, and the BMA agreed to sponsor for three years an annual national training course, organised by Basics, to equip volunteer doctors and other professionals to deal with major accidents and emergencies. A year later, on the anniversary of the bomb, the sundial was dedicated in a ceremony attended by staff, survivors and relatives of the victims. Each year on 7 July a shadow cast by a break in the sundial's stonework falls on a line marking 9.47, the exact time that the bomb exploded.

Over time the events of 7/7 were documented and analysed. There was a long and detailed police investigation, an official report to Parliament, a report by the London Assembly on the response of the emergency services and, in 2010–11, following pressure for a public enquiry, a series of Coroner's Inquests conducted by Lady Justice Hallett, at which several of those involved from the BMA were required to give evidence. The BMA reviewed its own response, located a trauma bag and a defibrillator in the building and entered a citation into the Book of Valour to acknowledge the selfless actions of those who had gone to the aid of the casualties.

The names of those who died are inscribed on a plaque attached to the railings close to the spot where the explosion took place and people at the BMA are still affected by this daily reminder of its appalling consequences. But they do not talk about 7/7 very much, finding it hard, it seems, to deal other than privately with the sad knowledge of the lives that were changed forever on that grey day, and with the painful memories that are regularly evoked by the media's favoured image of the London bombings – that picture of the wrecked number 30 bus framed by the familiar but blood-spattered facade of BMA House.

Chapter 15

The BMJ Publishing Group

In 2012, the activities of the BMJ Publishing Group (BMJPG)[1] extend from the traditional paper *British Medical Journal* (*BMJ*), via on-line editions of both this and its plethora of specialist journals, into learning and careers, quality improvement services, evidence based medicine and point of care tools and analytics services. Such a huge expansion of the work of the group could hardly have been envisaged in the early 1980s when routine use of the internet was at least 15 years in the future and the work of the BMJ Publishing Group was centred around the production of paper material, both the journal itself and books.

There are, though, some parallels between the BMJ Publishing Group of 1981 and that of 2012 and the seeds of some of its current activities were sown in the 1980s. Over the thirty or so years covered by this section, the group has striven to be at the forefront of medical publishing, using the latest means and technologies available at the time, it has continued to look overseas both for commercial opportunities and to support clinical decision making over a wide international area and, crucially for the BMA, its profits have for many years provided an important income stream for the BMA group (of which the BMJ Publishing Group is part), helping to plug the gap between income from subscriptions and expenditure on services to members. The BMJ Publishing Group's profits have never been taken for granted by the group itself nor by the BMA as threats to these have always been lurking in the shadows, often in the form of a new NHS jobs bulletin or website which would remove from the *BMJ* its lucrative classified advertisements. This was identified as long ago as 1983 when the group reported that it 'must constantly seek new ways of diversifying its activities, increasing its efficiency and improving its profitability.'

The 1981 accounts showed that the BMJ Publishing Group had made a very small profit of under £1,000 (it had actually expected to make a loss). To attract more advertising it split the *BMJ* into two

---

[1] Throughout this section the terms 'BMJ Publishing Group' and 'the group' are used. The term BMJ Publishing Group was first used in the 1991–92 Annual Report of Council. Prior to that the group was know as 'the Journal Group'.

editions: *Practice Observed* for GPs and *Clinical Research* for hospital doctors. It also reduced paper and postage costs by sending the 'compact' edition, which had no advertisements and was sent to overseas members, to retired members as well. These measures bore fruit and by the following year, the group reported a profit of more than £0.5 million. The contents of the journal at this time included old and popular features and some new ones, the latter including articles on dealing with the 'disadvantaged', alcohol and alcoholism and, reflecting the concerns of the time, a feature on 'medicine and the bomb'. There was also a regular letter from Chicago and one from the USSR.

By the end of 1983, the weekly print order for the *BMJ* reached 100,000 for the first time, the turn-over for the group was £8.9 million and each of the group's individual publications showed a profit. It was aware, though, that this could be reversed if, for example, there was a change in government policy on where to advertise NHS jobs, or a fall in the exchange rate for the US dollar, in which currency overseas subscriptions to the *BMJ* were made. But it hoped that these threats would be offset by continuing profits from the seven wholly-owned specialist journals, six co-owned journals and five journals published on behalf of others. It also hoped to make profits from publishing books of which, at the end of 1983, there were 34 titles. The group had also launched a series of limited editions of medical classics of the preceding 100 years. There were plans, too, to develop the *BMJ* as one of the leading international medical journals. It undertook a publicity campaign in Australia in 1983 and a similar one was proposed for the USA and the Nordic countries in 1984. Also, the BMA's Family Doctor Unit, which published a number of medical booklets for the public, was brought under the management of the *BMJ*.

In 1984 there was a serious threat to classified advertising revenue when an expert committee suggested to the Department of Health and Social Services (DHSS) that it might consider publishing its own jobs bulletins or creating a jobs agency.[2] The BMJ Publishing Group estimated that if either of these ideas had been taken up, it would have lost about £800,000 in a single year. The Editor of the *BMJ*, Stephen Lock, stressed to the Under-Secretary of State, John Patten, the important educational role of the journal and the fact that the expert committee itself had noted that the use of classified advertisements in the journal

---

[2] This was part of an efficiency scrutiny process of public services, begun by Lord Rayner in 1979, to advise on the promotion of efficiency in government.

was both economical and efficient. The government decided to cut the costs of advertising for NHS staff, but the *BMJ* would continue to carry classified advertisements for NHS posts. The storm had passed for now, but the threat of the loss of classified advertisements continued to hang over the group. By the time that the NHS jobs website was finally established in England and Wales in 2003, the group had had so much advance warning that it was well able to arm itself against the loss of revenue by diversification and the opening of a number of other revenue streams which had begun in earnest from the mid-1990s.

Back in the 1980s, the BMJ Publishing Group continued to draw attention to the heavy financial burden of posting a weekly copy of the *BMJ* to every member of the BMA, but its profits nevertheless carried on rising. The group continued to look beyond the UK and the number of international editions of the journal grew. By the end of the 1980s, these were available in Dutch, French, German, Italian and Spanish and worldwide circulation was almost 110,000.

A less positive development on the international front was the squeeze on many libraries and institutions which led to their economising on journal acquisition budgets, but the BMJ Publishing Group reported in 1986 that its 13 special journals maintained successful progress. By 1986 international subscriptions had been switched back from US dollars into sterling, which had saved the group money. Control of costs was a concern and the group reported in 1987 that the rising costs of production, distribution and staffing, as well as an increase in BMA membership, would combine to reduce the budget surplus. Vigorous efforts were being made to try to contain these costs and such containment would continue to be a constant preoccupation. Despite regular warnings from the group about the precarious state of the medical publishing market and threats to its income, it nevertheless continued to confound its own pessimistic forecasts throughout the 1980s with its turnover and profits often way ahead of budget. In the middle of the decade it was reporting record profits and, by 1987, the BMJPG's contribution to the BMA group's finances stood at £2.67 million, with another £500,000 being transferred in 1988.

The group's book publishing activities continued to grow throughout the decade and the books division was strengthened in 1987. Book sales boomed towards the end of the 1980s, with over 65,000 copies being sold in 1988, a rise of 20,000 on 1987, which had itself been a record year. The 'ABC' series was particularly successful and further expansion in book publication was planned. The 'Memoir Club' books were launched at the 1987 ARM with Sir Christopher Booth's *Doctors in Science and Society* and continued with Sir Douglas Black's *Recollections and Reflections*. Both authors had been recent Presidents of the BMA.

The 'look' of the flagship *BMJ* began to change during the 1980s, with the use of some colour being possible for the first time in 1986 as a result of the installation of new machines by the *BMJ*'s printers. In July 1988, after two years of planning, Stephen Lock launched a full redesign, the journal's first for 50 years. The intention was to make it easier for readers to find their way around the journal, to place emphasis on major news stories while continuing to ensure that the journal remained instantly recognisable and gave a high profile to peer-reviewed scientific papers. The redesigned journal was awarded the Charlesworth Group Award for Typographical Excellence in Journal and Serial Publishing the following year.[3] The editorial content of the journal continued to develop with an expansion of the news section being one of the changes. Another was a series by the editorial staff on research policy, 'conversations with consultants' and nursing grievances. The number of unsolicited manuscripts and letters increased; it was reported in 1986 that an average of almost 400 unsolicited manuscripts were submitted each month in that year and about 15% were selected for publication. A healthy sign of readers' interest was the number of letters received; this averaged around 60 a week, but in November 1986, there was a record 372. At around this time the journal's editorial staff was augmented by medical students and junior doctors as editorial registrars. Some of these went on to occupy senior positions in the journal – including as editor-in-chief.

On 3 October 1990 the *BMJ* celebrated its 150th anniversary with a special edition. It also commissioned an anthology of poetry written by doctors which was launched with a reading at the Poetry Society in London, an exhibition about the journal in BMA House and a specially-commissioned history of the *BMJ*.[4] There was also a symposium on the history of medical journals, which was organised jointly with the Wellcome Institute for Medical History. This resulted in *The Future of Medical Journals: in Commemoration of 150 Years of the British Medical Journal* edited by Stephen Lock. This was one of the

---

[3] The prestigious Charlesworth Group Award for Typographical Excellence is awarded by the Huddersfield-based Charlesworth Press.
[4] *Mirror of Medicine: A History of the British Medical Journal* by P W J Bartrip, *British Medical Journal* and Clarendon Press, 1990.

first books to question the quality of medical journals and it helped to start the practice of evidence based journals – a movement in which the *BMJ* played a leading part as it supported evidence-based medicine and quality improvement early on. In the 1990s the group launched several evidence based journals including *Quality & Safety in Health Care* in 1992. It also joined the Institute for Healthcare Improvement to run the annual International Forum on Quality and Safety in Healthcare which began in 1995 and is a yearly meeting of healthcare professionals involved in patient safety and quality improvement. By 2012 participants from around 90 countries were attending.

As the 1990s began and the *BMJ* celebrated its anniversary, the BMJ Publishing Group had good reasons to celebrate: the worldwide circulation of the *BMJ* continued at nearly 110,000 and it had maintained its market share in an increasingly competitive climate. 1991 saw the retirement of Stephen Lock as editor and the appointment of Richard Smith, a young doctor with a media profile and a degree in management science from Stanford. The journal's tradition of analysing medicosocial aspects of public policy continued with its series on health and housing and psychiatry in the community, the specialist journals were flourishing and book sales continued to grow. Yet the economic climate was worsening and that year BMJPG had a deficit of about £68,000. It reported in the 1990–91 annual report of Council that some of this was due to investment in new products (essential for diversification and growing the group), marketing and new technology, but the group had also had to face a bad debt and a fall in display advertising revenue.

By the end of 1991, the BMJ Publishing Group had taken stock of the situation and announced that its aim was to follow a strategy of finding new sources of revenue and part of this was 'to publish more and market it better'. The group immediately got to work on this strategy and, in the 1991–92 session, launched two new specialist journals, increased the size of several others, expanded its books publishing programme and, crucially for the future, increased its marketing activities to promote the *BMJ* and the specialist journals both in Europe and beyond. Looking to exploit markets beyond the UK had long been part of the group's aims and would continue to form a core part of its strategy in years to come. By 1994 the group was distributing, within the UK, the *Journal of the American Medical Association* (*JAMA*) and all of the American Medical Association's specialist journals. In 1998, the BMJ Publishing Group gained a base for its marketing activities in the USA with its purchase of the *Western Journal of Medicine*. This was a general medical journal serving the western states of the USA and would be jointly owned by the BMA and University of California San Francisco Healthcare. Sadly, the *Western Journal of Medicine* was ultimately unsustainable and ceased publication in May 2002. Although this was not a happy experience for the group, it did show its willingness to look overseas for growth opportunities.

By the end of 1992, the group was able to report that its strategy of increasing and diversifying its sources of revenue was beginning to pay off as its financial position was improving, helped by better than expected advertising revenue and decreased production costs. Better still, in 1993, the group finished the year ahead of budget at the same time as achieving its planned growth. It was noted that key sources of revenue for the group, pharmaceutical advertising and institutional subscriptions, were both declining and it was essential that the group's reliance on these was lessened by seeking out new opportunities. One of the BMJ Publishing Group's strengths has long been its keen awareness of the market in which it is operating and its ability both to detect an opportunity as well as to acknowledge when previously successful products are declining and to begin to look for ways in which to replace the eventual and inevitable loss of income. From its position of deficit in 1990, which was swiftly turned around, the group continued, throughout the 1990s, to remain strong financially (thanks to new product development and strict containment of costs) and to continue to contribute significant sums to the BMA group. In 1999, it reported an impressive net profit of £3,312,000.

The content of the *BMJ* itself continued to evolve and the news section was expanded at the beginning of the 1990s as a result of the many political and scientific developments which were affecting medical practice. In 1991 it commissioned responses to the government's health strategy, *The Health of the Nation,* and, in the same year, ran series on the environment and on Europe. In 1999, the *BMJ* introduced open peer review of its papers as a result of research into the effectiveness of peer review. The *BMJ* was an early supporter of open access publishing, which developed during the 1990s with the arrival of the internet. Several key funders of research, led by the National Institutes for Health in the USA, had started to advocate that the results of research that they funded should be made available free of charge. In 1999 the *BMJ* became the first general medical journal to join PubMedCentral, which had been developed by the USA's

National Library of Medicine to make the results of original research in the life sciences freely available via the internet. That year the BMJ Publishing Group also joined WorldSpace, an initiative to make recent contents freely available to health professionals caring for the world's most disadvantaged people.

The number of local editions of the *BMJ* was also growing and, by 1995, new editions had been launched in Bulgaria, Greece, Mexico, the Middle East, Poland and Romania. The *BMJ* was redesigned in January 1997 and this coincided with two new sections covering information in practice and clinical review. In the classified supplement, a new *Careers* section was included which covered advice on jobs and training. This soon became a valued part of the journal and was eventually transformed into a separate *Careers* supplement and, later, in to an on-line recruitment website for doctors which offered targeted job searching and an opportunity to set tailored job alerts for delivery to doctors via email.

The group announced the launch of the *Student BMJ* in 1992. This version of the *BMJ* was published monthly and contained a selection of articles from the *BMJ*, together with several pages written especially for medical students, many of which were written by medical students themselves. Later the *Student BMJ* would come to be edited by a medical student taking a year out from their studies and would evolve so that it explained how to read research papers, provided practical career advice and generally helped students put theory into practice.

Book sales continued to expand strongly throughout the 1990s. In 1990 over 85,000 copies were sold and 11 new titles or revised editions were added. In early 1993, the BMJ Bookshop moved to new and larger premises at the back of BMA House and many new book titles were commissioned that year. By the following year, income from the bookshop had more than doubled and the expansion of the books division was continuing with the number of titles growing from 27 in 1993 to 45 in 1994. Many of the books started as series in the *BMJ* or one of the specialist journals, but the books division began, in 1993, to commission some titles and the first of these, *Advanced Paediatric Life Support*, was published that year. The decision to create an independent books publishing programme was a sound one and in 1994–95, eight new titles appeared.

A new journal, *Evidence-Based Medicine,* was released during the 1995–96 session, produced jointly with the American College of

Physicians. This summarised the results of the world's best clinical trials and after one issue the new journal had more than 3,000 subscribers. Plans for *Clinical Evidence*, which was to become one of the BMJ Publishing Group's most influential products, were put in hand in 1998, and it was launched in the summer of 1999 to a positive reception.

New technology was rapidly changing working practices and in 1991 the group launched a new specialist journal, *Tobacco Control: an International Journal*, which had an editor in the USA, a deputy editor in Australia and a technical editor in London. Two years later, at the time of the stirring of the electronic revolution, classified advertisements in the *BMJ* were converted to electronic production in-house and moves were underway for a similar electronic system for the editorial pages of the *BMJ* and the specialist journals. In 1994 the annual report of Council noted that libraries and individual readers were seeking new ways of accessing information and so the group would be investing heavily in electronic products, such as CD-ROMs. This appears to be the first appearance in a BMA report of the term 'on-line'. It was then a new phrase but it would soon pass into everyday language, and on-line products would soon be among the group's most successful and innovative products.

In 1995, the *BMJ* joined the internet. Initially, the editorial home pages for the *BMJ* were added to the world wide web, making it one of the first major medical journals on the web. These pages were quickly followed by the contents pages of some of the specialist journals and later by the classified job advertisements for hospital posts. In 1998 the e*BMJ* (later bmj.com) was launched and became the first full text general medical journal website, with all content available free of charge. By this time, the full text of seven of the specialist journals was on the web and the *BMJ* bookshop had its own website. A new world had opened up for the BMJ Publishing Group and even as early as 1995, one of its journals, *Medicine and Global Survival*, was entirely electronic. The group seized the opportunities offered by new electronic means and in 1995 it marketed and distributed the *Cochrane Database of Systematic Reviews* and began to build a database with up-to-date information on doctors and hospitals in the UK. The group also continued to invest in electronic handling of the text for all of its journals.

From 1995 onwards, thanks to the internet, the work and the world of the BMJ Publishing Group would never be the same. Certainly, the group never lost sight of the value of its printed products, but attention would be focused more and more on the enormous potential of the internet for pioneering new products. The advent of the internet changed the way in which doctors worked and accessed information and it also massively increased the amount of medical material available to patients. The excitement felt within the group at the potential for change offered by the internet was coupled with concern at its probable effect on classified advertising. Therefore, at the end of the decade, as the group prepared its strategy for the five years ahead, it acknowledged that it had been prepared against 'a background of unprecedented change facing publishers and the arrival of the internet and electronic publishing'. Council was also warned that 'the Association could no longer rely on the journal's income' and that 'the Journal Committee had deep concerns that the Publishing Group's time as a profit centre was limited.' These worrying reports, it was explained to Council, were due to the emergence of electronic competitors to *BMJ Classified*, the possibility of pharmaceutical companies in the UK and Europe advertising direct to patients, pressure on library budgets worldwide and the plan by the US Library of Medicine and National Institutes of Health to launch PubMed Central. It was reported to Council that it was difficult to quantify the threats to the BMJ Publishing Group's income, but if it were to lose one quarter of its income then it would move from a profit centre to a neutral or loss-making one. This was not an optimistic assessment at the beginning of the new millennium and it was hoped that the group's decision to hedge its bets in this exciting, but also uncertain, new world by continuing publication of its existing products and carrying out research into new ones was the right one. In addition to the plan to develop new products, the group also continued to focus on ways in which to reduce its cost base and there were two important initiatives in 1996: an efficiency review and the decision to change the printers for the *BMJ*. These moves resulted in savings of around £2 million per annum.

The year 2000 opened with bad news: the NHS had announced the creation of a web-based jobs site for all NHS staff and there was no doubt that this would remove significant NHS business away from printed publications. This, or something similar, had been expected for years but, all the same, was a blow when it finally came. The group had considered whether *BMJ Classified* should bid to be the NHS's partner in this new business, but it decided that developing the existing features on its own website and providing services such as the new careers fair would be a better course of action. The imminent arrival of the NHS's jobs site prompted a warning from the BMJ Publishing Group that, although it had in 2000 made its highest ever contribution to the BMA group's finances, this profitability was unlikely to last. Another development likely to impact on profits from the group's journals were the changes to the publication of research as a result of open access publishing gathering pace. Although the group supported the movement, the financial effects were undeniable. To help counter this threat to its subscription income, the group's journals were developing their content to include, as well as research papers, more material that would be useful to doctors in their day to day work. In addition, it was reported in 2002 that the group had embarked on an investment programme to broaden its revenue base and range of activities. The main features of its strategy were to develop more products like *Clinical Evidence*, to sell more products outside the UK, to develop activities in quality improvement, to adopt an experimental approach to new products and services and to add value to existing products. The group increased its sales force and focused more on international sales, with a senior member of staff overseeing these. The group expected direct costs to grow by £3.1 million and overheads by £2.15 million in the three years following 2002 as a result of its investments.

Clinical Evidence, which had begun well when launched in 1999, took off spectacularly, becoming for a time one of the BMJ Publishing Group's strongest products. But there would be a commercial sting in its tail. In 2000, the NHS bought copies for GPs in England and Scotland; other clinicians would have access via the *Clinical Evidence* website. There had been a bulk-purchase deal negotiated in the USA which would see 400,000 copies distributed to doctors in the USA until 2003. Eventually, in the UK, *Clinical Evidence* would have to become a subscription only product due to the loss of the contract for providing it to the NHS in 2006. These problems were in the future, however, and, at the end of 2000, the BMJPG reported that its net profit was £5.9 million, which was £3.2 million ahead of budget and 50% higher than 1999's net profit. This strong performance continued: the net profit for 2001 was over £9 million, nearly £5 million better than budget, and it remained high at £8.8 million in 2002. These impressive figures were thanks in large part to the contribution of classified advertising, display advertising and subscription income from paper journals.

As signalled in its strategy, the group continued to look beyond the UK for opportunities. Although it had always had an eye on overseas markets and had long taken this business seriously, its overseas work moved up a gear from the early 2000s and, by the end of the decade, sixty per cent of its income was coming from outside the UK. The USA had always been an attractive market to the group and in 2002 a sales and marketing office was opened in Philadelphia. Although the office was subsequently closed because of the difficulty of attracting staff with the right skills from the catchment area, the group continued to employ sales and business development staff in the USA and to look for ways to expand its business there.

The *BMJ* continued at the heart of the Publishing Group. Paper and electronic versions of the *BMJ* started to complement each other, with full versions of original articles published on the website while the paper journal carried shorter versions of papers. The 'rapid responses' feature, which had appeared towards the end of the 1990s, was the first if its kind and still leads other medical journals in the number of comments posted by readers. Another change from the mid-1990s was a sudden reduction of reporting on the work of BMA committees and councils. Some members were unhappy about this, but the editorial change was defended on the grounds that the *BMJ* was not the BMA's house journal, but an international medical publication. Nevertheless, there was some regret at the passing of one of the journal's traditional and well-regarded regular features. In January 2002, *BMJ Classified* became *BMJ Careers* and the journal itself had a cover and contents page change. The number of themed issues of the *BMJ* was increasing, in response to reader requests for in-depth coverage of some issues. The specialist journals were also redesigned in 2001–2 and given their own websites.

An important change for the *BMJ* came at the beginning of 2005 with the decision to stop universal free access to bmj.com. The site would be free to BMA members and to readers in the world's poorest countries, but other users would have to pay for content after the first week of publication, with research material remaining free to all. By the following year, the annual report of Council reported that as a result of these controls subscription revenue had increased.

The paper journal and website were revamped in January 2007 after a major strategic review. As with other redesigns, the aim was to improve the content and usability of both and results from reader and user feedback indicated contentment with the new look of the journal and website. The improvements were also recognised by the industry as the *BMJ* won the Medical Journalist Association's Medical

Publication of the Year award in 2008 and two of the *BMJ*'s staff received awards for Health Editor of the Year and Medical Journalist of the Year. The *BMJ* was also able to announce in the 2008–9 annual report of Council that, for the first time, the syndicated research carried out twice a year showed the *BMJ* to have the highest readership among medical journals in the UK. The weekly *BMJ* is a valued BMA membership benefit and the journal has long had a critical influence on medical publishing and on the conduct and quality of medical journals both in the UK and abroad. It organised courses for editors of medical journals and played a leading role in what would become the International Committee of Medical Journal Editors.[5] The journal has also led a number of campaigns, the most recent being its 'open data' campaign for all data relating to clinical trials to be published and independently scrutinised. In the past it has campaigned against smoking, helped by the journal *Tobacco Control,* and on alcohol, housing, prisons, research fraud, research into peer review, conflict of interest, understanding Europe, nursing standards, end of life care and assisted dying.

In 2008 bmj.com moved to a model whereby it was updated daily, with all editorial processes geared towards on-line publication, which had itself been enhanced by online features such as polls, blogs and podcasts – a world away from the black and white paper journal. Throughout the 2000s, BMJ journals continued to flourish, with new journals being launched and acquired all the time. The journals division was eventually restructured to focus on growth through brand extensions, launches, acquisitions and society contracts. By 2012 the group had expanded its portfolio to 42 journals.

The early to mid-2000s saw some significant changes to the governance of the BMJ Publishing Group. In November 2000, Richard Smith, the Editor of the *BMJ* and Chief Executive of the BMJ Publishing Group, presented a paper to the BMA's Finance and General Purposes Committee which set out a number of problems with the current arrangements and suggested that the group should become a wholly-owned subsidiary of the BMA. This paper had the support of the Journal Committee. The problems that Richard Smith

---

[5] The International Committee of Medical Journal Editors (ICMJE) is a group of general medical journal editors, which includes the Editor of the *BMJ*, who meet each year to work on the Uniform Requirements for Manuscripts. These requirements are a set of guidelines produced by ICMJE to regulate the ethics, preparation and formatting of manuscripts submitted to medical journals for publication. Most leading medical journals insist that the requirements are met by authors.

identified had been present for some time and related to the lack of clarity about what the BMA expected from the group and the quality and speed of decision making by the Journal Committee (which oversaw the running of the BMJ Publishing Group and which was populated by BMA members elected by the Representative Body and Council). The Publishing Group was also currently obliged to use the BMA's corporate services and employ its staff on BMA terms and conditions and the group felt that it needed some freedom in respect of these in order to operate to maximum potential in a tough commercial market. The 'quality' of board decisions was an especially delicate matter. As was made clear in a document presented to Council in December 2000, 'members of the Journal Committee give generously of their time and some have made an outstanding contribution to the group. But they are doctors first and foremost. If they are experts in corporate management, finance, publishing, marketing or whatever this is pure accident.'

The publishing world was fast-moving and highly competitive and the time had now come when it was no longer feasible for the BMJ Publishing Group to operate in such an environment with a board largely composed of those who had taken their chances with the electoral system. The chairmanship of the Journal Committee had tended to be occupied by very distinguished and eminent BMA medico-politicians and they had led the group with great merit. However, as the Journal Committee itself acknowledged, the expansion of the BMJ Publishing Group and the environment within which it was operating, meant that it would become increasingly difficult to find a suitably qualified chairman, who had both political and business experience, from among BMA members.

Both the BMA's Finance and General Purposes Committee and Council agreed that the BMJ Publishing Group needed the freedom that status as a freestanding company would give it and Council agreed at its meeting in December 2000 that the Group should become a wholly-owned subsidiary of the BMA. Council also decided that a new Board of the BMJ Publishing Group would be established to replace the Journal Committee and the BMA would be responsible for appointing the Chairman of the new Board, with the group appointing the board's non-executive external directors. At its meeting in May 2001, Council considered how this new status would work in practice and received assurances that the BMA would continue to own in its entirety and to exercise full legal and economic control over the BMJPG once it was a separate legal entity. The transfer of the business into a separate legal entity took place with effect from 1 January 2003 and a memorandum of understanding was signed between the BMA and the new BMJ Publishing Group Limited, which included the following provisions:

- the BMA would continue to support the long-term development of the BMJ Publishing Group;
- the aims and objectives of the BMJ Publishing Group would be consistent with those of the Association;
- the Publishing Group would continue to publish the *BMJ* and circulate it to BMA members at no charge to the BMA;
- BMA Council would continue to appoint the Editor of the *BMJ*, but that the Editor's would continue to have 'editorial freedom';
- three-year financial projections and annual budgets would be sent to the BMA for review and acceptance;
- the Publishing Group would pay an annual dividend to the BMA (90% of annual profit after tax, subject to adjustment for approved investments, according to the memorandum of understanding).[6]

The fourth of these points, editorial freedom, was one to which Council attached enormous importance. Although the *BMJ* is owned by the British Medical Association, its Editor is free to publish research, articles, comment and letters that may not comply with BMA policy and which are sometimes critical of the Association.[7] A journal which is seen merely as a mouthpiece of the owners is unlikely to achieve the elevated national and international reputation of the *BMJ* and that is why, despite some uncomfortable reads, the BMA has maintained a strict hands-off policy with regard to the contents of the journal. As Richard Smith wrote, 'If readers once hear that important, relevant, and well argued articles are being suppressed or that articles are being published simply to fulfill hidden political agendas, then the credibility of the publication collapses—and everybody loses.'[8]

The BMJ Publishing Group had for some years made a sound financial contribution to the running of the BMA group but, as was noted at the time of the incorporation, there was some uncertainty about what exactly the BMA expected of its prosperous publishing arm. In the years ahead, clearer expectations were put on the table, beginning in 2003 when it was reported to Council that 'a single minimum profit

---

[6] Taken from the Memorandum of Understanding received at Council on 17 July 2002 (Doc C28, 2002–03).
[7] See for example *Is the BMA a 21st Century Organisation?* Nizam Mamode, *BMJ*, vol 329, 17 July 2004.
[8] *Editorial Independence at the BMJ. BMJ* 2004;329:0.8, published 8 July 2004.

expectation figure for future years for the group (excluding goodwill amortisation) of £5 million per year for the next three years had been agreed at the Publishing Group's board. It was clarified that this figure is neither a budget nor a target figure.' Council subsequently agreed a dividend policy in November 2008 and payments were made in December 2008 (£5 million), June 2009 (£5.4 million) and December 2010 (£6 million).

The changes in the governance of the BMJ Publishing Group did not end with the group's incorporation. There remained one inconsistency at the heart of the management of the arrangement: there was no one individual responsible for the management of both the BMA and the BMJ Publishing Group. Instead, the BMA Secretary was responsible for the BMA's secretariat and the Editor was responsible for the Publishing Group's staff and there was no formal management link between the two. In addition, within the Publishing Group itself, everything depended upon the Editor who was accountable both for the content and direction of the *BMJ* and the work of the expanding group. There were also questions about the size, composition and functioning of the board and it was noted that Reed Elsevier, a publicly quoted multi-national employing 36,000 people and the global market leader for scientific and medical publications, had a smaller board than the Publishing Group's. Therefore, a year after the incorporation of the group, it was reported to Council in March 2004 that the BMA's Finance Committee had commissioned the management consultants, KPMG, to 'review the board structure (including the roles and reporting structure of the executive directors) of the BMJPG in the light of the function and purpose of the board and the experience of its first year of operation . . . That, in view of the fact that this review would encompass board level executive responsibility for the BMJPG, KPMG be further requested to consider whether the new Secretary of the BMA[9] should have executive responsibility for the BMJPG and thus be appointed group chief executive of the BMA group.'[10]

KPMG's report two months later proposed a group chief executive officer with a single line of accountability for all of the BMA's operations. The group CEO needed to be given formal responsibility for line management in overseeing the Publishing Group's CEO to enable a formal management link to be established with the group.

---

[9] The then Secretary, Jeremy Strachan, was due to retire at the end of 2004 and the then Editor, Richard Smith, had resigned.
[10] From the remit given to KPMG in February 2004.

KPMG also suggested that the roles of the Publishing Group's CEO and Editor should be separated and that the roles of the Chairman of the Board of the Publishing Group, CEO, Editor and other executives should be clarified and recorded and their accountability for decision making be specified. The membership of the board of the Publishing Group should be reduced, with fewer practising doctors and more executive team members.[11]

All of these suggestions were accepted by the Finance Committee and subsequently by Council at its meeting in July 2004. The way was now clear for the final changes to be made to the governance of the Publishing Group. The new Chairman of the Board of the BMJPG had already been appointed in March 2004, Michael Chamberlain, not a member of the BMA, but someone who had extensive experience of journalism, magazine publishing and new media. Stella Dutton, the group's Executive Director, was subsequently appointed as its new CEO, Fiona Godlee, formally the Publishing Director/Executive Editor of *BMJ Knowledge* and lead developer of *Clinical Evidence*, became the Editor. In January 2005, Tony Bourne became the BMA's second non-medical Secretary and the first BMA group CEO. These changes coincided with the departure of two key *BMJ* figures: Sir Anthony Grabham, formerly a Chairman of Council and Chairman of BMA Services, who had served with distinction as Chairman of the Journal Committee for many years, and the Editor, Richard Smith, who had overseen the growth of the group from a division of the BMA to a wholly-owned subsidiary with a multi-million pound turn-over.

Following the changes at the top of the organisation, there was an expectation that relations between the BMA and BMJ Publishing Group would become closer and that there would be more cohesion between the work of the group and services for BMA members. As the Chairman of Council said at the time, 'We look forward to expanding the Publishing Group's business activities, and developing a closer relationship, particularly regarding services the Publishing Group might provide to BMA members.' Members of the BMA continued to receive the weekly printed edition of the *BMJ* as a benefit of membership and also had free access to bmj.com. Another membership benefit was free access to *BMJ Learning*. Members were also entitled to a 25% subscription discount for print and on-line BMJ journals and a 10% discount on all formats of *Clinical Evidence*. There are good working

---

[11] Subsequently, the BMA Treasurer was appointed to the Board of the BMJ Group as an observer to help protect the BMA's interests.

relations between *BMJ* staff and those in the BMA responsible for membership product development so that issues such as discounts for members can be addressed at an early stage. This also ensures that the BMA receives advance notice when new products are being considered by the group.

While the changes in the governance of the group were taking place, the group's publishing business and online ventures continued to develop. November 2003 saw the launch of one of the group's most valued products: *BMJ Learning*. This product almost died at birth, however, as the original intention was to sell the service to the NHS for the use of the proposed NHS University, which was launched in December 2003 and abolished just over 18 months later. With the loss of a major potential customer, the group proposed that the BMA buy the product to offer as a benefit of membership. The Finance Committee could not agree and discussions continued for a year until the committee finally decided to give financial backing to *BMJ Learning* and incorporate it into the member benefit package. By 2010 *BMJ Learning* had become the UK market leader in online continuing professional development and postgraduate training for doctors and other healthcare professionals. The site would come to contain more than 500 expert and peer-reviewed online courses, which were sorted by profession and speciality. Within just three years, *BMJ Learning* was the most popular and respected curriculum-led medical learning service in the UK, with over 38,000 BMA members registered, growing to 50,000 by 2005 and 90,000 UK users in 2008. By this time, the service was also accessible to over 1.5 million doctors in over 35 countries worldwide through distribution deals and country-wide partnerships. *BMJ Learning* was particularly valued by doctors for its help with appraisal preparation, and for its future use when revalidation became a reality. *BMJ Learning* continues to be offered free to BMA members and was voted as one of the most favoured perks of membership in a national membership survey.

The BMJ Publishing Group's commitment to offer learning opportunities to doctors extended in 2006 to BMJ Masterclasses and, by 2010, over 19,000 doctors[12] had attended these classes, which were held in locations around the UK and Ireland. The aim of the classes is to help those attending to change their practice and improve patient outcomes by using practical demonstrations and case histories. At the

---

[12] Figure of 19,000 taken from the BMJ Publishing Group's corporate brochure, created in August 2011 and accessed on its website in January 2012.

end of 2007, the group acquired OnExamination.com, which was the UK's market leader in on-line exam preparation for doctors, medical students and other healthcare professionals. The acquisition of OnExamination.com was an example of the group's renewed desire to increase revenue through the development of new products and from acquisitions. Its strategy document for 2006–9 makes this clear as a response to the threats of declining classified and display advertising markets. Another innovation was the sponsoring by *BMJ Careers* of annual careers fairs in London. These were tremendously successful and similar fairs would be held elsewhere in the UK.

All of these changes were set against the background of the development of the long-awaited NHS recruitment website. This had finally launched in England and Wales in 2003 and followed similar initiatives in Scotland and Wales. Although *BMJ Careers* would continue to carry job advertisements, it was now going to have to battle in a market where competition was becoming intense. It was ready for the challenge and its development of services for recruiters and jobseekers meant that it continued to be the place where the majority of advertisements were placed and where almost 100% of medical jobseekers looked for vacant posts. This was a remarkable achievement, but the loss of revenue was serious. By the end of 2010, *BMJ Careers* had experienced a 64% decline in hospital classified advertisements since 2003. The impact of this decline on revenue from classified advertising was mitigated to a certain extent by initiatives taken by the *BMJ Careers* staff to generate additional revenue online and to increase the revenue gained from each advertisement.

In the 2003–4 annual report of Council, the group drew attention to the continuing threats to its traditional income from classified advertising and journal subscriptions and especially the threats from internet campaigns for free and open access to all scientific research articles. In 2004, the group revised its mission and stated that it was set on a path to expand its activities and provide more services to doctors that would help them with decision making and improve outcomes for patients. Therefore, investment continued in *Clinical Evidence*, launched in 1999, so that, by the 2003–4 session, it had a new website available to the NHS, 300,000 copies being distributed in Italy, in addition to 500,000 copies being distributed every six months to doctors in the USA. Another important product in the *BMJ Knowledge* stable was the BestTreatments website. In the new era of web-based health information (not all of it trustworthy or reliable), this was designed to provide patients with the same evidence-based information as their doctors. It was made available in the USA to members of the United Health Group, which was one of the largest health maintenance organisations in the USA. BestTreatments was initially made available to members of the public in the UK via the NHS, but by 2006, it had been converted into a subscription based product in the UK.

The Publishing Group's books programme, which had been such a strong performer, was unable to maintain its momentum into the new millennium and, by May 2003, it was reported to the Board that attempts to make Books Publishing profitable had failed. After a long discussion, the Board sadly concluded that the focus of management had to be on the core business of the company, and this did not include publishing books. As was noted at that meeting, Books Publishing had high overheads and was a labour intensive operation. The scale of the BMJPG's operation was small, which made it more vulnerable to the ups and downs of the business and the downs were clear: the accounts for 2002 had shown a Books Publishing loss of £412,000. It was subsequently agreed at the end of 2003 that the books programme be sold to Blackwells, although the group would retain editorial control of the well-regarded ABC series.

In 2005 BMJ Publishing Group acquired the 50 per cent BMA shareholding in the *British National Formulary* (*BNF*), the reference tool for doctors, nurses and pharmacists; the other share was held by the Royal Pharmaceutical Society of Great Britain. That year also saw the celebration of the 50th anniversary of the *BNF* and the launch of the *BNF for Children*, which was designed to advise healthcare professionals when prescribing for childhood disorders. During the following year, work started on the digitalisation of the *BNF*, which was important in a digital prescribing environment. By 2011 the *BNF* was available in print, updated twice a year, and available in various digital versions including online, mobile and versions for incorporation in clinical systems. Following the transfer of the *BNF* procurement contract from the English Department of Health to the National Institute for Health and Clinical Excellence (NICE), the group had anxieties, 'we continue to work on the concern we have that NICE will be focused on its own needs in relation to the *BNF* rather than seeing the product holistically for the benefit of the practice of medicine, the Department of Health and the NHS.' These anxieties had deepened by the middle of 2010 when it was reported that the requirements of the new contract with NICE for the *BNF* included NICE wishing to hold a share of the intellectual property rights and profits and be given the right to attend meetings of the *BNF* Board. It was also asking for involvement in the production of the content and for all NICE-approved medicines to be specially marked, plus cost-savings of up to 5% each year for the three years of the contract. This dispute was eventually settled and NICE backed down over holding a share of the property rights, although it did insist on cost savings during the length of the contract and more frequent digital feeds.

The changes in the management of the BMJ Publishing Group had begun to bed down by 2005, but the following year was a disappointing one for the group as its operating profit was substantially down on budget and on that for 2005. This was almost entirely due to the predicted decline in classified advertising and the loss of the NHS contracts for both *Clinical Evidence* and *BestTreatments*. These contracts had been lucrative and the group had placed much dependence upon them, maybe too much, underlining the dangers of over-reliance on a small number of profitable customers. This was something of which the group was well aware and it had long striven to avoid, but the experiences of 2006 were a reminder that diversification was more important than ever if the BMJ Publishing Group was to thrive and it immediately began to increase its efforts and investments in new product development, creating a team specifically to develop new high quality products to respond to the changing needs of doctors.

Over the following five years various new products were launched including, in 2009, *Best Practice*, which is a decision-support tool designed for the digital environment to be integrated into electronic patient records. *Action Sets* followed in 2010. These are evidence-based check lists of actions that a clinician needs to take to deal with a particular condition and are also designed to be integrated into electronic patient records. The group also continued to expand its stable of journals and, as open access continued to develop as a business model for research publications, the BMJ Group launched an online-only open access general medical journal, *BMJ Open*, in 2011. This had a different business model to traditional subscription journals as authors pay to have their papers published and the papers are free for anyone to read. Eighteen months or so after launch, *BMJ Open* is publishing a large number of papers and is proving to be a successful model. Further open access journals are planned.

In 2006, the group decided to increase its sales staff in order to grow revenue worldwide from its existing products. To put this in context, by 2006, over half of the BMJ Publishing Group's revenue was derived from markets outside the UK (this remains the case in 2011) and over a third of all its revenue was from electronic business – just 11 years after it first joined the internet, showing the speed at which the business had had to change to embrace the new technology. Technological innovations continue to be made and the Publishing Group ensures that it acts quickly to develop products compatible with these. In 2010, in the new age of the tablet computer, the *BMJ* became the first medical journal in the world to launch a version for the Apple iPad, it has developed several 'apps' for the iPhone and summaries of *BMJ* case reports and blogs are available via the Amazon Kindle. The group continued to look for acquisitions and, at the beginning of 2012, it acquired a company called Informatica – a UK software company providing performance management systems for GPs. This represented a strategic shift for the group as it entered the important area of performance measurement and analytics software.

Following the disappointments of 2006 an improvement was quickly seen; at the end of 2007, the group finished with an operating profit 18% ahead of budget at £5.1 million and by the end of 2008, profits had risen to close to £9 million. This was due in the short-term to an unexpected upturn in classified advertising during these years, but was due mainly to the dividends from long-term investment in new product development and strategic acquisitions. The consolidation of recent innovations continued, with the growth of *BMJ Learning* and BMJ Masterclasses, and in 2008 the BMJ Evidence Centre was launched. This was designed to offer to the market not only products such as *Clinical Evidence*, but it also aimed to support doctors and institutions by providing trustworthy information in formats that were quickly and readily accessible at the point of care. Another initiative was a community website for doctors worldwide, doc2doc, which was launched at the beginning of 2009. The group's worldwide sales network continued to grow and, by 2009, it had sales staff in the USA, Europe, the Middle East, China, Japan and Australia. This has resulted in significant increases in new sales for all of the group's products and services and the group ended 2010 with an operating profit of £9.4 million.

In 2012, eight years after the 2004 changes to the governance of the BMJ Publishing Group, its staff numbers had risen from 170 to 420 and its annual profits from £3 million to over £11 million. As a result of this growth, the group reorganised into two divisions in the autumn of 2011: Journals and Clinical Improvement. By the middle of 2012, the BMJ Publishing Group was describing itself, with some justification, as a 'world leading provider of the most trusted medical information and services'.[13] Its aim is to deliver the 'highest standard of medical information and resources to improve outcomes for patients and the provision of healthcare worldwide'.[14] It wants to do this by stimulating and informing debate on health and healthcare and by creating the best evidence-based services and tools. Its global agenda has extended beyond merely selling UK-created products overseas to creating 'business hubs' in the emerging markets of Brazil, China and India where there are opportunities for the group to produce products and services especially to meet the needs of healthcare professionals working in these areas. By mid 2012 the group had offices in Mumbai and New Delhi which were employing some 20 staff. The group's aims and ambitions show the confidence of a company which is growing and adapting and is sure of its place at the forefront of medical publishing.

---

[13] Page 3 of the BMJ Publishing Group's corporate brochure, created in August 2012 and accessed on its website in January 2013.

[14] Page 1 of BMJ Publishing Group's corporate brochure, created in August 2012 and accessed on its website in January 2013.

Conclusions

National devolution, a revolution in electronic communication, increasing diversity in the medical profession and many changes in the organisation of the NHS have all been embraced by the British Medical Association over the past three decades. As this, the third volume of its history, comes to a close in the middle of 2012, it also looks back to bitter disputes with government, the resignation of a Chairman of Council, deep public antipathy towards doctors following Bristol and Shipman, and a lethal bomb blast outside its front door. It has emerged financially sound, with high membership levels, a thriving publishing group and strong democratic traditions. It remains the voice of doctors in the UK, but there are serious challenges ahead. In the short term these are likely to be the complexity and plurality of service delivery, the different ways in which doctors might be employed and the financial squeeze on the NHS. But others cannot be foreseen; who in 1982 (apart from the most visionary of technical experts) would have predicted the impact of the internet? The BMA must, therefore, remain alert, sensitive and responsive to the challenges of the future.

Doctors faced unprecedented upheavals from the late 1990s until the mid-2000s after several cases of severe medical malpractice and the subsequent reports. Although public confidence in doctors remained high, the profession's reputation was damaged. A small group of doctors was shown in the worst light and inquiries into their conduct concluded that procedures for regulating doctors were inadequate. The BMA shared the public's concern and dissociated itself from such unacceptable behaviour, but took the view that it should as far as possible protect self regulation and reassure the public that nearly all doctors were competent and reliable professionals. Despite its best efforts it could not stem the tide of directives from government aimed at regulating the profession more tightly and altering its regulatory body. After several false starts revalidation for doctors was introduced in 2012. It is a work in progress, but there is cautious optimism that the practical and fair system that the BMA has been working towards for many years may not be far away.

The BMA's biggest public health triumph in this period is its part in bringing about the ban on smoking in public places in 2007. It had campaigned for the ban for 20 years and learnt over that time the immense value of making alliances with like-minded bodies to pursue a common aim. This way of working, which involves several bodies chipping away at resistance at the same time, has been used to remarkable effect in other areas of public health, such as alcohol control and organ donation. In medical ethics the BMA's work has been groundbreaking, and in its human rights work it led the way for other medical associations.

The 2012 structure of the BMA is still recognisably that of 1982, with its national and UK councils, Representative Body, branch of practice and professional committees and divisions. But these bodies now work in very different ways: the single transferable vote, direct elections to the UK Council, changes to the composition of committees (sometimes to include non-medical voices), less formal debating and consultation methods, and more direct and rapid communications. These have all helped to make the BMA more inclusive and less hierarchical.

The branch of practice committees (with their direct accountability for negotiations) and the professional committees (with their high levels of expertise) are well tuned in to their constituents and speak with authority. But the question of how truly representative the BMA can be is still raised, inside and outside the organisation. Some criticise a culture in which electoral advancement is generally earned by knowledge and experience, favouring 'insiders', rather than those willing to challenge the status quo. Others fear that with doctors busier than ever, and hesitant to stand or vote in BMA elections, the organisation is, like other unions, at risk of being dominated by activists representing minority opinions. Electronic communication and social networks add a new dimension to this debate: they can inject a healthy dose of grassroots opinion and challenge, but can also introduce an aggressive tone that may stifle open discussion.

BMA Council, struggling to reconcile its corporate and representative roles, has sometimes found it difficult to reach a united view, leaving members frustrated and making the chairman's job particularly tough. But the BMA has never been a homogeneous or particularly harmonious organisation, bringing together as it does the members of a diverse profession comprising many tribes. Its great strength is to accommodate these different strands – facilitating robust debate while presenting a resolute face to government on issues that reflect the professional values that all doctors share. Meanwhile it supports its quasi-autonomous constituent bodies – branches of practice, professional committees and national councils – in vigorously pursuing the business in which they are expert.

The BMA has learnt during the past 30 years to work in closer partnership than would once have been thought wise – with patients' groups; charities; other trade unions and professions; educational, academic and regulatory bodies; commercial enterprises; and pressure groups. Collaboration has become a routine part of doctors' lives, bringing benefits such as broader perspectives, mutual understanding and new ways to exert influence. But in embracing these opportunities the BMA has made a positive choice to remain solely a doctors' organisation, underpinned by the ethos of a distinctive profession that all its members share and all its interlocutors recognise.

As a negotiating body, the BMA has enjoyed some success in this period. The turbulent contract negotiations of the early 2000s achieved significant gains, though these soon began to be eroded by government action. But the pensions dispute of 2011–12 brought a reminder of the vulnerability of a profession that works predominantly for a state employer, and of the need to ensure that it can deploy a range of bargaining tools. The BMA's influence has never come primarily from its industrial muscle, although it has at times been prepared to use this. Rather its reputation as an effective trade union – still often cited by other unions and employers – is based on a more complex armoury: an authoritative voice on scientific and ethical as well as health policy issues; tough, knowledgeable and principled leaders with the dedication, credibility and back-up to build working relationships with politicians; sympathy and respect from the public, which must be earned and maintained through a strong media presence; support from a large membership; and a willingness to lead positive change as well as to oppose developments that are not in patients' interests.

This book is full of examples of times when departments of health and governments did and did not listen to BMA advice or agree to its demands. But no government has been able to prise the BMA from its position of influence because in the end the NHS depends on the co-operation of the medical profession. Although they may be tempted to listen only to the medical voices that offer the most palatable advice, governments find in the end that such cooperation is best achieved through a dialogue with the organisation that is by a long stretch the largest and most representative of medical opinion. The BMA must use its position responsibly, for its part resisting the temptation to give undue weight to its most strident voices. As long as it can offer good protection and the right membership benefits to encourage doctors to join in their thousands, and as long as it keeps adapting to changing circumstances, then there is every reason to believe that the BMA's position as the voice of doctors is assured for the next 30 years.

Timeline of events 1982–2012

Secretaries of State and devolved nation equivalents	National events	NHS and healthcare related events	Health-related reports and legislation	BMA Chief Officers	BMA events
1982					
Norman Fowler	Unemployment in the UK reaches 3 million. Falklands War. HRH Prince William born. IRA bombings in London (Hyde Park and Regent's Park).	NHS reorganisation in England (abolition of health authorities and establishment of regional health authorities and district health authorities). The Steering Group on Health Services Information, chaired by Edith Körner, is established. The government-backed 'micros for GPs' scheme begins. GP vocational training becomes compulsory in the UK. Victoria Gillick fails to obtain assurances from her local health authority that her daughters will not be prescribed contraceptives without her knowledge or consent.	Motor Vehicles (Wearing of Seat Belts) Regulations 1982.	*President:* HRH The Prince of Wales *Chairman of RB:* John Marks *Chairman of Council:* Anthony Grabham *Treasurer:* Tony Keable Elliott	150th anniversary of the BMA. AGM at the Royal Festival Hall, London to install HRH The Prince of Wales as President. Associate Members Group established.

Secretaries of State and devolved nation equivalents	National events	NHS and healthcare related events	Health-related reports and legislation	BMA Chief Officers	BMA events
1983					
Norman Fowler	General election (Conservative majority of 144). Brink's-MAT robbery at Heathrow Airport.	The National Health Service privatises cleaning, catering and laundry services. The first heart and lung transplant carried out in Britain takes place at Harefield Hospital. Victoria Gillick loses case in the High Court against the DHSS to prevent the distribution of contraceptives to children under the age of 16 without parental consent.	*The NHS Management Inquiry* (Griffiths Report). Medical Act 1983 *Reflections on the Management of the National Health Service* (Professor Alain Enthoven, Nuffield Trust). Mental Health Act 1983 legislates for the detention of people deemed to be mentally ill and a risk to themselves or others, with or without their consent.	*President:* Ronald R Robertson *Chairman of RB:* John Marks *Chairman of Council:* Anthony Grabham *Treasurer:* Tony Keable Elliott	ARM Dundee. The weekly print order for the *BMJ* reaches 100,000 for the first time
1984					
Norman Fowler	Miners' strike. An IRA bomb explodes at Conservative Party conference hotel in Brighton.	First national No Smoking Day on 29 February 1984.	*The Report of the Committee of Inquiry into Human Fertilisation and Embryology* (Warnock Report). 1984 Data Protection Act	*President* Sir Douglas Black *Chairman of RB:* John Marks / James Kyle	ARM Manchester. Review of role and function of the BMA division and POWARS (July).

Year	Secretary of State	Events	Policy / medical events	BMA officers	BMA events
				Chairman of Council: Anthony Grabham/ John Marks *Treasurer:* Tony Keable Elliott	The BMA breaks off relations with the World Medical Association for a 10 year period.
1985	Norman Fowler	Trade Union Act requires all trade unions to elect their principal executive committee by secret ballot of all their voting members. Bradford football stadium fire. Heysel Stadium disaster. Riots in the Handsworth area of Birmingham, the Toxteth area of Liverpool and in Tottenham, Brixton and Peckham in London.	Family practitioner committees gain independent status. Gillick case is resolved when the House of Lords clarifies the right of doctors to help their young patients within the law without necessarily involving their parents.	*President:* Lord Pitt of Hampstead *Chairman of RB:* James Kyle *Chairman of Council:* John Marks *Treasurer:* Tony Keable Elliott	ARM Plymouth. Changes to BMA House in London to convert the lower section of the great hall into a library and the upper section into a suite of committee rooms.
1986	Norman Fowler	The UK signs the Single European Act. Greater London Council and 6 metropolitan councils abolished. *The Independent* newspaper is launched.	In November the government launches an advertising campaign (costing £20 million) to warn of the dangers of AIDS. Bovine spongiform encephalopathy (BSE) is identified in cattle. *Achieving a Balance* (report on medical workforce). European Directive (86/457/EEC) on specific training for general practice. The directive specifies that, from the beginning of 1995, no GP will be able to practise in the publicly-funded	*President:* Sir Christopher Booth *Chairman of RB:* James Kyle *Chairman of Council:* John Marks *Treasurer:* Tony Keable Elliott	ARM Scarborough. New Council membership directly elected for the first time as a result of the 1984 trade union legislation.

Secretaries of State and devolved nation equivalents	National events	NHS and healthcare related events	Health-related reports and legislation	BMA Chief Officers	BMA events
			health service of any member state unless he/she had undergone this training. Green paper: *Primary Healthcare: an Agenda for Discussion*. Green Paper: *Primary Care – Neighbourhood Nursing: A focus for care* (Cumberlege Report).		The Princess of Wales opens the new Nuffield Library at BMA House in London.
1987 Norman Fowler (until 13 June 1987) John Moore (from 13 June 1987)	General election (Conservative majority of 102). *Herald of Free Enterprise* capsizes off Zeebrugge. Hungerford massacre. Stock market crash in the City of London, known as 'Black Monday'. Enniskillen bombing at a Remembrance Day ceremony. Fire at King's Cross station in London.	It is reported that one person a day dies of AIDS in Britain. Government announces plans to abolish free eye tests. The first heart, lung and liver transplant is carried out at Papworth Hospital.	White Paper: *Promoting Better Health*. *Achieving a Balance: Plan for Action*.	*President:* David Bolt *Chairman of RB:* James Kyle/Benjamin Alexander *Chairman of Council:* John Marks *Treasurer:* Tony Keable Elliott / Alistair Riddell	ARM Bristol. Council sets up regional services working party (September).

1988 John Moore (until 25 July 1988) Kenneth Clarke (from 25 July 1988)	North Sea oil platform Piper Alpha is destroyed by explosion and fire. Pan Am flight 103 explodes over Lockerbie in Scotland.	The Prime Minister, Margaret Thatcher, announces a review of the NHS on the BBC's *Panorama* programme. National breast screening programme introduced. Health minister Edwina Currie claims that most of Britain's egg production is infected with the salmonella bacteria. She resigns shortly afterwards. Introduction of the Measles/mumps/rubella (MMR) vaccine.	*Public Health in England* (Acheson Report). Health and Medicines Act.	*President:* Sir David Innes Williams *Chairman of RB:* Benjamin Alexander *Chairman of Council:* John Marks *Treasurer:* Alistair Riddell	ARM Norwich. Regional services working party (May). The BMA Foundation for AIDS is set up as a charity.
1989 Kenneth Clarke	Kegworth air disaster. Hillsborough Stadium disaster. Prime Minister, Margaret Thatcher, along with American President, George Bush, and Soviet leader, Mikhail Gorbachev, declare the end of the Cold War.	In the case of *F v West Berkshire Area Health Authority* the House of Lords establishes the law on the non-emergency treatment of adults unable to give valid consent.	White Paper: *Working for Patients*. White Paper: *Caring for People*.	*President:* John Howell *Chairman of RB:* Benjamin Alexander / Alexander Macara *Chairman of Council:* John Marks *Treasurer:* Alistair Riddell	ARM Swansea. John Havard retires as Secretary and is replaced by Ian Field (July).

Secretaries of State and devolved nation equivalents	National events	NHS and healthcare related events	Health-related reports and legislation	BMA Chief Officers	BMA events
1990					
Kenneth Clarke (until 2 November 1990) William Waldegrave (from 2 November 1990)	Riots in London against Poll Tax which had been implemented in England and Wales. Margaret Thatcher resigns as Prime Minister and is succeeded by John Major.	New GP contract. France bans British beef and live cattle imports as a precaution against fears of Bovine spongiform encephalopathy (BSE) being spread. £42 million is made available by the government to 1,200 British haemophiliacs who were infected with the AIDS virus through blood transfusions.	Human Fertilisation and Embryology Act 1990. This introduces a 24 week upper limit for termination of pregnancy and establishes the Human Fertilisation and Embryology Authority. NHS and Community Care Act introduces an internal market into the NHS.	*President:* Dame Rosemary Rue *Chairman of RB:* Alexander Macara *Chairman of Council:* John Marks/ Jeremy Lee-Potter *Treasurer:* Alistair Riddell	ARM Bournemouth. Revised Council constitution approved in July. On 3 October 1990 the *BMJ* celebrates its 150th anniversary.
1991					
William Waldegrave	The Gulf War begins. In February the IRA launch a mortar attack against 10 Downing Street and later that month explode bombs in the early morning at Paddington and Victoria stations in London.	The *New Deal* agreement on junior doctors' hours. Changes to consultant contract following *Working for Patients*. 57 NHS trusts are established. First wave of GP fundholding practices.		*President:* Arthur Kennedy *Chairman of RB:* Alexander Macara *Chairman of Council:* Jeremy Lee-Potter *Treasurer:* Alistair Riddell	ARM Inverness. Stephen Lock retires as Editor of the *BMJ* and is replaced by Richard Smith. The BMA publishes *Leading for Health*.

Year	Minister	General events	Health events	Reports / White Papers	BMA officers	ARM / BMJ
1992	William Waldegrave (until 10 April 1992) Virginia Bottomley (from 10 April 1992)	Tim Berners-Lee establishes the first website at CERN. General election (Conservative majority of 21). The pound leaves the European Exchange Rate Mechanism on 'Black Wednesday'.	Patients Charter introduced. Human Fertilisation and Embryology Authority is established. The Department of Health reveals that AIDS cases among heterosexuals increased by 50% between 1990 and 1991.	White Paper: *Health of the Nation*. *Report of the Inquiry into London's Health Service, Medical Education and Research* (Tomlinson report). *Getting Better with Information* (NHS Management Executive).	*President:* John Reid *Chairman of RB:* Alexander Macara/ James Appleyard *Chairman of Council:* Jeremy Lee-Potter *Treasurer:* Alistair Riddell	ARM Nottingham. *Student BMJ* is launched.
1993	Virginia Bottomley	Black London teenager Stephen Lawrence is stabbed to death in London. IRA bombs in Warrington and Bishopsgate in London. Public sector trade union Unison is formed.	Tony Bland case (*Airedale NHS Trust v Bland*). The House of Lords decides that Tony Bland may be allowed to die as a result of the withdrawal of life-prolonging treatment of artificial nutrition and hydration. Government sets up a functions and manpower review and begins process of reorganising the NHS.	*Hospital Doctors: Training for the Future: The Report of the Working Group on Specialist Medical Training* (Calman report). *Making London Better* (Government response to Tomlinson).	*President:* James Birley *Chairman of RB:* James Appleyard *Chairman of Council:* Jeremy Lee-Potter/ Alexander Macara *Treasurer:* Alistair Riddell	ARM Torquay. Ian Field retires as BMA Secretary and is replaced by Mac Armstrong in November. Medline starts in June 1993, providing an index to much of the world's medical literature.

Secretaries of State and devolved nation equivalents	National events	NHS and healthcare related events	Health-related reports and legislation	BMA Chief Officers	BMA events
		In August the Department of Health reveals that the number of people on hospital waiting lists has reached 1,000,000 for the first time.			BMA organises a conference in March with the *BMJ*, the King's Fund and the Patients Association to consider rationing in the NHS. The *BMJ* subsequently commissioned a book on the subject *Rationing in Action* published later in 1993. The European Forum is established by the BMA to help the profession in the UK to present a united front in Europe.
1994 Virginia Bottomley	The Channel tunnel opens to traffic.	NHS Organ Donor Register is established to co-ordinate supply and demand of organs.	*Being Heard: The Report of a Review Committee on NHS Complaints Procedures* (Wilson report).	*President:* David Morrell *Chairman of RB:* James Appleyard	ARM Birmingham.

Year / Minister	National and world events	Health service events	Reports and legislation	BMA officers	BMA events
	Labour leader John Smith dies and is replaced by Tony Blair. The IRA declare a ceasefire.	Changes to the Defence Medical Services, including closure of military hospitals, cuts and mergers following *Options for Change*. The number of regional health authorities is reduced to eight as part of a reorganisation of the NHS.		*Chairman of Council:* Alexander Macara *Treasurer:* Alistair Riddell	The BMA launches the Core Values exercise at the ARM and holds a conference in November. The BMA opens an office in Brussels. The BMA rejoins the World Medical Association. Total membership reaches 100,000 – almost 80% of doctors in the UK are BMA members.
1995 Virginia Bottomley (until 5 July 1995) Stephen Dorrell (from 5 July 1995)	Barings Bank collapses following losses by Nick Leeson. British forces sent to help relieve the siege of Sarajevo during the war in Bosnia and Herzogovina.	GP out-of-hours dispute is settled.	*Acting on Complaints* (Government response to the Wilson report). Medical (Professional Performance) Act 1995. *Good Medical Practice* (GMC).	*President:* Sir Terence English *Chairman of RB:* James Appleyard/ Jane Richards *Chairman of Council:* Alexander Macara *Treasurer:* Alistair Riddell	ARM Harrogate. The *BMJ* website is launched. BMA cohort study of 1995 medical graduates begins.

Secretaries of State and devolved nation equivalents	National events	NHS and healthcare related events	Health-related reports and legislation	BMA Chief Officers	BMA events
1996					
Stephen Dorrell	IRA ceasefire ends with a bomb in London's docklands. A bomb explodes in Manchester later in the year.	New NHS complaints procedure begins in April.	White Paper: *Choice and Opportunity.*	*President:* Sir Donald Acheson	ARM Brighton. BMA's website is launched.
	Dunblane massacre.	Scientists in Scotland clone Dolly the sheep.	White Paper: *Primary Care: Delivering for the Future.*	*Chairman of RB:* Jane Richards	Council decides to close the majority of the BMA's overseas branches, retaining only those in Cyprus, Gibraltar, Hong Kong and Malta.
	EU bans exports of British beef because of BSE crisis.	Genetically modified food products go on sale in the UK for the first time.	White Paper: *The NHS: A Service with Ambitions.*	*Chairman of Council:* Alexander Macara	
		The NHS electronic network begins.		*Treasurer:* Alistair Riddell/ James Appleyard	
1997					
Stephen Dorrell (until 2 May 1997)	General election (Labour majority of 179).	The Specialist Register is introduced on 1 January 1997. From that date all doctors taking up posts as consultants must be on the register.	White Paper: *The New NHS: Modern, Dependable.*	*President:* Lord Kilpatrick of Kincraig	ARM Edinburgh.
Frank Dobson (from 3 May 1997)	Tony Blair becomes Prime Minister.	Introduction of GMC's Performance Procedures.	NHS (Primary Care) Act.	*Chairman of RB:* Jane Richards	
	The Princess of Wales dies in a car crash in Paris.	The new Labour government announces that it will ban tobacco sponsorship of sporting events.	Report of the Independent Task Force on Clinical Academic Careers (Richards Report).	*Chairman of Council:* Alexander Macara	
	Voters in Wales narrowly back plans for devolution and creation of a national assembly.		Independent Review of Higher Education Pay and Conditions (Bett Report).	*Treasurer:* James Appleyard	

Year		General events	Medical events	Reports and legislation	BMA officers	BMA events
1998	Frank Dobson	Voters in Scotland back plans for a national parliament. The IRA announces a ceasefire. The UK takes over the Presidency of the EC's Council of Ministers for six months until 30 June. Good Friday peace agreement in Northern Ireland. Car bomb explodes in Omagh killing 29 people. The government announces a total ban on the use of landmines by the British military.	New applicants for inclusion on the Specialist Register from 1 January 1998 must hold a certificate of completion of specialist training (CCST). NHS Direct is launched. Bristol and Ledward cases heard by the GMC. Harold Shipman is arrested on suspicion of murder in September. The President of the GMC proposes a system of revalidation. Bristol Royal Infirmary Inquiry is launched.	European Working Time Regulations (February). NHS Act 1998, reorganisation and change to the GMC. White Paper: *Smoking Kills*. Green Paper: *A First Class Service; Quality in the New NHS*. *Independent Inquiry in Inequalities in Health* (Acheson Report). *Information for Health: An Information Strategy for the Modern NHS 1998–2005*.	*President:* Sir Dillwyn Williams *Chairman of RB:* Jane Richards/ Brian Hopkinson *Chairman of Council:* Alexander Macara/ Ian Bogle *Treasurer:* James Appleyard	ARM Cardiff. The Representative Body agrees constitutional changes as a result of national devolution. The *eBMJ* (later bmj.com) is launched and becomes the first full text general medical journal website. BMA joins the Jubilee 2000 Coalition which campaigns for the burden of unpayable debt to be lifted from the poorest countries by the Millennium.

Secretaries of State and devolved nation equivalents	National events	NHS and healthcare related events	Health-related reports and legislation	BMA Chief Officers	BMA events
1999					
England Frank Dobson (until 11 October 1999)	The UK opts out of European Monetary Union.	National Institute for Health and Clinical Excellence (NICE) is established.	White Paper: *Saving Lives: Our Healthier Nation.*	*President:* Sir Peter Froggatt	ARM Belfast.
Alan Milburn (from 11 October 1999)	The first elections to the Scottish Parliament and Welsh Assembly are held in May.	The concept of 'clinical governance' is introduced which places a 'duty of quality' on all providers of NHS services.		*Chairman of RB:* Brian Hopkinson	BMA Audit Committee established.
Scotland Susan Deacon (from 16 May 1999)	The Scottish Parliament meets in Edinburgh for the first time. The Labour and Liberal Democrat parties form a coalition government in Scotland.	GP fundholding is abolished. Primary Care Groups are established.		*Chairman of Council:* Ian Bogle *Treasurer:* James Appleyard	The BMJ Publishing Group launches *Clinical Evidence.*
Wales Jane Hutt (from May 1999)	London's police force is accused of being 'institutionally racist' in the report into the murder of Stephen Lawrence.	Concerns are raised about organ retention at Alder Hey Children's Hospital.			
Northern Ireland Bairbre de Brún (from 2 December 1999)	A minimum wage is introduced throughout the UK.	The Royal Commission on Long Term Care reviews options for the ongoing funding of long-term care of older people.			
	Millennium celebrations are held across the country.				

2000

England
Alan Milburn

Scotland
Susan Deacon

Wales
Jane Hutt

Northern Ireland
Bairbre de Brún
Devolved government in Northern Ireland was suspended between 12 February 2000 and 30 May 2000.

Alex Salmond resigns as the leader of the Scottish National Party.

The Scottish Parliament is officially opened by the Queen.

In a protest about high fuel prices, entrances to oil refineries are blockaded. Panic buying leads to nationwide petrol shortages.

In a television interview in January, Prime Minister Tony Blair promises increased NHS spending to bring it up to average European levels.

Harold Shipman is convicted of 15 murders in January and sentenced to life imprisonment.

Juniors' new contract is implemented.

NHS walk-in centres are introduced.

Commission for Healthcare Improvement (CHI) is established.

Scientists with the International Human Genome Project release a draft of the human genome.

A Health Service of all the Talents: Developing the NHS Workforce (consultation document on the review of workforce planning).

White Paper: *The NHS Plan: A Plan for Investment, a Plan for Reform.*

Revalidating Doctors: Ensuring Standards, Securing the Future (GMC).

Our NHS (Scotland).

President:
Sir Christopher Paine

Chairman of RB:
Brian Hopkinson

Chairman of Council:
Ian Bogle

Treasurer:
James Appleyard

ARM London.

The Representative Body declares no confidence in the GMC.

Mac Armstrong resigns as BMA Secretary to become CMO for Scotland and is replaced by Jeremy Strachan, who becomes the BMA's first non-medical secretary (from January 2001).

The BMA establishes the Transplant Partnership, an alliance of 18 professional and patient groups which campaign for a radical review of the organ donation system.

Secretaries of State and devolved nation equivalents	National events	NHS and healthcare related events	Health-related reports and legislation	BMA Chief Officers	BMA events
2001					
England Alan Milburn (until 28 November 2001) **Scotland** Susan Deacon Malcolm Chisholm (from 28 November 2001) **Wales** Jane Hutt **Northern Ireland** Bairbre de Brún	General election (Labour majority of 167). Foot and mouth disease outbreak in UK from February until October. 11 September terrorist attacks in the USA. 67 UK nationals die. The IRA announces that it has began to decommission its weapons.	Shipman Inquiry, chaired by Dame Janet Smith, begins in February. National Clinical Assessment Service set up to support and advise the NHS, and doctors, and to help deal with failing doctors. Commission for Healthcare Improvement established. Diane Pretty case (*Pretty v Director of Public Prosecutions*). House of Lords holds that the European Convention on Human Rights does not oblige a state to legalise assisted suicide.	*The Report of the Public Inquiry into Children's Heart Surgery at the Bristol Royal Infirmary 1984–1995: Learning from Bristol* (The Kennedy Report). White Paper: *Shifting the Balance of Power.* Interim Wanless report on NHS Finance. Health and Social Care Act (2001). *Improving Health in Wales* (health authorities abolished).	*President:* Sir David Carter *Chairman of RB:* Brian Hopkinson/ George Rae *Chairman of Council:* Ian Bogle *Treasurer:* James Appleyard	ARM Bournemouth. The Representative Body agrees to give the Medical Students Committee full delegated authority and thus put it on the same constitutional basis as the other branch of practice committees. The BMA organises the Humanitarian Fund, which offers grants of up to £3,000 to current NHS employees for projects taking place in developing countries. The BMA publishes its *Healthcare Funding Review.*

2002

England
Alan Milburn

Scotland
Malcolm Chisholm

Wales
Jane Hutt

Northern Ireland
Bairbre de Brún.
Devolved government in Northern Ireland was suspended between 15 October 2002 and 8 May 2007.

Suspension of the Northern Ireland Assembly following spying allegations.

Deaths of Queen Elizabeth the Queen Mother and Princess Margaret.

The Queen's Golden Jubilee is celebrated.

The first public autopsy in the UK for 170 years is conducted by the German anatomist Gunther von Hagens in London.

Link between appraisal and revalidation is announced in a Joint GMC/Department of Health press release.

A modernised GMC comes into operation in July 2003. The size of the council is reduced from 104 to 35.

Ministry of Defence Medical Manning and Retention Review.

President:
Sir Anthony Grabham

Chairman of RB:
George Rae

Chairman of Council:
Ian Bogle

Treasurer:
James Appleyard/ David Pickersgill

Delivering the NHS Plan.

NHS Reform and Health Care Professions Act (more powers given to Commission for Healthcare Improvement, Council for the Regulation of Healthcare Professionals created and strategic health authorities replaced).

Securing our Future Health: Taking a Long-term View – (The Wanless Report).

Unfinished Business, Proposals for the Reform of the SHO Grade (consultation).

Delivering 21st Century IT Support for the NHS: National Strategic Programme (Department of Health).

Withholding and Withdrawing Life-prolonging Treatment: Good Practice and Decision Making (GMC).

ARM Harrogate.

Creation of the Directorate of Representational and Political Activities, the Directorate of Professional Activities and Boards overseeing the work of both directorates following a review of the BMA's governance.

Major review of the BMA's governance begins.

Abolition of the Non-Consultant Career Grades Subcommittee and creation of the Staff and Associate Specialists Committee as a branch of practice committee with full delegated authority.

Secretaries of State and devolved nation equivalents	National events	NHS and healthcare related events	Health-related reports and legislation	BMA Chief Officers	BMA events
					The consultant contract is rejected in October.
					BMA website is relaunched.
2003					
England Alan Milburn (until 13 June 2003)	UK forces involved in the invasion of Iraq.	General tobacco advertising is banned in the UK.	Working Time (Amendment) Regulations (March).	*President:* Sir Brian Jarman	ARM Torquay.
John Reid (from 13 June 2003)	The largest demonstration in British history takes place in February as over 2 million people in London protest against the war in Iraq.	The World Health Assembly adopts the World Health Organisation's Framework Convention on Tobacco Control.	The Postgraduate Medical Education and Training Board (PMETB) is established by the General and Specialist Medical Practice (Education, Training and Qualifications) Order 2003.	*Chairman of RB:* George Rae *Chairman of Council:* Ian Bogle/James Johnson	The Representative Body establishes its own Governance Committee.
Scotland Malcolm Chisholm					The BMJ Publishing Group becomes a wholly owned subsidiary of the BMA.
Wales Jane Hutt		GPs' and consultants' contract negotiations.		*Treasurer:* David Pickersgill	
Northern Ireland Devolved government in Northern Ireland was suspended between 15 October 2002 and 8 May 2007.	Scottish Parliamentary election with the ruling Labour and Liberal Democrat coalition, led by Jack McConnell, winning a majority of seats and staying in power.	Standardisation of pay and conditions for the majority of NHS staff as part of the Agenda for Change programme. Choose and Book is introduced. 2003 Licensing Act passed.	*NHS Complaints Reform: Making Things Right.* *Modernising Medical Careers.* Health and Social Care (Community Standards) Act (allowed the establishment of foundation trusts).		*BMJ Learning* is launched. The Retired Members Forum and the Patient Liaison Group are established.

2004

England
John Reid

Scotland
Malcolm Chisholm (until 6 October 2004)

Andy Kerr (from 6 October 2004)

Wales
Jane Hutt

Northern Ireland
Devolved government in Northern Ireland was suspended between 15 October 2002 and 8 May 2007.

The Higher Education Bill is passed in the Westminster Parliament. This introduced tuition fees and was only passed with the votes of Scottish Labour MPs, whose constituents would not be affected by the changes.

The Scottish Parliament building is opened in Edinburgh.

Harold Shipman commits suicide in his prison cell.

First wave of foundation trusts begin in April.

Implementation of new consultant and GP contracts.

Introduction of Alternative Provider Medical Services (APMS) in primary care.

European Working Time Directive takes effect for doctors in training from 1 August.

White Paper: NHS Improvement Plan.

Public Health White Paper: Choosing Health.

Modernising Medical Careers (reform of SHO grade and government response to *Unfinished Business*).

Fifth report of the Shipman Inquiry which looked at the handling of complaints against GPs, the GMC's procedures and its proposal for revalidation.

Building on the Best: Choice, Responsibility and Equality in the NHS.

A Licence to Practise and Revalidation (detailed guidance to doctors from the GMC on the operation of revalidation).

Mental Health (Care and Treatment) (Scotland) Act 2003.

The Health Protection Agency is established.

The BMA signs a strategic grant agreement with the Department for International Development.

President:
Sir Charles George

Chairman of RB:
George Rae/ Michael Wilks

Chairman of Council:
James Johnson

Treasurer:
David Pickersgill

ARM Llandudno.

The Representative Body votes to maintain the status quo with regard to the Association's governance.

Council agrees to a major reconfiguration of regional services and the closure of some regional offices.

Learning the Lessons exercise following contract negotiations.

Secretaries of State and devolved nation equivalents	National events	NHS and healthcare related events	Health-related reports and legislation	BMA Chief Officers	BMA events
		Ireland becomes the first country in the world to ban smoking in public places.			Jeremy Strachan retires as Secretary and is replaced in January 2005 by Tony Bourne who becomes the BMA's second non-medical Secretary and the first BMA group CEO.
		Payment by results is introduced.			
		Plans for revalidation put on hold as a result of criticisms in the Fifth report of the Shipman Inquiry.			
		Patient Choice Pilots are launched which gives all patients waiting longer than six months for an operation a choice of an alternative place of treatment.			
2005 **England** John Reid (until 6 May 2005) Patricia Hewitt (from 6 May 2005) **Scotland** Andy Kerr	General election (Labour majority of 66). Terrorist attacks in London on 7 July. Bomb explodes on a bus outside BMA House.	NHS Connecting for Health is formed on 1 April 2005 as a Directorate of the Department of Health. Its primary role is to deliver the National Programme for IT.	*Commissioning a Patient-led NHS* *Tomorrow's Doctors,* (GMC)	*President:* Dame Deirdre Hine *Chairman of RB:* Michael Wilks *Chairman of Council:* James Johnson	ARM Manchester. The Representative Body agrees changes to the constitution of Council and the RB.

Wales
Jane Hutt (until January 2005)

Brian Gibbons (from January 2005)

Northern Ireland
Devolved government in Northern Ireland was suspended between 15 October 2002 and 8 May 2007.

David Cameron becomes leader of the Conservative Party.

The Constitutional Reform Act provides for creation of a Supreme Court of the United Kingdom.

24 hour opening permitted for pubs in England and Wales.

It is announced in the Queen's speech that a health bill will contain clauses on a partial smoking ban in public places, thus paving the way for a more widespread ban.

Medically- and Dentally-Qualified Academic Staff: Recommendations for Training the Researchers and Educators of the Future (Walport Report on integrated career pathway for clinical academic trainees).

Building a Health Service Fit for the Future (Kerr Review (Scotland)).

Independent Review of Health and Social Care Services in Northern Ireland (Appleby Report).

The Mental Capacity Act 2005.

Treasurer: David Pickersgill

Universal free access to bmj.com stops. The site continues to be free to BMA members and to readers in the world's poorest countries.

Fiona Godlee replaces Richard Smith as Editor of the *BMJ* and Stella Dutton becomes the Chief Executive of the BMJ Publishing Group.

The BMJ Publishing Group acquires the 50 per cent BMA shareholding in the *British National Formulary*.

Council agrees to an ambitious plan to make significant changes to the BMA's headquarters building in Tavistock Square.

Secretaries of State and devolved nation equivalents	National events	NHS and healthcare related events	Health-related reports and legislation	BMA Chief Officers	BMA events
					Abolition of payment to members of compensation for earnings lost as a result of BMA work, introduction of fixed annual payments and new arrangements for payment of honoraria.
2006					
England Patricia Hewitt	Welsh Assembly building opened in Cardiff.	In February 2006 in a free vote in the House of Commons, MPs vote for a total ban on smoking in public places in England.	White Paper: *Our Health, Our Care, Our Say.*	*President:* Parveen Kumar	ARM Belfast.
Scotland Andy Kerr	Arrests are made in connection with a plot to blow up transatlantic aircraft.	Smoking is banned in enclosed public places in Scotland in March.	*Good Doctors, Safer Patients. Proposals to Strengthen the System to Assure and Improve the Performance of Doctors and to Protect the Safety of Patients.* (Chief Medical Officer for England).	*Chairman of RB:* Michael Wilks	NHS Together lobby of Parliament in November.
Wales Brian Gibbons		10 strategic health authorities are created. New primary care trusts are created.		*Chairman of Council:* James Johnson	New contract for staff and associate specialists doctors goes to ministers in November.
Northern Ireland Devolved government in Northern Ireland was suspended between 15 October 2002 and 8 May 2007.		NHS bowel cancer screening programme begins.		*Treasurer:* David Pickersgill	BMA cohort study of 2006 medical graduates begins.

2007

England
Patricia Hewitt (until 27 June 2007)

Alan Johnson (from 27 June 2007)

Scotland
Andy Kerr (until 16 May 2007)

Nicola Sturgeon (from 16 May 2007)

Wales
Brian Gibbons (until 25 May 2007)

Edwina Hart (from 25 May 2007)

Northern Ireland
Devolved government in Northern Ireland was suspended between 15 October 2002 and 8 May 2007.

Minister of Health, Social Services and Public Safety from 8 May 2007: Michael McGimpsey.

Gordon Brown succeeds Tony Blair as Prime Minister.

Nick Clegg becomes leader of the Liberal Democrats.

A power sharing executive is formed in Northern Ireland led by Ian Paisley (DUP) and Martin McGuinness (Sinn Féin).

Alex Salmond is elected First Minister of Scotland; the first person from the Scottish National Party to hold the post. His party forms a minority administration supported by the Scottish Green Party.

The Medical Training Application Service (MTAS) collapses in February.

Remedy march (March).

Smoking is banned in enclosed public places in Wales and Northern Ireland in April and in England in July. Enclosed public spaces in the whole UK are now smoke-free.

The first summary care records are uploaded in October.

White Paper: *Trust, Assurance and Safety – the Regulation of Health Professionals in the 21st Century*.

Our NHS, Our Future, report by Lord Darzi.

Health and Social Care Bill.

Aspiring to Excellence: Interim Report of the Independent Inquiry into Modernising Medical Careers (Tooke Report).

NHS Autonomy and Accountability: Proposals for Legislation (Conservative Party White Paper).

President: HRH The Princess Royal

Chairman of RB: Michael Wilks/ Peter Bennie

Chairman of Council: James Johnson until May, Sam Everington acting Chair of Council until Hamish Meldrum is elected in June

Treasurer: David Pickersgill

ARM Torquay.

The BMA celebrates its 175th anniversary.

The BMA publishes: *A Rational Way Forward for the NHS in England*.

Secretaries of State and devolved nation equivalents	National events	NHS and healthcare related events	Health-related reports and legislation	BMA Chief Officers	BMA events
2008					
England Alan Johnson	World wide financial crisis begins. Northern Rock is nationalised. As a response to the crisis, the UK government announces a package to rescue the banks which is worth around £500 billion.	60th anniversary of the NHS. Implementation of new contract for staff and associate specialist doctors. Reforms made to the NHS Pension Scheme. NHS foundation trusts now number 103. In October the High Court upholds as lawful the GMC's decision to withdraw the age exemption for payment of the annual retention fee for doctors who are 65 or over. Free choice is introduced on 1 April 2008. Patients can choose from any hospital or clinic that meets NHS standards.	*High Quality Care for All, Next Stage Review*, report by Lord Darzi. Health and Social Care Act (2008). Changed from the criminal to the civil standard of proof when GMC fitness to practise panels adjudicated upon concerns about a doctor's performance, health or conduct. Direct appointment to GMC Council. Healthcare and Associated Professions (Miscellaneous Amendments) Order 2008. Provided for equal numbers of medical and non-medical members on the Council of the GMC. *Aspiring to Excellence: Final Report of the Independent Inquiry into Modernising Medical Careers* (Tooke).	*President:* Sir Kenneth Calman *Chairman of RB:* Peter Bennie *Chairman of Council:* Hamish Meldrum *Treasurer:* David Pickersgill	ARM Edinburgh. The refurbished BMA House in London is formally opened by the Princess Royal.
Scotland Nicola Sturgeon					
Wales Edwina Hart					
Northern Ireland Michael McGimpsey					

2009

England
Alan Johnson
(until 5 June 2009)
Andy Burnham
(from 5 June 2009)

Scotland
Nicola Sturgeon

Wales
Edwina Hart

Northern Ireland
Michael
McGimpsey

Bank of England reduces interest rate to a record low of 0.5%, the lowest in the bank's 300 year history.

The Office for National Statistics announces that the United Kingdom's economy is officially in recession for the first time since 1991.

In October the Supreme Court of the United Kingdom officially opens and replaces the Law Lords in Parliament as the last court of appeal in UK in all matters other than criminal cases in Scotland.

H1N1 influenza outbreak. Meanwhile, The first Swine Flu related death in the United Kingdom is confirmed by the Scottish Government in June.

In July multiple sclerosis sufferer Debbie Purdy wins her battle to have the law on assisted suicide in England and Wales clarified after the House of Lords rules in her favour.

A report is published into the poor quality of care at Mid-Staffordshire NHS Foundation Trust.

Care Quality Commission takes over from Healthcare Commission.

One Wales: a Progressive Agenda for the Government of Wales (followed by reorganisation – 7 health boards and Public Health Wales).

NHS Constitution.

Transforming Community Services: Enabling New Patterns of Provision (Department of Health guidance for England).

White paper: *NHS 2010–2015: From Good to Great. Preventative, People-Centred, Productive.*

President:
Averil Mansfield
Chairman of RB:
Peter Bennie
Chairman of Council:
Hamish Meldrum
Treasurer:
David Pickersgill

ARM Liverpool.

The BMA launches a campaign to promote fair trade in medical supplies and sets up a Fair Medical and Ethical Trade Group.

Council agrees a set of principles for the use of BMA listservers.

Secretaries of State and devolved nation equivalents	National events	NHS and healthcare related events	Health-related reports and legislation	BMA Chief Officers	BMA events
	Expenses scandal hits Westminster Parliament.	'Nicholson Challenge' to the NHS to save £20 billion by 2015.			
		The size of the GMC's Council is reduced to 24 members, with equality of lay and medical members, all appointed by the NHS Appointments Commission.			
		In December the Department of Health in England announces a sudden and unexpected acceleration of the roll-out of the summary care record.			
2010					
England Andy Burnham (until 11 May 2010)	General election and establishment of coalition government of Conservative and Liberal Democrat Parties. David Cameron becomes Prime Minister.	As a result of the Purdey case, the Director of Public Prosecutions publishes guidance for prosecutors on assisted dying.	White Paper: *Equity and Excellence, Liberating the NHS.*	*President:* Sir Michael Marmot	ARM Brighton. *BMJ* becomes the first medical journal in the world to launch a version for the Apple iPad.
Andrew Lansley (from 11 May 2010)			Public Health White Paper: *Healthy Lives, Healthy People.*	*Chairman of RB:* Peter Bennie/Steve Hajioff	
Scotland Nicola Sturgeon				*Chairman of Council:* Hamish Meldrum	

Wales
Edwina Hart

Northern Ireland
Michael McGimpsey

Gordon Brown resigns as leader of the Labour Party and is replaced by Ed Miliband.

The Equality Act comes into effect, consolidating legislation requiring equal treatment in access to employment and services regardless of gender, race, health, disability, sexual orientation, belief and age.

In October the Chancellor George Osborne unveils the highest postwar cuts in public spending.

Revalidation: The Way Ahead GMC consultation and *Revalidation: A Statement of Intent.*

Treasurer:
David Pickersgill

The BMA publishes its *Seven Principles for Revalidation.*

2011

England
Andrew Lansley

Scotland
Nicola Sturgeon

Wales
Edwina Hart
(until 20 May 2011)
Lesley Griffiths
(from 20 May 2011)

The Scottish National Party wins an overall majority in elections to the Scottish parliament.

Elections to the Northern Ireland Assembly conclude with the DUP and Sinn Féin winning most of the 108 seats.

Andrew Lansley, the Secretary of State for Health in England, decides to discontinue the NHS Programme for IT.

The Dilnot Review calls for major reforms into the funding of adult social care.

Health and Social Care Bill.

Independent Public Service Pensions Commission: Final Report (Hutton Report).

Transforming Your Care (NI).

President:
David Haslam

Chairman of RB:
Steve Hajioff

Chairman of Council:
Hamish Meldrum

Treasurer:
David Pickersgill/
Andrew Dearden

ARM Cardiff.

Secretaries of State and devolved nation equivalents	National events	NHS and healthcare related events	Health-related reports and legislation	BMA Chief Officers	BMA events
Northern Ireland Michael McGimpsey (until 5 May 2011) Edwin Poots (from 16 May 2011)	The Welsh Labour Party wins 30 of the 60 seats in the Welsh Assembly and forms a government. Voters in Wales approved plans to give the Welsh Assembly more powers.				
	The mandatory retirement age is abolished.				
	Riots in English cities in August.				
2012					
England Andrew Lansley (until 4 September 2012)	Two men are convicted of the 1993 racist murder of Stephen Lawrence.	Doctors take industrial action in June in response to government changes to the NHS Pension Scheme.	Health and Social Care Act.	*President:* Professor Sheila the Baroness Hollins	ARM Bournemouth.
Jeremy Hunt (from 4 September 2012)	The Queen celebrates her Diamond Jubilee.	Establishment of the Medical Practitioners Tribunal Service (MPTS) in June 2012 which operates separately from the GMC.	DDRB report, *Review of Compensation Levels, Incentives and Clinical Excellence and Distinction Awards Scheme for NHS Consultants*. Signals negotiation on contract changes.	*Chairman of RB:* Steve Hajioff	BMA membership reaches 150,000 in August 2012.
Scotland Nicola Sturgeon (until 5 September 2012)	Olympic and Paralympic Games held in London.			*Chairman of Council:* Hamish Meldrum/ Mark Porter	Stella Dutton retires as Chief Executive of the BMJ Publishing Group and is replaced by Tim Brooks.
				Treasurer: Andrew Dearden	

Alex Neil
(from 5 September
2012)

Wales
Lesley Griffiths

Northern Ireland
Edwin Poots

Revalidation of doctors
begins in December.

Care and Support White
Paper and a draft Care
and Support Bill, which
outline the Government's
vision for reforming
adult care and support.

Index

Please see Abbreviations list on page xxiii

A
A First Class Service (green paper) (1998) 71
A health service for all the talents (DH, 2000) 114
A Licence to Practise and Revalidation (2003) 202
A Rational Way Forward for the NHS in England (2007) 81
abortion 279–281
  Abortion Act (1967) 279–280
  BMA position 279–280
  conscientious objection 280
    Janaway v Salford Health Authority 280
  Human Fertilisation and Embryology Act (1990) 280
    exceptions 280
  Northern Ireland 279–280
  Royal College of Obstetricians and Gynaecologists (RCOG) 281
  upper time limit 280
    BMA 24 week policy 280–281
    legislation, call for amendment 281
Abortion Act (1967) 279–280
Abrams, Michael 8, 9, 162
Abrams report 168–169
academic staff *see* medical academic staff
Academy of Medical Royal Colleges (AoMRC) 123, 188–189
accountancy services 341
Acheson, Sir Donald 14, 15, 167, 254–255
Acheson report 167
Achieving a balance (1986) 11–12, 23, 61, 101
  steering group (*Achieving a Balance: Plan for Action* (1987)) 12
Acquired Immune Deficiency Syndrome (AIDS) 258–260
  BMA advice 258
  BMA Foundation for AIDS 260
  BMA initiatives 258
  insurance queries about medical status 292
  Medical Foundation for AIDS and Sexual Health 260
  see also Human Immunodeficiency Virus (HIV)
Acting on Complaints (1995) 210
Action on Smoking and Health (ASH) 244
Action Sets 410
activists, BMA *see* BMA, activists
acupuncture 268
Additional Duty Hours (ADHs) 84
  The New Deal (1991) 25
advance directives
  BMA policy 308–309
  code of practice 308
  legal position 308
  Mental Capacity Act (2005) 309
advertising
  alcohol, ban debate 246
  publicity campaign (BMA) over NHS review 33–34
  smoking *see* smoking and smoking-related policy
advice services (BMA) 331–334, 340
  Doctors for Doctors 340
  Employer Advisory Service 338
  employment advice 334
  GPs as employers 338

legal support provision 333, 334
  BMA Law 340
  Court of Appeal 333
  employment tribunal 333
  satisfaction rates 333
  see also call centres
Advisory Committee on Medical Manpower (ACMM) 11
Advisory Committee on Medical Training (ACMT) 312
  specialist training charter 313
advisory committees 58
Advisory Group on Medical Education, Training and Staffing 63
advocacy unit (BMA) 332
age discrimination legislation 195–196
Agenda for Change programme 83–84, 89
AIDS *see* Acquired Immune Deficiency Syndrome (AIDS)
AIDS and You 259–260
Air Call 13
alcohol and alcohol-related policy 245–250
  advertising and promotion of alcohol 246
    ban debate 246
  Alcohol (Minimum Pricing) (Scotland) Bill 249
  alcohol misuse 245–246
  Alcohol Misuse: Tackling the UK Epidemic (2008) 248
  'binge drinking' 247
  BMA publications 246–247
  BMA Scotland role 151, 248, 250
  consumption rates 248
  crime and alcohol 247–248
  drink-drive limit 261–262
  drink-driving 246
  drinking guidelines 247
  government reliance on drinks industry 249–250
  Licensing Act (2003) (24-hour opening) 247
  pregnancy 247–248
  pricing/cost 248–249
    Scotland 248–249
  Public Health Responsibility Deal 249–250
  'sensible drinking' 245–246, 247
Alcohol (Minimum Pricing) Bill (2011) 249
Alcohol Misuse: Tackling the UK Epidemic (2008) 248
Alder Hey organs scandal 72, 89, 186, 297
Alment, Sir Anthony 197
alternative and complementary therapy 267–268
  acupuncture 268
  Alternative Therapy (1986) 267
  BMA position 268
  models of good practice 268
  orthodox *v* alternative medicine 267
Alternative Provider Medical Services (APMS) 78
anaesthetists 178
Anne HRH Princess (Princess Royal) 382, 384
Appleyard, James 320
Arbuthnott review 150
Armed Forces Committee (AFC) 173
armed forces doctors 172–174
  Armed Forces Committee (AFC) 173
  austerity programme effect 174

Bett report 173
Medical Manning and Retention Review 174
pay increase and pensions 173
Armed Forces Pay Review Body (AFPRB) 173, 174
Armstrong, Mac 56, 74, 87, 322
articles *see* constitution and governance (BMA)
askBMA 335, 339
Aspiring to Excellence (Tooke Report) 125–126
assisted dying/suicide *see* physician assisted suicide
    and euthanasia
associate specialists *see* staff and associate specialists
Association of British Insurers (ABI) 291–292
asylum seekers 292, 295
    see also human rights
audit, medical 29
Audit Committee (BMA) 358, 359
AUMTs (A Units of Medical Time) 22
austerity 139–141, 174
AXA PPP 178
    see also PPP
Ayling, Clifford 186, 187, 190

B
Ball, John 13
Being Heard (Wilson Committee report) 208, 210
Berry, Jacky 339–340
Best Practice 410
BestTreatments website 408–409, 410
Bett, Sir Michael 163
Bett report (1999) 163–164, 173
'The Big Kill' report 239
'The Big Opt Out Campaign' 222
Biko, Steve 319
'binge drinking' 247
    see also alcohol and alcohol-related policy
Bishop, John 359
Black, Sir Douglas 253, 254
    data protection 285
    Interprofessional Working Group on Access to
        Personal Information 285
Black report 253
    BMA response 254
'Black Wednesday', GPs' contract (2003) 100
Blair, Tony 72, 215
    contract negotiations 83
    on Summary Care Record 222
    see also Labour Party
Bland, Tony 304–305
Blood, Diane 277–278
'Blue Book' of ethical guidance 275
BMA
    150th anniversary celebrations i
    1930s-1982 ii
    activists 134
        Keep Our NHS Public pressure group 134
    advisory services *see* advice services (BMA)
    Annual Representative Meeting ('session') i, 233,
        282, 310, 353
        abortion legislation 281
        ban on promotion of alcohol and 246
        civil standard of proof and 193
        Constitution of Council recommendation
            366–367
        consultants' contract (2002) 92
        'Core Values' exercise and 56–57
        cycling safety 262
        drink-drive limit 261
        governance debates (2001/02) 360
        HIV testing 259
        local pay, rejection 69
        Marks' re-election 35–36
        physician-assisted suicide 301–302
        professional self-regulation and GMC 191
        Summary Care Records and 222, 224
        Systems Reform and 79–80
        trade union legislation and 344–345

Audit Committee 358, 359
    see also constitution and governance (BMA)
BMA House *see* BMA House
BMJ Publishing Group *see* BMJ Publishing
    Group (BMJPG)
Board of Representational and Political Activities
    Directorate (BRPAD) 360, 364
Board of Science and Education *see* Board of
    Science
Board of the Directorate of Professional Activities
    360, 361
carbon footprint 264
Caring for the NHS and 81
CCS Committee *see* Central Consultants and
    Specialists Committee (CCSC) (BMA)
committees *see* constitution and governance
    (BMA)
Communications Directorate 379–380
    Public Affairs Division (Padiv) 379–380, 381
conference on 'Core Values' exercise 56–57
constitution and governance *see* constitution and
    governance (BMA)
contract negotiations *see* contractual changes
control of 353, 354
core values exercise *see* 'Core Values' exercise
Council *see* Council (BMA)
devolved nations and *see* devolved nations
Diet, Nutrition and Health (1986) 250–251
Equal Opportunities Committee 333–334
Equality and Diversity Committee 362
feedback on activities from consumers 229–230
Finance Committee 360
finances *see* finances (BMA)
fundholding, views on 44–45
funding for NHS, call for increase (1985) 25
funding of NHS policy 73
GMC and *see* General Medical Council (GMC)
GMC Governance, proposed 11 principles
    188–189
Governance Committee *see* constitution and
    governance (BMA)
health policy and economic research unit
    (HPERU) 379
Information Fund 324
information technology (IT) *see* information,
    personal healthcare
inside the BMA 369–389
    see also BMA House; finances (BMA); staffing
        (BMA)
integrity of 186
international committee 311
international work *see* international work (BMA)
Interprofessional Working Group on Access to
    Personal Information 285, 286
Journal Committee (BMA) 403
library *see* library services
listservers *see* listservers and paperless committees
lobbying, public health 151
local negotiating committee (LNC) *see* Local
    Negotiating Committee (LNC)
local offices *see* structure, local (BMA)
London Regional Council 134
Look after our NHS campaign *see* Look after our
    NHS
Medical Ethics Committee *see* medical ethics
Medical Students Committee (MSC) *see* Medical
    Students Committee (MSC)
members *see* members (BMA)
modernisation board 73, 76
modernisation project 352–353
negotiations 415
    environment for 110
new technology and services for members 230–234
NHS review *see* National Health Service (NHS)
    review
Nominations Committee 360
in Northern Ireland *see* BMA Northern Ireland

objectives 236
Office of the Health Professions Adjudicator
  (OHPA), position on 195
officers 381–382
Organisation Committee 360
Oversight and Finance Committee 358
parliamentary unit 380–381
partnerships 415
Patient Liaison Group 361–362
Political Board 107
Presidents 381–382
  elections 381
  role definition 382
  royal 382
Private Practice Committee (PPC) 176, 179
professional activities 235
  achievements 235–236
  expenditure 236
  medical ethics *see* medical ethics
  profile 52, 53, 56, 125, 236, 331
    increased by *Working for Patients* 26
protocols, review of 125
Public Affairs Division (Padiv) 379–380, 381
publicity campaign, against *Working for Patients*
  see publicity campaign (BMA)
rationalisation of healthcare, response 50–60
Regaining the Confidence of the Profession 125
regional services, cost of 332
Representative Body *see* Representative Body (RB)
Retired Members Forum 361
revalidation, 7 principles document *see*
  revalidation
Road Transport and Health (1997) 261
roadshows, consultants' contract 92, 93
scope of representation over fundholding 45, 414
in Scotland *see* BMA Scotland
Senior Management Group (SMG) *see*
  constitution and governance (BMA)
senior secretariat 379
'session' *see* BMA, Annual Representative
  Meeting ('session')
Special Representative Meeting (SRM) on *Equity
  and Excellence* (2011) 143
Special Representative Meeting (SRM) on
  Working for Patients 31, 33
  see also publicity campaign (BMA)
staff pensions *see* pensions
strategic review 330
structure 414
  local *see* structure, local (BMA)
  staffing structure modernisation 332
  UK structure *see* devolved nations
  see also constitution and governance (BMA)
Supervisory Board of the Secretariat 356, 360
terrorism, impact on *see* terrorism, impact on
  BMA
Tobacco Control Resource Centre (TCRC)
  240–241
as trade union and professional association 235,
  345
  see also trade union(s)
in Wales *see* BMA Cymru Wales
website *see* world wide web
Working for Patients, response to *see* publicity
  campaign (BMA)
see also additional specific topics/issues
BMA BMJ Information Fund 323
BMA Council *see* Council (BMA)
BMA Cymru Wales 152–154
  advising WAG 152
  development 152
  organ donation 154
  reconfiguration proposals, role in 154
  smoking-related policy 154
  suntan salons policy 154
  WAG resolution of no confidence 153
BMA Foundation for AIDS 260

The BMA Guide to Alcohol and Accidents 246
BMA House 382–385
  Council chamber 384
  evacuation, London bombings 386
  formal opening 384
  Hastings Room 383, 384
  library 384
  office closure (bombings) 387
  property development programme 369–370
  reasons for upgrade 383
  refurbishment programme 372, 375
    costs 385
  state rooms 383
  terrorist bombings near 385–386, 388
  transformation 382–385
BMA Investments Limited 373
BMA Law 340
BMA News 343–344, 380
BMA News Review, Special Representative Meeting
  33
BMA Northern Ireland 154–156
  clinical excellence awards 156
  clinical leadership 156
  consultant contract *see* contractual changes
  development 155
  legal action clinical excellence awards 156
  'permissive managerialism' 155
BMA Professional Services (BMAPS) 341
BMA Scotland 149–152
  alcohol, minimum price 151, 248, 250
  contractual issues *see* contractual changes
  'devo-max' 152
  pensions 152
  premises 149–151
  profile 151
  relocation and premises 370
  SAS negotiations 151
  smoking in public places 151
  support of changes 151
  see also Scotland, healthcare in
BMA Services 340, 374
  see also financial services (BMA)
BMAtv 231
BMJ see British Medical Journal (BMJ)
BMJ Careers 401, 408
BMJ Classified 399, 401
BMJ Learning 406, 407
BMJ Open 410
BMJ Publishing Group (BMJPG) 391–412
  accounts 391–392, 396, 400, 411
  Action Sets 410
  activities 391
  Best Practice 410
  BestTreatments website 408–409, 410
  BMA and 391
    dividend policy 404
  BMA relationships 406
  BMJ Careers 401, 408
  BMJ Learning 406–407, 411
    market share 407
  Board 403
    reduction in members 405
    structure 405–406
  book sales 393–394, 397, 408
    BMJ Bookshop relocation 397
    Books Publishing sale 409
  *British Medical Journal (BMJ) see British Medical
    Journal (BMJ)*
  British National Formulary (BNF) 409
    for children 409
  'business hubs' 412
  classified advertisements 391, 410
    BMJ Classified 399, 401
  database 398
  deficit 395
  distribution of US journals 395–396
  diversification 391, 395, 400, 411

divisions 411–412
  Clinical Improvement 412
governance 405–406
group CEO 405
income generated by 370, 371, 372, 374, 376, 393, 404
  decline in 375
income sources 375, 396
  threat to 399, 408
Informatica, acquisition 411
international business
  emerging markets 412
  markets 400, 410–411
  offices 400–401
International Forum on Quality and Safety in Healthcare 395
Journal Committee (BMA) 403
Journal of the American Medical Association, distribution 395
journals 402
  BMJ see British Medical Journal (BMJ)
  BMJ Open 410
  Clinical Evidence 397–398, 400, 408, 410
    division 411
  evidence based journals 395
  Evidence-Based Medicine 397–398
  specialist journals 395
  NHS recruitment website 399–400, 408
  offices in India 412
  OnExamination.com 407
  profits 392, 393, 396, 400, 405, 410, 411
  separate legal entity from BMA 403
  staffing numbers 411
  technological advancements 398, 410
    internet opportunities 398–399
    online provision 398
  training opportunities 407
  Western Journal of Medicine 396
  see also BMJ Publishing Group Ltd
BMJ Publishing Group Ltd 403
  memorandum of understanding with BMA 403–404
  see also BMJ Publishing Group (BMJPG)
bmj.com 398, 401, 402
  new business model (daily updates) 402
Board of the Directorate of Professional Activities 360, 361
Board of Representational and Political Activities Directorate (BRPAD) 360, 364
  see also constitution and governance (BMA)
Board of Science (BMA) ii, 236, 254
  alcohol consumption and young people 245, 246–247
  alternative and complementary therapy 267, 268
  Alternative Therapy (1986) 267
  body image concerns 252
  cycling helmet use 262–263
  health inequalities recommendations 254
  housing inequalities 255
  nuclear war and civil defence 256–257
  nutrition and diet concerns 250
  passive smoking 242
  reports (1983–2011) 269–274
  risk, report 265
  smoking ban in public places 241
  Towards Smoke-Free Public Places (2002) 241
body image 252
Bogle, Ian
  Building Your Own Future (1991) 64
  Chairman of Council 71
  fundholding (GP) 44, 45
  junior doctors' pay and industrial action 85
  NHS proposals 73–74
  public confidence in doctors and 188
  revalidation and 198, 199, 201–202
  Smoking Kills white paper 240

Bolt, David 8, 9–10, 259
bombings (terrorist) see terrorism
Booze, Fags and Food (BMA report) 243
Borman, Edwin 60
Bottomley, Virginia 22–23, 40, 52, 55
  junior doctors, hours of work 22, 23
  London, healthcare in 59
  NHS reforms 56
Bourne, Tony 387, 406
boxing 265–267
  BMA campaign 266
  BMA report 266
  The Boxing Debate (1993) 266
  see also boxing
branches of practice 107, 147, 162–168
  autonomy 107
  structure 107
  see also community health; public health
Breathe Better in Scotland 244
Bristol Royal Infirmary 185, 198, 211
British Dental Association 165
British Medical Association see BMA
British Medical Journal (BMJ) 339, 391
  150th anniversary 394–395
  awards 394, 401–402
  BMA committees, reduction in reporting on 401
  BMA membership benefit 406
  bmj.com 398, 401, 402
  Careers supplement 397
  circulation levels 392, 401
    impact of economic climate 395
    international 393, 395
  classified advertisements 392–393
  Clinical Research 391–392
  content 396
  costs 393
  eBMJ 398
  editorial freedom 404
  editorial staff 394
  income for BMA 393
  International Committee of Medical Journal Editors and 402
  letters 394
  local editions 397
  market share 395
  open access publishing 396
  'open data' campaign 402
  peer review 396
  postage costs 393
  Practice Observed 391–392
  PubMedCentral 396
  'rapid responses' 401
  readership 391–392
  redesign 394
  strategic review (2007) 401
  Student BMJ 397
  submissions 394
  turnover 392
  universal free access stopped 401
British National Formulary (BNF) 409
  for children 409
  NICE share of intellectual property rights 409–410
British Postgraduate Medical Federation 22
Brown, Gordon 78, 125, 129
  see also Labour Party
Buckman, Laurence 131–132
budget holding see fundholding (GP)
Building on Progress: Where next for Organ Donation Policy in the UK? (2012) 296, 298
Building Your Own Future (1991) 64
BUPA/Bupa 176, 178
Burke, Leslie 307
Burnham, Andy 135, 144–145
Burrows, Maurice 25–26
bye-laws see constitution and governance (BMA)

C
C awards system 43, 67, 69–70
 see also distinction awards
Cadbury Report 359
call centres 334–339
 askBMA 335
 employment advice 334
 external call-centre, Essentia 334–335
Call for Delay 117
Calland, Tony 298
Calman, Sir Kenneth 56–57, 61
Calman Report 60–63
 new model of specialist training 61
 staffing 62
 training 61, 62
 working party 61
Cameron, David 120, 139
 pledges 142
 see also Conservative Party
capacity to consent *see* consent and capacity
capitation, General Practitioners (GPs) 19, 29
carbon footprint
 BMA 264
 NHS 264
Care Quality Commission (CQC) 179
Career Average Revalued Earnings (CARE) 146
Caring for the NHS 81
 lobbying MPs 81
 trade unions 81
Catto, Sir Graeme 189–190, 202
Central Committee for Community Medicine and
 Community Health (CCCMCH) 171
Central Consultants and Specialists Committee
 (CCSC) (BMA) 6, 31
 Chawner, John 49
 conferences 49
 conferences for doctors in trusts 49–50
 consultant's contract negotiations (1990–1991) 42,
  43
 consultant's contract negotiations (2001–2002) 89,
  90
 ballot result (rejection) 94
 European Working Time Directive and 110–111
 local negotiating committee (LNC) *see* Local
  Negotiating Committee (LNC)
 local pay, campaign 68, 69
 performance-related pay 67
 potential litigation 210
 public health 168
 revalidation appraisal, support of 200
 Ross, Paddy 6, 35
 self-governing trusts *see* self-governing hospital
  trusts
Certificate of Completion of Specialist Training
 (CCST) 103–104, 114, 315–316
Certificate of Completion of Training (CCT),
 oversupply 140
Certificate of Specialist Training (CST) 115
cessation, smoking *see* smoking and smoking-related
 policy
*Changing Conceptions of Motherhood: the Practice of
 Surrogacy in Britain* (1995) 279
 see also surrogacy
Charles, HRH The Prince of Wales 382
Chaudhary, Rajendra 333
Chawner, John 68, 176
 Central Consultants and Specialists Committee
  (CCSC) 49
 local pay campaign 69
 negotiations with LIG 60
 private practice 176
Chief Medical Officer (CMO)
 Calman, Sir Kenneth 56–57, 61
 Donaldson, Sir Liam 122, 123, 203
 Good Doctors, Safer Patients 191
 manpower initiative 9–10
 support for Liam Donaldson over MMC 123

child health services 171
children
 alcohol and 247
 cigarette advertising to children 238
 consent and capacity 287
  *Consent, Rights and Choices in Healthcare for
   Children and Young People* (2000) 289
  Gillick competence 287–289
  GMC guidance 288–289
 obesity prevention 251
China, organ transplantation 293
Chisholm, John 65, 97, 100
Choice and Opportunity (white paper) (2003) 66, 102
Choice Exercise (2010) 137–138
Choose and Book system 218, 219–220
 BMA position, and concerns 220
 BMA recommended improvements 221
 devolved nations 220
 DH guidance document (England) 221
 as established referral system 221
 GP criticisms 221
 referral process, impact on 220
Circle model 179
civil standard of proof 193
Clark, Alastair 328
Clarke, Kenneth
 deputising services (GPs) 13
 in Education department 41
 Joint Consultants Committee (JCC) and 31–32
 limited list (of drugs) 14
 NHS funding increase 27
 objectives of discussion with GMSC 16–17
 Primary Health Care: An Agenda for Discussion
  (green paper) 15
 Wilson Michael and 14–15, 18, 20
 Working for Patients (white paper) (1989) 17–18, 28
  introduction of contract 19, 20
  negotiations 19, 20–21
  poster targeting 37
Clegg, Nick 143
climate change 263–264
 BMA advice to doctors 264
 carbon footprint 264
clinical academics *see* medical academic staff
Clinical Commissioning Groups (CCGs) 145
clinical complaints *see* complaints (NHS)
Clinical Evidence 397–398, 400, 408, 410
clinical excellence awards 161
 Northern Ireland 156
clinical governance 71, 179, 190, 203
 Good Doctors, Safer Patients (2006) 191
clinical lecturer *see* medical academic staff
'clinical pathway groups' 130
 BMA response 130
clinical performance indicators 75
Clinical Research 391–392
Clinical Standards Advisory Group (CSAG) 39, 40
 BMA exclusion from 39–40
Coalition Government *see* Conservative/Liberal
 Democrat Coalition
'commercial private sector' 80
Commission for Healthcare Improvement 71
 Healthcare Commission 75
commissioning 72, 76, 143
 Lansley's proposal 142
Commissioning a patient-led NHS initiative 172
Commonwealth and International Medical Advisory
 Bureau 325
Commonwealth Human Rights Initiative 321
Commonwealth Medical Association (CMA)
 320–322
 BMA and 320–322
  membership resignation 322
 Commonwealth Human Rights Initiative 321
 funding 321
  subscriptions 321–322
 new constitution 321

Communications Directorate 379–380
  Public Affairs Division (Padiv) 379–380, 381
community health 171–172
  child health services 171
  providers 172
  provision structure 171
  senior clinical medical officers (SCMOs) 172
  working party (BMA) 171
  see also public health
community medicine *see* public health medicine
Compensation Committee 377
compensatory rest, European Working Time
    Directive-(EWTD) 112
competitive tendering *see* private sector provision
complaints (NHS)
  Acting on Complaints (1995) 210
  Being Heard (1994) 210
  clinical complaints 209
  contractual matters 209
  'defensive medicine' 210–211
  devolved nations 211–212
  disciplinary action 209
  England 211
  formal procedures 209–210
  independent review stage 210
  informal procedure 209
  mediation 210
  NHS Complaints Reform: Making Things Right
    (2003) 211
  potential litigation 210
  three-stage procedure 209
  Wilson, Professor Alan 209
  Wilson Committee report 210
    BMA response 210
complementary therapy *see* alternative and
    complementary therapy
confidentiality 284–286
  breach of/disclosure 284–285
    BMA advice 286
    BMA campaign 284
    GPC guidance for doctors 285
    Police and Criminal Evidence Bill 284
  contraception advice *see* contraception
  data protection, GP code of practice 286
  Data Protection Act (1984) 285
  Interprofessional Working Group on Access to
    Personal Information 285, 286
  of personal healthcare information 215
  statutory code 285
conscientious objection 280
consent, presumed 296
consent and capacity 286–292
  capacity 289–291
    adults 289–290
    advance directives *see* advance directives
    devolved nations 290
    non-emergency treatment and adults 289–290
    withholding/withdrawing treatment *see*
      withholding and withdrawing treatment
  children and young people 287
    *Consent, Rights and Choices in Healthcare for
      Children and Young People* (2000) 289
  contraception *see* contraception
  gamete collection 277
  Gillick competence *see* Gillick competence
  GMC guidance 289
  insurance company access to medical records
    291–292
    AIDS and HIV 292
    criteria for doctor compliance 291
    standard GP report package 292
  Police and Criminal Evidence Bill 287
    intimate body searches/samples consent 287
Conservative Government
  1982–1992 1–53
  1992–1997 55–70
  see also National Health Service (NHS), reforms

Conservative/Liberal Democrat Coalition (2010–
    2012) 139–148
  austerity 139–141, 174
  Equity and excellence (white paper) *see Equity and
    excellence: Liberating the NHS* (2010) (white
    paper)
  Future Forum *see* Future Forum
  Health and Social Care Act *see* Health and Social
    Care Act
  NHS funding 140
  pay freeze 139, 141, 161
  pensions *see* pensions
  smoking-related policy 245
Conservative Party
  1982–1992 1–53
  1992–1997, decline during 55–70
  coalition *see* Conservative/Liberal Democrat
    Coalition
  NHS funding 50–51
  prime ministers
    Cameron, David (2010–) 120
    Major, John (1990–1997) 51
    Thatcher, Margaret (1982–1990) 1–53
  re-election in 1992 52
  response to BMA, over 1989 White Paper 38
  Thatcher era, 1982–1992 1–53
Conservative Party Conference, BMA response to
    White Paper at (1989) 37
constitution and governance (BMA) 345–367
  Audit Committee 358, 359
  Board of Representational and Political Activities
    Directorate (BRPAD) 360, 364
  Board of the Directorate of Professional Activities
    360
  changes to committees 358–362
    new structure 360
    roles of main office-holders 360
  constitution of Council as recommended to 1985
    ARM 366–367
  Council *see* Council (BMA)
  devolution *see* devolved nations
  divergences of policy 365
  electoral process *see* electoral process
  Finance Committee 360
  governance 347–352
    Audit Committee, role of 359
    BMJ Publishing Group *see* BMJ Publishing Group
    governance project team 348
    Governance Project Team 350
    problems 348
    proposals 349
    reforms 347, 354
  Governance Committee 348
    elections 350
    opposition to 349
    Representative Body, of *see* Representative Body
    role of 359–360
    terms of reference 350
  lay members 361
  modernisation project 352–353
    articles, and bye-laws 352
  Nominations Committee 360
  options for change 350–351
    annual conference 351
    assembly 351
    board 351
    open debate 351–352
    senate 351
  Organisation Committee 347
  Oversight and Finance Committee 358
  Patient Liaison Group 361–362
  reporting structures 360–361
  Representative Body 352
  review 345
  Senior Management Group (SMG) 356
    role, and members 356
    threat of strike 356, 357, 358

Supervisory Board of the Secretariat 356, 360
Trade Union Act 1984 346
  see also trade union(s)
consultant(s)
  appraisal (revalidation) 200
  CCSC 31
    see also Central Consultants and Specialists
      Committee (CCSC) (BMA)
  Certificate of Completion of Training (CCT) 140
  'consultant-present' provision 140
  contracts 41–44, 88–96
    1990–1991 41–44, 88
    2001–2004 88–96
    amendments accepted 95
    appeal mechanism 42–43, 48
    appointment procedures 42
    ballot and rejection (2002) 94
    CCSC group role 89
    CCSC support 91
    clarification documents 93–94
    costing exercise 90
    costs and value for money? 95–96
    distinction awards *see* distinction awards
    district general manager 43
    intensity supplements 89
    introduction of changes (1990/91) 43
    JDC involvement 90–91
    'job-plans' 42
    MASC role 164
    negotiation process 89, 90
    NHS Plan (2000) 88
    NHSME negotiations (1990–1991) 42
    notional half days (NHDs) 42
    opposition 92
    organisation of duties 42
    proposal 89
    *Proposals for a new approach to the consultant
      contract* (2001) 88
    seven lean years 88, 90, 91
    successful conclusion (2004) 95
    Vote No campaign 92
    Wales 153, 154
    Working for Patients (1989) 29
    working pattern 42
  distinction awards *see* distinction awards
  European Working Time Directive 110
  expansion programme *see* consultant expansion
  Fidelio 121
  grades 62
  hospital
    deep specialisation 115
    generic skills 115
  job plans 42, 95
  Joint Consultants Committee 11–12
    Achieving a balance (1986) *see Achieving a
      Balance* (1986)
  junior 61–62
  junior doctor working hour agreement and (1990)
    23–24
  notional half days (NHDs) 42, 83
  pay increase 30–31, 67
    government 'betrayal' (1989) 30
    New Labour (2007) 82
  pay modernisation 83
  Private Consultant Work: BMA Guidelines (1989)
    177
  private practice *see* private practice
  programmed activities (PAs) 83, 91, 95
  redeployment negotiations 60
  senior 62
  'Short' 10
  supporting professional activities (SPAs) 96
  Welsh Consultants Committee 153
consultant-based service, *v* consultant-led service
  61–62
consultant expansion 8–9, 10, 62
  acceleration 61

Achieving a Balance (1986) *see Achieving a Balance*
  (1986)
  ballot, support and plans 10
  BMA position 9
  consultant concerns 9
  new model of specialist training and (1992/93)
    61–62
  number of new posts (1982) 10
  scope of 10
  Short Report and 8–9
  workforce figures 10, 12
consultant-led service, *v* consultant-based service
  61–62
'consultant-present' provision 140
Consultants Committee (CC) 140
Consultants' Committee 140
contraception 287–290
  doctors' role 289
    aiding/abetting unlawful intercourse 289
    guidance note for 289
  Gillick case 287, 288–289
  see also consent and capacity
contractual changes
  associate specialists *see* staff and associate
    specialists
  BMA negotiations 82–110
    approach 109
    background 83–84
    environment 110
    grasping negotiators 109
    'learning the lessons' exercise 82, 103, 107
    successes 82–83
    values 109
  consultants *see* consultant(s)
  GPs *see* General Practitioners (GPs)
  grass roots opinion 107
    BMA awareness 107
  junior doctors *see* junior doctors
  NHS and Community Care Bill 40, 41
  Northern Ireland 155
  reflections 107–110
    Learning the Lessons (2004) 82, 103, 107
  Scotland, SAS negotiations 151
  Scotland *v* England 151
  staff doctors *see* staff and associate specialists
  terms and conditions
    Core Services – taking the initiative 66
    Northern Ireland 154
    The New Deal (1991) 24–25
    Wales 154
Cook, Robin, NHS review 27, 52
core medical services 65–66
Core Services – taking the initiative 66
'Core Values' exercise 55–57
  Macara, Sir Alexander (Sandy) 56
  Reforming the NHS Reforms (1994) 56
Council (BMA) 353–358, 414
  Audit Committee *see* constitution and governance
    (BMA)
  conflicting pressures on Chairman (Johnson)
    126–127
  constitution of Council as recommended to 1985
    ARM 366–367
  control of BMA 353, 354
  Council chamber 383, 384
    refurbishment (1994) 372
    refurbishment (2007) 384
  directors, role of 355, 356
  electoral processes *see* electoral process
  emergency meeting after MMRC judicial review
    125
  role of 108, 353–354
  senior managers and 356–357
  support for junior doctors, hours of work 21–22
  trade union and company law responsibilities 355
  voting members, number (2005) 141
counterfeit medicines, world wide web 228

craft status 361
criminal standard of proof 193
Crisis in general practice (2001) 97
Crisp, Sir Nigel 77
Crockard, Professor Alan 122
'cross-branch of practice working' 107
    see also branches of practice
Cumberlege, Baroness, Julia 15
cycling
    helmets 262–263
    safety 262–263
Cycling Towards Health and Safety (1992) 262

D
Darke, Chris 334–335
Darzi, Sir Ara (Lord) 129, 132, 133
Darzi review *see* National Health Service (NHS)
    review
data protection *see* confidentiality; information,
    personal healthcare
Data Protection Act (1984) 285, 286
Davis, Jacky 80
Dawson, John, publicity campaign (BMA) 33
death certification 180–181
'deep specialisation' 115
defence body subscriptions 158–159
Defence Medical Services (DMS) *see* armed forces
    doctors
'defensive medicine' 210–211
Delivering 21st Century IT support for the NHS
    (2002) 217–218
    clinician role 218
Department for International Development 322, 323
Department of Health (DH)
    appraisal and revalidation of doctors 201, 203, 205
    BMA interface 58
    BNF procurement contract transfer to NICE 409
    FPC consultation 17
    GPC and GP contract 99
    Information for Health 215, 217
    NHS complaints 211
    NHS Connecting for Health *see* NHS Connecting
        for Health
    pensions dynamisation 132
deputising services, GPs *see* General Practitioners
    (GPs)
detailed care record (DCR) 222, 225
developing countries
    debts and international sanctions 322–323
    Humanitarian Fund and 323–324
devolution *see* devolved nations
devolved nations 73–74, 76, 93, 149–181
    autonomy 107, 108
    BMA and
        Articles of the Association 108
        constitutional changes 74
        Northern Ireland *see* BMA Northern Ireland
        role of 149, 150
        Scotland *see* BMA Scotland
        since devolution 149–156
        structure 74, 342, 343
        Wales *see* BMA Cymru Wales
    BMA premises requirements 372
    Choose and Book system 220
    complaints (NHS) 211–212
    consent and capacity 290
    constitution and governance of BMA 74, 364–365
        disputes 363
        divergences of policy 365
        UK Council and devolved Councils 363, 365
    consultant contract negotiations 94, 95
    'devo-max' 152
    medical academic staff 164, 166
    organ donation and transplantation 297
    pay freeze 161
    pensions 136–137

personal healthcare information systems 226–227
public health 170
    resourcing 74
    smoking-related policy 244
    staff and associate specialists contract 103, 105, 106
    structure, local (BMA) 342
    variations in documents 93
    workplace services (BMA) 329
Dhatta, Shree 140
diabetes 251
Diet, Nutrition and Health (1986) 250–251
Dignitas 302–303
Directed Enhanced Services, Scotland, healthcare
    in 151
Director of Public Health (DPH) 168
Director of Public Prosecutions (DPP) 303, 304
disciplinary measures
    separate from complaints investigation 209
    see also serious professional misconduct
disclosure, of confidential information *see*
    confidentiality
discretionary points scheme 70
distinction awards 42, 43, 67, 160, 161
    age limit 43
    alternatives to, *NHS Trusts – A Working Guide* 48
    C awards system 43, 67, 69–70
    delayed pensionability 42, 43
    discretionary points scheme 70
    'national' and 'local' awards 70
    national debate 67
    Scotland 151
    Treasury report 68
district health authority (DHA) 1, 57, 167
district management team (DMT) 2
district medical officer 167
Dobson, Frank 72, 86, 187, 216
doctor(s)
    armed forces *see* armed forces doctors
    duties of 184
    failing doctors *see* failing doctors
    GPs *see* General Practitioners
    human rights and *see* human rights
    junior *see* junior doctors
    as medical managers *see* medical managers
    Medical Workforce Standing Advisory Committee
        114
    overseas *see* overseas doctors
    physician assisted suicide *see* physician assisted
        suicide and euthanasia
    registrars *see* registrars
    registration of 184, 195–196
    relationship with government 52–53
    role in contraception advice 288, 289
    role of 3–4
    specialty, new grade (2008) 106
    staff *see* staff and associate specialists
    women *see* women doctors
    see also grades
doctor–patient relationship 185
    contraception for young adults 288
    internet changing 228, 229
    medical information for insurance purposes and 291
Doctors' and Dentists' Review Body (DDRB) 156
    government cut/phasing of award (1990) 159
    government interference 156–157
    GP remuneration package (1994) 65
    history of recommendations 156–162
        1987 and defence body subscriptions 158–159
        1990 and government phasing of award 159
        1992 pay increase restrictions 160
        1997 comparative pay and GPs 160
        2003–2006 across-the-board increase 160
        2007 small increase and phasing 160–161
        BMA approach 159, 160, 161, 162
    negotiations 156
    Northern Ireland 157
    pay increases 160

performance-related pay 66–67
proposed fee scale 96
purpose 162
recommendations and government response
    156–162
redefining role (2007) 131
regional variations 157
Scotland and 151
terms of reference 157
Working for Patients (1989), after 30
see also remuneration
Doctors and Tobacco 240–241
Doctors for Doctors 340
doctors.net.uk 92, 229–230, 232
Doll, Sir Richard 244
Donaldson, Sir Liam 122, 123, 203
Dorrell, Stephen 65, 142–143
Douglas, Professor Sir Neil 119, 121
Dr Foster website 228
drink-drive limit 261–262
    testing and consent 262
drink-driving 246, 261–262
The Drinking Driver (BMA publication) 246
drinking guidelines 247
drinks industry 248, 249–250
drug budgets, indicative 29, 37
drugs, limited list *see* limited list (of drugs)
Duncan, George 171
'duty of quality' 190

E
eating disorders 252
eBMJ 398
electoral process (BMA)
    alternative voting method 351–352
    Council 346, 347, 352
        Trade Union Act 1984, impact of 346
    doctor categorisation 347
    Governance Committee 350
    lay members 361
    Nominations Committee 360
    presidents 381
    Representative Body 352
        formal complaint 353
        two-stage appointment process 353
        unused seats 353
    single UK election proposal 352–353
        constraints 352–353
        geographical zones 353
    'staging' of elections 347
    two-year terms of office 347
    voting rights 347
electronic books 230, 340
electronic communication 92
    negative aspects 232
    see also social media
electronic journals 230, 340
    library services 230
Elizabeth II, HM the Queen 382
Ellis, Norman 328–329
emails 232, 356
    misuse and unwanted effects 233
embryonic stem cells 283
emerging markets 412
'enabling clause' 68
    industrial action 69, 70
    sanctions 69
    see also local pay campaign
end of life issues 299–309
    advance directives *see* advance directives
    BMA position 299–300
    criminal law position 299, 300
    physician assisted suicide *see* physician assisted
        suicide and euthanasia
    withholding/withdrawing treatment *see*
        withholding and withdrawing treatment

England, BMA structure 363–364
England, healthcare in
    Choose and Book system 221–222
    complaints (NHS) 211
        see also complaints (NHS)
    consent and capacity 290–291
    differences between Scotland and 150
    NHS Plan 72–74, 83, 88, 150
    NHS Programme for IT 217–218, 225
        see also NHS Connecting for Health
    Public Health England (PHE) 170
    summary care record (SCR) *see* Summary Care
        Record (SCR)
    see also National Health Service (NHS)
English, Sir Terence 40
    The New Deal (1991) 24
    'the English clause' 24
Enthoven, Professor Alain 27
environment 260–265
    climate change *see* climate change
    genetically modified (GM) food 263
    hazardous waste 261
    transport *see* transport
Equal Opportunities Committee 333–334
Equality and Diversity Committee 362
Equity and excellence: Liberating the NHS (2010)
    (white paper) 18, 142
    amendments 144
    BMA response/concerns 142
        call for bill withdrawal 144
        formal opposition 144
        Special Representatives Meeting (SRM) 143
    campaign priorities 143
    Future Forum 143
    public opposition 142
    see also Health and Social Care Act (2012)
Essentia 334–335
    see also call centres
Ethical Procurement for Health (2011) 324
ethics, medical *see* medical ethics
Ethics Department (BMA) 236, 275
    confidentiality 284, 286
    guidance notes 286
European institutions 312–314
    BMA, main objectives 312
    implications of proposed policy initiatives 312
    medical training *see* training
European Working Time Directive (EWTD) 110–113
    active and inactive time, definition 112
    BMA response 112
    clarification of law, consultation process 141
    compensatory rest 112
    compliance with 112
    derogations 110, 113
    disadvantages/problems 140
    exemptions 110
    full implementation 111
    implementation 112
    negotiations 111
    rest periods 112
    review of impact on junior doctors 140–141
    shift patterns 112
euthanasia *see* physician assisted suicide and
    euthanasia
Everington, Sam 124, 125, 386
    junior doctors, hours of work 21, 22
Evidence-Based Medicine 397–398
expectations, public 211
extra-contractual referrals 41

F
Facebook 231
failing doctors
    BMA support for 184
    National Clinical Assessment Service 190–191
    standard of proof *see* standard of proof

Fair and Ethical Trade Group 324
Family Health Service Authorities 57
family planning speciality 172
family practitioner committees (FPCs) 1
    composition 17
    deputising services and 13
    Key Ministerial Aims for FPCs 1989–1991 16–17
Farrar, Mike 97
fee(s)
    professional 179–180
    schedule, private practice 177
    specialist, private practice 178
    see also remuneration
fee scale
    GPs contract (2003) 96
    out-of-hours services (GPs) 65
fertility treatment 276
    access to 276
    Human Fertilisation and Embryology Act (1990)
        277, 280, 284
    Human Fertilisation and Embryology Authority
        (HFEA) 277
    IVF *see* in-vitro fertilisation (IVF)
    statutory licensing body 276–277
    surrogacy *see* surrogacy
fetal alcohol spectrum disorders 248
Fidelio 121
Field, Ian 33, 37
Field, Steve 144
Fielden, Jonathan 119, 120, 121
Finance and General Purposes Committee 373
Finance Committee (BMA) i, 341, 360, 373
    2001–2002 360, 373
    BMJ Publishing Group and 405, 407
    Oversight and Finance Committee 358
finances (BMA) 369–378
    BMA House refurbishment programme 372, 375
    BMA Staff Pension Scheme 373–374
    budgets
        1987–1989 370–371
        1992 371–372
        2003 report 374
        global financial crisis effect 375–376
    devolution and premises requirements 372
    expenditure 370
        campaigns 373
    impact of NHS Review 370–371
    investments 371
        see also investments and rental income (BMA)
    members' services 376
    membership levels 371
    payment to members *see* members (BMA)
    Professional Affinity Group Services Limited 374
    recession 371
    regional network expansion funding 372
    sources of funding 369, 375
        BMJ Publishing Group *see* BMJ Publishing
            Group
        investments and rental income *see* investments
            and rental income (BMA)
        membership subscription *see* subscriptions
            (BMA)
    staffing and departments 378–381
    staffing costs 370, 374
    subscriptions *see* subscriptions (BMA)
    treasurers 369, 370, 372, 374
financial crisis (2008, UK) 132–134
    austerity under coalition government 139–141, 174
    impact on BMA finances 375–376
    NHS funding 133
    pensions reforms 136–138
financial services (BMA) 339–341
    accountancy services 341
    BMA Professional Services (BMAPS) 341
    BMA Services 340, 374
    Jardine Glanville 340
    Professional Affinity Group Services Limited 340

A First Class Service (green paper) (1998) 71
First Point of Call 339
fitness to practise 193, 194
    Bogle, Ian 199
    GMC 'affiliate' *see* General Medical Council
        (GMC)
    GMC proposal consultation 199
    Good Doctors, Safer Patients (2006) 203–204
    Johnson, James and 199
    Medical Practitioners Tribunal Service (MPTS)
        195
    revalidation process and 199
    standard of proof *see* standard of proof
fixed annual payments 378
'flagship hospitals' 48
flexible trainees 87
The Follett Principles 164
food deserts 253
    see also health inequalities
Forensic Medical Committee 178, 180
forensic medicine 180–181
    death certification 180–181
    Forensic Medical Committee 178, 180
    national coroner service 181
    Offender Health 180
Foster, Andrew 92, 93
Foundation for AIDS 260
Foundation Trusts 75, 178, 331
    v primary care trusts 77
Fowler, Norman 13, 14, 15, 26
Framework Convention on Tobacco Control (WHO)
    241–242
A Framework for Action, Healthcare for London 129
Functions and Manpower Review (1993) 57, 168
    result of 58
fundholding (GP) 27, 31, 43–46, 57, 72
    BMA opposition 44
    Bogle, Ian and 44
    clinical need criterion 45
    'first wave' 44
    GMSC
        concerns over reductions 41
        conferences 45
        opposition 43–44, 45–46
        working party 44
    Labour promise to replace 72
    National Association of Fundholding Practices
        (NAFP) 45–46
    objections to 31
    policy statement (GMSC) 44
    scope of BMA representation 45
Future Forum 144
    report 144

G
general managers (NHS) 3
    appointment process 4
    candidates 3
    management board 5
        BMA concerns 5
    negotiations with CCHMS and GMSC 4
    payment for clinicians 4
General Medical Council (GMC)
    abolishment 187
    'affiliate' 204
        BMA consultation 204–205
        BMA response 204
        'responsible officer' 205
    'Blue Book' of ethical guidance 275
    BMA and 183–196
        concerns 183, 194
        no confidence 187
        relations 183
    Bogle, Ian 198
    certificate to work as specialist in Europe 61
    children, consent and capacity guidance 288–289

civil standard of proof *v* criminal standard 193
education committee, Medical Students
  Committee (MSC) and 175
Fitness to Practise panel
  1990s 126–127
  Johnson, James 126–127
funding 191–192
Good Medical Practice (1995) 184, 190
governance, proposed 11 principles of 188–189
A Licence to Practise and Revalidation (2003) 202
medical register 184
  BMA position 196
  payment exemption 195
members 189
  lay membership 188, 189
  medical members 191, 193, 194
  number 196
modernised GMC 189
performance procedures 184
  failing doctors *see* failing doctors
  motivation for GMC to adopt 184
  retraining 184
powers 183
revalidation *see* revalidation
Revalidation: The Way Ahead (2010) 205, 206
self-regulation *see* self-regulation (GMC)
serious professional misconduct *see* serious
  professional misconduct
Spearing, Nigel 183
structure reform 188, 189
  election procedures 188
  GMC conference 188
  proposed 11 principles of GMC Governance
    188–189
withholding and withdrawing treatment guidance
  306–307
General Medical Services Committee (GMSC)
  conferences for fundholders 45
  extraordinary meeting (new GP contract) 20
  fundholding opposition 43–44, 45–46
  fundholding subcommittee 46
  Help us to Help You campaign 64
  limited list campaign 14
  new contract (GPs) discussions (1983/84) 13, 14
  new contract (GPs) negotiations (1990) 18, 19
    contract imposition by government 20
    debate over changes (1991) 64
  objectives of discussion with Kenneth Clarke
    16–17
  Promoting Better Health (white paper) (1987) 16
  response to *Key Ministerial Aims for FPCs 1989–
    1991* 16–17
  Wilson, Michael 14
  Working for Patients (white paper) (1989) 17–18
    negotiations and 11-point document 19, 20–21
general practice administration system for Scotland
  (GPASS) 226–227
General Practitioners (GPs)
  2005 London terrorist bombings, help at 386
  access time for patients, increase proposed by
    government (2007) 131
  access to surgeries 77, 131
  Alternative Provider Medical Services (APMS) 78
  appraisal, revalidation 201–202
  ballot on resignation 97
  BMA support services 338
  budget-holders proposal 27, 31
  budgets *see* fundholding (GP)
  Building Your Own Future (1991) 64
  capitation 19, 29
  Choose and Book system 221
    see also Choose and Book system
  commissioning 72, 76, 143
    role proposed by Lansley 142
  conduct *see* serious professional misconduct
  contract (1990)
    debate over changes to (1991) 64

extraordinary meeting (GMSC) 20
  imposition 20
  introduction 19, 20, 30
  negotiations 13, 18, 19, 21
  'overpayment' and claw back 63–64
  rejection 19
contract (2003) 96–101
  ballot in favour of 101
  'Black Wednesday' 100
    see also global sum letters
  costings 98
  DDRB proposed fee scale 96
  deadline/announcement 98, 99
  funding formula 108–109
  funding formula, GPC opposition to 100
  global sum letters *see* global sum letters
  government reneging on deal (2006) 130
  minor changes in 2010 139
  negotiation team 97
  NHS Confederation negotiations 97, 101
  PMS contracts 96
  'principled negotiation' 97
  proposals rejected 101
  roadshows 100
  Special LMC Conference 100–101
  timeframe 98
  working groups 98
  Your contract your future 98
contract (2007), negotiations 131
Crisis in general practice (2001) 97
deputising services 13, 64
  BMA support against government 13
  debate over in 1991 64
  government proposals 13
  limitation of use by Clarke (Kenneth) 13
  monitoring 13–14
    see also out-of-hours services
European standards 313
fundholding *see* fundholding (GP)
General Practitioners Defence Fund 377
generalist register 197
Good Medical Practice for General Practitioners
  (2000) 201
health centres led by 132, 133
  costs 134
  scheme termination 134
  tender, bidding process 133–134
Informatica 411
limited list *see* limited list (of drugs)
media criticism of 129–130
morale 65, 97
  listening exercise 65–66
negotiations (1980s) 13–21
  contract *see* General Practitioners (GPs),
    contract (1990)
  deputising services 13–14
  limited list of drugs *see* limited list (of drugs)
  pay *see* General Practitioners (GPs), pay
  Promoting Better Health 16
  Working for Patients and 17, 18, 19
    see also General Medical Services Committee
      (GMSC)
negotiations (2003), out-of-hours *see* out-of-hours
  services
negotiations (2007), contract 131
new services, pressure to offer (2006) 77
online reviews 228–229
  BMA response 229
out-of-hours work *see* out-of-hours services
patient relationship, internet changing 228, 229
pay ii, 78, 82, 160
  2003–2006 and DDRB's role 160
  2010 161–162
  criticism in media over 129–130
  DDRB involvement (1995/96) 65
  DDRB role (2007) 78, 161
  DDRB role (2010/11) 161

Dorrell's (Stephen) involvement 65
  modernisation 83
  no increase in 2007 78, 161
  'overpayment' and claw back 64
  performance-related 66
  salaried option 65–66, 76
policy priorities 65
Practice Observed 391–392
practices 147, 229
  boundaries 139
  diseconomies of scale 99
  Minimum Practice Income Guarantee (MPIG)
    100, 109
  patient feedback 229
Primary Care Under Pressure (1987) 25–26
private companies *see* private sector provision
quality outcomes framework (QOF) 83, 98
referral
  extra-contractual 41
  freedom of 40–41
senior academic GPs 164
sessional *see* General Practitioners Committee
    (GPC)
swine flu 136
terms and conditions of service 58
values 109
views on fundholding status 44
Working for Patients (white paper) (1989) 17
  response to 18, 19
Your Choices for the Future 64
General Practitioners Committee (GPC) 96–97
  Choose and Book, criticisms 221
  concerns over commissioning (2010) 142
  concerns over Darzi report 131–132
  contract negotiation (2001) 97, 98, 99
    see also General Practitioners (GPs), contract
  data protection
    GP code of practice 286
    guidance 285
  pensions, legal challenge 130
  response to surgery opening hours 131–132
  sessional GPs subcommittee 139–140
  structure change (2011) 139–140
  Support your Surgery 132
  swine flu vaccination 136
General Practitioners Defence Fund 377
genetically modified (GM) food 263
genetics *see* human genetics
Gerada, Clare 143
Gillick, Victoria 287–288
Gillick competence 287–289
  BMA response to Court of Appeal 288
  misinterpretation of 288
global sum letters 100
  BMA
    costings under new formula 100
    opposition 100
GM food 263
GMC *see* General Medical Council (GMC)
GMC (education committee), Medical Students
    Committee (MSC) and 175
Good Doctors, Safer Patients (2006) 191, 203–204
Good Medical Practice (1995) 184, 190
Good Medical Practice for General Practitioners
    (2000) 201
'good practice' allowance 15
governance (BMA) *see* constitution and governance
    (BMA)
GPs *see* General Practitioners (GPs)
Grabham, Anthony 10, 11–12, 35, 346
  exclusion from CSAG meeting 39–40
grades
  implementation 116
  post-CCST (Certificate of Completion of
    Specialist Training) 114
  registrars, unification of grades 61
  senior house officer 114, 116

specialist *see* specialist training
  sub-consultant – specialist grade 114
Granger, Richard 217
grass roots (BMA) 31, 101, 107, 348
  opinions on new contract negotiation 107
green papers
  A First Class Service (1998) 71
  Primary Health Care: An Agenda for Discussion
    (1986) 15, 16
Greenfield Report (1982), limited list (of drugs) 14
Grey-Turner, Elston i–ii
Griffiths, Roy 3
Griffiths report, *The NHS Management Inquiry*
    (1983) 3, 167
  see also National Health Service (NHS)
Gulf War 173
Gullick, David 176–177

H
Hangartner, Robert 9
Havard, John 33, 235, 321, 378
Hawker, Peter 89, 90, 93, 94
  revalidation and 200
hazardous waste 260, 261
health and safety legislation *see* European Working
    Time Directive (EWTD)
Health and Security Adjudications Bill 2
Health and Social Care Act (2012) 141–145
  amendments 145
  BMA response 141, 192–193
    united position 141
  BMA role 145
  Labour Party opposition 143
  launch of bill 143
  'listen, engage, and amend' process 143–144
    see also Future Forum
  PCT dismantling before 143
  royal assent 145, 192
  see also Equity and excellence: Liberating the NHS
    (2010) (white paper)
Health and Social Care Bill (2007) 190, 192
  BMA reservations 192
health authorities 75
  district (DHA) 1, 57, 167
  Family Health Service Authorities 57
  Wales 153
  see also regional health authority; strategic health
    authorities (SHAs)
Health Authorities Act (1995) 57
Health Bill *see* Health and Social Care Act
health boards
  Scotland 150, 170
  unified 150, 153
  Wales 153, 170
  see also health authorities
health centres, GP-led *see* General Practitioners (GPs)
health inequalities 253–256
  Black report *see* Black report
  Board of Science recommendations 254
  history of 253–254
  housing 255
  Inquiry in Inequalities in Health (1998) 255
  Labour Party and New Labour 254–255
  low income 253
  obesity 253
  Saving Lives: our healthier nation (white paper)
    (1999) 256
  *Social Determinants of Health: What Doctors Can
    Do* 256
  socio-economic status 253
  'water poverty' 254–255
Health of the Nation (1991) 51, 396
  Reforming the NHS Reforms (1994) and 56
health of the public *see* public health
health policy and economic research unit (HPERU)
    379

health promotion clinics 63
Health Protection Agency 170
A Health service for all the talents (2000) 114
health services, comparative data on website 228
health strategy, *The Health of the Nation* (1991) 51, 396
Healthcall 13
healthcare, international *see* international work (BMA)
Healthcare Commission 75
Healthcare for London 129, 131
  Framework for Action 129
healthcare information *see* information, personal healthcare
Healthcare Information for All by 2015 (HIFA) 323
healthcare market 135
  see also private sector provision
Healthy Housing Taskforce 255
Healthy Lives, Healthy People 169
Help Us to Help You campaign 64
hereditary diseases *see* human genetics
Hewitt, Patricia 77, 78, 116
  replacement 125
High Quality Care for All: NHS Next Stage review (2008) 129
  BMA response 132
Higher Education
  funding reduction 164–165, 175
  see also medical academic staff; medical students
Higher Education Funding Council for England 165
Higher Education white paper (2003) 166
Hilborne, Jo 119, 120, 121
  standing down 126
Holdcroft, Anita 166
Holden, Peter 178, 386
home-working 336
  member response 337
  senior management team role 337
  staff response 337–338
Horner, Stuart 278
Hospital at Night 111
hospital consultant *see* consultant(s)
Hospital Junior Staff Committee (HJSC)
  Borman, Edwin 60
  conference in 1990 over working hours 23
  hours of work 8, 9, 24
  Hunter, Stephen 24
  New Deal 24–25, 60
  private member's bill (Lord Rees) 21
  Short Report and 7–8
  specialist training *see* specialist training
hospital treatment tariff 75
hours of work *see* European Working Time Directive (EWTD); junior doctors
housing 255
Human Bodies, Human Choices (2001) 297
The Human Cost of Tobacco (BMA report) 242
Human Fertilisation and Embryology Act (1990) 277, 280, 284
  see also fertility treatment
Human Fertilisation and Embryology Authority (HFEA) 277
  see also fertility treatment
human genetics 281–284
  BMA approach 282
  genetic testing 282
  Human Genetics: Choice and Responsibility (1998) 281–282
  International Human Genome Project 282–283
  stem cell research *see* stem cell research
Human Genetics: Choice and Responsibility (1998) 281–282
Human Immunodeficiency Virus (HIV) 258–259
  antibody testing and consent 259
  BMA advice 258
  insurance queries about medical status 292
  public education 259–260

  see also Acquired Immune Deficiency Syndrome (AIDS)
human rights 292–295
  abuses 292
    abuse of medical skills 293
    BMA reporting 292–293
    Medicine Betrayed (1992) 293
    torture 292–293
  asylum seekers 292, 295
  Commonwealth Human Rights Initiative 321
  The Medical Profession and Human Rights: Handbook for a Changing Agenda (2001) 293
  oppressive regimes' targets 292, 294
    Bahrani case 294–295
    BMA support of victims 294
    international publicity 294
Human Tissue Act (2004) 297
Human Tissue Authority 297
Humanitarian Fund 323–324
Hunt, Jeremy 148
Hunt, Lord (Phillip) 105
Hunter, Stephen 24
Hutton, Lord 145–146

I
immigration *see* overseas doctors
immigration controls *see under* overseas doctors
Improving Health for the World's Poor – What can Health Professionals do? (2007) 324
Improving health in Wales 153
in-vitro fertilisation (IVF) 276
  Blood (Diane) case 277–278
    BMA response 278
  donor anonymity 278
    legislation 278–279
  gamete collection consent 277
  payment to donors 278
    BMA response 278
    expenses 278
  see also fertility treatment
Independent Sector Treatment Centres (ISTCs) 79, 81
  'additionality' principle 79
  BMA concerns 79
  contractual details 79
  first wave 79
  GP response 79
industrial action 81, 356, 357, 358, 361
  ballot by junior doctors 23
  BMA position 85
    ballot 147
  Junior Doctors Committee (JDC) 84, 85
  local pay campaign 69, 70
  pensions *see* pensions
  trade unions 147
  see also trade union(s)
Industrial Relations Officers (IROs) (BMA) 328, 329
  workloads 335
inequalities, health *see* health inequalities
infertility *see* reproductive technology
influenza, swine flu 136
Informatica 411
information, personal healthcare
  access to 213–225, 285
    code of practice 214
    Interprofessional Working Group on Access to Personal Information 285, 286
  administrative *v* clinical information systems 213, 215–216
  barriers to effective use of IT 217
  BMA
    concerns 215, 217
    opinion 225
    security policy for clinical information systems 215
    working party 215

confidentiality 215
Data Protection Act (1984) 286
data transmission protocol 214
Delivering 21st Century IT support for the NHS: National Strategic Programme (2002) 217–218
devolved nations 226–227
draft bill (1996) 286
Information for Health (1998) *see Information for Health* (1998)
Information Strategy for the NHS (1998) *see Information for Health* (1998)
insurance companies' access to medical records 291–292
  lifestyle choices and 291
  standard GP report package 292
listservers and paperless committees *see* listservers and paperless committees
NHS Management Executive (NHSME) information strategy 214
Northern Ireland *see* Northern Ireland, healthcare in
problems, failings and strategic document 217
Scotland *see* Scotland, healthcare in
Wales *see* Wales, healthcare in
Wanless report 216–217
world wide web *see* world wide web
Information for Health (1998) 215–216
  elements of 216
Information Strategy for the NHS (1998) *see Information for Health* (1998)
Information Technology (IT) 213–234
  BMA's use of new technology 230–232
  internet *see* world wide web (www)
  listservers *see* listservers and paperless committees
  personal healthcare information *see* information, personal healthcare
Information Technology Working Party (BMA) 214
Inquiry in Inequalities in Health (1998), BMA response 255
insurance companies, information for 291–292
  see also information, personal healthcare
intensity supplements 89
internal market 27, 28, 72
  campaign against 32
  continuation in 1997, commissioning 72
  problems 50–51
  royal colleges and debate 31–32
International Committee of Medical Journal Editors (ICMJE) 402
International Forum on Quality and Safety in Healthcare 395
International Human Genome Project 282–283
  BMA response 282–283
international medical associations 318–322
  BMA membership 311
  Commonwealth Medical Association (CMA) *see* Commonwealth Medical Association (CMA)
  Medical Association of South Africa (MASA) *see* Medical Association of South Africa (MASA)
  World Medical Association (WMA) *see* World Medical Association (WMA)
international sanctions *see* international work (BMA)
international work (BMA) 311–325
  BMA Information Fund 324
  closure of overseas branches 312
  Commonwealth and International Medical Advisory Bureau 325
  European institutions *see* European institutions
  Fair and Ethical Trade Group 324
  history 311
  Humanitarian Fund 323–324
  immigration *see* overseas doctors
  Improving Health for the World's Poor – What can Health Professionals do? (2007) 324
  international healthcare
    Healthcare Information for All by 2015 (HIFA) 323

international medical associations *see* international medical associations
international sanctions
  BMA BMJ Information fund 323
  Iraq 322–323
  medical equipment, ethical procurement of 324
    Ethical Procurement for Health (2011) 324
  scope of activities 311
  strategic grant agreement 323
  third-world debt
    Department for International Development 322, 323
    Jubilee 2000 Coalition 322
internet 398–399
  see also world wide web (www)
Interprofessional Working Group on Access to Personal Information 285, 286
investments and rental income (BMA) 375–376
  impact on BMA Staff Pension Scheme 375–376
  investment policy 371
  recession impact 371, 372
  recovery of market (1996) 372
Iraq, international sanctions 322–323
Irvine, Sir Donald 184, 185, 187
  revalidation and 198, 200
IT (Information Technology) *see* Information Technology (IT)

J
Jaeger judgement 111, 112
Janaway v Salford Health Authority 280
Jardine, Glanville 340
'job-plans' 42
Johnson, Alan 125, 129, 316, 317
Johnson, James (Jim) 69, 77, 80, 189, 204, 337–338
  allegations over clinical practice 126–127
  lack of support for 124
  passive smoking report 242
  resignation 124
  resumption of clinical practice 127
  revalidation and 199, 203, 204
  support of junior doctors 119, 121
  The Times letter 123
Johnstone, Chris 22
Joint Consultants Committee (JCC)
  Achieving a Balance (1986) *see Achieving a Balance* (1986)
  Clarke, Kenneth and 31–32
  Grabham, Anthony 11–12
  Johnson, James 189
  proposed 11 principles of GMC Governance 188–189
  Ross, Paddy 41
Joint Planning Advisory Committee (JPAC) 11
Joseph, Sir Keith 164, 165
Journal Committee (BMA) 403
Journal of the American Medical Association (JAMA) 395
journals *see* BMJ Publishing Group
Jubilee 2000 Coalition 322
junior consultants 61–62
  training *see* specialist training
junior doctors
  accommodation and support 23
  additional duty hours (ADHs) 84
  banding appeals 112
  BMA membership levels 344
  European Working Time Directive 110
  hours of work 21–25
    agreement of 72-hour week 23
    annual conference 21
    attendance at 1990 conference with Bottomley 23
    ballot on industrial action 23
    BMA council support 22
    Bottomley, Virginia 22–23

call for legislation on 21–22
decrease under EWTD, and pay impact 112
demands made to Bottomley 22–23
Everington, Sam and 21, 22
exclusion from European Working Time
 Directive 111
full shifts and training impact 113, 140
ministerial working group 23
national terms and conditions of service 40
The New Deal (1991) 24–25, 110, 111
NHS and Community Care Bill (1989) 40
on-call classification 111
private member's bill (Lord Rees) 21–22
reduction in hours to 48 hours/week 111, 141
shift systems 23, 112, 140
'the English clause' 24
training hours required 23, 111, 140
industrial action 23, 84, 85
legislation on hours 8–9
MMC (2003) *see Modernising Medical Careers*
 (MMC) (2003)
new contracts (Coalition government) 141
pay
 ballot 86
 banding 87, 88
 banding appeals 88
 BMA advice 87
 BMA position 86
 flexible trainees 87
 impact of EWTD 112
 increase (1995) 63
 increase (2004–2007) 82
 industrial action 85
 JDC negotiations 86
 Mamode, Nizam 86, 87
 modernisation 83
 negotiation strategy 87
 out-of-hours 84–88
 overtime 84
 part-time contracts 87
 rejection of proposed agreement 86
RemedyUK *see* RemedyUK
rotas, changes 9, 22, 23
Scotland 151
Situation Critical campaign 85
specialist training *see* specialist training
training *see* training
units of medical time (UMTs) 84
see also Junior Doctors Committee (JDC)
Junior Doctors Committee (JDC) 61
 BMA support, MMC 119
 Call for Delay 117
 European Working Time Directive and 111, 113,
 140
 findings after implementation 113
 Hospital at Night 111–112
 industrial action 84, 86
 junior doctors' out-of-hours pay and negotiations
 84, 86
 lobbying on overseas doctors 116–117
 MMC 116, 121
 BMA support for JDC 119
 implementation delay needed 116, 117
 improvements and press release 118
 outcry and suspension sought 119
 RemedyUK deputation 118
 motion of no confidence in leadership 122
 new contracts for juniors pressed 141
 role in consultant contract negotiations 90–91
 support group for 123
 Train not Drain campaign 117
 see also junior doctors

K
Keep Our NHS Public pressure group 134
Kendell, Professor Robert 67, 68

Kendell Committee 67, 68, 69, 70
Kerr, David 150
Kerr, William 186, 187
Key Ministerial Aims for FPCs 1989–1991 16–17
Khan, Mohib 101, 103, 105
Körner, Dame Edith 213
Körner Committee 214
KPMG (management consultants) 359, 405–406

L
Labour Party
 1997–2007 71–126
 see also National Health Service (NHS)
 modernisation (1997–2007)
 2007–2010 129–138
 Darzi review *see* National Health Service (NHS)
 review
 financial crisis and 132–134
 election campaign (1992) 52
 fundholding, abolition 46
 health inequalities 255
 NHS Programme for IT 225
 opposition to Health and Social Care bill 143
 Prime Ministers
 Blair, Tony *see* Blair, Tony
 Brown, Gordon 129
 publicists 52
 Smoking Kills (white paper) (1998) 240
 smoking-related policy 239–240
 Standards for Better Health (2004) 190
Lansley, Andrew 142, 143, 148, 225
lay members
 BMA 361
 GMC 188, 189
Leading Change (2001) 73
Leading for Health (1991) 51
Learning the Lessons (2004) 82, 103, 107
Ledward, Rodney 72, 186
Lee-Potter, Jeremy 41, 51–52, 55
 criticism of 50–51
 models for health service provision 51
 NHS resource problems 50–51
Liberal Democrat Party, coalition *see* Conservative/
 Liberal Democrat Coalition (2010–2012)
Library anywhere app 230–231
library services (BMA) 230–232, 339
 Berry, Jackie 339–340
 electronic books 230, 340
 electronic journals 230, 340
 Library anywhere app 230–231
 Medline/Medline Plus 230
 new Library (2008) 384
 online catalogue 230
 relocation 339
A Licence to Practise and Revalidation (2003) 202
Licensing Act (2003) 247
'life check' 77
life-style, risk 265
limited list (of drugs) 15
 BMA support 14–15
 campaign (GMSC) 14
 Clarke, Kenneth and 14
 Greenfield Report (1982) 14
 introduction by government 14–15
 review mechanism 15
listservers and paperless committees 232–234, 356
 inappropriate use 233
 principles for BMA listservers 233
 telephone and video conferencing 233
lobbying, BMA, on public health 151
local enhanced services (LESs) 109
local health resilience partnerships (LHRPs) 170
local improvement finance programme (LIFT) 76
 see also private finance initiative (PFI)
local medical committees (LMCs)
 conference (1986) 15

conference (1989) and GP contract rejection 19
conference (1990) and GP contract imposition
    20–21
GP contracts, negotiations (2002) 98, 99
    Special LMC Conference 100–101
primary care system opposition 16
Primary Health Care: An Agenda for Discussion
    (green paper) (1986) 15, 16
Local Negotiating Committee (LNC) 49, 331
    activities 330
    BMA policy, and Chawner (John) 49
    BMA support 49, 330
    consultant contract negotiations 94
    impact on BMA membership levels 330–331
    local pay scheme 68
    online training 339
local pay campaign 66–70, 68
    BMA rejection 69
    'enabling clause' 68, 69, 70
    industrial action 69, 70
    Local Negotiating Committees (LNCs) 68
    publicity 69
    sanctions 69
    'transitional local pay' 70
    see also performance-related pay
local structure (BMA) *see* structure, local (BMA)
Lock, Stephen 393, 394
London, healthcare in 58–60
    Bottomley, Virginia 59
    Healthcare for London *see* Healthcare for London
    London Implementation Group (LIG) 59
    'London initiatives zone' 59
    London Local Medical Committees (LMCs) 60
    London Regional Council (BMA) 134
    Making London Better (1993) 59
    rationalisation 59, 60
        BMA response 59–60
    Strategic Health Authorities, consortium 129
    see also Tomlinson report
London bombings *see* terrorism, impact on BMA
London Implementation Group (LIG) 59
'London initiatives zone' 59
London Local Medical Committees (LMCs) 60
London Regional Council (BMA) 134
Look after our NHS campaign (BMA) 134
    costs and progress 135
    disadvantages 135
    ending 136
    principles 134
    surveys 135
low income 253
    see also health inequalities

M
Macara, Sir Alexander (Sandy) 55–56, 171, 215
    BMA and bad doctors 186
    CMO for England, response to 56
    Core Values exercise 56–57
    third world debt and 322
Machin, Derek 89, 90, 94, 179
Major, John 50–51
Making London Better (1993) 59
    London Implementation Group (LIG) 59
Malone, Gerry 65
malpractice *see* serious professional misconduct
Mamode, Nizam 84–85, 87, 94
management, of NHS *see* National Health Service
    (NHS)
management board (NHS) *see* general managers
    (NHS)
Markham, Professor Alex 243–244
Marks, John 28, 321
    campaign against internal market 32, 33
    publicity campaign (BMA) 34, 35, 36
        BMA member concerns 34–35
    re-election 35–36

retirement as BMA chairman 41
    seven-point plan 38
Marks, Sue 39, 380–381
Marmot, Sir Michael 255, 256
Mawhinney, Brian 52, 62, 68
McColl, Ian, self-governing hospital trusts 46, 47
McDonald, Graeme 22, 23
McKim Thompson, Ian 329
media
    eating disorders, role in 252
    images of women, voluntary code 252
media skills training 380
medical academic staff 162–167
    academic careers 166
    academic clinical fellowships 166
    BMA role 164
    career structure and progression 164
    clinical academics 162–163, 164
        pay award 163
    devolved nations 164
    The Follett Principles 165
    Higher Education Funding Council for England
        165
    Higher Education funding reduction 164–165
    loss of posts 164, 165, 166
    Medical Academic Staff Committee (MASC) *see*
        Medical Academic Staff Committee (MASC)
    medical schools 164
    medical student numbers 166
    Medical Students Committee (MSC) *see* Medical
        Students Committee (MSC)
    NHS salary levels comparison 163
    RAE 166
    research infrastructure 165
    Richards report 166
    Scotland 166
    senior academic GPs 164
    teachers and researchers 162
    University Grants Committee (UGC) 165
    women 166–167
Medical Academic Staff Committee (MASC)
    basic pay award 163
    conference on academic careers 166
    consultant contracts 164
    The Follett Principles 164
    monitoring of impact of university cuts 165
    Rees, Professor Michael 164
    survey, unfilled vacancies 165
    women in academic medicine 166–167
Medical Academic Staff Committee (MASC)
    (BMA) 162
    campaigns 163
Medical Act (1983), serious professional misconduct
    183
Medical Appraisal Guide (2012) 207
Medical Association of South Africa (MASA) 319
    WMA and 319
medical audit 29
medical equipment, ethical procurement *see*
    international work (BMA)
medical ethics 236, 275–309
    abortion *see* abortion
    BMA Department *see* Ethics Department (BMA)
    BMA Medical Ethics Committee 275
    confidentiality *see* confidentiality
    consent and capacity *see* consent and capacity
    end of life issues *see* end of life issues
    ethical guidance
        GMC 'Blue Book' 275
        Medical Ethics Today (BMA) 275
    human genetics *see* human genetics
    human rights *see* human rights
    organ donation and transplantation *see* organ
        donation and transplantation
    reproductive technology *see* reproductive technology
    scope of issues covered 275
    social media and 232

Medical Ethics Committee (BMA) 275
Medical Ethics Today (BMA) 275
Medical Foundation for AIDS and Sexual Health 260
medical malpractice *see* serious professional misconduct
medical managers 5
  committee 5
  medical director appointments 6
Medical Manning and Retention Review 174
Medical Practitioners Tribunal Service (MPTS) 195
medical profession, regulation *see* regulation, medical profession
The Medical Profession and Human Rights: Handbook for a Changing Agenda (2001) 293, 295
medical records
  insurance company access, consent and 291–292
  see also information, personal healthcare
medical register 184, 196
  age limit and fees 195–196
  payment exemption 195
medical scandals 71–72, 73, 76, 89
  see also serious professional misconduct
medical schools *see* medical students
Medical Schools Council (TMSC), Medical Students Committee (MSC) and 175
medical students 174–176
  Advisory Committee on Medical Manpower (ACMM) 11
  BMA committee (MSC) 174
  European standards 313, 314
  finance
    Scotland 151
    Wales 154
  higher education funding 175
  intake, increase 114
  library services 340
  medical schools, new 114
  Medical Schools Council (TMSC) 175
  Medical Students Committee (MSC) 174
    see also Medical Students Committee (MSC)
  Medical Workforce Standing Advisory Committee 114
  NHS bursary scheme 175
  numbers 166
  overseas medical students 175–176
  postgraduate medical education *see* postgraduate medical education
  Regional Education and Development Group (REDG) 57
  Tomorrow's Doctors (2005) 175
  workforce problems (NHS) 7, 8, 9
    freeze on intake, BMA position 8, 9
Medical Students Committee (MSC) 174, 361
  GMC (education committee) and 175
  higher education funding 175
  Medical Schools Council (TMSC) and 175
  members 174
  Modernising Medical Careers (MMC), role in 176
  NHS bursary scheme 175
  status 174
  Tomorrow's Doctors (2005) 175
  see also medical students
Medical Training Application Service (MTAS) 115
  abandoned 122
  applications 118
  computer system procurement 117
  effect on BMA membership 129
  evaluation and analysis 125
  mistrust of, and chaos 118
  modified 122
  Tooke report 125–126
  see also Modernising Medical Careers (MMC) (2003)
Medical Workforce Standing Advisory Committee 114
Medicine Betrayed (1992) 293
  see also human rights

Medicines and Healthcare Products Regulatory Authority (MHRA) 228
medico-political activity 342–343
Medline/Medline Plus 230, 339
Meldrum, Hamish 65, 134, 192, 316
  alcohol-related policy and 249
  as Chairman of Council 125, 129, 130
  GP-led health centres 134
  ICT 219
  revalidation 206, 208
  self-diagnosis and self-prescribing 228
Mellor, David 18–19, 22
members (BMA) 327–344
  advocacy unit 332
  benefits 328, 334, 339
    BMA library *see* library services (BMA)
    BMJ see British Medical Journal (BMJ)
    BMJ Learning 406
  communication
    BMA News 343–344
    BMA website 344
    methods 343
    website 376
  decline in numbers 129
  doctors' perceptions of BMA 327–328
  financial services *see* financial services (BMA)
  library services *see* library services (BMA)
  local structures *see* structure, local (BMA)
  medico-political activity 342–343
  membership levels 327, 344, 371, 372, 375
    external influencing factors 327
    growth rate 327
    junior doctors 344
    LNCs, impact of 330–331
    women doctors 327
  modernisation 332
    service delivery 332
    staffing structure 332
  participation 341
  payment to 377–378
    Compensation Committee 377
    expenses 377
    fixed annual payments 378
    General Practitioners Defence Fund 377
    review of 377–378
    standard daily payments 378
  regional services 328–339
    advice, demand for *see* advice services (BMA)
    call centre provision *see* call centres
    costs 339
    First Point of Call 339
    GPs as employers 338
    home-working *see* home-working
    Industrial Relations Officers (IROs) *see* Industrial Relations Officers (IROs)
    Place of Work Accredited Representatives (Powars) *see* Place of Work Accredited Representatives (Powars)
    workplace services *see* workplace services (BMA)
  retired 181
Mental Capacity Act (2005) 290, 309
mental incapacity *see* consent and capacity
Merrison Committee 197
Milburn, Alan 72, 74, 89, 187
  resignation 77, 95
military *see* armed forces doctors
Miller, Paul 94
Mills, Ian 5
Minimum Practice Income Guarantee (MPIG) 100, 109
misconduct *see* serious professional misconduct
misuse, alcohol *see* alcohol and alcohol-related policy
modernisation of BMA House *see* BMA House
modernisation of NHS *see* National Health Service (NHS) modernisation (1997–2007)
modernised GMC *see* General Medical Council (GMC)

Modernising Medical Careers (MMC) (2003) 102, 115
  background and proposal 114–115
  BMA position 118
  competency-based curricula 116
  delivery board 115, 116, 117
  evaluation and analysis 125
  grades *see* grades
  Hilborne, Jo 119, 120
  implementation risks 116
  Junior Doctors Committee (JDC) engagement 116
  Medical Academic Staff Committee (MASC) role
    166
  Medical Students Committee (MSC) role in 176
  offers withdrawn from juniors 120
  outcry from junior doctors 119
  processes and procedures 117, 118, 120
    apology for failure 122
    application number from EU doctors 121
    applications 117, 118, 121
    interview panels 118
    interviews 118–119, 121, 123
    new, after judicial review 124, 125
    new proposals 121
    selection systems 116, 117, 118
    shortlisting chaos 118–119
    training post number 117
  RemedyUK *see* RemedyUK
  review group 119–120
    BMA defence of role 122
    BMA return to 121–122
    BMA withdrawal 121
    Hilborne rejoining 121
    juniors' anger towards 122
    meetings 119–120
    RemedyUK legal challenge ruling 124
  review group and meetings 120
  service grade 103
  start date 116
  The Times letter 123
    Junior doctors' response 123–124
  Tooke report 125
  training *see* training
  transition arrangements 116
  see also Medical Training Application Service
    (MTAS)
modified MTAS 122
Monitor (regulator) 143
Monopolies and Mergers Commission (MMC)
  private practice 177–178
  ruling on BMA 178
Moorthy, Ram 126

N
National Association of Fundholding Practices
  (NAFP) 45–46
  consultant grade 62
National Association of Health Authorities and
  Trusts (NAHAT) 62
National Audit Office
  consultants' contract costs 95
  NHS Programme for IT 225
National Clinical Assessment Service 190–191
National Coroner Service 181
National Health Service (NHS)
  appraisal *see* revalidation
  bursary scheme 175
  carbon footprint 264
  charter 81
  complaints *see* complaints (NHS)
  constitution 81
  consultant expansion *see* consultant expansion
  core values 81, 109
  finance 5–6
    resource management initiative *see* resource
      management initiative (RMI)
  founding 52–53

funding
  2008 financial crisis impact 133
  Arbuthnott review 150
  balanced (2007) 78
  Blair, Tony and 72
  BMA call for 25, 26, 27, 51
  Coalition government statement 140
  concerns (1992–1997) 55
  deficit (2005–2006) 77
  increased (2007–2010) 78
  long-term requirements 72
  Major, John and 50, 51
  NHS Plan (2000) 72
  problems 55
  Quality Innovation Productivity and Prevention
    (QIPP) 133
  response to 2008 financial crisis 133
  Royal Colleges' statement 26
  savings by 2015 140
  steering group review (2001) 73
general managers *see* general managers (NHS)
government and doctors relationship 52–53
government proposals, BMA response to 38
information technology (IT) *see* information,
  personal healthcare
liability for actions of staff 159
local pay campaign *see* local pay campaign
management 2–6
  1982 reorganisation 2–3
  BMA response to management teams 3
  budgeting 5
  cost cutting 133
  doctors' role in management 3–4
  general managers *see* general managers (NHS)
  medical managers *see* medical managers
  models 5
  self-governing hospital trusts *see* self-governing
    hospital trusts
  structure, *Working for Patients* 28–29
modernisation (1997–2007) *see* National Health
  Service (NHS) modernisation (1997–2007)
NHS management executive (NHSME) *see* NHS
  management executive (NHSME)
NHS University proposal 407
Northern Ireland *see* Northern Ireland, healthcare
  in
operation in times of war 257
  see also weapons and warfare
pensions *see* pensions
personal healthcare information *see* information,
  personal healthcare
public confidence, fall in 1999 72
re-organisation
  1982–1992 1–2
  1993 57–58
  1997–2007 72, 74–76
    see also National Health Service (NHS)
      modernisation (1997–2007)
  BMA response to 57
  by Coalition government 142–145
    see also Equity *and excellence: Liberating the
      NHS* (2010) (white paper)
  DHA 1
  district management team (DMT) 2
  FPCs 1, 17
recruitment website 399–400, 408
reforms (1982–1992) 1–53
  aftermath (1990–1992) 50–52
  Bottomley's response 56
  campaign against white paper *see* publicity
    campaign (BMA)
  consultants' contracts *see* consultant(s)
  Functions and Manpower Review *see* Functions
    and Manpower Review (1993)
  GP fundholding *see* fundholding (GP)
  GP negotiations *see* General Practitioners (GPs)
  Health and Security Adjudications Bill 2

The Health of the Nation 51
junior doctors' working hours *see* junior doctors
Macara's opposition 55–56
management *see* National Health Service
  (NHS), management
NHS and Community Care Bill *see* NHS and
  Community Care Bill (1989)
review and white paper *see* National Health
  Service (NHS) review; *Working for Patients*
  (white paper) (1989)
self-governing trusts *see* self-governing hospital
  trusts
workforce *see* workforce problems (NHS)
reforms, reforming the (1992–1997) 55–70
  Calman Report *see* Calman Report
  Core Values *see* 'Core Values' exercise
  GP out-of-hours services *see* out-of-hours
    services
  local pay campaign *see* local pay campaign
  London healthcare *see* London, healthcare in
  Macara (Sir Alexander) and 56–57
  NHS re-organisation 57–58
  specialist training *see* specialist training
reforms and modernisation (1997–2007) *see*
  National Health Service (NHS) modernisation
  (1997–2007)
review *see* National Health Service (NHS) review
Scotland *see* Scotland, healthcare in
Standards for Better Health (2004) 190
vicarious liability 159
Wales *see* Wales, healthcare in
workforce problems *see* workforce problems
  (NHS)
see also entries beginning NHS
National Health Service Executive (NHSE)
consultant contract (2000–2002) 88, 89
  local implementation after rejection in ballot 94
fee scale, out-of-hours 65
Information Strategy for the NHS (1998) 215–216
performance-related pay and 65
regional offices abolition 71
replacing regional health authorities 57
roadshows, consultants' contract 92–93
National Health Service (NHS) modernisation
  (1997–2007) 71–74
Alternative Provider Medical Services (APMS) 78
BMA position 76
BMA seat on board 73, 76
clinical performance indicators 75
Commission for Healthcare Improvement 71
contractual changes (1999–2007) 74–82
  BMA negotiations *see* contractual changes
  see also specific grades of doctors
EU Working Time Directive *see* European
  Working Time Directive (EWTD)
A First Class Service (green paper) (1998) 71
funding limitations (2004) 102–103
Independent Sector Treatment Centres *see*
  Independent Sector Treatment Centres
  (ISTCs)
Johnson, James 77
Leading Change (2001) 73
local improvement finance programme (LIFT) 76
long-term funding requirements 72
medical careers and MTAS *see* training
Modernising Medical Careers (MMC) *see*
  Modernising Medical Careers (MMC) (2003)
National Institute for Clinical Excellence (NICE)
  71, 190, 409–410
The New NHS – Modern, Dependable (white
  paper) (1997) 71
NHS Direct 75
NHS Improvement Plan 77
NHS Plan (2000) 72, 83, 88, 150
  proposals 72–74
patient choice *see* patient choice
pay modernisation *see* remuneration

Payment by Results 75
Personal Medical Services *see* personal medical
  services (PMS)
private finance initiative (PFI) 75
A Rational Way Forward for the NHS in England
  (2007) 81
scandals, implications of 76
staffing 114
  A health service for all the talents (2000) 114
'systems reform' 79–80
waiting times 75, 78
National Health Service (NHS) review
1988 16, 25–28
  aftermath of, and Lee-Potter, Jeremy 50–51
  Bill *see* NHS and Community Care Bill
  BMA memorandum of evidence 27
  BMA response to process 27
  campaign *see* publicity campaign (BMA)
  capitation, General Practitioners (GPs) 19, 29
  chaired by Thatcher 27
  Clarke's assurance to GPs 17
  conduct and duration 26–27
  consultants contracts *see* consultant(s)
  Cook, Robin 28
  funding increase 25
  GP fundholding *see* fundholding (GP)
  joint reports, BMA 25–26
  medical audit 29
  self-governing hospitals *see* self-governing
    hospital trusts
  white paper *see* *Working for Patients* (white
    paper) (1989)
2008 (Darzi) 129–132
  BMA concerns 132
  'clinical pathway groups' *see* 'clinical pathway
    groups'
  consultations 131
  GPC concerns 130, 131–132
  *High Quality Care for All: NHS Next Stage
    review* (2008) 129, 132
  implementation 133
  London *see* London, healthcare in
  BMA finances, impact on 370–371
National Institute for Health and Clinical Excellence
  (NICE) 71, 190, 409–410
National Institute for Health Research 166
National Programme for IT (NPfIT) 217–218, 219,
  224, 225
  costs 225
  discontinuation 225
  see also NHS Connecting for Health
Neale, Richard 72, 186
The New Deal (1991) 24–25, 110, 111
  Additional Duty Hours (ADHs) 25
  contractual changes 24–25
  English, Terence 24–25
  pay rise 24–25
  'the English clause' 24–25
New Labour 1997–2007
  see also Labour Party
The New NHS – Modern, Dependable (white paper)
  (1997) 71
NHS *see* National Health Service (NHS)
NHS: Medical Education England 125, 126
  BMA representation 126
NHS 111 139
NHS and Community Care Bill (1989) 38–42
  BMA evaluation 38–39
  concessions made 39
  contractual changes 41
  junior doctors, working hours 40
  NHS Supporters Party 39
  opinion polls 39
  publication by government 38
  Royal Assent 41
  Thatcher, Margaret, concerns and 39–40
NHS and Social Care Act (2012) 169

NHS bursary scheme 175
NHS Care Records Service 218, 219, 222
NHS Choices 229
NHS Complaints Reform: Making Things Right
  (2003) 211
NHS Confederation 97, 101
NHS Connecting for Health 222, 225
  BMA, concerns, response and role 219
  BMA links 218–219
  Choose and Book system *see* Choose and Book
    system
  National Programme for IT (NPfIT) *see* National
    Programme for IT (NPfIT)
  role 218
  Summary Care Record (SCR) *see* Summary Care
    Record (SCR)
NHS Direct 75–76
NHS Evaluation Programme 39–40
  BMA exclusion from CSAG meeting 39–40
NHS Executive (NHSE) *see* National Health Service
  Executive (NHSE)
NHS Improvement Plan 77
NHS Management Executive (NHSME) 28–29, 57
  consultants' contracts (1990–1992) 42, 43
  fundholding evaluation 45
  information strategy 214
  see also National Health Service Executive
    (NHSE)
The NHS Management Inquiry (1983) 3
  see also National Health Service (NHS)
NHS modernisation *see* National Health Service
  (NHS) modernisation (1997–2007)
NHS pension scheme (NHSPS) 136, 146
  see also pensions
NHS Plan (2000) 72–74, 83, 150
  consultant contract 88
'NHS preferred provider' policy 135
NHS Programme for IT *see* National Programme
  for IT (NPfIT)
NHS Supporters Party 39
NHS Together 81
NHS Trusts – A Working Guide (1989) 48
Nicholl, Duncan 31
Nicholson, Sir David 140, 142
No Smoking Day 237
Nominations Committee (BMA) 360
Northern Ireland
  abortion 279–280
  ban on smoking in public places 244
  consent and capacity 290
  detainees, treatment 292
  remuneration 157
Northern Ireland, healthcare in
  administrative units 154
  doctors, pay and terms/conditions 154
  emergency care summary record 226
  Health and Social Care Board 155
  Information and Communication Programme
    227
  Patient and Client Council 155
  public health 170
  Public Health Agency 155
  Review of Public Administration 155
  Transforming your care 155
  trusts 155
notional half days (NHDs) 42, 83
nuclear war
  criteria for selecting casualties 257
  medical effects of 256–257
nutrition 250–253
  diabetes 251
  Diet, Nutrition and Health (1986) 250–251
  eating disorders 252
  guidelines and public health message 250–251
  obesity 251
  over-eating 251
  'traffic-light approach' 251

O
obesity 251
Offender Health 180
Office of Fair Trading (OFT) 178
Office of the Health Professions Adjudicator
  (OHPA) 193, 194, 195
  BMA position 195
Office of the Immigration Services Commissioner
  317
Okunnu, Rob 381
*One Wales: a progressive agenda for the government of
  Wales* (2007) 153
OnExamination.com 408
online healthcare resources *see* world wide web
online learning, *BMJ Learning* 407
online self-diagnosis 227–228
open access publishing, *British Medical Journal
  (BMJ)* 396
'open data' campaign 402
organ donation and transplantation 295–299
  Alder Hey organs scandal 297
  BMA Cymru Wales role 154
  BMA position 296
  BMA report (2012) 298
  China, human rights violations 293
  consent 295–296
  devolved nations 297
    Wales 154, 299
  Human Bodies, Human Choices (2001) 297
  Human Tissue Act (2004) 298
    Scotland 298
  Human Tissue Authority 297
  Human Tissue Bill amendments 297
    BMA response 297
  legal position 296
  opt-out system 296, 297, 298
    *Building on Progress: Where next for Organ
      Donation Policy in the UK?* (2012) 296, 298
    Wales 299
  Organ Donation Taskforce 298
  techniques for acquiring organs 295
  Transplant Partnership 296
*Organ Donation in the 21st Century – Time for a
  Consolidated Approach* (2000) 296
Organ Donation Taskforce 298
Organ Donor Register 299
orthodox medicine, alternative medicine *v* 267
Our Health, Our Care, Our Say (2006) 77
Our NHS (2000) 150
out-of-hours development fund 65
out-of-hours services 140
  consultants 95
  GPs *see* out-of-hours services (GPs)
  pay, junior doctors *see* junior doctors
  provision, 2010–2012 140
out-of-hours services (GPs) 13, 64, 66, 99, 108
  BMA conflict of interest 13
    see also General Practitioners (GPs)
  deputising services 64
  fee scale 65
  format 64
  health promotion clinics 63
  Help us to Help You campaign 64
  listening exercise 65
  LMC conference 64
  negotiations 63–66
  opposition to NHSE proposal 65
  opting out, price of 99
  out-of-hours development fund 65
  reducing burden not opting out 64–65
over-eating 251
overseas doctors 101, 114, 116
  BMA advice service 317
  BMA support for 315
  European law and qualifications 315
  immigration 314–318
    BMA policy 314

immigration controls 11, 116–117, 315
  BMA response 316, 317
  points-based system 316, 317
  non-EEA 316
  refugees 317–318
    BMA support initiatives 318
    government funding 318
    Refugee Council 318
  training legislation 313, 315
  training scheme 11
  work permit 316
  workforce problems (NHS) 8
overseas medical students 175–176
Oversight and Finance Committee (BMA) 358

P
PACT (Prescribing Analysis and Cost) 17
Padiv (Public Affairs Division) 379–380, 381
pandemic 136
parliamentary unit 380–381
passive smoking *see* smoking and smoking-related policy
patient choice 75
  private sector provision 75
Patient Liaison Group 361–362
Patient's Charter (1991) 51
Patterns of Hospital Medical Staffing (report) 22
pay modernisation *see* remuneration
pay rise *see* remuneration
Payment by Results 75, 220
pensions 136–138
  1995 scheme 137–138
  2008 financial crisis impact 133
  2008 scheme 136–137, 138
  armed forces doctors 173
  BMA Staff Pension Scheme 373–374
    investment in global financial markets 375–376
    recovery plan 376
  Career Average Revalued Earnings (CARE) 146
  Choice Exercise (2010) 137–138
  coalition government and 145–148
    BMA response 146, 147
    contributions, staged increases 146
    increase based on CPI not RPI 146
    pre-negotiation changes 146
    trade union actions 146–147
  conditions 138
  current situation 148
  devolved nations 136
  dynamisation 132, 137
  final salary scheme 137
    CARE scheme *v* 146
    exclusions 137
  government agenda 137
  GPs 130
    legal challenge 130, 132
  increased contributions 137, 138
  industrial action 146, 147
    extent of support 147
    public opinion 148
    scope of action 147
  negotiations 137
  NHS pension scheme (NHSPS) 136, 146
  reform (2008–2010) 136–138
  retirement age change 138
  Scotland 152
  unions 137
performance-related pay 66
  DDRB response 66–67
persistent vegetative state (PVS) 304–305
personal healthcare information *see* information, personal healthcare
personal medical services (PMS) 66, 76, 96
  contract renewal 139
petrol, leaded and unleaded 261
physician assisted suicide and euthanasia 299–304

bills and legislation 301
  BMA guidance to doctors 303, 304
  BMA position 300–301, 301–302
    2005 position shift 301–302
    open debates 301–302
  criminal charges 299, 300, 303
  Dignitas 302–303
  Director of Public Prosecutions (DPP) 303, 304
    rules for prosecutors 304
  distinctions between physician assisted suicide and euthanasia 300, 301
  impact on society 300–301
  Pretty, Diane 303
  Purdey, Debbie 303
  terminology 299–300
Pickersgill, David 209, 374, 383
Pickersgill, Trevor 91
Picture Archiving and Communications Systems (PACs) 218
Pilkington Commission ii
Pilkington Report 156
Place of Work Accredited Representatives (Powars) 328, 329
  BMA profile, role in 331
  services 329
  termination 331
Plymouth, self-governing hospital trusts 48–49
podcasts 231
Police and Criminal Evidence Bill 284, 287
  intimate body samples/searches consent 287
Political Board, BMA 107
pollution 260
  see also environment
'polyclinics' 129, 132
Porter, Mark 89, 140, 148
postgraduate medical education 57
  NHS Medical Education England 125
Postgraduate Medical Education Training Board (PMETB) 102, 115
PPP 176
  AXA PPP 178
Practice Observed 391–392
pregnancy, alcohol and 247–248
Prescribing Analysis and Cost (PACT) 17
prescription medicines, online access 228
presidents (BMA) *see* staffing (BMA)
Pretty, Diane 303
Primary Care: delivering the future (white paper) 66
Primary Care Act (1997) 66
Primary Care Group (PCG) 71, 75, 169
  see also Primary Care Trusts (PCTs)
primary care system
  financial incentives 16
  local medical committees (LMCs) opposition 16
  Promoting Better Care (white paper) (1987) 16
Primary Care Trusts (PCTs) 75, 169
  closure/dismantling 143
  deficit and demands made on 77
  foundation trusts *v* 77
  funding deficit (2005–2006) 77
  GP-led health centres 133
  local enhanced services (LESs) 108
  mergers and scaling down 139
  reduction in number 77
  redundancies 78
  Transforming Community Services initiative 135
Primary Care Under Pressure (1987) 25–26
Primary Health Care: An Agenda for Discussion (green paper) (1986) 15
  local medical committees (LMCs) 15, 16
Prince of Wales, Charles (HRH Prince Charles) 382
Princess Royal, HRH Princess Anne 382, 384
Princess Royal Trust for Carers 382
prison medical services 180
prisoners, human rights abuses 293
Private Consultant Work: BMA Guidelines (1989) 177

Private Finance Initiative (PFI) 75, 76, 176
  BMA opposition 75, 76
private practice 176–181, 179
  anaesthetists, local fee setting 178
  BUPA/Bupa 176, 178
  consultants fees 176–177
  consultants' hours for NHS 91
  forensic medicine *see* forensic medicine
  Gullick, David 176–177
  Machin, Derek 179
  monopolies, BMA role 178
  Monopolies and Mergers Commission *see*
    Monopolies and Mergers Commission (MMC)
  Office of Fair Trading (OFT) 177, 178
  PPP/AXA PPP 176, 178
  Private Consultant Work: BMA Guidelines (1989)
    177
    response to 177
  Private Practice and Professional Fees Committee
    (PPPFC) 177, 178
  Private Practice Committee (PPC) *see* Private
    Practice Committee (PPC)
  professional fees 179–180
  quality guidelines 179
  schedule of fees 177
  specialist fees 178
Private Practice and Professional Fees Committee
  (PPPFC) 177, 178
  Forensic Medical Committee 178, 180
  Professional Fees Committee 178, 180
  see also Private Practice Committee (PPC)
Private Practice Committee (PPC) 176
  Chawner, John 176
  role in initiatives 179
private sector provision 75, 80
  Alternative Provider Medical Services (APMS) 78
  'commercial private sector' 80
  community health 168
  competitive tendering 135–136
  concerns over NHS destabilisation by 135
  general practice, concerns 131–132
  GP-led health centres, tendering 133
  'NHS preferred provider' policy 135
  role of, BMA surveys 135
  Scotland 150
  Transforming Community Services initiative 135
pro-choice groups (abortion) 280
Professional Affinity Group Services Limited 340, 374
professional fees 179–180
  see also private practice
Professional Fees Committee 178, 180
professional misconduct *see* serious professional
  misconduct
Promoting Better Health (white paper) (1987) 16
  financial incentives 16
  GMSC response 16
Proposals for a new approach to the consultant contract
  (2001) 88
public affairs (BMA) 379–380, 381
Public Affairs Division (Padiv) 379–380, 381
public expectations 211
Public Health: Our Voice 170–171
Public Health Agency, Northern Ireland 155
Public Health England (PHE) 170
public health medicine 167–172, 235–274
  Abrams report 168–169
  AIDS *see* Acquired Immune Deficiency
    Syndrome (AIDS)
  alcohol *see* alcohol and alcohol-related policy
  alternative and complementary therapy *see*
    alternative and complementary therapy
  body image 252
  boxing *see* boxing
  Central Consultants and Specialists Committee
    (CCSC) 168
  community health *see* community health
  devolved nations 170

director of public health (DPH) 168
  BMA support 168
district health authorities (DHAs) 167
district medical officer 167
environment *see* environment
Functions and Manpower Review (1993) 168
health inequalities *see* health inequalities
Healthy Lives, Healthy People 169
HIV *see* Human Immunodeficiency Virus (HIV)
local authorities 169
local health resilience partnerships (LHRPs) 170
nutrition *see* nutrition
Primary Care Trusts (PCTs) 169
Public Health: Our Voice 170–171
Public Health England (PHE) 170
Public Health Medicine Committee (PHMC) 169,
  170–171
Public Health Responsibility Deal 249–250
  BMA response 249–250
risk *see* risk
smoking *see* smoking and smoking-related policy
strategic health authorities 169
tobacco *see* smoking and smoking-related policy
transport *see* environment
weapons and warfare *see* weapons and warfare
Working for Patients (white paper) (1989) 168
Public Health Medicine Committee (PHMC) 169,
  170–171
Public Health Responsibility Deal 249–250
  see also public health medicine
Public Health Wales 153
public opinion of the profession 183, 187
Public Sector Pay Committee 104
publicity campaign (BMA) 32
  'flagship hospitals' 48
  NHS review (1989, *Working for Patients*) 34–39
    action group 32–33
    advertisements 33–34
    BMA members' responses 34–35
    BMA tensions as result of 34–35
    chief officers 32–33
    Clarke, Kenneth response to 35
    costs 38
    Dawson, John 33
    lobbying MPs 34
    Marks, John 34, 35, 36, 38
    poster targeting Clarke (Kenneth) 37
    poster themes 36–37
    posters 36–37
    posters, Conservative response 37–38
    public meetings 34
    public response and concerns 34
    research 34
    response to bill publication 38–39
    Taylor, Pamela 33, 39
    see also Marks, John; NHS and Community
      Care Bill (1989)
  self-governing trusts 48
  trade unions, links with 49
PubMedCentral 396
Purdey, Debbie 303

Q
quality assurance 65–66, 133
  see also clinical governance
Quality Innovation Productivity and Prevention
  (QIPP) 133
quality outcomes framework (QOF) 83
  General Practitioners (GPs) 98
Queen Elizabeth II, HM 382

R
RAE (Research Assessment Exercise) 166
A Rational Way Forward for the NHS in England
  (2007) 81, 130

rationalisation of healthcare
  BMA response 50–60
  Tomlinson Report and 50–60
re-certification 204
  see also revalidation
re-licensure 197, 204
  see also revalidation
reaccreditation 198
  see also revalidation
recession 371
  see also financial crisis (2008, UK)
Recognition and Reward (2003) 102
Rees, Lord (private member's bill), junior doctors
    21–22
Rees, Professor Michael 7–8, 164
referral(s), GPs 41, 221
referral management schemes 78
referral process, Choose and Book system, impact
    of 220
Reforming NHS Financial Flows (2002) 75
Reforming the NHS Reforms (1994) 56
reforms, NHS *see* National Health Service (NHS)
Refugee Council 318
refugees
  asylum seekers 292, 295
  see also overseas doctors
Regaining the Confidence of the Profession 125
Regional Director of Public Health (RDPH) 58
Regional Education and Development Group
    (REDG) 57
regional health authority 1
  replacement with NHS Executive (NHSE) offices
    57
  see also National Health Service Executive
    (NHSE)
registrars
  Achieving a balance (1986) 12
  specialist 63
    contract negotiations 63
    route 102
  unification of grades 61
registration 184, 195–196
  see also medical register
regulation, medical profession 183–212
  civil standard of proof *v* criminal standard 193
  fitness to practise *see* fitness to practise
  Good Doctors, Safer Patients (2006) 203–204
  Good Medical Practice for General Practitioners
    (2000) 201
  Office of the Health Professions Adjudicator
    (OHPA) 193, 194, 195
  revalidation *see* revalidation
  serious professional misconduct *see* serious
    professional misconduct
  standard of proof *see* standard of proof
  see also revalidation
Reid, John 77, 95
RemedyUK 118, 119, 120
  BMA and 120
  legal challenge 122
    judicial review 124
    ruling 124
  support for march 120
remuneration 156–162
  armed forces doctors 173
  consultants *see* consultant(s)
  DDRB *see* Doctors' and Dentists' Review Body
    (DDRB)
  defence body subscriptions 158–159
  devolved nations *see* devolved nations
  GPs *see* General Practitioners (GPs)
  history of DDRB's recommendations 157–162
    see also Doctors' and Dentists' Review Body
      (DDRB)
  junior doctors *see* junior doctors
  local pay campaign *see* local pay campaign
  medical academic staff 163

NHS modernisation *see* National Health Service
    (NHS) modernisation (1997–2007)
out-of-hours *see* out-of-hours services
pay freeze 139, 141, 160, 161
pay modernisation 83
  consultant(s) 83
  GPs 83
  junior doctors 83
pay rise
  2003–2006 160
  2007 160
  The New Deal (1991) 24–25
performance-related pay *see* performance-related
    pay
Scotland 161
self-governing hospital trusts *see* self-governing
    hospital trusts
Representative Body (RB) 171, 348, 352
  abortion 279, 280
  anonymity of egg/sperm donors 278
  control of BMA 353, 354
  electoral processes *see* electoral process
  Governance Committee of 350, 351, 352
  medical reports for insurance purposes 291
  open debate on governance 351–352
  physician-assisted dying 301–302
  role of 353–354
  surrogacy 279
reproductive health 241
  smoking and 241
reproductive technology 276–279
  BMA early policy development 276
  fertility treatment *see* fertility treatment
  IVF *see* in-vitro fertilisation (IVF)
  Warnock Inquiry *see* Warnock Inquiry
Research Assessment Exercise (RAE) 163–164, 166
researchers *see* medical academic staff
Resource Management Initiative 47
resource management initiative (RMI) 6, 29
  CCHMS support, Ross, P 6
  Central Consultants and Specialists Committee
    (CCSC) 6
  clinical directorates, need for 6
  Working for Patients (white paper) (1989) 6
  'responsible officer' 205
    see also revalidation
rest periods 112
retired doctors 181
  medical register and 195–196
Retired Members Forum 181, 361
retirement age 138
retraining 184
revalidation 197–209, 413
  'affiliate', GMC *see* General Medical Council
    (GMC)
  appraisal (NHS) 199, 201–202, 208
    CCSC support 200
    consultants 200
    GMC support 200, 201, 202
    GPs 201–202
    A Licence to Practise and Revalidation (2003)
      202
    quality, doubts over 201–202
  appraisal route 202
  BMA 7 principles document 206
  BMA response to proposals 199–200, 201, 204
    concerns 199, 200, 203
  Bogle, Ian and 201–202
  clinical governance, role of 203
  cost-effectiveness evaluation 207, 208
  doctor's folders 202–203
  extended pilot period 207, 208
  fitness to practise *see* fitness to practise
  GMC and BMA, press release 198
  GMC and DH collaboration 201
  Good Medical Practice for General Practitioners
    (2000) 201

implementation date 208, 209
independent route 202
introduction of 209
in Medical Act 1983 amendment 203–204
Medical Appraisal Guide (2012) 207
preparation for 205
process
   BMA concerns 199, 200, 203
   independent route proposal 202
   three-stage process 199
   'responsible officer' 205, 208
   Revalidation: The Way Ahead (2010) 205, 206
   BMA response 206–207
UK Revalidation Programme Board, members
   207–208
review body and remuneration *see* Doctors' and
   Dentists' Review Body (DDRB); remuneration
Richards, Sir Rex 166
Richards report 166
risk 265
   estimation/evaluation methods 265
   life-style 265
   public health issues 265
Risk: What's Your Perspective? 265
Road Transport and Health (1997) 261
Robertson, George 174
Ross, Paddy 31, 32, 35, 37, 41
   Resource Management Initiative 47
   self-governing hospital trusts 47
Rowe, Alan 311
Royal College of Obstetricians and Gynaecologists
   (RCOG) 281
royal colleges
   accreditation, specialist 61
   alternative to CMO's initiative on consultants 10
   Equity and excellence: Liberating the NHS (2010)
      (white paper) 144
   internal market debate 32
   NHS Evaluation Programme 39–40
   NHS funding statement 26
   training input 115

S
'safety net' 12
Saving Lives: our healthier nation (white paper)
   (1999) 256
scandals, medical *see* serious professional misconduct
Scotland
   Alcohol (Minimum Pricing) Bill 249
   alcohol pricing 248–249
   ban on smoking in public places 244
   BMA in *see* BMA Scotland
   consent and capacity 290–291
   health boards 150, 170
   medical academic staff 166
   Staff and Associate Specialists Committee
      (SASC) 105, 364
      response to strike 356
   withholding and withdrawing treatment 306
Scotland, healthcare in
   Arbuthnott review 150
   collaborative approach 150
   differences between England and 150
   Directed Enhanced Services 151
   distinction awards 151
   e-Health Strategy 226, 227
   emergency care summary 226
   general practice administration system for
      Scotland (GPASS) 226–227
   Human Tissue Act (Scotland) (2004) 298
   junior doctors 151
   medical student finance 151
   Our NHS (2000) 150
   private sector provision 150
   public health 170
   remuneration 161

   structure 150
   trusts 150
   unified health boards 150
   see also BMA Scotland
Scottish Clinical Research Excellence Development
   Scheme 166
seat belts 261
self-governing hospital trusts 27, 28, 29, 46–50
   advantages 46, 47
   autonomy 66
   campaign (BMA) *see* publicity campaign (BMA)
   CCSC 49
      conferences for doctors in 49–50
      debate 47
      information pack 47–48
      opinion of 31
      survey of consultants 47
   conference 36, 49–50
   'expressions of interest' 47
   LNCs and 49–50
   management 48–49
   McColl, Ian 46–47
   meetings with management 48
   NHS reforms 57
   NHS Trusts – A Working Guide (1989) 48
   opposition to 46–47
   performance-related pay 66
   Plymouth 48
   Ross, Paddy 47
   Royal Assent to Bill for 48
   trusts' individual proposals 50
self-regulation (GMC) 184, 189, 191, 196
   BMA support 196
   failings 185
   Irvine, Sir Donald 185
   Trust, Assurance and Safety (2007) 191
Selsdon Park Hotel (Surrey), meetings 18
senior clinical medical officer (SCMO) 172
senior consultants *see* consultant(s)
senior house officer *see* grades
Senior Management Group (SMG) *see* constitution
   and governance (BMA)
senior secretariat (BMA) 379
serious professional misconduct 183, 413
   Alder Hey organs scandal 186
   Bristol Royal Infirmary 185
   Medical Act (1983) 183
   responses to 187
   scandals, medical 71–72, 73, 76, 89
   Shipman, Harold 186, 203, 211, 359
   standard of proof *see* standard of proof
service doctors *see* armed forces doctors
service grade 103, 115
'sessional' doctors, concerns over GPC 139–140
'seven lean years' proposal 88, 90, 91
seven-point plan 38
sexually transmitted infections 292
   see also Human Immunodeficiency Virus (HIV)
Shipman, Harold 186, 203, 211, 359
Shipman Inquiry 73, 181, 186, 203, 211
Shock, Sir Maurice 56
Short, Renée *see* Short Report
'Short' consultants 9–10
Short Report (House of Commons Social Services
   Committee) (1981) 7
   central recommendation 7, 8–9
   government acceptance 9–10
   HJSC and CCHMS joint response 7–8
   hospital career structure 7–8
   workforce planning 7–9, 12–13
      consultant expansion *see* consultant expansion
      general practice (GP) 9
      junior doctors *see* junior doctors
      medical students 8
      overseas doctors *see* overseas doctors
SIMAP case 111, 112
Situation Critical campaign 85

'Slide 9' 92
Smith, Colin 165
Smith, Richard 395, 402
Smoking and Carcinoma of the Lung 237
smoking and smoking-related policy 236–245, 413
    Action on Smoking and Health (ASH) 244
    ban in private vehicles 244
    ban in public places 236, 237, 242, 413–414
        BMA response 242, 243
        partial 242, 243
        survey and MORI poll 243
        welcome for ban 243–244
    BMA
        Booze, Fags and Food 243
        publicity 238
        role 237
        Scotland role 151
    BMA Cymru Wales role 154
        publications 239
    cessation 239
    Coalition government 245
    devolved nations 244
    Framework Convention on Tobacco Control
        (WHO) 241–242
    Labour government 239–240
    other tobacco-related campaigns 244–245
    passive smoking 240–244
        in cars 244–245
    public education 239, 245
    reproductive health 241
    Smoking Kills (white paper) (1998) 240
        BMA response 240
    statistics 239
    'The Big Kill' report 239
    tobacco advertising and sponsorship 237–240
        advertising to children 238
        ban 240
        BMA campaign 237
        motor sports exemption 240
        voluntary code on sports sponsorship 238
    Tobacco Control Resource Centre (TCRC) 240–241
        Doctors and Tobacco 240–241
    tobacco tax 239
    Towards Smoke-Free Public Places (2002) 241
Smoking Kills (white paper) (1998) 240
*Social Determinants of Health: What Doctors Can
    Do* 256
social inequalities 253, 255
    see also health inequalities
social media
    BMA use of 231, 232
        ethics, and practicalities 232
    doctors' use of 231–232
Social Partnership Forum 135
socio-economic status *see* health inequalities
Sommerville, Ann 293
Spearing, Nigel 183
Special Representative Meeting (SRM), *Working for
    Patients* (white paper) (1989) 31, 33
specialist fees *see* private practice
specialist register 103
    revalidation *see* revalidation
    see also medical register; specialist training
specialist registrars (SpRs) *see* specialist training
specialist training 60–63, 113, 117
    ACMT training charter 313
    Advisory Group on Medical Education, Training
        and Staffing 63
    available posts 117
    Call for Delay 117
    Calman Report 60–63, 62
    Certificate of Completion of Specialist Training
        (CCST) 103–104, 114, 315–316
    Certificate of Specialist Training (CST) 115,
        315–316
    double standards 61
    grades unified 61, 116

new model of specialist training 61
overseas doctors 315–316
post-CCST (Certificate of Completion of
    Specialist Training) grade 114
selection process 116–117
Specialist Workforce Advisory Group 63
specialty doctor 106
sub-consultant – specialist grade 114
    see also Calman report
Specialist Training Authority 102
Specialist Workforce Advisory Group 63
specialists, associate *see* staff and associate specialists
specialty doctor 106
sponsorship, tobacco products *see* smoking and
    smoking-related policy
sports, sponsorship of tobacco products *see* smoking
    and smoking-related policy
Staff and Associate Specialists Committee (SASC)
    101
    contract
        barriers to negotiation 102, 104
        campaign 105
    Modernising Medical Careers (MMC) (2003) *see
        Modernising Medical Careers* (MMC) (2003)
    postgraduate training *see* postgraduate medical
        education
    scope of representation 101
    Scotland *v* UK 105
staff doctors and associate specialists 101–106
    Achieving a balance (1986) 12
    Choice and Opportunity (white paper) (2003) 102
    composition of group 102
    continuing professional development (CPD) 102
    contract 101–106
        approval 104–105
        ballot 104
        costings concern 105
        frustration (2007) 129
        government approval 106
        implementation (2008) 106
        Lord Hunt 105
        reopening of negotiations 104
    contract campaign 105
    craft status 361
    funding 106
    Khan, Mohib 103
    negotiations 102
        mandate 103
    Recognition and Reward (2003) 102
    regrading and acceptance 106
    SASC *see* Staff and Associate Specialists
        Committee (SASC)
    Scotland 364
    service grade 103
staffing (BMA) 378–381
    chief officers 381
    expansion 378–379
    media skills training 380
    Presidents *see under* BMA
    senior secretariat 379
staffing (NHS) *see* workforce problems (NHS)
standard daily payments 378
standard of proof 193, 194
    civil 191, 192, 193
    criminal 191, 192
        BMA support 193
    criminal *v* civil 191
    Health and Social Care Bill (2007) 192
Standards for Better Health (2004) 190
stem cell research 282–283
    BMA position 283–284
    debate 283
    embryonic *v* adult 283
    Warnock Inquiry 283
Strachan, Jeremy 332, 337, 405
strategic health authorities (SHAs) 75
    reduction 77, 169

strike *see* industrial action
structure, local (BMA) 335, 341–344
    devolved nations 342, 343
    expenditure 335
    home-working *see* home-working
    Local Medical Committees 342
    medico-political activity coordination 342–343
    rationalisation (England and Scotland) 336
    regional co-ordinators 343
    regional committees 342
    regional councils (England) 342–343
Student BMJ 397
students *see* medical students
subscriptions (BMA) 329
    increase 369, 374
Summary Care Record (SCR) 219, 221–222
    BMA criticism of DH 223
    concerns about 223
    consent model 222, 224
    costs 225
    delays 225
    detailed care record (DCR) 222
        delays 225
    'early adopter' sites 222
    implementation, rushed 223
    information limitations 224–225
    suspension of system 222–224
    'The Big Opt Out Campaign' 222
    UCL report 223, 224
suntan salons, BMA Cymru Wales role 154
Supervisory Board of the Secretariat (BMA) 356,
    360
Support your Surgery 132
supporting professional activities (SPAs) 96
    reduction of 140
        CC response 140
surgical trainees 24, 113
    see also training
surrogacy 278–279
    *Changing Conceptions of Motherhood: the Practice
        of Surrogacy in Britain* (1995) 279
    regulation of organisation of surrogacy 279
    Warnock Inquiry, BMA response 279
swine flu 136
'systems reform' 79–80

T
Taylor, Hugh 85, 86, 87, 89
Taylor, Pamela 33, 39, 380, 381
teachers *see* medical academic staff
Temple, Professor Sir John 140–141
tendering *see* private sector provision
terrorism, impact on BMA (London, 2005) 385–389
    BMA evidence 389
    buses 385
    emergency assistance from BMA 385–386
    evacuation of BMA House 386
    memorials 389
    office closure 387
    remembrance service 388
    sponsored training course 389
    tube station 385
Thatcher, Margaret, NHS review and white paper
    16, 25, 27
Thatcher era, 1982–1992 1–53
'The Big Kill' report 239
'The Big Opt Out Campaign' 222
The Health of the Nation (1991) *see Health of the
    Nation*
The New Deal (1991) *see The New Deal (1991)
    (under New . . .)*
The Way Ahead (2010) *see* revalidation
third-world debt *see* international work (BMA)
Time's Running Out 112
Time's Up 112
Timmins, Nick 37, 141, 142, 144

tobacco *see* smoking and smoking-related policy
Tobacco Control Resource Centre (TCRC)
    240–241
    Towards Smoke-Free Public Places (2002) 241
'tobacco-free society' 244
tobacco industry 238
Tomlinson, Sir Bernard 59
    see also Tomlinson Report
Tomlinson Report (1992) 58–60
    BMA response 59–60
    'London initiatives zone' 59
    Making London Better (1993) *see Making London
        Better* (1993)
    recommendations 59
Tomorrow's Doctors (2005) 175
Tooke, Professor Sir John 122
    see also Tooke report
Tooke report 125–126
    government response 126
'Toronto Group' 320
torture 292–293
    see also human rights
Towards Smoke-Free Public Places (2002) 241
trade union(s)
    BMA
        NHS Together and 81
        trade union and company law responsibilities
            355
        trade union status 235, 345
    NHS, pension scheme (2011–2012) 146, 147
    trade union action *see* industrial action
    Trade Union Bill 346–347
Trade Union Act 1984 345–347
    constitutional changes required 346
    impact on electoral process 346
Train not Drain campaign 117
'trained doctor' provision 140
training 113–126
    BMA sponsored course due to London bombings
        389
    BMJ publishing group 407
    budgets 77
    competency-based curricula 116
    European standards 312
        Advisory Committee on Medical Training
            (ACMT) 312–313
        BMA role 314
        general practice 313
        higher education diplomas 314
        medical students 313
    European Working Hours Directive impact 113
    full shifts impact 113, 140
    hours 23, 111, 113, 140
    juniors' concerns 116
    media skills training 380
    Medical Training Application Service (MTAS)
        115
    MMC *see Modernising Medical Careers* (MMC)
        (2003)
    number of posts (2006) 117
    postgraduate *see* postgraduate medical education
    royal colleges role 115
    specialist *see* specialist training
    students *see* medical students
    surgical 24, 113
    Train not Drain campaign 117
    'trust doctors' 113
    see also medical students
Transforming Community Services initiative 135, 172
Transforming your Care 155
'transitional local pay' 70
Transplant Partnership 296
transplantation *see* organ donation and
    transplantation
transport
    cycling *see* cycling
    drink-drive limit *see* drink-drive limit

leaded petrol 261
Road Transport and Health (1997) 261
seat belts 261
Treatment Agency for Substance Abuse 170
treatment tariff 75
trust(s)
  foundation *see* foundation trusts
  primary care *see* Primary Care Trusts (PCTs)
  self-governing *see* self-governing hospital trusts
*Trust, Assurance and Safety – The Regulation of
  Health Professionals in the 21st Century* (2007)
  191, 192, 205
  BMA response 191
'trust doctors' 114
Twitter 231

U
UK Revalidation Programme Board *see* revalidation
unions *see* trade union(s)
units of medical time (UMTs) 84
  see also additional duty hours (ADHs)
universities
  funding decline 165
  staff *see* medical academic staff
  students *see* medical students
University Grants Committee (UGC) 165
USA, BMJPG sales and marketing office 400–401

V
validation
  specialist register 197
  see also revalidation
video-conferencing 233
Vision and Recommendations for a Health Service
  156
Vote No campaign 92
voting rights *see* electoral process

W
Wain, Eileen 167
waiting times 75, 78
Waldegrave, William 41, 50, 51
Wales
  ban on smoking in public places 244
  BMA in *see* BMA Cymru Wales
Wales, healthcare in 152–154
  'clinical portal' 227
  consent and capacity 290
  consultant contracts 153
  Improving health in Wales 153
  individual health record 226
  *One Wales: a progressive agenda for the government
    of Wales* (2007) 153
  organ donation and transplantation, opt-out
    system 299
  public health 170
  Public Health Wales 153
  reconfiguration proposals 154
  WAG resolution of no confidence 153
  see also BMA Cymru Wales
Walford, Diana 11
walk-in centres 133
Walport Report 166
Walshaw, Russell 348, 349
Wanless, Sir Derek 72
Wanless report 216–217
Warner, Lord Norman 109, 111
Warnock, Dame Mary 276
  see also Warnock Inquiry
Warnock Inquiry 276, 283
  BMA response 276, 279
'water poverty' 254–255
Watkins, Stephen 172
The Way Ahead (2010) *see* revalidation

weapons and warfare 256–258
  nuclear war *see* nuclear war
  operation of NHS in times of war 257
webcasting 231
webpages *see* world wide web
website (BMA) *see under* world wide web (www)
Welsh Assembly Government (WAG) 152–153
Welsh Consultants Committee, WAG resolution of
  no confidence 153
Western Journal of Medicine 396
white papers
  Choice and Opportunity (2003) 66
  Equity and excellence: Liberating the NHS (2010)
    142
  The New NHS – Modern, Dependable (1997) 71
  Primary Care: delivering the future 66
  Promoting Better Health (1987) 16
  Saving Lives: our healthier nation (1999) 256
  Smoking Kills (1998) 240
  *Trust, Assurance and Safety – The Regulation of
    Health Professionals in the 21st Century* (2007)
    191
  Working for Patients (1989) *see Working for Patients*
    (white paper) (1989)
Whitelaw, William 284
Whittingham, Leigh 383
Wilks, Michael 80, 282
Williams, Baroness 144, 145
Wilson, Ian 350, 352
Wilson, Michael
  Clarke, Kenneth and 14–15, 18, 19–20
  General Medical Services Committee (GMSC) 14
  Working for Patients (white paper) (1989) 17–18
    negotiations and 11-point document 19
Wilson, Professor Alan 209
Wilson Committee report 210
  see also complaints (NHS)
Winning, Sally 104
*Withholding and Withdrawing Life-Prolonging
  Medical Treatment* (1999) 306
withholding and withdrawing treatment 304–307
  Bland, Tony 304–305
  BMA
    guidance 305, 306
    public consultation 305
    *Withholding and Withdrawing Life-Prolonging
      Medical Treatment* (1999) 306
  Burke, Leslie 307
  capacity 306
  GMC guidance 307
  human rights issues 307
  persistent vegetative state (PVS) 304–305
  Scotland 306
women doctors 101
  medical academic staff 166–167
  members (BMA) 327
  part-time training opportunities 11
  working hours 113
workforce problems (NHS) 7–13, 113–114
  CMO's initiative on manpower 7
    resistance to 8, 10
  'consultant-provided service' 8
    see also consultant expansion
  junior and senior doctors imbalance 7
  medical students *see* medical students
  overseas doctors *see* overseas doctors
  recruitment problems 114
  seniority of staff 7
  Short Report and 7–9
  staffing levels 7
  traditional staffing structures 114
Working for Patients (white paper) (1989) 6, 17, 18,
  26–27, 28–34, 168
  Bill *see* NHS and Community Care Bill (1989)
  BMA response 28, 29–30
  campaign against *see* publicity campaign (BMA)
  Clarke, Kenneth 17–18, 19, 28

concerns from doctors 29, 31
follow on working papers 30
geographical scope 29
GP response to 18, 19
implications for GPs 17
key elements 28–29
LMC conference, contract rejection 19
negotiations and 11-point document 19
rejection of proposed contract 19
Special Representative Meeting (SRM) 31, 33
timeframe 29
Wilson, Michael 18
see also NHS and Community Care Bill (1989)
working hours *see* European Working Time
    Directive (EWTD); junior doctors
Working Time (Amendment) Regulations (2003)
    111
workplace services (BMA) 329–331
    devolved nations 329
    foundation trusts 331
    Local Negotiating Committees (LNCs) *see* Local
        Negotiating Committee (LNC)
    Powars *see* Place of Work Accredited
        Representatives (Powars)
    strategic review 330
    subscriptions, direct debit 329
World Health Organization (WHO), Framework
    Convention on Tobacco Control (WHO)
    241–242
World Medical Association (WMA) 319–320
    BMA and 319–320
    BMA withdrawal 319
    constitution, BMA concerns 319
    MASA and 319
    weighted voting system 319
world wide web (www) 227–230
    Best Health webpages 228

Best Treatments webpages 228
BMA 231–232
    BMAtv 231
    customer feedback on 229–230
    electronic newsletter 231
    live streaming 231
    podcasts 231
    relaunch 231
    website 231, 344
    YouTube 231
comparative data on health services 228–229
counterfeit medicines 228
development of 213
doctors.net.uk 229–230, 232
GP rating and comment facility 229
health-related information availability 227
library services *see* library services
misinformation 228, 229–230
NHS Choices 229
prescription medicines, online 228
self-diagnosis, online 228
service reviews, online 228–229
social media *see* social media
telephone and video conferencing 233

Y
You and Your GP 20
young people
    consent and capacity, *Consent, Rights and Choices
        in Healthcare for Children and Young People*
        (2000) 289
    see also children
Young People and Alcohol (BMA report) 246–247
Your Choices for the Future 64
Your contract your future 98
YouTube 231